TEACHER'S EDITION

Algebra

STRUCTURE AND METHOD
BOOK 1

Mary P. Dolciani
William Wooton
Robert H. Sorgenfrey
Richard G. Brown

Editorial Advisers
Andrew M. Gleason
Albert E. Meder, Jr.

Houghton Mifflin Company • Boston

Atlanta   Dallas   Geneva, Illinois
Hopewell, New Jersey   Palo Alto

ABOUT THE AUTHORS

Mary P. Dolciani, University Dean for Academic Development and Professor of Mathematics, Hunter College, City University of New York.

William Wooton, Mathematics Consultant, Vista, California, Unified School District.

Robert H. Sorgenfrey, Professor of Mathematics, University of California, Los Angeles.

Richard G. Brown, Mathematics Teacher, The Phillips Exeter Academy, Exeter, New Hampshire.

ABOUT THE EDITORIAL ADVISERS

Andrew M. Gleason, Hollis Professor of Mathematics and Natural Philosophy, Harvard University.

Albert E. Meder, Jr., Dean and Vice Provost and Professor of Mathematics, Emeritus, Rutgers, The State University of New Jersey.

The authors of *ALGEBRA, Structure and Method, Book 1* wish to express appreciation to Professor Frank Ebos, Associate Professor of Mathematics, Faculty of Education, University of Toronto, for his valuable contribution to this Teacher's Edition.

Printed in the United States of America

Teacher's Edition   ISBN: 0-395-21672-9

CONTENTS

INTRODUCTION

Houghton Mifflin Company is proud to introduce *ALGEBRA, Structure and Method, Book 1,* a completely new text for the initial course in algebra. The format, organization, exercises, and features are innovative yet the text retains the mathematical soundness of previous editions.

We invite you to browse through the next few pages of this Teacher's Edition, which illustrate many of the features of this new edition by showing reduced sample pages from the text.

Features

1. *ALGEBRA, Structure and Method, Book 1,* covers all the essentials of first-year algebra.
2. Concepts and skills are developed in a direct, logically ordered sequence.
3. Expository sections are short and readable, without sacrificing mathematical accuracy. Abundant illustrative examples and diagrams promote understanding.
4. The expository material and the exercises employ a problem-solving approach which gives students an increased awareness of how algebra relates to everyday life. In this context the relevance of the study of algebra is apparent.
5. Oral Exercises provide opportunities for student-teacher interaction.
6. A multitude of carefully selected exercises and verbal problems are graded in difficulty, to allow for student differences.
7. Self-Tests, Chapter Summaries, Chapter Tests, Programmed Chapter Reviews, and Cumulative Reviews serve as built-in evaluation aids.
8. Maintaining Skills sections provide opportunities for students to practice basic arithmetic and algebraic skills.
9. Excellent enrichment features are numerous and varied. Consumer Notes sections add new and practical information often missing in academic courses. Other features include the following: Career Notes, Biographical Notes, Historical Notes, Just for Fun, Puzzle Time, Computer Activity, Applications, and Extra for Experts.
10. Topics such as inequalities, division of polynomials, and quadratic functions and equations, which are necessary but which can be difficult for students, are reserved for the latter part of the course, allowing students time to grow into these topics.
11. The imaginative, streamlined design motivates interest and helps organize the flow of material. Red panels highlight the objectives and key concepts.
12. The book contains answers to Self-Tests and odd-numbered exercises, all tables needed for the course, extra practice in problem solving, a list of symbols, and a complete glossary and index.

Organization of the Text

The text consists of twelve chapters, each divided into at least two major sections. The main sections are in turn divided into numbered lessons, each of which begins with one stated objective, and ends with a generous number of oral and written exercises.

1

The Language of Algebra

1-1 Numerals and Expressions

OBJECTIVE To learn how to simplify numerical expressions.

The numerical expressions

$$5 - 1, \quad 3.5 + 0.5, \quad 36 \div 9,$$
$$1 + 1 + 1 + 1, \quad 34 - 30,$$
$$2 \times 2 \text{ or } 2 \cdot 2 \quad [\cdot \text{ means } \times]$$

all have the *value four*. A numeral, or numerical expression, is a *name* for a number. The number is the value of the expression.

To say that any two of the expressions, such as "36 ÷ 9" and "4", name the same number, you use the equality symbol, =. You write

$$36 \div 9 = 4$$

and say, "thirty-six divided by nine equals (or is equal to) four." Of course, "4" is the *simplest* name for *four*.

Whenever you replace a numerical expression by the simplest, or most common, name of its value, you say that you have **simplified the expression.**

★ *Self-Test 1*

Be sure that you understand these terms:

inequality (p. 255)   between (p. 256)   equal sets (p. 258)
subset (p. 258)   finite set (p. 258)   infinite set (p. 258)

Be sure that you understand these symbols:

$<$ (p. 255) $>$ (p. 255) $\subset$ (p. 258)

Replace each __?__ with $<$ or $>$ to make a true statement.

1. 2 _?_ -1 2. -3 _?_ 2   Objective 7-1, p. 255

Translate into words.

Chapter Summary

1. The solution set of a system of open sentences in two variables is the set of ordered pairs of numbers that satisfy all the sentences of the system.
2. The solutions of pairs of linear equations in two variables may be estimated by graphing, and computed by the substitution or the addition-or-subtraction method.
3. The graph of the solution set of a system of inequalities is the intersection of the graphs of the inequalities.

Chapter Test

9-1   1. Solve graphically: $x - y = 3$
                              $x + y = 7$

Programmed Chapter Review

9-1   1. __?__ lines are lines that lie in the same plane, but have no point in common.   Parallel

       2. The graphs of "$y = -x + 1$" and "$y = -x + 3$" __?__ (intersect, coincide, have no common point).   have no common point

9-2   3. In order to solve the system $\begin{array}{l} 3x + 2y = -18 \\ x - 3y = -6 \end{array}$ by substitution, transform the second equation to $x =$ __?__. $3y - 6$

       4. Substituting in the first equation in Exercise 3 gives __?__ = __?__. $3(3y - 6) + 2y = -18$

       5. A system equivalent to the one in Exercise 3 is:

Cumulative Review, Chapters 1–6

Simplify each expression.

1. $3(19 - 11)$ 2. $4(-2) + 8$ 3. $-11 + (-15) + 20$

4. $(-3)^2(-2) + 4$ 5. $\dfrac{12 - 18}{-2} + 3(5)$ 6. $(-6)^2 + 3(-2) + 4$

If $x = 3$, $y = -2$, $z = 0$, and $w = 4$, evaluate each expression.

7. $2x + w$ 8. $3y - 2z$ 9. xy^2 10. $wx - 2y^3$

11. $xz^2 + 2wy$ 12. $xw + 6y + 3z$ 13. $\dfrac{xy - w}{5}$ 14. $\dfrac{-7wy}{x^2w + y^3}$

Self-Tests at the end of each major section include questions which are keyed specifically to the objectives stated at the beginning of each lesson within the section. Answers to these questions are provided at the back of the text. In addition to questions, each self-test includes, where applicable, a review of new vocabulary and symbols, complete with page references.

Each chapter is followed by a Chapter Summary, a Chapter Test, and a Programmed Chapter Review. The tests and reviews are keyed to the numbered lessons in the text. Alternate Chapter Tests are provided in this Teacher's Edition, beginning on page T15.

After every three chapters there is a Cumulative Review, a total of four in all.

T6

Pedagogical Features

Diagnostic Tests in Arithmetic precede the text and are helpful in pinpointing difficulties students may have with computational skills. The tests cover the operations with whole numbers and rational numbers, including work with decimals and percents.

The text is easy to read and generously illustrated. Lesson objectives and key concepts are highlighted with colored panels to help students grasp and review essentials quickly. Each topic is presented clearly in a short, concise section. Many illustrative examples with complete solutions appear in both the text and the exercises. Clear, accurate diagrams make effective use of color.

Diagnostic Tests in Arithmetic*

1. Whole Numbers—Addition

1. $\begin{array}{r} 6 \\ +9 \\ \hline \end{array}$	2. $\begin{array}{r} 2 \\ 2 \\ +3 \\ \hline \end{array}$	3. $\begin{array}{r} 4 \\ 6 \\ +7 \\ \hline \end{array}$	4. $\begin{array}{r} 55 \\ +25 \\ \hline \end{array}$	5. $\begin{array}{r} 68 \\ +15 \\ \hline \end{array}$
6. $\begin{array}{r} 575 \\ +371 \\ \hline \end{array}$	7. $\begin{array}{r} 778 \\ +177 \\ \hline \end{array}$	8. $\begin{array}{r} 814 \\ 857 \\ +311 \\ \hline \end{array}$	9. $\begin{array}{r} 7456 \\ 3701 \\ 6101 \\ +5592 \\ \hline \end{array}$	

---

52 *Chapter 2*

2-6 Subtraction of Real Numbers

> **OBJECTIVE** To learn how to express differences and how to simplify expressions containing differences.

If you buy a 20-cent candy bar and give the clerk a quarter, he may hand you a nickel and say

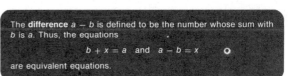

"20 and 5 is 25."

The clerk uses addition,

$$20 + 5 = 25,$$

to do subtraction,

$$25 - 20 = 5.$$

In general:

> The **difference** $a - b$ is defined to be the number whose sum with b is a. Thus, the equations
> $$b + x = a \quad \text{and} \quad a - b = x$$
> are equivalent equations.

Example 1 State an equation involving x to fit the diagram below, and solve the equation.

Solution Each of the following equations fits the diagram:

(1) $3 + x = 7$ (2) $x = 7 - 3$

The solution of each equation is 4. *Answer*

Oral Exercises

Use the distributive property to simplify each expression.

1. $2(40 + 3)$
2. $3(50 + 4)$
3. $5(20 + 4)$
4. $4(30 + 5)$
5. $2(20 - 4)$
6. $3(40 - 3)$
7. $4(500 - 1)$
8. $5(300 - 2)$
9. $8(2.5)$
10. $6(5.5)$
11. $6(7.5)$
12. $4(9.5)$

Written Exercises

Evaluate each of the following expressions in two ways.

Sample $(-2)[4 + (-1)]$

Solution

1. Simplify the sum $[4 + (-1)]$ and then multiply it by -2:

$$(-2)[4 + (-1)] = (-2)(3) = -6 \quad \textit{Answer}$$

2. Apply the distributive property to $(-2)[4 + (-1)]$ and then simplify the resulting expression:

$$(-2)[4 + (-1)] = (-2)(4) + (-2)(-1)$$
$$= -8 + 2 = -6 \quad \textit{Answer}$$

A 1. $(-6)(6 + 4)$ 2. $(-3)[(-1) + (-7)]$ 3. $[18 + (-5)](-2)$
   4. $(-5 + 20)(0)$ 5. $0[-3 + (-21)]$ 6. $27[2 + (-2)]$

Problems

Solve each problem. If no diagram is given, make a sketch.

A 1. The screen of a Model 610 television set is a rectangle, 10 centimeters (cm) wider than it is high. Model 702 has a screen which is 2 cm wider and 3 cm higher and has 240 square centimeters more area. Find the dimensions of the Model 610 screen.

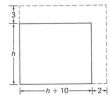

2. A tunnel is to have a rectangular cross sec-

Find the area of the building if the area devoted to seats is 7200 square meters.

5. An Ace paving machine can pave a strip five times as long as it is wide in one hour. A Goliath machine paves a strip one meter wider than the Ace. In one hour the Goliath travels 3 meters farther than the Ace and paves an area 27 square meters greater. Find the width of the strip each machine paves.

6. When a ditch 2 meters wide and 1 meter deep was dug around a square building (and adjacent to it) the volume of earth removed was 192 cubic meters. Find the dimensions of the building.

7. The figure shows a cross section of a semicircular tunnel. The concrete is 1 meter thick

Looking Ahead ▶ You have now learned the basic methods for solving simple equations. In order to be able to solve more complicated equations, you need to learn how to operate with expressions called *polynomials*. You will also need to learn how to work with *fractions*. The next three chapters are devoted to these topics.

There is an abundance of exercises, both oral and written. Most exercises are arranged "in parallel"; that is, the odd-numbered exercises in a set provide the same type of practice as the even-numbered exercises. Written Exercises are graded by the letters A, B, and C, in order of increasing difficulty.

Current word problems test understanding of material and, by providing applications, help make algebraic concepts more meaningful. The metric system of measurement is used to a great extent. Seven pages of Extra Practice in Problem Solving are provided at the end of the text.

Looking Ahead features help students see the direction they are going and understand the relationship between what they have learned and what they are about to learn.

The following references provide students with quick access to specific information and page references to appropriate sections of the text:

Special Features

Maintaining Skills pages occur at the end of chapters and answer the need for continuing practice of basic arithmetic and algebraic skills. Each section reviews only a few specific skills, and an example with a complete solution is provided for each skill.

Maintaining Skills

Remember how?

$$2\frac{1}{3} = 2 + \frac{1}{3} = \frac{6}{3} + \frac{1}{3} = \frac{7}{3}$$

$$8\frac{2}{5} = 8 + \frac{2}{5} = \frac{40}{5} + \frac{2}{5} = \frac{42}{5}$$

Now practice:

1. $5\frac{2}{3}$ 2. $6\frac{1}{8}$ 3. $4\frac{3}{5}$ 4. $7\frac{3}{8}$

5. $2\frac{11}{23}$ 6. $1\frac{21}{28}$ 7. $42\frac{1}{3}$ 8. $67\frac{2}{5}$

Remember how?

$$\frac{42}{5} = 8\frac{2}{5} \qquad 5\overline{)42} \;\; \begin{array}{r} 8 \\ \underline{40} \\ 2 \end{array}$$

Now practice:

9. $\frac{17}{10}$ 10. $\frac{24}{5}$ 11. $\frac{61}{11}$ 12. $\frac{33}{2}$

13. $\frac{48}{17}$ 14. $\frac{52}{6}$ 15. $\frac{38}{3}$ 16. $\frac{105}{12}$

Remember how?

$$3\frac{1}{4} + 6\frac{2}{5} = \frac{13}{4} + \frac{32}{5}$$

$$= \frac{13 \cdot 5}{4 \cdot 5} + \frac{32 \cdot 4}{5 \cdot 4}$$

$$= \frac{65}{20} + \frac{128}{20} = \frac{193}{20} = 9\frac{13}{20}$$

Now practice:

17. $1\frac{1}{3} + 2\frac{3}{4}$ 18. $4\frac{1}{2} + 7\frac{3}{8}$

19. $12\frac{2}{5} - 11\frac{1}{3}$ 20. $7\frac{1}{4} - 5\frac{2}{3}$

21. $12\frac{5}{6} + 7\frac{1}{3}$ 22. $18\frac{5}{6} - 1\frac{1}{2}$

Remember how?

$$3\frac{1}{3} \times 4\frac{1}{5} = \frac{\overset{2}{\cancel{10}}}{\cancel{3}} \times \frac{\overset{7}{\cancel{21}}}{\cancel{5}} = 14$$

Now practice:

23. $2\frac{1}{3} \times 4\frac{1}{2}$ 24. $3\frac{1}{5} \times 5\frac{3}{10}$ 25. $8\frac{3}{4} \times \frac{2}{5}$

26. $5\frac{1}{2} \times \frac{11}{12}$ 27. $3\frac{6}{7} \times 2\frac{1}{3}$ 28. $1\frac{1}{8} \times 3\frac{11}{15}$

Remember how?

$$2\frac{3}{4} \div 5\frac{1}{2} = \frac{11}{4} \div \frac{11}{2}$$

$$= \frac{\overset{1}{\cancel{11}}}{\underset{2}{\cancel{4}}} \times \frac{\overset{1}{\cancel{2}}}{\underset{1}{\cancel{11}}} = \frac{1}{2}$$

Now practice:

29. $3\frac{1}{2} \div 1\frac{3}{4}$ 30. $3\frac{1}{4} \div 2\frac{5}{8}$ 31. $2\frac{1}{2} \div 3\frac{2}{3}$

32. $1\frac{3}{8} \div 5\frac{1}{2}$ 33. $1\frac{2}{7} \div 4\frac{1}{3}$ 34. $5\frac{3}{4} \div 3\frac{3}{4}$

195

Consumer Note $$
Nutrition Labeling

Have you noticed the nutrition information that is printed on the labels of many canned foods? For example, a can of corn has:

Nutrition Information per Serving

Calories 230	Carbohydrates 50 grams
Protein 4 grams	Fat 2 grams

Percentage of U.S. Recommended Daily Allowance (U.S. RDA) per Serving

Protein	6	Riboflavin (B$_2$)	6
Vitamin A	4	Niacin	8
Vitamin C	20	Calcium	Less than 2
Thiamin (B$_1$)	2	Iron	4

Biographical Note
Doris Margaret Wills

Doris Margaret Wills (1902–1963) was born in Maryland. She received her bachelor's degree from Cornell University and did graduate work at George Washington University. At first her interests were in astronomy. She worked at the Harvard Observatory and became acting director of the Maria Mitchell Observatory in 1928. In 1942 she became a research engineer for Brown Instruments Division of Minneapolis-Honeywell Regulator Company, which later became Honeywell, Incorporated. There she achieved recognition as an authority on the theory of control system engineering. Control systems may be used to regulate things such as the temperature of the rooms

Career Note
Environmental Health Technician

Environmental health technicians may work on air and water pollution control, noise control, or the enforcement of sanitation laws. They may be employed in health laboratories, food processing companies, water treatment plants, or sewage disposal plants. Their work includes chemical and bacteriological analyses of food or water samples. There are positions for environmental health technicians in local, state, and federal government agencies. These technicians inspect restaurants and hotels to see that sanitation regulations are observed.

The usual educational requirement is an associate degree or two years of college with courses in the natural

Historical Note
Greater than—less than

The symbols for "greater than" and "less than" were invented by Thomas Harriot (1560–1621), an English mathematician and astronomer. They appeared in his algebra book, which was published in 1631, ten years after his death. He also used Recorde's symbol of equality (page 9). Harriot was appointed geographer for Sir Walter Raleigh's expedition to Roanoke, Virginia, in 1585–1586. His report of that trip was included in Hakluyt's *Voyages*, published in 1600.

Many interesting topics are explored in sections headed *Consumer Note, Biographical Note, Career Note,* and *Historical Note.* Consumer Notes offer up-to-date practical information about a variety of subjects. Biographical Notes present background material about famous people. Career Notes lead students to think about various occupations and their educational requirements. Historical Notes give interesting insights into the history of mathematical notation.

Fourteen *optional* sections entitled *Computer Activity* offer a computer approach to solving problems that students encounter in algebra. The programs (in BASIC) are given to the students, and no attempt is made to teach BASIC as such.

Extra for Experts sections challenge students who want to extend their understanding of algebra.

Computer Activity

If you have access to a computer that will accept BASIC, try this program. It will test factors for you.

```
10  PRINT "WHAT IS YOUR INTEGER";
20  INPUT N
30  PRINT "WHAT FACTOR DO YOU WISH TO TEST";
40  INPUT F
50  LET Q=N/F
60  IF Q=INT(Q) THEN 90
70  PRINT "NOT A FACTOR; TRY AGAIN."
80  GOTO 30
90  PRINT "CORRECT. ";F;" IS A FACTOR OF ";N;"."
100 END
```

Note. "IF Q=INT(Q)" in line 60 tests whether the divisor is a factor.

280 *Chapter 7*

Extra for Experts ExtraExtraExtraExtraExtraExt
Equations and Inequalities
Involving Absolute Value

Equations and inequalities involving absolute value (Section 2-3) occur frequently in higher mathematics.

Consider the following sentences and their graphs:

$|x| = 3$

$|x| > 3$

$|x| < 3$

From these graphs, you can see that

"$|x| = 3$" means "$x = 3$ or $x = -3$";

"$|x| > 3$" means "$x > 3$ or $x < -3$";

"$|x| < 3$" means "$x < 3$ and $x > -3$";

that is, "$-3 < x < 3$."

Example 1 Solve $|2t - 5| = 3$.

Solution $|2t - 5| = 3$ means the *disjunction*:

$2t - 5 = 3$	or	$2t - 5 = -3$
$2t = 8$	or	$2t = 2$
$t = 4$	or	$t = 1$

∴ the solution set is $\{1, 4\}$. *Answer*

Example 2 Solve $|2t - 5| > 3$.

Solution $|2t - 5| > 3$ means the *disjunction*:

$2t - 5 > 3$ or $2t - 5 < -3$

Completing the solution is left to you. You should find that the solution set is

$\{$all real numbers that are less than 1 or greater than 4$\}$. *Answer*

Just for Fun ○○○○○○○○○○○○○○○○

Suppose that you earned 2¢ for each problem that you solved correctly, but had to pay back 1¢ for each problem that you failed to solve correctly. Suppose that after doing 45 problems, you were 15¢ ahead. How many problems had you solved correctly?

Just for Fun and *Puzzle Time* activities break the pace and provide mathematical puzzles and intriguing problems.

Puzzle Time ○○○○○○○○○○○○○○○○

Suppose a semicircle with radius 1 is drawn with its center at the vertex, *B*, of ∠*ABC*. Suppose also that ∠*DEB* and ∠*FGB* are right angles. Then:

$$\cos \angle ABC = \frac{BE}{1} = BE$$

$$\sin \angle ABC = \frac{DE}{1} = DE$$

Find the segment whose length is tan ∠*ABC*.

Applications sections give students an opportunity to use their knowledge to solve problems.

Applications
Electrical Power and Energy

Power is associated with the flow of an electric current in a circuit. Electrical power is measured in watts. The amount of power that is used depends on the voltage of the source of electricity and on the current. Current is the rate of flow of electrical charge, measured in amperes. Most household appliances (with the exception of large ones, such as stoves or clothes dryers) operate at between 115 and 125 volts. Look at some electrical appliances in your home. The voltage and power are usually labeled.

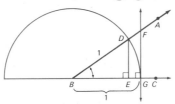

The watt, ampere, and volt are units in the metric system. Using these units of measurement, power (*P*) is related to voltage (*V*) and current (*I*) by the formula

$$P = VI.$$

Example 1 If current from a 120-volt source flows through a 100-watt light bulb, find the amount of current flowing in the circuit.

Solution You are given *V* = 120 and *P* = 100. Use the formula:

$$P = VI$$
$$100 = 120 \cdot I$$
$$I = \frac{100}{120} = \frac{5}{6}$$
$$I = \frac{5}{6} \text{ or about 0.83 ampere } \quad \textit{Answer}$$

Supplementary Materials

This Teacher's Edition contains section-by-section commentary on the student text: mathematical background material, teaching suggestions, chalkboard examples, and extensions. Annotated alternate chapter tests, an individualized assignment guide, and a table of related references are also provided. Answers to oral and written exercises, problems, and puzzles are included, most appearing right on the full-sized facsimiles of the student pages.

The Solution Key provides step-by-step solutions for every written exercise and problem.

For use after section 9-2 of text ALGEBRA: Structure and Method, Book 1 Sheet 59

NAME _____ SCORE _____

Solution by the Graphic Method; Solution by the Substitution Method

Solve each system by graphing.

1. $x - y = 3$
$x + y = 7$

2. $x + y = 3$
$x - y = 5$

3. $x + y = 9$
$x = 3 + y$

4. $x - 4y = -1$
$x + 4y = 7$

5. $x = -4 - y$
$y = 8 + x$

6. $3x - 2y = 6$
$x + y = 2$

7. $x + y = 1$
$y = -2x$

8. $x = 6$
$2x - $

Write an equation of a line parallel to the line w
given value as y-intercept.

10. $y = \frac{2}{3}x + 1; \ -3$

11. $y = $

Solve each system of equations using the substit
first variable in the first equation as the first com

13. $3x + y = 16$
$x = 5y$

14. $a + $

16. $2e - f = 6$
$e + 2f = 8$

17. $x - $
$\frac{1}{5}(x + $

NAME _____ CLASS _____ DATE _____ SCORE _____

2 Test 5 **TRANSFORMING EQUATIONS** (2-5 through 2-7)

Directions: Write the answers in the spaces provided.

QUESTIONS

Section 2-5

Solve each equation using transformation by addition.

1. $y + (-3) = 4$

2. $x + 9 = 19$

3. $7 + n = -5$

4. $16 = p + (-4)$

5. $5 = (-m) + (-2)$

Write equations and solve.

6. A number plus 7 equals -4. Find the number.

7. What number must be added to -24 to get a sum of 11?

ANSWERS

1. _____ (5)
2. _____ (5)
3. _____ (5)
4. _____ (5)
5. _____ (5)
6. _____ (5)
7. _____ (5)
8. _____ (5)
9. _____ (5)
10. _____ (5)
11. _____ (5)
12. _____ (5)
13. _____ (5)

Section 2-6

Simplify.

8. $26 - 8$

9. $13 - (-7)$

10. $-30 - (-9 + 7)$

11. $(75 - 25) - (100 - 75)$

12. $(7 - 21) - (-18 + 2)$

13. $4 - 8 - 6 + 16 - 4$

Duplicating Masters offer extra practice for students who need reinforcement. Each duplicating master is keyed to the student text.

Progress Tests are a convenient way to measure achievement and to keep track of each student's performance. Each test is keyed to the student text. Answers to all tests appear in the Teacher's Annotated Editions of the Progress Tests.

Basic Philosophy

This textbook has been designed for the wide range of students taking first-year algebra. It covers all the essentials of such a course, but certain mathematical refinements have been left for a second course in algebra. The emphasis in this course is on teaching elementary algebra as an aid to solving everyday problems. This is carried out through carefully chosen sets of problems and extra sections on Applications and Consumer Notes.

Organization

The text consists of twelve chapters, each divided into at least two major sections. The main sections are in turn divided into lessons each of which begins with one stated objective, and ends with a generous number of oral and written exercises. Each major section includes at least one Self-Test, and each chapter ends with a Chapter Summary, a Chapter Test, and a Programmed Chapter Review.

A glance through the Contents of this text reveals that the material falls naturally into four parts —Chapters 1–3, 4–6, 7–9, and 10–12—each of which is followed by a Cumulative Review.

The first part, Chapters 1–3, deals with the four fundamental operations on real numbers and their use in the solution of simple equations and related problems. (The chapter-opening illustrations for this part are chosen from the field of fine arts.)

The second part, Chapters 4–6, treats polynomials, factoring, and fractions, leading to the solution of more complicated problems. Division of polynomials is discussed following mixed expressions. (The chapter-opening illustrations for this part are selected from the physical sciences.)

The third part, Chapters 7–9, discusses inequalities, functions and relations, and systems of open sentences, extending the range of problems that can be solved. Graphing of straight lines in the coordinate plane is presented. (The chapter-opening illustrations for this part are chosen from the biological sciences.)

The fourth part, Chapters 10–12, introduces work with irrational numbers and presents quadratic functions and equations, again extending the problem-solving capabilities of the student. This part concludes with a brief introduction to geometry and trigonometry. (The chapter-opening illustrations for this part come from the social sciences.)

Suggestions for Teaching

The best way to use any particular textbook varies from teacher to teacher and from student to student. Therefore, any printed suggestions such as these cannot be expected to fit all situations. Nevertheless, some general comments may serve to clarify the authors' point of view.

First, it is important that students learn how to use this textbook. They should be encouraged to read the explanations and to ask questions about what they have read. Reading mathematics is not like reading a story; it is a special skill which has to be developed with practice. Every sentence and every word must be considered with care. Patience and perseverance at the beginning will pay large dividends later on. By encouraging students to develop their ability to read mathematical material, you will help them acquire a skill that will be of inestimable value in all their future work.

Discuss the organization of the text with the students. For example, call their attention to the panels that display the objective and key concepts of each section and the Self-Tests within each chapter. The students will find the Table of Symbols (p. x), the Glossary (pp. 493–501), and the Index (pp. 502–510) helpful references.

Uses of the Exercise and Review Material

Chapters 1–11 contain approximately 5800 oral, written, review, and test exercises. The oral exercises may be used in a number of ways.

1. They may be used to determine whether or not the students have understood the concepts developed in a section. The exercises have been carefully designed to probe the key ideas presented in the section.
2. The teacher may elect to use them, in whole or in part, as written assignments.
3. They may be used as a basis for group chalkboard work.

In assigning the written exercises, the teacher should keep in mind the following factors.

1. The exercise sets in most cases contain more exercises than a student can complete in a reasonable length of time. Care should be taken not to overload students with assignments.

2. In many instances the exercises are designed in pairs so that an assignment of a number of odd-numbered exercises provides the same practice as the assignment of the corresponding even-numbered exercises.

3. Generally, the teacher may use some written exercises for supervised study in the classroom and still have sufficient exercise material in the same section for a homework assignment.

The tests and reviews in the textbook may be used for individual or class review. Alternate Chapter Tests are given in this Teacher's Edition, beginning on this page.

Arithmetic skills may be tested by using the Diagnostic Tests on pages xi–xiii. The skills are maintained by continual use in connection with the algebraic work and specifically on the "Maintaining Skills" pages following each of Chapters 1–5.

ALTERNATE CHAPTER TESTS

Test for Chapter 1

Simplify.

1-1   **1.** $\dfrac{3(12 - 2)}{5}$ 6   **2.** $\dfrac{8 + (18 \div 3)}{2 \times 7}$ 1

1-2   **3.** Evaluate $\dfrac{36}{a + b}$ if $a = 2$ and $b = 4$.   6

1-3   **4.** Write $3x^3y^2$ in factored form.
$3 \cdot x \cdot x \cdot x \cdot y \cdot y$

   5. Write the product of "a squared" and "b cubed" in exponential form. a^2b^3

1-4   **6.** Evaluate $a^2 - 2ab$ if $a = 4$ and $b = 2$.   0

1-5   **7.** Find the value of V if $V = \pi r^2h$, $\pi \doteq \frac{22}{7}$, $r = 7$ and $h = 6$.   924

   If $n \in \{0, 1, 2, 3, 4, 5\}$, write the solution set of:

1-6   **8.** $3x + 1 = 10$ $\{3\}$

   9. $n + 3 \neq 7$ $\{0, 1, 2, 3, 5\}$

1-7   **10.** Write a variable expression for:
   a. the number n increased by 5. $n + 5$
   b. the product of 4 and the number n, decreased by 1. $4n - 1$

   11. Write an equation for this word sentence: Eight more than one-half the number t is 18. $\frac{1}{2}t + 8 = 18$

1-8   **12.** Use the 5 step method to solve this problem: There are three times as many students in the drama club as there are in the camera club. If there are 45 students in the drama club, how many are in the camera club?   15 students

Test for Chapter 2

2-1   **1.** Graph $\{^-4, ^-2, 0, 1\}$ on a number line.

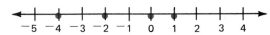

2-2   **2.** Use a number line to show how you would find $^-6 + 4$.

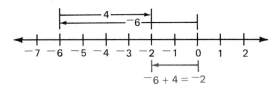

   3. Simplify $(12 + ^-20) + ^-6$. $^-14$

   Simplify.

2-3   **4.** $-(^-8 + 6)$ 2   **5.** $|^-2| + |^-6|$ 8

2-4   **6.** $5 + (-6) = (-6) + 5$ is an illustration of the ___?___ property for addition.
   commutative

   7. Simplify:
   $23 + (-6) + (-2) + 18 + (-12)$.   21

   Solve.

2-5   **8.** $k + 5 = 13$ $k = 8$

   9. $-3 = -6 + y$ $y = 3$

   10. Solve by using an equation: Twelve more than a number is 8. Find the number. -4

2-6   **11.** Simplify $-4 - (-2) + 8$.   6

Solve.

2-7   **12.** $r + 4 = 9$ $r = 5$

     13. $-3 = k - 8$ $k = 5$

14. Solve this problem by using an equation: Jean said, "Three less than my number is -12." Find Jean's number. -9

Test for Chapter 3

Simplify.

3-1   **1.** $(-1)(-4)(5)$ 20

     2. $(3)(-2)^2(-4)$ -48

3-2   **3.** $-6(-3) + (-2)$ 16

     4. $-3[4 + (-6)]$ 6

5. Evaluate in the simplest way:
$21 \cdot 196 + 23 \cdot 196$. 8624

Simplify.

3-3   **6.** $3xy(-\frac{1}{3})$ $-xy$

     7. $\frac{1}{2}(4x + 8y)$ $2x + 4y$

Solve.

3-4   **8.** $\frac{1}{3}c = -24$ $c = -72$

     9. $\frac{3}{2} = -3z$ $z = -\frac{1}{2}$

Simplify.

3-5   **10.** $\frac{64}{-8}$ -8 **11.** $-50 \div (-10)$ 5

     12. $(-16) \div (-\frac{1}{2})$ 32

Solve.

3-6   **13.** $12a = -36$ $a = -3$

     14. $-39 = -13x$ $x = 3$

3-7   **15.** $\frac{b}{3} + 3 = 9$ $b = 18$

     16. $-8 = 2 - 5k$ $k = 2$

17. Solve: Twenty-one increased by twice a number is 9. Find the number. -6

3-8   **18.** Give the reason.
$$2x + 6 = 20$$
$$(2x + 6) - 6 = 20 - 6 \qquad \underline{\quad?\quad}$$
Add. prop. of equality and rule for subtr.

Test for Chapter 4

Simplify.

4-1   **1.** $16x + 3y - 30x + 9y$ $-14x + 12y$

     2. $3x^2 - 2xy + 4x^2 + 8xy + y^3$
       $7x^2 + 6xy + y^3$

Solve.

4-2   **3.** $6y - 2y = -16$ $y = -4$

     4. $5(k - 2) - 2(k + 4) = 6$ $k = 8$

4-3   **5.** $6x - 5 = x + 10$ $x = 3$

     6. $3(2 + r) - 2r = 2r + 11$ $r = -5$

4-4   **7.** Michael is 6 years older than his sister Lesley. In three years he will be twice as old as she. How old are they now? Michael: 9 yr; Lesley: 3 yr

4-5   **8.** Find three consecutive odd numbers whose sum is 93.   29, 31, 33

4-6   **9.** Subtract $2w^2 - 3w + 2$ from $4w^2 - 2w + 5$. $2w^2 + w + 3$

     10. Find the sum of $2x^2 + xy$, $-y^2 - xy$, and $-2xy + x^2 + y^2$. $3x^2 - 2xy$

Simplify.

4-7   **11.** $(4a^2b)(3ab^2)$ $12a^3b^3$

     12. $(-k)(-k^2n)(3kn^2)$ $3k^4n^3$

4-8   **13.** $2s(-2st)^2$ $8s^3t^2$

     14. $(3x^2)^3(-2x)^2$ $108x^8$

4-9   **15.** $2x(x^2 - 3x + 5)$ $2x^3 - 6x^2 + 10x$

     16. $3ab(a^2 - ab + 2b^2)$ $3a^3b - 3a^2b^2 + 6ab^3$

4-10   **17.** $(2s - 3)(3s - 2)$ $6s^2 - 13s + 6$

     18. $(2u - v)(u + v)$ $2u^2 + uv - v^2$

4-11   **19.** Find a polynomial expression in x for the shaded area. $16x + 16$

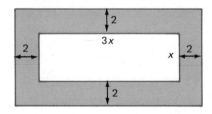

20. A rectangular parking lot is 6 meters longer than it is wide. A border 2 meters wide is painted white around the edge as a no-parking area. The area painted is 200 square meters. Find the dimensions of the parking lot.   20 m by 26 m

Test for Chapter 5

5-1   **1.** Find the prime factorization of 420.
$2^2 \cdot 3 \cdot 5 \cdot 7$

2. Find the greatest common factor of 150 and 210.   30

5-2   **3.** Simplify $\dfrac{-8x^3y^4}{4x^5y^2} \cdot -\dfrac{2y^2}{x^2}$

4. Find the missing factor:
$36a^3b^5c^3 = (-12ab^2c)(\underline{\ ?\ })$. $-3a^2b^3c^2$

Simplify.

5-3   **5.** $\dfrac{10x^3 - 5x^2}{5x}$ $2x^2 - x$

6. $\dfrac{k^2 + 2k}{k} - \dfrac{2k^2 - 6k}{2k}$ 5

7. Factor $10x^2 + 15x^2y$. $5x^2(2 + 3y)$

5-4   **8.** Express $c^2(a^2 + 2c)(a^2 - 2c)$ as a polynomial. $a^4c^2 - 4c^4$

9. Factor $25d^2 - 16$. $(5d + 4)(5d - 4)$

Express each product as a polynomial.

5-5   **10.** $(2a - 3b)^2$ $4a^2 - 12ab + 9b^2$

11. $(u^2 - 2a^2v^2)^2$ $u^4 - 4u^2a^2v^2 + 4a^4v^4$

Factor.

12. $25x^2 + 10x + 1$ $(5x + 1)(5x + 1)$

13. $x^2 - 6xy + 9y^2$ $(x - 3y)(x - 3y)$

Express each product as a polynomial.

5-6   **14.** $(2a - 3b)(3a - 2b)$ $6a^2 - 13ab + 6b^2$

15. $(j - 2k)(4j + 3k)$ $4j^2 - 5jk - 6k^2$

Factor.

5-7   **16.** $f^2 - 4f + 3$ $(f - 3)(f - 1)$

17. $g^2 + 5gh + 6h^2$ $(g + 3h)(g + 2h)$

5-8   **18.** $y^2 - 5y - 50$ $(y - 10)(y + 5)$

19. $y^2 - yx - 6x^2$ $(y - 3x)(y + 2x)$

5-9   **20.** $5w^2 - 2w - 7$ $(5w - 7)(w + 1)$

21. $2m^2 - 7mn - 4n^2$ $(2m + n)(m - 4n)$

5-10   **22.** $3a^3 + 2a^2 + 6a + 4$ $(a^2 + 2)(3a + 2)$

23. $3p^2 - 2r - 6p + pr$ $(3p + r)(p - 2)$

5-11   **24.** $x^2z^4 - x^6$ $x^2(z + x)(z - x)(z^2 + x^2)$

25. $2cy^3 + 6c^2y^2 + 4c^3y$ $2cy(y + 2c)(y + c)$

Solve.

5-12   **26.** $(x - 3)(x + 4) = 0$ $\{3, -4\}$

27. $x(x - 1)(x - 4) = 0$ $\{0, 1, 4\}$

5-13   **28.** $y^2 + 2y - 8 = 0$ $\{-4, 2\}$

29. $3z^2 + 2z = 1$ $\{\frac{1}{3}, -1\}$

5-14   **30.** The length of a side of one square is 3 cm longer than the length of a side of another square. Their combined area is 149 cm². Find the length of each side.   10 cm, 7 cm

Mid-Chapter Test for Chapter 6

Write in lowest terms, noting all necessary restrictions on values of the variables.

6-1   **1.** $\dfrac{2y^2 - 10y}{y^2 - 6y + 5}$ $\dfrac{2y}{y - 1}$; $y \neq 5, y \neq 1$

2. $\dfrac{x^3 - x}{x^3 - 2x^2 - 3x}$ $\dfrac{x - 1}{x - 3}$; $x \neq 0, x \neq 3$, $x \neq -1$

6-2   **3.** Give the ratio of 2 hours to 2 days in lowest terms.   1:24

4. Find the ratio $x:y$ in lowest terms: $8x - 6y = 0$.   3:4

6-3   **5.** $\dfrac{24x^2y^2}{3x} \cdot \dfrac{-4x}{2y}$ $-16x^2y$

6. $\dfrac{n^2 - 4}{n^2 - 1} \cdot \dfrac{n - 1}{n - 2}$ $\dfrac{n + 2}{n + 1}$

Simplify.

6-4   **7.** $\dfrac{a^2 - 4}{6a^2} \div \dfrac{a + 2}{3a}$ $\dfrac{a - 2}{2a}$

8. $\dfrac{v^2 + 3v^3}{4 - v^2} \div \dfrac{3v^3 + 4v^2 + v}{2v + v^2}$

$\dfrac{v^2(2 + v^2)}{(2 + v)(2 - v)(v + 1)}$

6-5 **9.** $\dfrac{x^2 - 7x + 12}{x^2 - 9} \cdot \dfrac{x}{x^2 - 16} \div \dfrac{x}{x + 3}$

$\dfrac{1}{x + 4}$

6-6 **10.** $\dfrac{3w + 1}{4} + \dfrac{w - 2}{8}$ $\dfrac{7w}{8}$

11. $\dfrac{3x + 2y}{3y} - \dfrac{x + 2y}{6x}$ $\dfrac{6x^2 + 3xy = 2y^2}{6xy}$

Write each fraction as a mixed expression.

6-7 **12.** $\dfrac{8 + 12c^2}{2c}$ $\dfrac{4}{c} + 6c$

13. $\dfrac{15ab^2 + 10ab}{5ab}$ $3b + 2$

6-8 **14.** Divide $3x^2 + 8x + 8$ by $x + 1$.

$3x + 5 + \dfrac{3}{x + 1}$

Solve.

6-9 **15.** $\dfrac{z}{2} - \dfrac{z}{3} = 8$ $z = 48$

16. $\dfrac{x + 2}{2} = \dfrac{2x}{3}$ $x = 6$

6-10 **17.** $\dfrac{1 + y}{y} = \dfrac{3}{y}$ $y = 2$

18. $\dfrac{4}{2y - 3} - 2 = \dfrac{7}{y}$ $y = \dfrac{21}{8}$

6-11 **19.** Express $\dfrac{1}{25}$ as a percent. 4%

20. Change $87\dfrac{1}{2}\%$ to a fraction. $\dfrac{7}{8}$

6-2 **4.** $\dfrac{x^2 - 5x - 6}{12 + 4x - x^2} - \dfrac{x + 1}{x + 2}$; $x \neq 6$, $x \neq -2$

6-2 **5.** Express the ratio of 2 kilograms to 50 grams in lowest terms. 40:1

6. Find the ratio $x:y$ from $3(7x - y) = 4y$.
1:3

Express as a single fraction in lowest terms.

6-3 **7.** $\dfrac{-10xy}{5y^2} \cdot \dfrac{12x}{6x^2y}$ $-\dfrac{4}{y^2}$

8. $\dfrac{z - 1}{z - 2} \cdot \dfrac{z^2 - 4}{z^2 - 1}$ $\dfrac{z + 2}{z + 1}$

6-4 **9.** $\dfrac{y + 2}{y^2 - 16} \div \dfrac{y + 2}{y - 4}$ $\dfrac{1}{y + 4}$

10. $\dfrac{b^2 - 9}{b} \div b^2 - 3b$ $\dfrac{b + 3}{b^2}$

11. $\dfrac{t^2 + 4t + 4}{t^2 - 4} \div \dfrac{t^2 + 2t}{t^2 - 2t}$ 1

6-5 **12.** $\dfrac{n^2 - 1}{n^2 - 9} \cdot \dfrac{n^2 + 3n}{n^2 - n - 2} \div \dfrac{n^2 - n}{n^2 - 3n}$ $\dfrac{n}{n - 2}$

6-6 **13.** $\dfrac{2 + x}{4x} + \dfrac{x - 1}{4x} + \dfrac{1 - 2x}{4x}$ $\dfrac{1}{2x}$

14. $\dfrac{a + 2b}{2} - \dfrac{a - b}{4}$ $\dfrac{a + 5b}{4}$

15. $\dfrac{3}{x + 4} - \dfrac{3}{x - 4} + \dfrac{24}{x^2 - 16}$ 0

6-7 **16.** Change to a mixed expression:

$\dfrac{6t + 3t - 2}{6t} \cdot \dfrac{3}{2} - \dfrac{1}{3t}$

17. Express as a fraction: $h - 2 - \dfrac{h - 2}{h - 1}$.

$\dfrac{(h - 2)(h - 2)}{h - 1}$

6-8 **18.** Divide $k^3 + k^2 - 3k + 8$ by $k + 3$.

$k^2 - 2k + 3 - \dfrac{1}{k + 3}$

Solve.

6-9 **19.** $\dfrac{4}{6} + b = \dfrac{5b}{6}$ $b = -4$

20. $\dfrac{3y - 6}{10} + \dfrac{3}{2} = \dfrac{y + 1}{5}$ $y = -7$

6-10 **21.** $\dfrac{x}{x + 3} - 1 = \dfrac{3}{2x}$ $x = -1$

Test for Chapter 6

Write each fraction in lowest terms, noting all necessary restrictions on values of the variables.

6-1 **1.** $\dfrac{ax^2 - 7ax + 12a}{ax^2 - 9a}$ $\dfrac{x - 4}{x + 3}$; $x \neq 3$, $x \neq -3$, $a \neq 0$

2. $\dfrac{x + 16}{x^2 - 36}$ $\dfrac{x + 16}{(x + 6)(x - 6)}$; $x \neq 6$, $x \neq -6$

3. $\dfrac{4x - 8y}{x^2 - y^2}$ $\dfrac{4(x - 2y)}{(x + y)(x - y)}$; $x \neq y$, $x \neq -y$

22. $\dfrac{3}{k+1} - \dfrac{15}{1-k^2} = \dfrac{4}{k-1}$ $k=8$

6-11 **23.** The sales tax on \$230 is \$16.10. Find the rate of sales tax.   7%

6-12 **24.** A chemist has 60 grams of a 12% solution. She wishes to dilute it to a 5% solution by adding water. How many grams of water should be added?   84 g

25. A 60% solution of acid is obtained by adding 1 liter of water to an 80% solution. Find the total number of liters in the original 80% solution.   3 ℓ

6-13 **26.** Divide \$120 into two parts so that 5% of the smaller part together with 2% of the larger part is \$3.   \$20, \$100

6-14 **27.** Pat, traveling on a motorcycle at 40 kilometers per hour, takes two hours less in going a certain distance than Sal, traveling on a motor scooter going 24 kilometers per hour. Find this distance.   120 km

6-15 **28.** Jean can count a certain amount of pennies in 12 minutes, but when Helen helps her, together they can count the same amount of pennies in 8 minutes. Find how long it would take Helen to count the pennies alone.   24 min

Test for Chapter 7

Insert a symbol to make a true statement.

7-1 **1.** $\frac{1}{4}$ _?_ $\frac{1}{8}$ >   **2.** -3 _?_ -8 >

7-2 **3.** $\{4,5\}$ _?_ $\{4,5,6,7\}$ $\subset$

4. 4 _?_ $\{4,5,6,7\}$ $\in$

7-3 **5.** Solve and graph the solution set of $3k+9 < 5(5+k)$. $k > -8$

7-4 **6.** One integer is three times another. The sum of these integers increased by 12 is less than 5 times the smaller. Find the smallest possible values for the integers.   13, 39

7-5 **7.** If $M = \{0,3,6,9\}$ and $N = \{1,2,3,4,5,6\}$, draw a Venn diagram to illustrate $M \cap N$.

7-6 **8.** Solve and graph the solution set of $-3 \le 3k+2 < 9$. $-1\frac{2}{3} \le k < 2\frac{1}{3}$

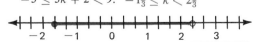

Test for Chapter 8

8-1 **1.** Find the range of the function
$$g : y \to 2y^2 + 4$$
if the domain is $\{-2, -1, 0, 1, 2\}$. $\{4, 6, 12\}$

2. A function f is defined by $f(x) = -3x + \dfrac{1}{x}$. Find $f(-1)$.   2

8-2 **3.** For an experiment the temperature of a liquid is recorded each hour for 5 hours. Make a broken-line graph from this information:

Time	Temperature
9:00 AM	8°C
10:00 AM	12°C
11:00 AM	15°C
12:00 PM	18°C
1:00 PM	20°C

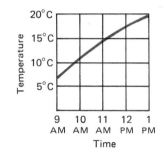

In the ordered pair $(-4, 3)$:

8-3 **4.** Name the abscissa. -4

5. Name the ordinate. 3

6. Name the quadrant in the coordinate plane in which its graph lies. Second

8-4 **7.** The graph of a relation is shown below. Is the relation a function? List the members of the domain.
No; $\{-4, -3, -2, -1, 0, 1, 2, 3, 4\}$

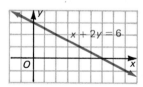

8-5 **8.** The ordered pair $(3, \underline{\ ?\ })$ is a solution of $2x - 3y = 3$. Find the missing value. 1

9. Find the solution set of $y = x + 3$ if the replacement set for x is $\{-1, 0, 1\}$.
$\{(-1, 2), (0, 3), (1, 4)\}$

8-6 **10.** Graph $x + 2y = 6$ in the coordinate plane.

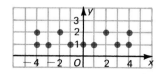

11. Does the point $(2, 3)$ satisfy $x + 2y = 6$?
No

8-7 **12.** Find the slope of the straight line passing through $(-2, 1)$ and $(3, -9)$. -2

8-8 **13.** Find the slope and y-intercept of a line from its equation $y = \frac{2}{3}x - 5$. Slope, $\frac{2}{3}$; y-intercept, -5

14. Change the equation $2x - y = 6$ into slope-intercept form. $y = 2x - 6$

8-9 **15.** Write an equation in standard form of the line passing through the point $(-1, 5)$ and having a slope of -3. $3x + y = 2$

16. Write an equation in standard form of the line passing through the points $(-2, 5)$ and $(-7, 10)$. $x + y = 3$

8-10 **17.** If s varies directly as t, and $s = 12$ when $t = 2$, find s when $t = 8$. 48

Test for Chapter 9

9-1 **1.** Solve graphically: $x + 2y = 8$
$2x - y = 1$

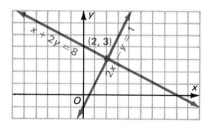

Solve by substitution.

9-2 **2.** $x + y = -3$
$2x - 3y = -21$
$(-6, 3)$

3. $m + 2n = 4$
$3m - 2n = -12$
$(-2, 3)$

9-3 **4.** Solve: An amount of $230 is made up of $5 bills and $1 bills. If there are 86 bills all together, find how many bills of each kind there are. 36 $5 bills, 50 $1 bills

Solve each system by addition or subtraction.

9-4 **5.** $2x + y = 1$
$3x + y = -1$
$(-2, 5)$

6. $-2a + b = 8$
$2a - 3b = -12$
$(-3, 2)$

9-5 **7.** $2m + 3n = 7$
$3m + 6n = 15$
$(-1, 3)$

8. $3x + 2y = 18$
$2x - 3y = -1$
$(4, 3)$

9-6 **9.** A two-digit number is 8 times the sum of its digits. If 6 times the units digit is 5 more than the tens digit, what is the number? 72

9-7 **10.** Pete left Jackson at the same time Juan left Freeport to meet each other. Pete drove at a rate of 5 km/h faster than Juan. If the cities are 780 km apart, and they met after 4 hours, how far did Pete and Juan each drive? Pete: 400 km, Juan, 380 km

Graph.

9-8 **11.** $y - 4x > 8$

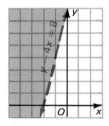

12. $y \leq 2x + 1$
   $x - y < 3$

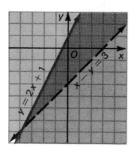

Test for Chapter 10

10-1 **1.** Determine which rational number is the greater: $-\frac{22}{5}$ or $-\frac{32}{7}$. $-\frac{22}{5}$

2. Arrange in order from least to greatest: $\frac{7}{24}, \frac{1}{3}, \frac{3}{8}, \frac{1}{4}$. $\frac{1}{4}, \frac{7}{24}, \frac{1}{3}, \frac{3}{8}$

3. Find the number halfway between $-\frac{7}{16}$ and $-\frac{8}{32}$. $-\frac{11}{32}$

Write each as a terminating or a repeating decimal.

10-2 **4.** $\frac{6}{41}$ $0.\overline{14634}$ **5.** $-\frac{19}{101}$ $-0.\overline{1881}$

Express each as a common fraction in lowest terms.

6. 3.045 $\frac{609}{200}$ **7.** $0.6\overline{5}$ $\frac{59}{90}$

Simplify.

10-3 **8.** $\sqrt{3025}$ 55   **9.** $-\sqrt{\dfrac{256}{64}}$ -2

10-4 **10.** Compute the square root of 224 to the nearest hundredth. 14.97

Find the solution set.

10-5 **11.** $a^2 = 625$ $\{25, -25\}$
12. $27y^2 - 675 = 0$ $\{5, -5\}$

Find the missing measures for the right triangles.

10-6 **13.** 34   **14.** 48

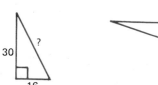

15. A ladder 8 meters long leans against a wall. The base of the ladder is 2 meters from the wall. Calculate to the nearest tenth of a meter, how far up the wall the ladder will reach. 7.7 m

Simplify.

10-7 **16.** $\dfrac{3\sqrt{10}}{6\sqrt{50}}$ $\dfrac{\sqrt{5}}{10}$

17. $(2\sqrt{6})(3\sqrt{2})(2\sqrt{3})$ 72

10-8 **18.** $2\sqrt{5} + 3\sqrt{2} - \sqrt{5} - 4\sqrt{2}$ $\sqrt{5} - \sqrt{2}$
19. $12\sqrt{2} + \sqrt{75} - \sqrt{98}$ $5\sqrt{2} + 5\sqrt{3}$

10-9 **20.** $(3 - \sqrt{2})(3 + \sqrt{2})$ 7
21. $(\sqrt{2} - \sqrt{3})^2$ $5 - 2\sqrt{6}$
22. $(3\sqrt{2} - 2\sqrt{3})(4\sqrt{2} + 3\sqrt{3})$ $6 + \sqrt{6}$
23. $\dfrac{8}{24 - 2\sqrt{5}}$ $\dfrac{48 + 4\sqrt{5}}{139}$

Solve.

10-10 **24.** $\sqrt{3x - 1} = 7$ $x = \frac{50}{3}$
25. $\sqrt{2a^2 - 25} - 5 = 0$ $a = 5$ or $a = -5$

Test for Chapter 11

11-1 **1.** y varies directly as x^2. If y is 8 when x is 5, find the value of y when x is 4. 5.12

2. Graph $y = -2x^2$.

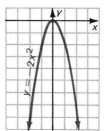

11-2 **3.** y varies inversely as x. When x is 6, y is 8. Find the value of x when y is 24. 2

4. At 25 km/h, how long does a trip take if it takes 10 hours at 10 km/h? 4 hr

11-3 **5.** If y varies inversely as x^2, and x is 4 when y is 25, find x when y is 4. 10

11-4   **6.** Find the greatest value of y, if
$y = -x^2 + x$. $\frac{1}{4}$

11-5   **7.** Draw the graph of $y = x^2 - 3x$.

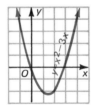

8. Write the coordinates of the vertex for the graph named in Exercise 7. $(1\frac{1}{2}, -2\frac{1}{4})$

Solve, using the property of square roots of equal numbers.

11-6   **9.** $x^2 = 144$ $x = \pm 12$

10. $3x^2 = 75$ $x = \pm 5$

11. $3y^2 - 300 = 0$ $y = \pm 10$

12. $2(z + 5)^2 = 50$ $z = -10$ or $z = 0$

11-7   **13.** Complete the square:
$x^2 - 16x + \underline{\ ?\ } = (x - \underline{\ ?\ })^2$.   64; 8

14. Solve by completing the square:
$t^2 - 2t - 143 = 0$. $t = 13$ or $t = -11$

Solve by using the quadratic formula. Express irrational answers in simplest radical form.

11-8   **15.** $x^2 + 7x + 3 = 0$ $x = \dfrac{-7 \pm \sqrt{37}}{2}$

16. $12y^2 = 7 - 6y$ $y = -\frac{1}{4} \pm \frac{1}{12}\sqrt{93}$

Find the value of the discriminant and tell how many different real roots each quadratic equation has.

17. $4c^2 - 9c - 2 = 0$ 113; two

18. $2q^2 + 3q + 25 = 0$ -191; none

Solve.

11-9   **19.** Find two integers whose sum is -5 and whose product is -24. -8 and 3

20. What must be added to the length of a rectangle 40 cm by 30 cm to increase the diagonal by 10 cm? Express your answer to the nearest hundredth.   11.96 cm

Test for Chapter 12

12-1   **1.** Graph the solution set for $3 \le x \le 5$.

2. Determine whether each of the following measures indicates an acute, obtuse, or right angle.
a. $23°$ **b.** $89°$ **c.** $136°$ **d.** $90°$
a, b. acute;   **c.** obtuse;   **d.** right

12-2   **3.** The measure of an angle is $46°$ more than the measure of its supplement. Find the measure of the supplement of the angle. $67°$

12-3   **4.** A triangle has angles with measures $36°$ and $52°$. Find the measure of the remaining angle. $92°$

5. In $\triangle ABC$, $AB = 14$, $CA = 48$ and $BC = 50$. Show whether the triangle is a right triangle or not.   Yes, since $(AB)^2 + (CA)^2 = (BC)^2$.

12-4   **6.** Given: $\triangle ABC \sim \triangle DEF$ and $\dfrac{AB}{DE} = \dfrac{3}{2}$. If $DF = 20$, find AC.   30

12-5   **7.** Find $\tan A$ to the nearest tenth.   1.9

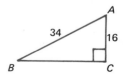

12-6   **8.** Use the table of trigonometric values on page 488 to find:
a. $\cos 38°$ 0.7880   **b.** $\tan 56°$ 1.4826
c. the measure of $\angle A$ to the nearest degree if $\sin A = 0.9820$. $79°$

12-7   **9.** A ramp is shown in the diagram. Calculate the measure of $\angle C$ to the nearest degree. (Use the table on page 488.) $15°$

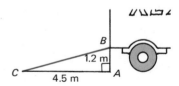

GUIDE TO INDIVIDUALIZED ASSIGNMENTS

The following Guide may be of some help to you in planning your basic assignments for a minimum course, an average course, or a maximum course. Of course, only you can tailor the assignments to the needs of your students. By keeping a check on the amount of time your students spend on homework, you can adapt the assignments to conform to the policies of your school.

You will also want to make use of some of the optional features provided in the book, according to the interests of your students. If you have access to a computer that will accept BASIC, you may wish to allow a little time to show your students how to use it. They do not need to learn the BASIC language in order to use the Computer Activities.

All the assignments refer to written exercises, with the letter *P* indicating word problems. The letter **S** identifies the "spiraled" portion of the assignment, which reviews earlier work.

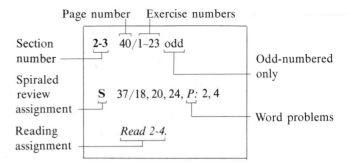

Summary Time Schedule for the Assignments

Chapter	1	2	3	4	5	6	7	8	9	10	11	12	Total
Minimum Course	13	12	13	16	25	32	9	15	13	12	0	0	160
Average Course	11	12	14	15	22	25	9	15	12	12	13	0	160
Maximum Course	9	11	12	14	22	19	9	13	13	12	12	14	160

LESSON	MINIMUM COURSE		AVERAGE COURSE		MAXIMUM COURSE	
1	1-1	3/1–16, 17, 19	1-1	3/1–16, 17, 19, 21	1-1 1-2	3/7–23 odd 6/13–25 odd
2	1-2 S	6/1–23 odd 3/18, 20, 21	1-2 S	6/1–25 odd 3/18, 20, 22	1-3 S	9/1–35 odd 3/18–24 even 6/Self-Test 1 Read 1-4.
3	1-3 S	9/1–33 odd. 3/22, 24; 6/24, 25	1-3 S	9/11–39 odd 3/23, 24; 6/22, 24	1-4 S	11/1–29 odd 9/20–44 even Read 1-5.

LESSON	MINIMUM COURSE		AVERAGE COURSE		MAXIMUM COURSE	
4	1-4 S	9/10–36 even 3/23; 6/26; 6/Self-Test 1	1-4 S	11/1–18 6/Self-Test 1 9/16, 18, 43	1-5 S	13/1–24 11/20–36 even Read 1-6.
5	1-4 S	11/1–25 odd 9/37, 38, 39	1-5 S	13/1–11 odd 9/38, 40, 42; 11/19–29 odd	1-5 1-6	14/26–46 even 19/1–16 Read 1-7.
6	1-5 S	13/1–23 odd 9/40, 42; 11/27, 29	1-5 S	13–14/13–30 11/31–36	1-7 S	21/1–10 14/25–41 odd 16/Self-Test 2 Read 1-8.
7	1-5 S	13–14/14–18 even, 25–41 odd 11/31, 33	1-5	14–15/31–52 16/Self-Test 2	1-8 S	24/1–6 15/47–52
8	1-5 S	14–15/43, 44, 47, 49; 16/Self-Test 2 11/26, 28	1-6 1-7	19/1–15 odd 21/1–9 odd	\[Maximum\]	Announce chapter test. 25/Self-Test 3 28/Programmed Chapter Review
9	1-6 S	19/1–15 odd 15/48–50	1-8 S	24/1–6 19/10, 12, 14; 21/8, 10		Administer chapter test. Read 2-1. 34/1–11 odd
10	1-7 S	21/1–9 odd 19/2, 4, 6	 S	Announce chapter test. 25/Self-Test 3 6/18, 20, 26; 9/32, 34, 44	2-2 S	36/1–12 34/2–24 even Read 2-3.
11	1-8 S	24/1–5 odd 28/Programmed Chapter Review 19/8, 10, 12; 21/2, 8		Administer chapter test. Read 2-1. 34/1–11 odd	2-3 S	40/9–23 odd 34/13, 15, 21; 37/13–19 odd Read 2-4.
12	 S	Announce chapter test. 24/2, 4 25/Self-Test 3 9/43; 11/8–22 even; 13–14/4, 6, 10, 24, 46	2-1	34/4–12 even, 13, 15, 17, 21 Read 2-2.	S	37/14–24 even, P: 1–6; 40/18–24 even
13		Administer chapter test. 29/Maintaining Skills Read 2-1.	2-2 S	36/1–12 34/14, 16, 18, 22	2-4	44/7–18; 45/P: 1–4 Read 2-5.
14	2-1	Discuss test. 34/1–23 odd Read 2-2.	2-2	37/13–24, P: 1–5	2-5 S	50/1–23 odd 45/P: 5, 6 45–46/Self-Test 1
15	2-2 S	36/1–12 34/8, 10, 14, 18, 22	2-3 S	40/1–23 odd 37/P: 6	2-5	51/25–36, P: 1–6 Read 2-6.

LESSON	MINIMUM COURSE		AVERAGE COURSE		MAXIMUM COURSE	
16	2-2 S	37/13–23 odd, *P:* 1, 3 34/2, 4, 6, 16, 20, 24 *Read 2-3.*	2-4 S	44/2–18 even 40/16, 18, 20, 24	2-6 S	55/1–29 odd, *P:* 1–3 51/*P:* 7, 8 *Read 2-7.*
17	2-3 S	40/1–23 odd 37/18, 20, 24, *P:* 2, 4 *Read 2-4.*	2-5 S	50/8–18 even; 51/*P:* 1–4 45/*P:* 1–4	2-7 S	57/1–23 odd 51/*P:* 9, 10; 55/*P:* 4–6
18	2-4 S	44/1–17 odd 40/2–24 even *Read 41/Career Note.*	2-6 S	55/1–19 odd 45/*P:* 5, 6; 50/15, 17, 19; 51/*P:* 7, 8	2-7	57/2–24 even, *P:* 1–6
19	2-4	44/10–18 even; 45/*P:* 1, 3, 5 45–46/*Self-Test 1* *Read 2-5.*	2-6 S	55/10–30 even 45/*P:* 7; 51/*P:* 9 45–46/*Self-Test 1*		*Announce chapter test.* 57/*P:* 7–10 58/*Self-Test 2*
20	2-5	50/1–24 *Read 47/Consumer Note.* *Read 2-6.*	2-7	57/2–24 even, *P:* 1–4		*Administer chapter test.* *Read 3-1.* 65/1–10
21	2-6 S	55/1–21 odd 51/25–35 odd, *P:* 1, 3, 5	2-7	57/13–23 odd; *P:* 5–9 58/*Self-Test 2*	3-1	65/11–25 odd, *P:* 1, 2, 3 *Read 3-2.*
22	2-6 S	55/22–30, *P:* 1–4 51/*P:* 2, 4, 6 *Read 2-7.*	S	*Announce chapter test.* 40/10, 12, 14; 44/13, 15, 17; 50/21, 23	3-2 S	68–69/1–23 odd 65/*P:* 4 *Read 3-3.*
23	2-7	57/1–23 odd, *P:* 1–5 58/*Self-Test 2*		*Administer chapter test.* *Read 3-1.*	3-3 S	71–72/1–24 69/25–35 odd *Read 3-4.*
24		*Announce chapter test.* 57/4–24 even 60/*Programmed Chapter Review*	3-1	65/1–20, *P:* 1, 2, 4	3-4 S	76/10–20; 77/*P:* 1, 2 69/37, 38, 40 *Read 3-5.*
25		*Administer chapter test.* 61/*Maintaining Skills* *Read 3-1.*	3-2 S	68–69/1–23 odd 65/23, 25, 27, *P:* 3	3-5 S	81/1–16 72/*Self-Test 1* 76/21–24; 77/*P:* 3–4
26	3-1	65/1–15, *P:* 1, 2	3-2	69/25–35	3-5 S	81/17–31 odd 77/*P:* 5, 6 *Read 3-6.*
27	3-2 S	68–69/1–23 odd 65/16–20, *P:* 3	3-3 S	71/1–23 odd 69/36, 38, 40	3-6 S	83/1–23 odd, *P:* 1, 2 81/18, 22, 28 *Read 3-7.*

LESSON	MINIMUM COURSE		AVERAGE COURSE		MAXIMUM COURSE	
28	3-3 S	71/1–15 69/25–30	3-4 S	76/1–23 odd; 77/P: 1, 2 72/Self-Test 1	3-7 S	86–87/5–25 odd 83/P: 5, 6
29	3-4 S	76/1–10 69/31–36; 72/16–24	3-5 S	81/1–16 76/12–18 even 77/P: 3, 4	3-7	87/26–36 even, P: 1–5 Read 3-8.
30	3-4	76/13–24; 77/P: 1, 2 72/Self-Test 1	3-5 S	81/17–32 77/P: 5, 6	3-8 S	90/1, 2; 91/7 87/P: 11, 12
31	3-5 S	81/1–25 odd 77/P: 6, 7	3-6	83/13–23; P: 1, 2		Announce chapter test. 92/12, 13 94/Self-Test 2
32	3-6 S	83/1–24 81/27, 29	3-7 S	86/1–20 83/P: 5, 6		Administer chapter test. Read 4-1.
33	3-7 S	86/1–10 81/31, 32; 83/P: 1–3	3-7	87/25–35 odd, P: 1–5	4-1	103/9–21 odd Read 4-2.
34	3-7	86–87/12–30 even; 87/P: 1, 2, 3	3-8 S	90/1–6 87/P: 6, 8, 11	4-2 S	105/9–29 odd, P: 1, 2 103/8, 12, 14
35	3-8 S	90/1–6; 92/9 87/25, 27, P: 5, 6, 7	3-8 S	91/7, 8; 92/12, 13 76/20, 22, 24 87/P: 12, 13	4-2 S	105–106/P: 3, 5, 7–12 103/16, 18, 20; 105/20, 24 Read 4-3.
36	3-8 S	94/Self-Test 2 87/P: 11, 12, 13; 93/17		Announce chapter test. 94/Self-Test 2 97/Programmed Chapter Review	4-3 S	108–109/15–39 odd 105/28, 30 Read 4-4.
37		Announce chapter test. 97/Programmed Chapter Review		Administer chapter test. Read 4-1.	4-4 S	111/P: 1–8 106/P: 17, 18; 108–109/26, 28, 34 Read 4-5.
38		Administer chapter test. 99/Maintaining Skills	4-1	103/1–20	4-5 S	115/P: 1–10 109/P: 1–5 Read 4-6.
39	4-1	103/1–21 odd	4-2 S	105/1–23 odd 103/21, 22	4-6 S	118/1, 7, 11, 13, 19, 23 109/P: 6–10; 115/13–18 111–112/Self-Test 1 Read 4-7.
40	4-2 S	105/1–19 odd 103/12–22 even	4-3 S	108/1–23 odd 105/P: 3, 5, 7	4-7 S	121/11–31 odd 118–119/25–35 odd Read 4-8.

LESSON	MINIMUM COURSE		AVERAGE COURSE		MAXIMUM COURSE	
41	4-3 S	108/1–15 105/21, 23, *P:* 1, 2	4-3 S	108–109/25–39 odd 105/*P:* 6, 8	4-8 S	23/1–25, 27, 29 121/12–32 even 119/*Self-Test 2* *Read 4-9.*
42	4-3 S	108/16–30 even; 109/*P:* 1–4 106/*P:* 9, 10	4-4 S	111/*P:* 1–6 106/*P:* 9, 10; 109/*P:* 1–6	4-9	125–126/9, 11, 12, 17, 21, 25, 29, 31, 33, 37, 41, 42 127/*Extra for* *Experts* *Read 4-10.*
43	4-4	111/*P:* 1–4 111–112/*Self-Test 1* 112/*Applications*	4-5 S	115/*P:* 1–6, 13–17 odd 111/*P:* 7,8	4-10 S	130/9–39 odd 125/20, 22, 28; 126/34, 36 *Read 4-11.*
44	4-5 4-6	115/*P:* 1–6 118/1–6	4-6	118/1–29 odd 111–112/*Self-Test 1*	4-11 S	132/*P:* 1–6 125/30, 32; 126/43, 44; 130/43, 45
45	4-6	118/7–27 odd 119/*Self-Test 2*	4-7 S	121/1–31 odd 119/31, 33	*Announce chapter test.* S	132/*P:* 7, 8 133/*Self-Test 3* 130/42, 44
46	4-7 S	121/1–27 odd 105/*P:* 3, 4, 6	4-8 S	123/1–29 odd 121/16–30 even	*Administer chapter test.* *Read 5-1.*	
47	4-8 S	123/1–25 odd 121/16–30 even	4-9	125/1–31 odd 119/*Self-Test 2*	5-1	141/9–35 odd; 142/49, 51 *Read 5-2.*
48	4-9	125/1–23 odd	4-10	130/1–24	5-2	147/1–33 144/*Extra for* *Experts* 1–8 149/*Applications* 1–6 *Read 5-3.*
49	4-9	125–126/25–43 odd	4-10	130/25–45 odd	5-3	153/5–45 odd *Read 5-4.*
50	4-10	130/1–31 odd	4-11 S	132/*P:* 1–8 130/26–46 even	5-4 S	158/1–12 153/26–46 even; 154/1–6
51	4-10	130/32–46 even	*Announce chapter test.* 133/*Self-Test 3*		5-4	158–159/13–51 odd 155/*Self-Test 1* *Read 5-5.*
52	4-11	132/*P:* 1–5 133/*Self-Test 3*	*Administer chapter test.* *Read 5-1.*		5-5 S	162–1–35 odd 158/22, 26, 34, 36
53	*Announce chapter test.* 135–136/*Programmed* *Chapter Review*		5-1	141/1–35 odd *Read 5-2.*	5-5	162/37–50; 163/51, 53, 56 *Read 5-6.*

LESSON	MINIMUM COURSE		AVERAGE COURSE		MAXIMUM COURSE	
54		*Administer chapter test.* 137/*Maintaining* *Skills*	5-2	147/1–33 odd 148–150/*Applications* *Read 5-3.*	5-6 S	166/1–12 153/2–12 even; 163/52, 54, 58
55	5-1	141/1–23 odd, 25, 27, 37, 39	5-3	153/1–23 odd 149/*Applications 1–6*	5-6 S	166/13–31 odd 154/7; 158/18, 30, 32; 162/34, 36 *Read 5-7.*
56	5-2 S	147/1–19 odd 141/6, 8, 10; 142/49, 50, 51	5-3	153/20, 22, 25–45 odd; 154/1–8 150/*Applications 7–9* *Read 150/Historical* *Note.*	5-7 S	169/5–35 odd 163/59, 60; 166/28, 30 *Read 5-8.*
57	5-2 S	147/21, 23 149–150/*Applications* *1–5 odd, 7, 8, 9* 141/14, 16, 18; 142/54	5-4	158/1–19 odd 155/*Self-Test 1* *Read 5-5.*	5-8 S	171/5–35 odd 164/*Self-Test 2* 169/18, 20, 26, 30 *Read 5-9.*
58	5-3 S	153/1–23 odd 147/25, 29	5-5 S	162/1–12 158–159/21–47 odd *Read 155/Career* *Note.*	5-9 S	174/1–31 odd 171/18, 20, 26, 30 *Read 5-10.*
59	5-3	153/25–45 odd; 154/1, 2, 6	S	158–159/22–28 even, 34–48 even *Read 5-6.*	5-10 S	176/6–22 174/26–40 even *Read 5-11.*
60	5-4 S	158/1–11 odd, 13, 17 153/10, 14, 42	5-6 S	166/1–12 163/51, 52, 53, 54 164/*Self-Test 2*	5-11	178/6–36 even 174/*Self-Test 3* *Read 155/Career* *Note.*
61	5-4 S	158–159/19, 21–41 odd 154/2, 12 155/*Self-Test 1*	5-6	166/13–31 odd *Read 5-7.*	5-11	178/37–59 odd *Read 179/Metric* *System.* *Read 5-12.*
62	5-5 S	162/1–35 odd 158/12, 22, 28, 34	5-7	169/1–39 odd *Read 5-8.*	5-12	181–182/1–19 *Read 5-13.*
63	5-5	162–163/24, 28, 30, 37–57 odd *Read 155/Career* *Note.*	5-8 S	171/1–31 odd 169/26, 28, 32, 36 *Read 5-9.*	5-13 S	185/1–35 odd 178/38, 40, 42 *Read 5-14.*
64	5-6	166/1–12 164/*Self-Test 2*	5-9 S	174/5–35 odd 171/14–34 even *Read 5-10.*	5-14 S	188/*P:* 1–6 178/44, 50; 185/40, 44, 46
65	5-6	166/13–31 odd	5-10	176/1–23 odd 174/*Self-Test 3*	5-14	188/*P:* 7–13 179/*Self-Test 4*

LESSON	MINIMUM COURSE	AVERAGE COURSE	MAXIMUM COURSE
66	5-7 169/1–27 odd	S 141/20, 22; 147/14, 24, 28; 153/14, 18, 28, 44; 158/18, 20, 30, 32	5-14 188–189/P: 14–22 190/Self-Test 5
67	5-8 171/1–23 odd S 169/26–36 even	5-11 178/1–49 odd Read 179/Metric System. Read 5-12.	Announce chapter test. 192–194/Programmed Chapter Review
68	5-9 174/1–23 odd S 171/25–35 odd	5-12 181–182/1–19 179/Self-Test 4 Read 5-13.	Administer chapter test. Read 6-1.
69	5-10 176/1–23 174/Self-Test 3	5-13 185/1–35 odd Read 5-14.	6-1 199–200/1–39 odd Read 200/Historical Note. Read 6-2.
70	5-11 178/1–35 odd	5-14 188/P: 1–6 S 185/26–36 even	6-2 202–203/1–12, 13–25 odd S 200/34, 38, 40 Read 6-3.
71	5-11 178/6–46 even 179/Self-Test 4	5-14 188/P: 7–12 S 185/37–47 odd, 50, 52	6-3 207/9–39 odd S 203/18, 22, 24 204/Self-Test-1 Read 6-4.
72	5-12 181–182/1–17 odd S 178/49–52	5-14 188–189/P: 13–20 190/Self-Test 5	6-4 209/11–31 odd S 204/P: 1–9 odd; 207/28, 30, 34 Read 6-5.
73	S 141/20, 22; 147/14, 24, 28; 153/18, 28, 44; 158/18, 20, 30, 32	Announce chapter test. 192–194/Programmed Chapter Review	6-5 212/7–17 odd Read 213/Consumer Note. S 210/33–51 odd Read 6-6.
74	5-13 185/1–35 odd	Administer chapter test. Read 6-1.	6-6 217/17–35 odd S 212/14, 16, 18 Read 6-7.
75	5-14 188/P: 1–6 S 185/10–30 even	6-1 199/1–31 odd Read 200/Historical Note. Read 6-2.	6-7 219/1–20, Just for Fun 212–213/Self-Test 2 Read 6-8.
76	5-14 188/7–12 190/Self-Test 5	6-2 202–203/1–23 odd S 199/22, 28; 200/33–41 odd Read 6-3.	6-8 221–222/7–37 odd, Just For Fun Read 6-9.
77	5-14 188/P: 13, 14, 15 192/Programmed Chapter Review 1–18	6-3 204/1–9 odd S 199/24, 26; 200/34, 38; 203/4, 12, 18, 22	6-9 225/7–29 odd, Puzzle Time 223/Self-Test 3 Read 6-10.

LESSON	MINIMUM COURSE		AVERAGE COURSE		MAXIMUM COURSE	
78		*Announce chapter test.* 188/16, 17 193–194/*Programmed* *Chapter Review* 19–47	6-3	207/9–39 odd 204/*Self-Test 1* *Read 6-4.*	6-10 S	227/13–23 odd 221–222/8, 12, 14; 225/10, 12, 16 *Read 6-11.*
79		*Administer chapter test.* 195/*Maintaining Skills*	6-4	209/1–31 odd *Read* 213/*Consumer* *Note.*	6-11	230/1–16; 231/*P:* 1–11 odd
80	6-1	199/1–20	6-4 S	210/33–51 odd 207/28, 30, 34 *Read 6-5.*	6-11	*P:* 13, 15 232/*Self-Test 4*
81	6-1	199/21–32 *Read* 200/*Historical* *Note.*	6-5	212/1–17 odd 212–213/*Self-Test 2* *Read 6-6.*	6-11	231/*P:* 14, 16, 18; 233/*Mid-Chapter Test* *Read* 232/*Career* *Note,* 233/*Looking* *Ahead.* *Read 6-12.*
82	6-2 S	202–203/1–8 200/33, 35	6-6	217/1–35 odd *Read 6-7.*	6-12	235/*P:* 1–10 *Read 6-13.*
83	6-2	203/9–23 odd; 204/*P:* 1, 2	S	199/32; 203/24, 26; 204/*P:* 4, 6; 207/16, 18, 26; 209/22, 24, 28; 210/38, 42; 212/14, 16; 217/22, 26, 32	6-13	237/*P:* 1–10 *Read* 238/*Consumer* *Note.* *Read 6-14.*
84	6-3 S	207/1–19 odd 204/*P:* 3, 4, 6	6-7	219/1–20, *Just for* *Fun* *Read 6-8.*	6-14	242/1–10 *Read 6-15.*
85	6-3 S	207/21–35 odd 204/*P:* 7, 10 204/*Self-Test 1*	6-8	221–222/1–19 odd *Read* 223/*Historical* *Note.* *Read 6-9.*	6-15	244–245/1–11 odd 245/*Self-Test 5* *Read* 246/*Looking* *Ahead.*
86	6-4 S	209/1–12 207/16–26 even	6-8	222/14, 16, 18, 25–35 odd, *Just for Fun* 223/*Self-Test 3*		*Announce chapter test.* 248–250/*Programmed* *Chapter Review*
87	6-4 S	209/13–31 odd 207/32, 34, 36	6-9	224–225/1–29 odd, *Puzzle Time* *Read 6-10.*		*Administer chapter test.* *Read 7-1.*
88	6-4	209/22–32 even; 210/37–51 odd	6-10 S	227/7–23 odd 225/16, 20, 24 *Read 6-11.*	7-1	257/1–33 odd *Read* 257/*Historical* *Note.* *Read 7-2.*
89	6-5 S	212/1–12 210/38–48 even	6-11 S	230/1–16; 231/*P:* 1–7 odd 225/18, 22; 227/18, 20	7-2 S	260/1–12 257/20, 22, 32 260/*Self-Test 1* *Read 7-3.*

LESSON	MINIMUM COURSE		AVERAGE COURSE		MAXIMUM COURSE	
90	6-5	212/13–16 212/Self-Test 2	6-11	231/P: 2, 4, 6, 9–15 odd Read 232/Career Note.	7-3	265/1–31 odd Read 265/ Biographical Note. 266/Extra for Experts. Read 7-4.
91	6-6	217/1–23 odd	6-11	232/Self-Test 4	7-4 S	268/1–6 268–269/Applications 265/18, 22, 28 Read 7-5.
92	6-6	217/14–24 even, 25–33 odd	6-11	231/P: 8, 10, 12, 16; 233/Mid-Chapter Test Read 6-12.	7-5	272–273/3–29 odd 269/Puzzle Time Read 7-6.
93	6-7 S	219/1–15 217/26, 30, 34	6-12	235/P: 1–6 Read 235/Biographical Note. Read 6-13.	7-6	277–278/1–29 odd Read 278/Career Note.
94	6-8	221/1–8 219/Just for Fun	6-13 S	237/1–7 235/P: 7, 9 Read 238/Consumer Note.	S	257/18, 24, 30
95	6-8	222/9–29 odd, 35	6-14 S	242/1–8 237/9, 10	Announce chapter test. 282/Self-Test 2	
96	6-8	222/18–28 even 223/Self-Test 3	6-15 S	244–245/P: 1–6 242/9, 10	Administer chapter test. Read 8-1.	
97	6-9 S	224–225/1–21 odd 222/36, Just for Fun	6-15	245/P: 7–10 245/Self-Test 5 Read 246/Looking Ahead.	8-1	290/1–43 odd Read 290/Historical Note. Read 8-2.
98	6-10 S	227/1–17 odd 225/14–24 even	Announce chapter test. 248–250/Programmed Chapter Review		8-2	294/1–6 295/Self-Test 1 Read 8-3.
99	6-11 S	230/1–16 225/25, 27; 227/14, 18, 20	Administer chapter test. Read 7-1.		8-3	300/1–23 odd, 24 Read 300/Historical Note. Read 8-4.
100	6-11 S	231/P: 1–5 225/29, 30; 227/19, 21	7-1	257/1–33 odd Read 257/Historical Note. Read 7-2.	8-4	304/1–14 Read 305/Consumer Note. Read 8-5.
101	6-11	231/P: 6–10 Read 232/Career Note.	7-2	260/1–12 Read 265/Biog. Note. Read 7-3.	8-5	308–309/1–23 odd Read 8-6.
102	6-11	231/P: 11–16; 233/Mid-Chapter Test Read 235/ Biographical Note.	7-3 S	265/1–25 odd 257/10, 12, 16, 20 Read 7-4.	8-6 S	314/1–35 odd 309/29–35 odd Read 310/Career Note. Read 8-7.

LESSON	MINIMUM COURSE		AVERAGE COURSE		MAXIMUM COURSE	
103	6-12	235/P: 1–6 232/Self-Test 4	7-4	268/P: 1–6 268–269/Applic. 2, 4 260/Self-Test 1 Read 7-5.	8-7	317–318/9–19 odd, 25, 27, 29, 33, 35 309–310/Self-Test 2 Read 8-8.
104	6-13 S	237/P: 1–5 235/P: 8, 10	7-5	272/1–25 odd, 27, 28, 29 Read 7-6.	8-8 S	323/5–25 odd 318–319/18, 20, 26, 34, 42, 44 Read 8-9.
105	6-13	237/P: 6–10 Read 238/Consumer Note.	7-6	277–278/1–29 odd Read 278/Career Note.	8-9 S	325/1–23 odd 323/14–30 even Read 8-10.
106	6-14	242/P: 1–5	S	257/18, 24, 30; 265/18, 22, 28 282/Self-Test 2 Read 284/Consumer Note.	8-10 S	330/1–27 odd 325/14–24 even
107	6-14	242/P: 6–10 248/Programmed Chapter Review 1–13		Announce chapter test. 283–284/Programmed Chapter Review	8-10	330/18–28 even; 331/P: 1–8
108	6-15	244/P: 1–5 249/Programmed Chapter Review 14–27		Administer chapter test. Read 8-1.		Announce chapter test. 331/Self-Test 3 333–334/Programmed Chapter Review
109	6-15	245/P: 6–8 245/Self-Test 5 Read 246/Looking Ahead.	8-1	290/7–39 odd Read 290/Historical Note. Read 8-2.		Administer chapter test. Read 9-1.
110		Announce chapter test. 250/Programmed Chapter Review 28–41	8-2 S	294/1–6 290/32, 34, 42 295/Self-Test 1 Read 8-3.	9-1	339/1–12 Read 9-2.
111		Administer chapter test. 253/Maintaining Skills	8-3	300/1–4, 10, 12, 13–20 Read 300/Historical Note. Read 8-4.	9-2 S	342/1–19 odd Read 342/Applications 339/17, 19 Read 9-3.
112	7-1	257/1–33 odd Read 257/Historical Note.	8-4	304/1–13 odd Read 305/Consumer Note. Read 8-5.	9-3 S	345/P: 1–5 339/21, 22, 23; 343/3–7 Read 9-4.
113	7-2	260/1–12 Read 265/ Biographical Note.	8-5 S	308–309/1–27 odd 304/10, 12 Read 8-6.	9-4 S	347/9–19 odd, P: 1, 3, 6 Read 348/Applications. 345/P: 6–8
114	7-3 S	265/1–25 odd 257/10, 12, 16, 20	8-6 S	314/1–27 odd 309/12, 18, 22, 29–35 odd Read 8-7.	9-4	347/P: 5, 7, 9 348–349/Applications Read 9-5.

LESSON	MINIMUM COURSE		AVERAGE COURSE		MAXIMUM COURSE	
115	7-4	268/P: 1–6 268–269/Applications 2, 4 260/Self-Test 1	8-7 S	317–318/1–23 odd 314/33, 35 Read 310/Career Note.	9-5	351–352/5–15 odd, P: 1–5 Read 354/Career Note. Read 9-6.
116	7-5	272/1–14	8-7 S	318–319/25–45 odd 309/24, 26; 314/14, 22, 30 Read 8-8.	9-6 S	356/Digit Problems 1, 3, 5; Age Problems 1, 3, 5 352–353/P: 6, 7, 8
117	7-5	273/15–29 odd, 24, 30 Read 278/Career Note.	8-8	323/5–11 odd, 17–23 odd, 27, 29 309–310/Self-Test 2 Read 8-9.	9-6	357/P: 1–6 354/Self-Test 1 Read 9-7.
118	7-6	277–278/1–25 odd Read 284/Consumer Note.	8-9 S	325/1–23 odd 323/10, 12, 22, 28 Read 8-10.	9-7	358–359/P: 1–11 odd 359/Self-Test 2 Read 9-8.
119		Announce chapter test. 282/Self-Test 2 283–284/Programmed Chapter Review	8-10 S	330/1–21 odd 325/14, 18, 22	9-8 S	363/1, 3, 11, 13, 17, 19 357/8; 359/8, 10
120		Administer chapter test. 285/Maintaining Skills	8-10	330/22–28; 331/P: 1–3	9-8 S	363/18, 22 339/24; 347/P: 8, 10 364/Self-Test 3
121	8-1	290/3, 5, 11–29 odd Read 290/Historical Note.	8-10	331/P: 4–8 331/Self-Test 3		Announce chapter test. 365–366/Programmed Chapter Review
122	8-2	294/1–6 295/Self-Test 1		Announce chapter test. 333–334/Programmed Chapter Review		Administer chapter test. Read 10-1.
123	8-3 S	300/1–21 odd Read 300/Historical Note. 290/4, 8, 12		Administer chapter test. Read 9-1.	10-1	375/1–31 odd Read 376-377/Extra for Experts. Read 10-2.
124	8-4	304/1–13 odd Read 305/Consumer Note.	9-1	339/1–12 Read 9-2.	10-2	381/1–29 odd Read 10-3.
125	8-5 S	308–309/1–11 304/6, 8	9-2	342/1–19 odd Read 342/Applications. Read 9-3.	10-3	384/1–29 odd 385/Self-Test 1 Read 385/Career Note. Read 10-4.
126	8-6	309/13–33 odd 309–310/Self-Test 2 Read 310/Career Note.	9-3 S	345/P: 1–6 343/Applications 3–8 Read 9-4.	10-4	390/1–18 Read 10-5.

LESSON	MINIMUM COURSE	AVERAGE COURSE	MAXIMUM COURSE
127	8-6 314/1–16	9-4 347/3–19 odd, *P:* 1–6 *Read 348/Applications.* *Read 9-5.*	10-5 392/1–21 odd; 393/*P:* 1–3 *Read 393/* *Biographical Note.* *Read 10-6.*
128	8-6 314/17–33 odd	9-5 351–352/1–15, *P:* 1, 2, 3, 7 *Read 9-6.*	10-6 396/1–11 odd; 397/*P:* 1–3 S 393/*P:* 4–6 *Read 10-7.*

129	8-7 317–318/5–27 odd	9-5 353/*P:* 8–10
		 354/*Self-Test 1*
		 Read 354/Career
		   Note.
		 Read 9-6.
			10-7 399–400/7–27 odd
			 S 393/*P:* 7, 8;
			      397/*P:* 4–6
			 Read 10-8.

130	8-8 323/1–23 odd
	 S 318/33, 37;
	      319/42
		9-6 356/*Digit Problems*
		   1–5, Age Problems
		   1–5;
		      357/*P:* 1–5
		 Read 9-7.
			10-8 403/9–29 odd
			 S 400/28–36 even
			 Read 400/Consumer
			   Note.
			 Read 10-9.

131	8-9 325/1–23 odd S 323/25, 27, 28	9-7 358–359/*P:* 1–8 359/*Self-Test 2* *Read 9-8.*	10-9 405/1–29 odd S 401/*P:* 1–5 *Read 10-10.*
132	8-10 330/1–15 odd S 325/10, 12, 18, 20	9-8 363/1–10 S 359/*P:* 9–12	10-10 407/9–29 odd, *P:* 1, 3, 7 397/*Self-Test 2*

133	8-10 330/4–24 even;
	      331/*P:* 1–4
	 S 325/16, 24
		9-8 363/11–27 odd
		 364/*Self-Test 3*
			Announce chapter test.
			    408/*Self-Test 3*
			    410–411/
			     Programmed
			     Chapter Review

134	*Announce chapter test.*
	    330/25–28
	    331/*Self-Test 3*
	    333–334/
	     Programmed
	     Chapter Review
		Announce chapter test.
		    365–366/
		     Programmed
		     Chapter Review
			Administer chapter test.
			    Read 11-1.

135	*Administer chapter test.*
	    335/*Maintaining Skills*
		Administer chapter test.
		    Read 10-1.
			11-1 418/1, 3, 11,
			      P: 1, 3, 5
			 Read 11-2.

136	9-1 339/1–12
	 Read 9-2.
		10-1 375/1–31 odd
		 376–377/*Extra for*
		   Experts 1–4
		 Read 10-2.
			11-2 422/1–7 odd, *P:* 1, 3
			 Read 423/Career
			   Note.
			 S 418/*P:* 9, 10
			 Read 11-3.

137	9-2 342/1–15 odd S 339/13, 15, 17 *Read 9-3.*	10-2 381/1–29 odd S 377/*Extra for* *Experts 5–12* *Read 10-3.*	11-3 425/1–6, *P:* 1–4 S 422–423/*P:* 2, 6, 7 *Read 11-4.*

LESSON	MINIMUM COURSE	AVERAGE COURSE	MAXIMUM COURSE
138	9-3 345/*P:* 1–5 S 339/19, 21; 342/17, 19 *Read 9-4.*	10-3 384/1–29 odd *Read 385/Career* *Note.* *Read 10-4.*	11-4 428–429/1–23 odd 429/*Self-Test 1* *Read 11-5.*
139	9-4 347/1–15 odd	10-4 390/1–18 385/*Self-Test 1* *Read 10-5.*	11-5 431/1–6 *Read 11-6.*
140	9-4 347/17–20, *P:* 1, 3, 4 *Read 9-5.*	10-5 392/1–21 odd; 393/*P:* 1, 3, 5, 7 *Read 10-6.*	11-6 434/9–49 odd, *Just* *for Fun* *Read 11-7.*
141	9-5 351–352/1–11 odd S 347/*P:* 2, 6 *Read 9-6.*	10-6 396/1–11 odd; 397/*P:* 1–5 397/*Self-Test 2* *Read 10-7.*	11-7 437/1–31 odd *Read 11-8.*
142	9-6 356/*Digit Problems* 1, 2, 3 S 352/10, 14; *P:* 1, 2 354/*Self-Test 1*	10-7 399–400/1–35 odd *Read 400/Consumer* *Note.* *Read 10-8.*	11-8 439/1–9 odd; 440/13–21 odd *Study 440/Samples.*
143	9-6 356/*Age Problems* 1, 2, 3 S 352–353/*P:* 3, 8	10-8 403/1–23 odd S 401/*P:* 1, 3, 6 *Read 10-9.*	11-8 439/2, 4, 6; 441/23–33 *Read 11-9.*
144	9-6 357/*P:* 1–5 *Read 9-7.*	10-9 405/1–31 odd S 401/*P:* 2, 4 *Read 10-10.*	11-9 444–445/1–13 odd, *P:* 1, 3, 5 *Read 445/Extra for* *Experts.*
145	9-7 358–359/*P:* 1–8 359/*Self-Test 2* *Read 9-8.*	10-10 407/3–25 odd, *P:* 1–5 odd 408/*Self-Test 3*	*Announce chapter test.* 446–447/*Self-Test 2* 449–450/*Programmed* *Chapter Review*
146	9-8 363/1–15 odd 364/*Self-Test 3*	*Announce chapter test.* 410–411/*Programmed* *Chapter Review*	*Administer chapter test.* *Read 12-1.*
147	*Announce chapter test.* 365–366/ *Programmed* *Chapter Review*	*Administer chapter test.* *Read 11-1.*	12-1 455/1–14 *Read 12-2.*
148	*Administer chapter test.* 369/*Maintaining* *Skills*	11-1 418/3–6, *P:* 1, 4, 5 *Read 11-2.*	12-2 458/1–4, *P:* 1–4 458/*Self-Test 1* *Read 12-3.*
149	10-1 375/1–29 odd *Read 10-2.*	11-2 422/1–10, *P:* 1–5 *Read 11-3.*	12-3 460/1–12
150	10-2 381/1–25 odd *Read 10-3.*	11-3 425/1–6, *P:* 1–4 *Read 423/Career* *Note.* *Read 11-4.*	12-3 460/*P:* 1–8 *Read 12-4.*

LESSON	MINIMUM COURSE		AVERAGE COURSE		MAXIMUM COURSE	
151	10-3	384/1–29 odd *Read 10-4.*	11-4	428–429/1–23 odd *Read 11-5.*	12-4	462/1–5 463/*Self-Test 2* *Read 12-5.*
152	10-4	390/1–17 385/*Self-Test 1* *Read 10-5.*	11-5 S	431/1–6 429/*Self-Test 1* *Read 11-6.*	12-5 S	466/1–9 odd 462/6–9 *Read 463/Historical Note.*
153	10-5	392/1–15 odd; 393/*P:* 1, 3, 5 *Read 10-6.*	11-6	433–434/1–39 odd *Read 11-7.*	12-6	468/1–20 *Read 12-7.*
154	10-6	396/1–9 odd; 397/*P:* 1, 3, 5 397/*Self-Test 2* *Read 10-7.*	11-7 S	437/1–27 odd 434/41–49 odd *Read 11-8.*	12-7	470/1–6
155	10-7	399–400/1–35 odd *Read 400/Consumer Note.* *Read 10-8.*	11-8	439–440/1–21 odd *Read 11-9.*	12-7	471/*P:* 1–6
156	10-8 S	403/1–23 odd 401/*P:* 1, 3 *Read 10-9.*	11-9 S	444/1–13 odd 441/23–33 odd	12-7	472/*P:* 7–10 473/*Self-Test 3*
157	10-9	405/1–31 odd *Read 10-10.*	11-9	444–445/*P:* 1–5 odd 446–447/*Self-Test 2*		*Announce chapter test.* 474–476/*Programmed Chapter Review*
158	10-10	407/1–29 408/*Self-Test 3*	S	418/7, 9, 11, *P:* 7, 9 423/*P:* 7, 9, 11		*Administer chapter test.* 476/*Cumulative Review 1–24*
159		*Announce chapter test.* 410–411/ *Programmed Chapter Review*		*Announce chapter test.* 449–450/ *Programmed Chapter Review*		476–477/*Cumulative Review 25–48*
160		*Administer chapter test.*		*Administer chapter test.*		477–478/*Cumulative Review 49–72*

TABLE OF RELATED REFERENCES

For use after Section	Duplicating Masters	Progress Tests	Computer Resource Book
1-2	Sheet 1	Test 1	
1-3	Sheet 2		
1-4	Sheet 3		
1-5		Test 2	
1-6	Sheet 4		
1-8	Sheet 5	Test 3	
2-1	Sheet 6		
2-3	Sheet 7		
2-4		Test 4	
2-5	Sheet 8		
2-7	Sheet 9	Test 5	
3-1	Sheet 10		
3-3	Sheet 11	Test 6	
3-4	Sheet 12		
3-6	Sheet 13		
3-8	Sheet 14	Test 7	
Cumulative Review/Test	Sheet 15	Test 8	
4-1	Sheet 16		
4-2	Sheet 17		
4-3	Sheet 18	Test 9	
4-5	Sheet 19		
4-6	Sheet 20	Test 10	
4-7	Sheet 21		
4-8	Sheet 22		
4-9	Sheet 23		

For use after Section	Duplicating Masters	Progress Tests	Computer Resource Book
4-11	Sheet 24	Test 11	
5-2	Sheet 25		
5-3	Sheet 26	Test 12	
5-4	Sheet 27		
5-5	Sheet 28		
5-6	Sheet 29		
5-7	Sheet 30		
5-8	Sheet 31		
5-9		Test 13	
5-10	Sheet 32		
5-11	Sheet 33	Test 14	
5-12	Sheet 34		
5-13	Sheet 35		
5-14	Sheet 36	Test 15	
6-1	Sheet 37		
6-2		Test 16	
6-3	Sheet 38		
6-5	Sheet 39	Test 17	
6-6	Sheet 40		
6-7	Sheet 41		
6-8	Sheet 42	Test 18	
6-9	Sheet 43		
6-10	Sheet 44		
6-11	Sheet 45	Test 19	
6-13	Sheet 46		
6-15	Sheet 47	Test 20	

For use after Section	Duplicating Masters	Progress Tests	Computer Resource Book
Cumulative Review/Test	Sheet 48	Test 21	
7-1			Units 1A, B
7-2	Sheet 49	Test 22	
7-4	Sheet 50	Test 23	Unit 1C
7-6	Sheet 51	Test 24	Unit 2A
8-1			Unit 3A
8-2	Sheet 52		Unit 4C
8-3			Units 5A, B
8-4	Sheet 53		
8-5	Sheet 54	Test 25	
8-6	Sheet 55		Unit 5C
8-8	Sheet 56		Unit 5D
8-9	Sheet 57		
8-10	Sheet 58	Test 26	
9-2	Sheet 59		
9-3	Sheet 60	Test 27	
9-4	Sheet 61		
9-5	Sheet 62	Test 28	Unit 6A
9-6	Sheet 63		

For use after Section	Duplicating Masters	Progress Tests	Computer Resource Book
9-7	Sheet 64		
9-8	Sheet 65	Test 29	
Cumulative Review/Test	Sheet 66	Test 30	
10-2	Sheet 67	Test 31	
10-3			
10-4	Sheet 68	Test 32	
10-6	Sheet 69		
10-7	Sheet 70		
10-9	Sheet 71	Test 33	Unit 7A
10-10	Sheet 72		
11-3	Sheet 73	Test 34	
11-4	Sheet 74		
11-6	Sheet 75		
11-7	Sheet 76		
11-8			Units 7C, D
11-9	Sheet 77	Test 35	Units 10C, D, E
12-4	Sheet 78	Test 36	
12-7	Sheet 79	Test 37	
Cumulative Review/Test	Sheet 80	Test 38	

1 Introduction to Algebra

CHAPTER OVERVIEW

The main objective of this chapter is to introduce the mathematical vocabulary and skills that are essential to solving simple word problems. The equations written for the various word problems are solved by inspection. In subsequent chapters students will work with more systematic methods for solving equations.

This chapter reviews the essential skills related to arithmetical operations and then develops the comparable skills related to the study of algebra. Throughout the development, care is taken to illustrate the meaning of each term introduced.

SECTION-BY-SECTION COMMENTARY

1-1 NUMERALS AND EXPRESSIONS

Key Mathematical Ideas Essential to problem solving is the student's ability to simplify numerical expressions. Throughout the student's work in mathematics this skill will be required, especially in evaluating formulas and other equations. Grouping symbols, such as parentheses, brackets, and fraction bars specify the order of operations in simplifying expressions.

As students gain experience in recognizing and evaluating numerical expressions, they will be acquiring the skills needed for working with variable expressions in Section 1-2.

Teaching Suggestions Students should be familiar with the concept of *different names for a number;* a brief comment about the distinction between a number and a numeral should suffice.

You may wish to start the lesson with this class activity: Have the class choose a number from one to ten, say five. Make a list of the students' suggestions for the different ways to combine numerals and other symbols to form numerical expressions with the value five. It should be emphasized that there are *many* names for *one* number.

Students interested in the origin of the equality symbol may be referred to the Historical Note on text page 9.

Chalkboard Examples

Simplify.

1. $(40 - 30) + 5 = 10 + 5 = 15$

2. $40 - (30 + 5) = 40 - 35 = 5$

3. $16 \div [8 \div (4 \div 2)] = 16 \div [8 \div 2] = 16 \div 4 = 4$

4. $[(7 \times 10) + 2] \div \dfrac{4 \times 4}{2 + 6} = [70 + 2] \div \dfrac{16}{8}$
$$= 72 \div 2 = 36$$

Suggested Extensions

1. Ask students to write a numerical expression for each number from 0 to 9. Each expression should include at least three numerals from 0 to 9, and involve at least two of the operations addition, subtraction, multiplication, and division. For example,

Number	Expression
0	$(4 \times 2) - 8$
1	$(1 \times 3) - 2$
2	$5 + 1 - 4$

and so on.

2. Challenge each student to write as many expressions for a particular number, say eight, as he or she can in a given time limit.

1-2 VARIABLES AND EXPRESSIONS

Key Mathematical Ideas In the previous section students learned how to simplify numerical expressions. Here, the development is extended to their work with variable expressions.

You will want to be certain that students understand the importance of specifying the domain of a variable used in an expression. In subsequent sections, students will work with open sentences such as

$$n + 5 = 8 \text{ where } n \in \{1, 2, 3, 4, 5\}.$$

An open sentence is neither true nor false until the variable is replaced by the numeral for a given value of the variable. Reinforcement of the concepts *variable*, *domain*, and *open* will be helpful for students' later work.

Teaching Suggestions To motivate the class, challenge them to develop variable expressions to represent such quantities as the number of centimeters in n meters. If a visual presentation is preferable, you may wish to use a box and cubes or dice and have the class develop the expression for the number of faces in n cubes.

Draw one cube and ask the class how many faces the cube has. Then draw two cubes and ask how many faces they have in all. Continue the pattern. Then say: "There are a number of cubes in the box but I don't know how many." Have the class develop the expression $6n$ for the number of faces in n cubes.

You may wish to point out that when braces are used to specify a set, they are *not* grouping symbols.

Chalkboard Examples

1. Explain the meaning of each expression, first in symbols and then in words.

   a. $\dfrac{10}{bc} \quad \dfrac{10}{b \times c}$; 10 divided by the product of b and c

   b. $xy(t + s) \quad (x \times y)(t + s)$; add t and s, and then multiply the sum by the product of x and y (Other answers are possible.)

2. If $x = 3$ and $y = 2$, evaluate $\dfrac{2x + 9}{3x - 2y}$.

   $$\frac{2x + 9}{3x - 2y} = \frac{2(3) + 9}{3(3) - 2(2)} = \frac{6 + 9}{9 - 4} = \frac{15}{5} = 3$$

   (Remind students to simplify numerical expressions completely.)

Suggested Extensions

1. The Suggested Extensions of Section 1-1 may be developed as follows: Ask students to write variable expressions where the domain of the variable is $\{0, 1, 2, \ldots, 9\}$ and each expression has the value t when the variable has the value t. For example,

if b is the variable, then expressions can be written as shown in the table.

b	Expression	Value of Expression
0	$3b$	0
1	$5b - 4$	1
2	$\dfrac{b}{8} + \dfrac{7}{4}$	2

2. Exercise 1 can be extended to include two variables where the value of the second variable may be selected by the student. For example, if a and b are the variables, then expressions can be written as shown in the table.

a	b	Expression	Value of Expression
0	5	$6ab$	0
1	1	$3a - 2b$	1
2	3	$ab - 4$	2

A Self-Test appears after every major division of each chapter, and is designed to help students evaluate their progress as they move through the course. The first part of each test is a review of vocabulary and symbols with page references included. The second part is composed of questions keyed to the behavioral objectives listed at the beginning of each section. Note that the answers to each Self-Test can be found at the back of the book.

1-3 FACTORS AND EXPONENTS

Key Mathematical Ideas The basic objective of this section is to practice writing and evaluating exponential expressions. Most students will not be familiar with the notation x^n; extensive explanation and discussion may be necessary.

Teaching Suggestions You may wish to introduce the lesson by reminding students that symbols are often used in mathematics to write numerical expressions in a concise form. The sum of equal addends can be concisely expressed using multiplication. For example, $2 + 2 + 2 + 2$ can be written more simply as 4×2. Similarly, a product of equal factors can be concisely expressed using exponential form. For example, $2 \times 2 \times 2 \times 2$ can be written more simply as 2^4. The number 2 is the base (or factor); the number 4 is the exponent (or number of factors).

If students ask why the second and third powers are read differently from other powers, you can show them geometric models of a square and a cube. If s is the length of a side of a square, then the square has area s^2 or "s squared."

Similarly, the third power of a number s can be related to the volume of a cube with sides of length s.

Chalkboard Examples

1. Name the base and the exponent. Then read the expression in factored form.
   a. 4^5 Base, 4;   exponent, 5; $4 \cdot 4 \cdot 4 \cdot 4 \cdot 4$
   b. 5^4 Base, 5;   exponent, 4; $5 \cdot 5 \cdot 5 \cdot 5$
   c. a^3 Base, a;   exponent, 3; $a \cdot a \cdot a$

2. Write each expression in exponential form.
   a. $7 \cdot s \cdot s \cdot s$ $7s^3$
   b. $5x(x + y)(x + y)$ $5x(x + y)^2$
   c. The sixth power of $m - n$ $(m - n)^6$

3. If $m = 2$ and $n = 3$, evaluate each expression.
   a. $(m \times n)^4 = (2 \times 3)^4 = 6^4 = 6 \cdot 6 \cdot 6 \cdot 6 = 1296$
   b. $m \times n^4 = 2 \times 3^4 = 2 \cdot (3 \cdot 3 \cdot 3 \cdot 3)$
      $= 2(81) = 162$
   c. $m^4 + n^4 = 2^4 + 3^4 = (2 \cdot 2 \cdot 2 \cdot 2) + (3 \cdot 3 \cdot 3 \cdot 3)$
      $= 16 + 81 = 97$
   d. $(m + n)^4 = (2 + 3)^4 = 5^4 = 5 \cdot 5 \cdot 5 \cdot 5 = 625$

Suggested Extensions

1. Show that these expressions differ in value.
   a. $3a^2$ and $(3a)^2$ if $a = 4$
   b. $m^2 + n^2$, $(m + n)^2$, and $(mn)^2$ if $m = 2$ and $n = 3$

2. Show that these expressions have the same value.
   a. $4y(4y)^2$ and $(4y)^3$ if $y = 2$
   b. $(x + 1)^3$ and $(x + 1)(x + 1)^2$ if $x = 1$

3. An extension of Exercises 37–44: Find a variable expression using a, b, and c such that the value of the expression is **a.** 10;   **b.** 50.

(Answers may vary. For example,

$$\frac{3bc}{2a} = \frac{3(4)(5)}{2(3)} = 10$$

and $b^2c - 2ac = 4^2(5) - 2(3)(5) = 50$.)

1-4 ORDER OF OPERATIONS

Key Mathematical Ideas   At this point, students know how to evaluate expressions containing grouping symbols. In this section, rules are established to clarify the meaning of expressions which lack grouping symbols. A good grasp of the order of operations will be important in later sections when the student is confronted with evaluating challenging algebraic expressions.

Teaching Suggestions   As a review and as an introduction into this section have each student work through these exercises and record his or her answers.

$(2 + 3)^2$	$2 + 3^2$
$(6 + 8) \div (4 + 3)$	$6 + 8 \div 4 + 3$
$(16 \div 8) - (6 \div 3)$	$16 \div 8 - 6 \div 3$

Students should have little difficulty with the exercises on the left. However, collectively, students will obtain different answers for the exercises on the right. This difference will demonstrate the need for well-defined steps in simplifying numerical expressions that do not contain grouping symbols. Refer students to the summary of order of operations on page 10. A brief comment should be made that these rules are merely conventions; mathematicians have *agreed* to use these rules to avoid confusion.

Chalkboard Examples

Simplify each expression.

1. $\dfrac{2 + 24 \div 4}{64 \div 8} = \dfrac{2 + 6}{8} = \dfrac{8}{8} = 1$

2. $2(3^2 - 2 \cdot 3) \div (6 - 3) = 2(9 - 2 \cdot 3) \div 3$
   $= 2(9 - 6) \div 3$
   $= 2(3) \div 3 = 6 \div 3 = 2$

3. Evaluate $5a + 2b \div c$ if $a = 2$, $b = 6$, and $c = 2$.
   $5a + 2b \div c = 5(2) + 2(6) \div (2) = 10 + 12 \div 2$
   $= 10 + 6 = 16$

Suggested Extensions

1. Using only three 3's and the operations addition, subtraction, multiplication, division, and raising to a power, write numerical expressions for as many numbers between 0 and 100 as possible. For example,

$$0 = 3(3 - 3)$$

$$1 = \left(\frac{3}{3}\right)^3$$

$$2 = 3 - \frac{3}{3}$$

$$3 = 3 \cdot 3 \div 3$$

$$4 = 3 + \frac{3}{3}$$

$$6 = 3 \cdot 3 - 3$$

and so on. In some cases, more than one numerical expression exists for a given number. For example,

$$2 = 3 - \frac{3}{3} = \frac{3 + 3}{3}.$$

Place grouping symbols so that the expression has the given value.

2. $8 \div 4 + 4$; 1 $\qquad 8 \div (4 + 4)$

3. $12 + 4 \div 4 + 4$; 2 $\qquad (12 + 4) \div (4 + 4)$

4. $3 \cdot 2 + 3 + 5 \div 4$; 5 $\qquad [3 \cdot (2 + 3) + 5] \div 4$

1-5   FORMULAS FROM GEOMETRY

Key Mathematical Ideas Formulas occur frequently in the application of mathematics. Working with formulas, students will become aware of the practicality of the study of algebra.

Teaching Suggestions In students' early experience with measurement, they probably computed the area of a region by counting the number of unit squares contained in the region. Point out how much easier it is to evaluate a variable expression.

Useful formulas occur in many branches of mathematics. A common formula that would interest students is the one for the sum, S, of the first n positive integers:

$$S = \frac{n(n + 1)}{2} \text{ where } n \in \{1, 2, 3, \ldots\}$$

You may wish to point out that formulas related to circles, cylinders, spheres, and so on always involve the constant π (pi). Of course, π is an irrational number, and hence we must work with rational approximations of π. To twenty decimal places,

$$\pi \doteq 3.14159265358979323846.$$

More useful approximations are 3.14159 and $\frac{22}{7}$. The latter is correct to two decimal places.

Chalkboard Examples

1. Find the perimeter of the square shown below if $P = 4s$, and $s = 8$. $P = 4s = 4(8) = 32$

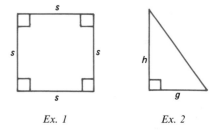

Ex. 1   *Ex. 2*

2. Find the area of the region bounded by the right triangle shown above if $A = \frac{1}{2}gh$, $g = 4$, and $h = 7$. $A = \frac{1}{2}gh = \frac{1}{2}(4)(7) = 14$

3. Find the perimeter of a rectangle if the length is 6 and the width is 5.
$P = 2l + 2w = 2(6) + 2(5) = 12 + 10 = 22$

Suggested Extensions

1. You may wish to challenge the class to explain how some of the formulas are derived. For instance, the perimeter of a square is given by $s + s + s + s$, or $4s$. The perimeter of a rectangle is given by $l + w + l + w$, or $2l + 2w$. Challenge students to explain the formula for the perimeter of the figure given in Exercises 17 and 18.

The meaning of *equivalent formulas* may be discussed. Point out that the formula for the perimeter of a general quadrilateral (Ex. 9) has no simpler equivalent form.

2. Ask the class to create figures based on circles, rectangles, squares, and so on. The originator of each figure should assign variables to represent lengths. He or she then should write a formula for the perimeter of the figure and, if possible, a formula for the area bounded by the figure. For example, the figure shown at the top of the next page is based on four semicircles and a square.

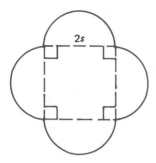

The perimeter of the figure is given by

$$P = 4\pi s$$

and the area is given by

$$A = 4s^2 + 2\pi s^2.$$

1-6 EQUATIONS AND INEQUALITIES

Key Mathematical Ideas In this section, the key concepts of *equation* and *inequality* are introduced along with the related vocabulary. Students should understand that equations and inequalities are types of mathematical sentences. A sentence that can be labeled as "true" or "false" is called a *statement;* a sentence that cannot be so labeled (one containing a non-constant variable) is called an *open sentence.* The solution set of an open sentence depends upon its domain.

Teaching Suggestions You may wish to write the following statements on the chalkboard and ask the class which ones are true and which are false:

$$8 \div 4 + 3 = 5 \quad \text{(true)}$$
$$6 + 3 \times 3 = 27 \quad \text{(false)}$$
$$16 \div 8 \div 2 = 4 \quad \text{(false)}$$

Then ask the class whether the statement

$$n + 8 = 12$$

is true or false. A class discussion might follow, focusing on the major concepts of the section.

Chalkboard Examples

1. Refer to the equation introduced in the Teaching Suggestions above: $n + 8 = 12$. If $n \in \{1, 2, 3, 4, 5\}$, what is the solution set of the given equation? $\{4\}$

2. If $n \in \{1, 2, 3, 4, 5\}$, what is the solution set of $n + 8 \neq 12$? $\{1, 2, 3, 5\}$

Suggested Extensions Any symbol may be transformed into a "not" symbol by using "/". For example:

$= $ means *is equal to;*

$\neq$ means *is not equal to;*

$\in$ means *is a member of;*

$\notin$ means *is not a member of.*

In fact, a slash is used internationally to indicate restricted movement. You probably have noticed signs such as the following:

means *No parking*

means *No right turn*

means *No U-turn*

See if you can find other signs which use the slash.

1-7 CONVERTING WORDS INTO SYMBOLS

Key Mathematical Ideas One of the main difficulties students have in solving word problems is translating the words into mathematical symbols. The symbol "+" may be verbalized by "is added to," "is increased by," "the sum of," and "is greater than." The equality symbol can mean "has the value of," "is equal to," or "represents the same number as." By practicing translating words into symbols, students gain essential preparation for solving word problems in Section 1-8.

Teaching Suggestions Point out that we learn mathematics in order to apply our skills to solving problems. The first part of this task is being able to express words in terms of mathematical symbols. You will probably want to discuss the chalkboard exercises or the oral exercises with the class to be certain that students are reading carefully.

Chalkboard Examples

Convert each phrase into a variable expression. Use *n* to represent the given number.

1. Four times the number $4n$

2. The number increased by six $n + 6$

3. Thirteen decreased by the number $13 - n$

4. The quotient when the number is divided by ten
$n \div 10$

5-8. Write a word sentence for each phrase in Exercises 1-4. Then write the appropriate open sentence to represent the word sentence.

Answers to Exercises 5-8 may vary.

5. Four times the number is twelve; $4n = 12$.

6. The number increased by six is twenty-five; $n + 6 = 25$ (or $6 + n = 25$).

7. Thirteen decreased by the number is three greater than the number; $13 - n = 3 + n$ (or $13 - n = n + 3$).

8. The quotient when the number is divided by ten is six less than one-half the number; $\frac{n}{10} = \frac{1}{2}n - 6$ $\left(\text{or } \frac{n}{10} + 6 = \frac{1}{2}n \right)$.

1-8 USING EQUATIONS TO SOLVE PROBLEMS

Key Mathematical Ideas This section represents the culmination of skills acquired in Chapter 1. Students use equations to represent simple numerical relationships that occur in real-life situations. They are also able to solve the equations they have written and to use the information to answer questions.

Teaching Suggestions Many students have difficulty solving word problems. The five-step plan presented on page 23 provides students with an organized way to deal with word problems. Some additional suggestions are as follows:

a. When reading the problem, identify the arithmetical steps involved and the numbers asked for.

b. Identify the unit when choosing a variable. For example: Let $t =$ the number *of minutes* that . . .

c. Check your result with the *original word problem* rather than the open sentence written in Step 3. (The sentence may have been incorrectly written.)

d. Answer the question posed by the problem *in words*.

Chalkboard Examples

Exercises 1 and 2 illustrate how the *same* open sentence is written to solve *different* problems. Arrange the problems side-by-side so that their solutions may be compared. (An outline of each solution is given.)

1. The sum of a number and seven is twelve. Find the number. $n + 7 = 12$; 5

2. The total number of students in the chess club is twelve. If there are seven girls in the club, how many boys are there? $b + 7 = 12$; 5

3. The perimeter of a square is 72 centimeters. Find the measure of a side of the square. $4s = 72$; 18 cm

Suggested Extensions

1. Some students may claim that they can solve problems mentally and that they therefore do not need to learn the plan for solving a word problem. Challenge these students with the following problem:

   When the product of 3 and a number is decreased by 4, the same result is obtained as when the number is doubled and then increased by 15. Find the number. 19

2. Write some open sentences on the chalkboard and ask students to create word problems that "fit" the open sentences. For example, if you write $3n - 12 = 2n$, a student might volunteer the following problem: Twelve less than the product of 3 and a number is the same as the number doubled. Find the number.

Throughout this book some very simple Computer Activities are suggested for those schools that have access to a computer that will accept BASIC. No attempt is made to teach BASIC, although students using these programs will very likely pick up some of the statements and techniques.

Students and teachers who wish to learn more about computer programming may refer to *A Guided Tour of Computer Programming in BASIC* by Thomas A. Dwyer and Michael S. Kaufman (Boston: Houghton Mifflin Company, 1973). For more extensive work, the more elementary portions of *Computer Resource Book—Algebra* by Thomas A. Dwyer and Margot Critchfield (Boston: Houghton Mifflin Company, 1975) may be used. (See the table of related references on pages T37 and T38.)

2 Addition and Subtraction

CHAPTER OVERVIEW

The main objective of this chapter is to teach the addition and subtraction of real numbers. This is accomplished by means of a visual presentation on the number line. The related concepts of *the opposite of a number* and *the absolute value of a number* are also developed. The second half of the chapter focuses on systematic methods for solving equations: transformation by substitution, by addition, and by subtraction. Transforming an equation by one of these methods produces an equivalent equation whose solution can be seen by inspection. Throughout the chapter, problem sections provide many opportunities for students to apply newly-acquired skills.

SECTION-BY-SECTION COMMENTARY

2-1 GRAPHING SETS OF REAL NUMBERS

Key Mathematical Ideas The addition and subtraction of real numbers may be effectively illustrated using a number line. The related vocabulary introduced in the section is also important for later work.

Teaching Suggestions If students ask why they should learn about graphing, you can point out that a visual presentation of information is usually the simplest to interpret. For example, by arranging dots as shown below,

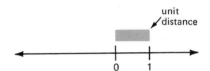

and so on,

a pattern can easily be seen for the square numbers. To "picture" sets of numbers, it is helpful to use a number line.

Build a number line with the class. (Draw a line on the chalkboard or, if you prefer, use masking tape.) Choose a starting point and label it "0" (zero).

Discuss why the term "origin" is a suitable name to describe the point marked by 0. Choose a strip of paper or a ruler to use as a fixed length and use it to locate the point corresponding to "1."

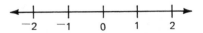

The use of this device reinforces the fact that a uniform scale is used on the number line. Point out that mathematicians have agreed to use the right-hand side of the number line to represent the positive direction; if each of us were to draw our number lines differently, we would find it difficult to compare graphs.

Use the unit distance to locate points corresponding to other integers, both positive and negative. Remind students that although the "+" may be omitted when writing positive numbers, the "−" must always be written to indicate the numeral for a negative number.

Once the number line has been constructed (with arrowheads to indicate that the line continues indefinitely in both directions), use a finite set of integers such as $\{0, 1, 2\}$ to introduce the meaning of the terms *graph* and *coordinate*. Then extend the example to illustrate how to graph infinite sets:

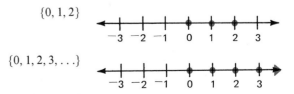

Chalkboard Examples

1. Draw a number line on the chalkboard. Pair the letters of the alphabet with the points and their coordinates as follows: pair A with the point whose coordinate is $^-12$, and B with the point whose coordinate is $^-11$; continue up to Z which has coordinate 13.

   a. Ask students to name the coordinates of the given points:

$$I, T, A, L, Y.$$

   Choose a suitable collection of names for your geographical region.

   b. Ask students to name the points with the given coordinates:

$$^-10, 2, ^-1, 8, 0, ^-11, 8, 6.$$

   (The letters spell out "Columbus.") Choose other suitable lists of coordinates.

2. Graph each set on a separate number line.

   a. $\{^-5, ^-4, 2\}$

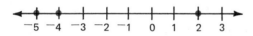

   b. $\{^-3, ^-\frac{1}{2}, 0, 1\frac{1}{2}\}$

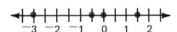

Suggested Extensions Use the number line described in Exercise 1 of the Chalkboard Exercises. For each list of coordinates, have students name the points and unscramble the letters to spell famous geographic locations. If they have difficulty guessing the answer, give students the accompanying hint.

1. $^-8, ^-4, ^-1, 1$
   (*Hint:* The longest river in the world)
2. $^-8, ^-4, ^-3, 3, 5, 7, 8$
   (*Hint:* The largest planet in the solar system)
3. $^-10, ^-8, ^-4, ^-2, ^-1, 0, 1, 12$
   (*Hint:* The highest mountain in North America)
4. $^-12, ^-8, ^-1, 0, 6$
   (*Hint:* The capital of Oregon)

Solutions

1. Nile River   2. Jupiter
3. Mt. McKinley   4. Salem

2-2 ADDITION ON THE NUMBER LINE

Key Mathematical Ideas The key idea of this section is that the number line can be used as an aid for adding real numbers. When an arrow is drawn to represent a real number, certain conventions are followed: the magnitude of the number is indicated by the length of the arrow, and the "sign" of the number is indicated by the direction of the arrow.

Teaching Suggestions Draw a number line on the chalkboard (or make one out of masking tape). Introduce the use of an arrow to represent a positive number, say 3.

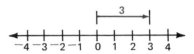

Discuss where the arrow begins and ends and what its length represents. Next, draw an arrow to represent a negative number, say $^-3$.

Now use the number line to illustrate these sums:

    1. $4 + 3$ 2. $^-4 + ^-3$
    3. $4 + ^-3$ 4. $^-3 + 4$

Point out that $4 + ^-3 = ^-3 + 4$ since each is equal to 1. You may wish to introduce the term *commutative,* using the number line to show that addition is commutative.

Chalkboard Examples

1. Draw a diagram to represent the sum $5 + ^-3$.

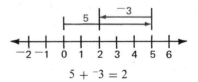

$$5 + ^-3 = 2$$

2. Encourage students to find these sums mentally.

    a. $^-3 + ^-2$ $^-5$ b. $^-4 + 2$ $^-2$
    c. $4 + ^-2$ 2 d. $^-2 + 4$ 2
    e. $^-3 + 2$ $^-1$ f. $^-2 + 2$ 0

3. Simplify $[^-4 + (^-3 + 5)] + ^-8$.

$$[^-4 + (^-3 + 5)] + ^-8 = [^-4 + 2] + ^-8$$
$$= ^-2 + ^-8 = ^-10$$

4. Solve $^-3 + y = 4$ by using the number line.

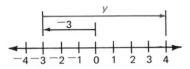

To arrive at 4 from $^-3$, we need to move 7 units in the positive direction. Thus $y = 7$.

2-3 OPPOSITES AND ABSOLUTE VALUES

Key Mathematical Ideas This section utilizes the number line to show intuitively that every real number has an additive inverse. The expressions *the opposite of a number, the additive inverse of a number* and *the negative of a number* are equivalent. Because the opposite of a positive number is a negative number, we can use the symbol -6, for example, to denote both the number "negative six" and the "opposite of six." Hence we no longer need raised minus signs on numerals for negative numbers.

In any pair of nonzero opposites, one is positive and the other is negative. The absolute value of any pair of nonzero opposites is then simply defined as the positive number of the pair.

Teaching Suggestions Draw a number line on the chalkboard. Use arrows to illustrate the sums $3 + ^-3$ and $^-3 + 3$. Point out that any pair of numbers a and ^-a are *additive inverses* since $a + ^-a = 0$.

Now ask the class to name the additive inverse (opposite) of each of the following numbers: $3, ^-2, ^+2\frac{1}{2}$, $\frac{3}{4}$, and 0. Use the students' answers to introduce the use of the minus sign to denote *the opposite of*. That is, -3 means the opposite of 3. But the opposite of 3 is $^-3$. Therefore $^-3 = -3$. Point out that every real number has an opposite. Remind students that a symbol such as $-x$ may represent a positive number, a negative number, or zero, depending on the value of x.

To introduce the concept of *absolute value*, draw arrows on the number line to represent 3 and -3. The arrows point in opposite directions, but each is 3 units long. Thus $|3| = |-3| = 3$. We can think of the absolute value of a real number as the number of units in

the arrow representing the real number. The absolute value of a number is always greater than or equal to zero.

Chalkboard Examples

Simplify.

1. $-[-(-4)] = -[4] = -4$

2. $-|-(-4)| = -|4| = -4$

3. $-[-3 - (-4)] = -[-3 + 4] = -[1] = -1$

4. $-(-3 - |-4|) = -(-3 - 4) = -(-7) = 7$

5. $-3|2| + 4|-2| = -3(2) + 4(2) = -6 + 8 = 2$

Suggested Extension Challenge students to write an equation using the following symbols:

$$7, -8, 15, +, =, |\ |$$

Possible answers are $7 + |-8| = 15$ and $|-8| + 7 = 15$. Provide an opportunity for students to write such exercises and then exchange them. The practice students obtain in attempting to write such equations will reinforce their understanding of absolute value.

2-4 RULES FOR ADDITION

Key Mathematical Ideas This section specifies the rules for adding real numbers. These rules will enable students to add numbers without the direct use of a number line. The section also reviews the commutative and associative properties of addition.

Teaching Suggestions Some students will have intuitively developed methods for adding real numbers mentally. Others may need some explanation. You may wish to draw number line diagrams to illustrate each of the four rules. In any case, students are better off thinking of the number line than memorizing the rules given in the book.

The commutative and associative properties of addition may also be illustrated using the number line if that seems advisable. Alternately, you may prefer to work through the chalkboard examples with the class.

Chalkboard Examples

Simplify.

1. $-2 + 5 = 5 + (-2) = 5 - 2 = 3$

2. $-9 + 3 = -(9 - 3) = -6$

3. $4 + [9 + (-8)] = 4 + [9 - 8] = 4 + 1 = 5$

4. $[4 + 9] + (-8) = 13 + (-8) = 13 - 8 = 5$

5. $[4 + (-8)] + 9 = [-(8 - 4)] + 9 = -4 + 9$
$$= 9 + (-4) = 9 - 4 = 5$$

6. $-6 + 9 + (-12) + 8$

Method 1

$-6 + 9 + (-12) + 8 = 3 + (-12) + 8$
$$= -9 + 8 = -1$$

Method 2

$-6 + (-12) = -18; \ 9 + 8 = 17;$
$-18 + 17 = -1$

The computer programs on text page 46 will give students practice in using a computer terminal, although a minicalculator would also be appropriate for solving simple addition problems.

In the first program, notice that the computer types a question mark for each number to be input. If students input very large numbers, the computer may print the sum in exponential notation (see text page 66).

In the second program, the GOTO statement in line 70 directs the computer back to the INPUT statement in line 40 until 0 (zero) is typed in response to a question mark. (This zero is used to tell the computer that the last number to be added has been typed in.) When zero is typed in, the computer skips to line 80 where the accumulated sum is printed. In line 60, LET S = S + N means "Take the value that is in S, add the value of N to it, and store the result back in S."

Suggest that students try $1 + 2 + 3 + \cdots + 10$ and $1 + 3 + 5 + \cdots + 19$. Let them explore other patterns.

2-5 TRANSFORMING EQUATIONS BY ADDITION

Key Mathematical Ideas This section introduces two methods for solving linear equations which cannot be solved by inspection: transformation by substitution and transformation by addition. When applied to an equation, these transformations can be used to produce an equivalent equation whose solution *can* be obtained by inspection. Transformation by substitution is based on the substitution principle (text page 2); transformation by addition is based on the addition property of equality.

Teaching Suggestions To introduce the concept of *transformation by addition*, write the equation $x = 3$ on the chalkboard and illustrate how the addition property of equality can be used to transform the equation. For example,

$$x = 3$$
$$x + 3 = 3 + 3$$
$$x + 3 = 6$$

Ask the class how each of the following equations are obtained from the equation $x = 3$:

$x + (-8) = -5$	$x + 9 = 12$
$-3 + x = 0$	$11 + x = 14$

Ask the class to suggest other equations that can be obtained from $x = 3$ using the addition property of equality. Point out that all of the equations obtained are *equivalent* to $x = 3$ since each resulted from validly transforming this equation.

Now explain that the process of *solving an equation* is the reverse of the process described above. We are given an equation whose solution cannot be seen by inspection, and we are to use the addition property of equality to change the given equation into one of the forms

variable = number or number = variable.

Encourage students to check their work. It is important that they substitute each root in the *original* equation.

Chalkboard Examples

For each equation, state whether the given number is a root of the equation. (Either solve the equation and compare the root with the given number or substitute the given number in the equation.)

1. $x + 8 = 4; \quad -4$ Yes

2. $2 + k = -6; \quad 8$ No

3. $4 = -5 + q; \quad 9$ Yes

4. $r + (-3) = 2; \quad -1$ No

5. $-29 = 16 + s; \quad -13$ No

6. $-7 + z = 17; \quad 24$ Yes

Use transformation by addition to solve each equation.

7. $\qquad t + (-6) = 8$
$$t + (-6) + 6 = 8 + 6$$
$$t = 14$$

Check: $14 + (-6) = 8 \ \checkmark$

$\therefore$ the solution is 14.

8.
$$0 = k + 4$$
$$0 + (-4) = k + 4 + (-4)$$
$$-4 = k$$
Check: $0 = -4 + 4$ ✓
∴ the solution is -4.

(Remind students that the solution of an equation is a *number* and not another equation. In Exercise 7 above, for example, the equation $t = 14$ is not the solution; the number 14 is.)

Suggested Extensions

1. Identify the equations that are equivalent.

   a. $x + 2 = 4$ **b.** $-8 = -10 + x$
   c. $10 + x = 8$ **d.** $x + (-1) = 1$
   e. $-12 = -10 + x$ **f.** $12 = x + 14$
   g. $3 = 5 + x$ **h.** $-9 + x = -7$

   Equations a, b, d, and h are equivalent; equations c, e, f, and g are equivalent.

2. Solve the equation $[-y + 3] + (-4) = 6$.

   Solution 1
   $$[-y + 3] + (-4) = 6$$
   $$[-y + 3] + (-4) + 4 = 6 + 4$$
   $$-y + 3 = 10$$
   $$-y + 3 + (-3) = 10 + (-3)$$
   $$-y = 7$$
   $$y = -7$$

   Solution 2
   $$[-y + 3] + (-4) = 6$$
   $$-y + [3 + (-4)] = 6$$
   $$-y + (-1) = 6$$
   $$-y + (-1) + 1 = 6 + 1$$
   $$-y = 7$$
   $$y = -7$$

   (Point out that if the opposite of y is 7, then y is the opposite of 7, that is -7.)

2-6 SUBTRACTION OF REAL NUMBERS

Key Mathematical Ideas In this section students learn to subtract real numbers. The key concept is the relationship between addition and subtraction, expressed by the rule for subtraction: $a - b = a + (-b)$.

The significance of this rule is that any difference can be expressed as a sum and conversely. Numerical examples are used to demonstrate that subtraction is neither commutative nor associative.

Teaching Suggestions Draw the diagram shown below on the chalkboard.

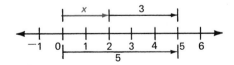

Ask the class to state an equation to fit the diagram. Some student should volunteer $x + 3 = 5$. Now draw this diagram on the chalkboard:

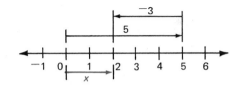

One equation that fits this diagram is $5 + (-3) = x$. Another is $5 - 3 = x$. These equations and the equation $x + 3 = 5$ are all equivalent to the equation $x = 2$. Point out that we can consider the difference $5 - 3$ as either the number whose sum with 3 is 5 or as the sum of 5 and the opposite of 3. In general, to find the difference $a - b$, we add the opposite of b to a, namely $a - b$.

Chalkboard Examples

Simplify.

1. $2 - 3 + 8 - 6 + 5 = (2 + 8 + 5) - (3 + 6)$
   $$= 15 - 9 = 6$$

2. $7 - (-15) - 9 + 4 = 7 + 15 - 9 + 4$
   $$= (7 + 15 + 4) - 9$$
   $$= 26 - 9 = 17$$

   (Point out that to subtract -15, we add the opposite of -15, that is, 15.)

3. $(11 - 16) + (-7 + 3) = -5 + (-4)$
   $$= -5 - 4 = -9$$

4. $(11 - 16) - (-7 + 3) = -5 - (-4)$
   $$= -5 + 4 = -1$$

5. $(11 - 16) - |-7 + 3| = -5 - |-4|$
   $$= -5 - 4 = -9$$

Suggested Extensions

1. Ask students to clip the weather report from their newspapers. Have them make a chart indicating the high temperature, the low temperature, and the difference of these temperatures for several cities listed in the weather report.

2. Ask students to write and exchange word problems, such as those on text page 55, basing their problems on the following data:

Place	Elevation above sea level
Mount Everest (Tibet)	8848 m
Mount McKinley (Alaska)	6194 m
Mount Logan (Canada)	6050 m
Pike's Peak (Colorado)	4301 m

	Below sea level
Dead Sea (Israel-Jordan)	396 m
Death Valley (California)	86 m
Peninsula Valdés (Argentina)	40 m
Lake Eyre (S. Australia)	16 m

2-7   TRANSFORMING EQUATIONS INVOLVING SUBTRACTION

Key Mathematical Ideas In Section 2-5 students learned how to use transformation by addition to solve simple linear equations. In this section their work is extended to solving equations which involve subtraction.

Teaching Suggestions In order to solve the equation $y - 4 = 6$, we may use the rule for subtraction and the substitution principle to rewrite the equation as $y + (-4) = 6$. We may then solve the equation by the method of Section 2-5. However, once students understand transformation by subtraction, encourage them to use the condensed method illustrated on text page 56. Also, be sure that they check their work by substituting the solution in the original equation.

Chalkboard Examples

Solve.

1. $k + 8 = -3$

Method 1

$$k + 8 = -3$$
$$k + 8 + (-8) = -3 + (-8)$$
$$k = -11$$

Method 2

$$k + 8 = -3$$
$$k + 8 - 8 = -3 - 8$$
$$k = -11$$

Check: $-11 + 8 = -3$ ✓

∴ the solution is -11.

(Students should realize that transformation by subtraction is another form of transformation by addition.)

2. $z + |3 - 6| = -3$

$$z + 3 = -3$$
$$z + 3 - 3 = -3 - 3$$
$$z = -6$$

Check: $-6 + |3 - 6| = -6 + 3 = -3$ ✓

∴ the solution is -6.

3 Multiplication and Division

CHAPTER OVERVIEW

The chapter opens with the basic rules and concepts related to the multiplication of real numbers: the commutative and associative properties of multiplication, the distributive property, and reciprocals. The solution of equations is then extended to include a new technique: transformation by multiplication. After a section devoted to the meaning of division of real numbers, the method of transforming equations by division is developed. The chapter concludes with a look at the axioms of algebra and the nature of deductive proof.

SECTION-BY-SECTION COMMENTARY

3-1 RULES FOR MULTIPLICATION

Key Mathematical Ideas The main objective of this section is to learn to multiply real numbers. From students' earlier work with addition on number lines they should intuitively understand why $2 \times (-1) = -2$ (see text page 63). The development of multiplying real numbers is then based on the multiplicative property of -1: $a(-1) = -a$ and $(-1)a = a$.

Teaching Suggestions Students have often seen statements such as the following:

$$2 \times 3 = 3 + 3 = 6$$
$$3 \times 1 = 1 + 1 + 1 = 3$$

If we substitute -1 for 3 in the first statement above and -1 for 1 in the second, we obtain the statements shown on text page 63:

$$2 \times (-1) = -1 + (-1) = -2$$
$$3 \times (-1) = -1 + (-1) + (-1) = -3$$

Students should come to the realization that multiplying a real number by -1 produces the opposite of the number. Since multiplication is commutative, the same effect is achieved by multiplying -1 by a real number. Introduce this rule, the multiplicative property of -1, emphasizing the special case $(-1)(-1) = 1$. From this special case, students should see why $(-3)(-4) = 12$ (see text page 64).

Chalkboard Examples

1. The product of two positive numbers is __?__ (a positive number, a negative number, zero).
   a positive number

2. Simplify $6(-5)$ and justify each step.

$6(-5) =$	
$6[5(-1)] =$	Mult. prop. of -1
$(6 \cdot 5)(-1) =$	Associative prop. for mult.
$30(-1) =$	Mult. fact
-30	Mult. prop. of -1

   Generalize: The product of a positive number and a negative number is __?__ (a positive number, a negative number, zero). a negative number

3. Simplify $(-5)(6)$ and justify each step.

$(-5)(6) =$	
$(6)(-5) =$	Commutative prop. for mult.
-30	Exercise 2

   Generalize: The product of a negative number and a positive number is __?__ (a positive number, a negative number, zero). a negative number

4. Simplify $(-6)(-5)$ and justify each step.

$(-6)(-5) =$	
$(-1 \cdot 6)(-1 \cdot 5) =$	Mult. prop. of -1
$[-1(-1)](6 \cdot 5) =$	Commutative prop. for mult. and associative prop. for mult.
$1(6 \cdot 5) =$	Mult. prop. of -1
$1(30) = 30$	Mult. fact

   Generalize: The product of two negative numbers is __?__ (a positive number, a negative number, zero). a positive number

5. Simplify $(-1)^2(4)^3$.

   $$(-1)^2(4)^3 = [(-1)(-1)] \cdot [4(4)(4)]$$
   $$= 1 \cdot 64 = 64$$

Suggested Extension Have students decide, without evaluating, whether each of the following products represents a positive or a negative number.

$(-2)(-1)$	Positive
$(-3)(-2)(-1)$	Negative
$(-4)(-3)(-2)(-1)$	Positive
$(-5)(-4)(-3)(-2)(-1)$	Negative
$(-6)(-5)(-4)(-3)(-2)(-1)$	Positive

Generalize: A product involving an *even* number of negative numbers is a ___?___ (positive, negative) number. positive

Generalize: A product involving an *odd* number of negative numbers is a ___?___ number. negative

Point out that in a product which has both positive and negative factors, one need count only the number of *negative* factors to determine whether the product represents a positive or a negative number. For example, $(-1)^2(4)(5)$ (Exercise 13 on text page 65) has *two* negative factors and therefore represents a positive number.

The computer program on text page 65 corresponds exactly to the first program on text page 46. Here a discussion of the BASIC exponential notation is given (compare this with the discussion of scientific notation on text pages 148 and 149). The activities suggested in this computer activity could equally well be done on a minicalculator.

3-2 THE DISTRIBUTIVE PROPERTY

Key Mathematical Ideas In earlier grades students learned how to multiply two-digit numbers by using the distributive property. For example, to find the product 3×12, students used the following steps:

$$3 \times 12 = 3 \times (10 + 2)$$
$$= (3 \times 10) + (3 \times 2)$$
$$= 30 + 6 = 36$$

The use of the distributive property is extended in this section to apply to the real numbers.

Teaching Suggestions To motivate the class, illustrate how quickly you can multiply a two-digit number by 21. Ask the class to suggest a two-digit number, say 36. The product $21 \cdot 36$ can be quickly computed in your head using the distributive property. *Think:* $21 \cdot 36 = (20 + 1)36 = 720 + 36 = 756$.

Next, introduce the distributive property to the class, using squared paper as shown below:

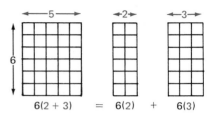

$$6(2 + 3) = 6(2) + 6(3)$$

Regroup the strips of paper to illustrate that $6(1 + 4) = 6(1) + 6(4)$. Other examples can be illustrated using a similar approach.

Now tell the class how you were able to multiply by 21 so quickly. Challenge members of the class to perform similar multiplications mentally. (You may wish to use the Oral Exercises for this purpose. See also Suggested Extension 2 on page T53.)

Chalkboard Examples

Simplify.

1. $12 \cdot 6 + 12 \cdot 8 - 12 \cdot 11 = 12(6 + 8 - 11)$
$$= 12(3) = 36$$

2. $23[12 \cdot 8 - 12 \cdot 6] = 23[12(8 - 6)]$
$$= 23[12(2)]$$
$$= 23(24) = 552$$

3. $12 \cdot 25 + 14 \cdot 25 = (12 + 14)(25)$
$$= (20 + 6)(25)$$
$$= 20(25) + 6(25)$$
$$= 500 + 150 = 650$$

Suggested Extensions

1. In this section, students have learned to use the distributive property of multiplication with respect to addition. This property can be extended to include the distributive property with respect to subtraction. For example, we can evaluate the product $4[16 + (-4)]$ in the following ways:

$4[16 + (-4)] =$	$4[16 + (-4)] =$
$4(16) + 4(-4) =$	$4[16 - 4] =$
$64 + (-16) =$	$4(16) - 4(4) =$
48	$64 - 16 = 48$

In general:

$$a(b - c) = ab - ac \quad \text{and} \quad (b - c)a = ba - ca.$$

2. Students may enjoy finding the products listed below in their heads. This can be accomplished informally or perhaps as a contest. (You may wish to divide the class into teams. Write a product on the chalkboard; the person who calls out the correct answer first earns a point for his or her team.)

32(21)	672	12(73)	876
49(14)	686	12(88)	1056
64(11)	704	35(31)	1085
15(39)	585	44(22)	968
54(19)	1026	29(41)	1189
51(25)	1275	69(11)	759

3-3 THE RECIPROCAL OF A REAL NUMBER

Key Mathematical Ideas The main objective is to introduce the meaning of the *reciprocal* or *multiplicative inverse* of a real number. The work in this section prepares the students for transforming equations by multiplication in Section 3-4.

Teaching Suggestions Introduce the class to *the reciprocal of a number* by asking, "What number should I multiply each of the following numbers by to obtain 1?"

Number	Response
8	$\frac{1}{8}$
-2	$-\frac{1}{2}$
1	1
$\frac{1}{3}$	3
$-\frac{1}{2}$	2
-1	-1

Introduce the definition that numbers whose product is 1 are called *reciprocals*. Discuss why the number 0 has no reciprocal. (The product of any number and 0 is always 0 and never 1.) Work some examples with the class before referring them to the generalization on text page 70.

Chalkboard Examples

Simplify.

1. $3 \cdot \frac{1}{4} \cdot \frac{1}{3} = \left(3 \cdot \frac{1}{3}\right) \cdot \frac{1}{4} = 1 \cdot \frac{1}{4} = \frac{1}{4}$

2. $\left(-\frac{1}{8}\right)(-40) = \left(-\frac{1}{8}\right)(-8)(5) = 5$

3. $\frac{1}{s}(12st) = \left(\frac{1}{s} \cdot s\right)(12t) = 12t \quad (s \neq 0)$

4. $-36ab\left(-\frac{1}{6}\right) = -36\left(-\frac{1}{6}\right)(ab)$

$\qquad = \left[6(-6)\left(-\frac{1}{6}\right)\right](ab)$

$\qquad = 6(ab) = 6ab$

5. $\frac{1}{3}(15a + 9) = \frac{1}{3}(15a) + \frac{1}{3}(9)$

$\qquad = \frac{1}{3}(3)(5a) + \frac{1}{3}(3)(3)$

$\qquad = 5a + 3$

6. $\left(-\frac{1}{3}\right)[-9x + (-3y)]$

$\qquad = \left(-\frac{1}{3}\right)(-9x) + \left(-\frac{1}{3}\right)(-3)y$

$\qquad = \left(-\frac{1}{3}\right)(-3)(3x) + y$

$\qquad = 3x + y$

(Point out in Exercises 5 and 6 that the expressions in parentheses/brackets cannot be simplified. In both cases, the grouping symbols indicate that the distributive property should be applied. Point out, too, that as students become familiar with using reciprocals, they will perform some of the intermediate steps shown above in their heads.)

Suggested Extension You may wish to discuss the relationship between *identity element* and *inverse* (see text page 88). We call 0 the identity element for addition for the following reason: For any real number a, $a + 0 = 0 + a = a$. The symbol $-a$ denotes the additive inverse of a for the following reason: For any real number a, $a + (-a) = -a + a = 0$ (See text page 38.).

Similar analogies can be made for multiplication. 1 is the identity element for multiplication because for any nonzero real number a, $a \cdot 1 = 1 \cdot a = a$. The symbol $\frac{1}{a}$ denotes the multiplicative inverse of a because for any nonzero real number a, $a \cdot \frac{1}{a} = \frac{1}{a} \cdot a = 1$.

3-4 TRANSFORMING EQUATIONS BY MULTIPLICATION

Key Mathematical Ideas The concept of *reciprocal* is applied in this section to the solution of simple linear equations. Transformation by multiplication is based on the multiplication property of equality. This transformation is directly analogous to transformation by addition: in each case, an equation is transformed by using an inverse.

Teaching Suggestions You may wish to start the lesson by reviewing transformation by addition and transformation by subtraction. As part of this review, you might write out complete solutions for the equations $y - 23 = -12$ and $3 + k = 14$. Remind students that their objective is to transform the given equation into an equivalent equation whose solution can be seen by inspection. You will want to be sure that students remember the terms *solve, solution set,* and *root.* By this time, students should be in the habit of checking their work.

To introduce the multiplication property of equality, compare it to the addition property of equality. If the same number is added to (multiplied by) equal numbers, then the sums (products) are equal. Extend the method used in the Teaching Suggestions of Section 2-5 to show how the multiplication property of equality can be used to transform an equation such as $x = 3$.

Introduce transformation by multiplication. Be sure students understand why zero must not be used as a multiplier to transform an equation (discuss the example at the bottom of text page 74).

Chalkboard Examples

Solve each equation.

1. $6x = 30$

    $\frac{1}{6}(6x) = \frac{1}{6}(30)$

    $x = 5$

    Check: $6(5) = 30$ ✓

    ∴ the solution is 5.

2. $-\frac{1}{3}y = 4$

    $(-3)\left(-\frac{1}{3}y\right) = (-3)(4)$

    $y = -12$

Check: $-\frac{1}{3}(-12) = 4$ ✓

∴ the solution is -12.

3. $6 = \frac{1}{3}z$

    $3(6) = 3\left(\frac{1}{3}z\right)$

    $18 = z$

    Check: $6 = \frac{1}{3}(18)$ ✓

    ∴ the solution is 18.

Suggested Extension Provide students with the opportunity to write equations such that the sum of their roots has a particular value. For example, the sum of the roots of the following equations is zero.

$$\frac{1}{3}y = \frac{4}{3} \qquad\qquad 4 + (-6) + 15 + (-18) + 5 = 0$$

$$-2x = 12$$

$$-3 = -\frac{1}{5}k$$

$$-\frac{2}{3}u = 12$$

$$10 = 2y$$

3-5 DIVISION OF REAL NUMBERS

Key Mathematical Ideas The main objective of this section is to learn to express a quotient $a \div b$ $(b \neq 0)$ in the forms $\frac{a}{b}$ and $a \cdot \frac{1}{b}$. Using the rule for division, any quotient can be expressed as a product and conversely. A key idea of the section is the exclusion of zero as a divisor.

Teaching Suggestions The difference $a - b$ was defined in Section 2-6 as the number whose sum with b is a. Thus, for example, $6 - 4 = 2$ because $4 + 2 = 6$. The same approach is used to define division. The quotient $a \div b$ $(b \neq 0)$ is defined as the number whose product with b is a. Thus, for example, $10 \div 2 = 5$ because $2 \cdot 5 = 10$. Students may find it helpful if you point out that division is related to multiplication just as subtraction is to addition.

In previous mathematics courses students have used the rule for division to simplify numerical expressions. They should have little difficulty extending the rule to variable expressions.

Chalkboard Examples

Rewrite each quotient as a product and simplify.

1. $45 \div (-9) = 45 \cdot \left(-\dfrac{1}{9}\right) = -5$

2. $-18 \div \left(-\dfrac{1}{3}\right) = -18 \cdot (-3) = 54$

3. $12c \div \dfrac{4c}{3} = 12c \cdot \dfrac{3}{4c} = \dfrac{12c}{4c} \cdot 3 = 3 \cdot 3 = 9$
$(c \neq 0)$

4. If $a = 3$, $b = -4$, and $c = 5$, evaluate $\dfrac{b^2 - 2c}{a}$.

$\dfrac{b^2 - 2c}{a} = \dfrac{(-4)^2 - 2(5)}{3} = \dfrac{16 - 10}{3} = \dfrac{6}{3} = 2$

Suggested Extension In the Suggested Extension of Section 3-3, the concept of *identity element* was discussed in relation to addition and multiplication. If you introduced those concepts to your students, you may wish to extend their work to subtraction and division. Ask students to decide whether there is an identity element for subtraction or for division. They should reach the following conclusions:

1. There is an identity element for subtraction if and only if there is some real number x such that $a - x = a$ and $x - a = a$ for every real number a. If $x = 0$, then $a - 0 = a$ for every real number a, but $0 - a \neq a$ for every real number a. Since there is no number x that satisfies the conditions, there is no identity element for subtraction.

2. There is an identity element for division if and only if there is some real number x such that $a \div x = a$ and $x \div a = a$ for every real number a. If $x = 1$, then $a \div 1 = a$, but $1 \div a \neq a$ for every real number a. Hence, division has no identity element.

3-6 TRANSFORMING EQUATIONS INVOLVING DIVISION

Key Mathematical Ideas The groundwork for this section was established in Sections 3-4 and 3-5. The "new" method for solving equations, transformation by division, is just transformation by multiplication written in a different form. The link between the two methods is the equivalence of $a \div b$, $\dfrac{a}{b}$, and $a \cdot \dfrac{1}{b}$
$(b \neq 0)$.

Teaching Suggestions You may wish to begin the lesson by reviewing the method of transformation by multiplication. Write out the solution to an equation such as $20x = 40$; stress that we *multiply by the reciprocal* of 20 to solve this equation. However, the rule for division states that multiplying by the reciprocal of 20 is the same as dividing by 20, that is $\dfrac{1}{20}(20x) = \dfrac{20x}{20}$. Thus, using transformation by division, the equation can be solved as follows:

$$20x = 40$$
$$\frac{20x}{20} = \frac{40}{20}$$
$$x = 2$$

As always, students may need to be reminded to check their work.

Chalkboard Examples

Describe how each equation may be transformed into one having a variable alone as a member.

1. $-12 = -\dfrac{k}{2}$ Multiply each member by -2.

2. $5q = 20$ Multiply each member by $\dfrac{1}{5}$ or divide each member by 5.

3. $\dfrac{2}{3}t = 15$ Multiply each member by $\dfrac{3}{2}$ or divide each member by $\dfrac{2}{3}$.

Solve.

4. $0 = 18w$
$\dfrac{0}{18} = \dfrac{18w}{18}$
$0 = w$

Check: $0 = 18(0)$ ✓
∴ the solution set is $\{0\}$.

5. $-8d = 64$
$\dfrac{-8d}{-8} = \dfrac{64}{-8}$
$d = -8$

Check: $-8(-8) = 64$ ✓
∴ the solution set is $\{-8\}$.

3-7 USING SEVERAL TRANSFORMATIONS

Key Mathematical Ideas This section brings together the methods of four earlier sections for solving equations:

    Section 2-5   Transformation by Addition
    Section 2-7   Transformation by Subtraction
    Section 3-4   Transformation by Multiplication
    Section 3-6   Transformation by Division

In this section students use more than one transformation to solve equations. This is accomplished by selecting the appropriate inverse operation to simplify the equation successively until it can be solved by inspection.

Teaching Suggestions It may be helpful for you to discuss the example on text page 85. Stress that an equation is simplified by applying inverse operations to the equation. Then discuss the plan for solving an equation given on text page 85.

Students should realize that there is often more than one way to solve an equation. For example, to solve the equation $\frac{1}{3}k - 10 = 4$ one might first multiply each member by 3; alternatively, one might first add 10 to both members. Although both methods are valid, one method may be preferable over another.

Chalkboard Examples

Solve.

1. $12 - 2(z - 2) = 12$

    $12 - 2z - 2(-2) = 12$

      $12 - 2z + 4 = 12$

        $-2z + 16 = 12$

    $-2z + 16 - 16 = 12 - 16$

          $-2z = -4$

          $\dfrac{-2z}{-2} = \dfrac{-4}{-2}$

           $z = 2$

  Check: $12 - 2(2 - 2) = 12 - 2(0) = 12$ ✓

  $\therefore$ the solution is 2.

2. $\dfrac{x}{3} - 7 = 5$

    $\dfrac{x}{3} - 7 + 7 = 5 + 7$

        $\dfrac{x}{3} = 12$

$$3\left(\frac{x}{3}\right) = 3(12)$$

$$x = 36$$

Check: $\dfrac{36}{3} - 7 = 12 - 7 = 5$ ✓

$\therefore$ the solution is 36.

3. If 8 is added to the product of 3 and a number, the result is 6 less than the number. Find the number.

Step 1   Find the number.

Step 2   Let $n = $ the number.

Step 3 $3n + 8 = n - 6$

Step 4 $3n - n = -6 - 8$

          $2n = -14$

          $n = -7$

Step 5   Check.

$\therefore$ the number is -7.

3-8 AXIOMS OF ALGEBRA

Key Mathematical Ideas This section reviews some of the basic rules and properties relating to real numbers. These properties, along with other theorems, are then used to justify steps in algebraic proofs. The section introduces a fundamental fact: The structure of algebra is based on axioms, theorems, and logical reasoning.

Teaching Suggestions Students may be overwhelmed if challenged to memorize all of the vocabulary and rules of this section. It may be effective to have students discuss and record answers to the Oral Exercises, working in pairs. Also, many students will better understand the properties of real numbers if they prepare a chart like the one given on text page 88, substituting specific numbers for a, b, and c.

Chalkboard Examples Before attempting an algebraic proof with the class, you may want to write out some numerical examples.

Give the missing reasons.

1. $8 + (3 + 2) = $
  a. $8 + (2 + 3) = $
  b. $(8 + 2) + 3 = $
  c. $10 + 3 = 13$

a. Commutative axiom for add.

b. Associative axiom for add.

c. Substitution principle

2. *Prove:* If $a + b = 0$, then $a = -b$.

Proof:

a. $a + b = 0$

b. $(a + b) + (-b) = 0 + (-b)$

c. $a + [b + (-b)] = 0 + (-b)$

d. $a + 0 = 0 + (-b)$

e. $a = -b$

a. Given

b. Add. prop. of equality
(Sample 2, text page 91)

c. Associative axiom for add.

d. Axiom of inverses for add.

e. Identity axiom for add.

The program in the Computer Activity on text page 95 uses a FOR-NEXT loop to determine the number of exercises specified by the user. The loop begins in line 40 and ends in line 260. If N is given the value 5 at the beginning, then 5 exercises will be generated.

Lines 50, 60, and 70 use the BASIC random number function. Line 50 generates numbers (A) selected at random from $\{1, 2, 3\}$. Lines 60 and 70 generate numbers (B and C) selected at random from $\{-8, -7, \ldots, 0, \ldots, 7, 8\}$.

In line 90 the value of A causes the computer to go to line 100 for an addition exercise, to line 150 for a subtraction exercise, or to line 200 for a multiplication exercise.

If students would like to try more difficult exercises, suggest that they change one of the numbers to a number from 10 to 20 by using

60   LET B=INT(11*RND(1)+10)

or to a number from -10 to -20 by using

60   LET B=$-$INT(11*RND(1)+10).

4 Working with Polynomials

CHAPTER OVERVIEW

This chapter covers the addition, subtraction, and multiplication of polynomials. The solution of equations is extended to include equations with similar terms. Students are given many opportunities to apply their skills to solving a variety of word problems.

SECTION-BY-SECTION COMMENTARY

4-1 SIMILAR TERMS

Key Mathematical Ideas This section introduces the vocabulary and concepts basic to the study of polynomials. Students learn to combine similar terms by using the distributive property introduced in Section 3-2.

Teaching Suggestions Familiarize the students with the vocabulary introduced in this section. Then write the expression $3a - 2b - 2a + 3b$ on the chalkboard. Evaluate the expression for $a = -2$ and $b = 3$:

$$3a - 2b - 2a + 3b =$$
$$3(-2) - 2(3) - 2(-2) + 3(3) =$$
$$-6 - 6 + 4 + 9 = 1$$

Now write the expression $a + b$ on the chalkboard and evaluate for $a = -2$ and $b = 3$.

$$a + b = -2 + 3 = 1$$

Evaluate the expressions for other values of a and b and show that in each case the expressions have the same value. Write out a proof to show that for every real number a and b, $3a - 2b - 2a + 3b = a + b$. Discuss how the distributive property may be used to simplify expressions containing similar terms.

Chalkboard Examples

Simplify.

1. $4n^2 + (-8n) - 12n^2 + 9n = -8n^2 + n$
2. $(-12s + 20k) - (2s - 15k)$
$$= -12s + 20k - 2s + 15k$$
$$= -14s + 35k$$
3. $2(4x - 3y) + 2(2y - 4x) = 8x - 6y + 4y - 8x$
$$= -2y$$

4. $-3[9 + (-j)] + 6(k - j - 4)$
$$= -27 + 3j + 6k - 6j - 24$$
$$= -51 - 3j + 6k$$

4-2 EQUATIONS WITH SIMILAR TERMS

Key Mathematical Ideas In the previous section students learned to simplify expressions containing similar terms. This skill is applied in this section to solving linear equations having a variable in only one member.

Teaching Suggestions Review the use of the distributive property to simplify expressions containing similar terms. Point out that students have solved equations such as

$$2a + 3 = 10 \quad \text{and} \quad 3 - 6d = -72.$$

In this section students learn to solve equations such as $2a + 3a = 10$.

$$2a + 3a = 10$$
$$(2 + 3)a = 10*$$
$$5a = 10$$
$$\frac{5a}{5} = \frac{10}{5}*$$
$$a = 2$$

You may wish to let the more capable students omit the starred steps above.

The word problems on text pages 105 and 106 are more difficult than those students have previously solved. It may be beneficial for you to work through one or two problems with the class before assigning homework from that set.

Chalkboard Examples

Solve.

1. $-2r + 6 + 5r = -9$

$-2r + 5r + 6 = -9$

$(-2 + 5)r = -15$

$3r = -15$

$r = -5$

Check: $-2(-5) + 6 + 5(-5) = 10 + 6 + (-25)$

$= -9 \checkmark$

$\therefore$ The solution is -5.

2. $3(s - 2) + 2(2 - s) = -12$

$3s - 6 + 4 - 2s = -12$

$(3 - 2)s + (-6 + 4) = -12$

$s + (-2) = -12$

$s = -10$

Check: $3(-10 - 2) + 2[2 - (-10)] =$

$3(-12) + 2(12) = -36 + 24 = -12 \checkmark$

$\therefore$ The solution is -10.

Chalkboard Examples

Solve.

1. $2(y + 7) - 3y = 4(y - 4)$

$2y + 14 - 3y = 4y - 16$

$14 - y = 4y - 16$

$14 + 16 = 4y + y$

$30 = 5y$

$6 = y$

Check: $2(6 + 7) - 3(6) = 2(13) - 18$

$= 26 - 18 = 8$

$4(6 - 4) = 4(2) = 8 \checkmark$

$\therefore$ The solution is 6.

2. $\frac{1}{2}(14w + 1) + \frac{3}{2} = 10(w - 1) - (3w - 12)$

$7w + \frac{1}{2} + \frac{3}{2} = 10w - 10 - 3w + 12$

$7w + 2 = 7w + 2$

$\therefore$ The solution set is the set of real numbers.

4-3 EQUATIONS HAVING THE VARIABLE IN BOTH MEMBERS

Key Mathematical Ideas In this section, students' work with solving equations is extended one more step: an equation having a variable in both members is transformed by adding or by subtracting the same polynomial from each member of the equation. This method is an extension of transformation by addition introduced in Section 2-5.

Teaching Suggestions Equations of the type studied in this section have the following characteristic: each may be satisfied by just one real number, by no real number, or by every real number. Point out that it may not be immediately obvious how many roots a particular equation has; however, the given equation can be transformed in order to determine how many real roots it has. If the given equation is equivalent to a false statement such as $0 = 2$, then the equation has no root; if the given equation can be transformed to the true statement $0 = 0$, then it is an identity, satisfied by every real number.

4-4 AGE PROBLEMS

Key Mathematical Ideas Students now have the background to solve many types of problems involving one variable. The age problems solved in this section will prepare students for solving age problems using two variables in Section 9-6.

Teaching Suggestions You may wish to introduce this lesson by asking students to translate verbal phrases into mathematical symbols. For example, if Victor's present age is v years:

What will be his age next year? $(v + 1)$

Five years from now? $(v + 5)$

What was his age last year? $(v - 1)$

Six years ago? $(v - 6)$

Jean is four fifths as old as Victor.

What is her age? $(\frac{4}{5}v)$

Victor's sister's age is ten years more than half Victor's age. What is her age? $(10 + \frac{1}{2}v$ or $\frac{1}{2}v + 10)$

Chalkboard Example Carla is twelve years older than her niece, Sofia. In six years Carla will be twice as old as Sofia. How old is Carla now?

Solution

Step 1 The problem asks us to find Carla's present age.

Step 2 Let $c = $ Carla's age.

Step 3

	Carla	Sofia
Age now	c	$c - 12$
Age in 6 yr	$c + 6$	$c - 6$

$$\underbrace{\text{C's age will be}}_{c+6} \quad \downarrow = \quad \underbrace{\text{twice S's age in 6 yr}}_{2(c-6)}$$

Step 4
$$c + 6 = 2c - 12$$
$$6 + 12 = 2c - c$$
$$18 = c$$
$$6 = c - 12$$

Step 5 *Check:* Is Carla 12 years older than Sofia?
$$18 = 6 + 12 \checkmark$$
In 6 years their ages will be 24 and 12; will Carla be twice as old as Sofia? $24 = 2(12) \checkmark$

∴ Carla is 18 years old.

4-5 PROBLEMS INVOLVING INTEGERS

Key Mathematical Ideas In this section students learn to solve word problems involving integers, consecutive even integers, and consecutive odd integers.

Teaching Suggestions To motivate the class, discuss the method used by Gauss as a child to evaluate an arithmetic series. Carl Friedrich Gauss (1777–1855), the famous mathematician, was able to evaluate the sum of many numbers very quickly by recognizing patterns. One example follows.

$$1 + 2 + 3 + 4 + 5 + 6 + 7 + 8 + 9 + 10$$

(with brackets showing pairs summing to 11)

The sum $1 + 2 + 3 + \cdots + 10$ equals 55 since $5(11) = 55$. Ask students to draw similar diagrams to illustrate the sums $1 + 2 + 3 + \cdots + 26$ and $1 + 2 + 3 + \cdots + 50$.

Using the examples discussed above, introduce the concept of *consecutive integers* as integers that differ by one. Illustrate how variables are used to represent consecutive integers. Finally, introduce consecutive even integers and consecutive odd integers, pointing out that each are integers that differ by two. Hence n, $n + 2, n + 4, \ldots$ can denote either consecutive even or consecutive odd integers, and similarly $n - 1, n + 1$, $n + 3, \ldots$ can represent them.

Chalkboard Example Find three consecutive integers such that three times the largest is 40 greater than the sum of the other two.

Outline of Solution

Step 1 We are to find three consecutive integers such that three times the largest is 40 greater than the sum of the other two.

Step 2 Let $n = $ the least integer. Then the other integers are $n + 1$ and $n + 2$. Three times the largest $= 3(n + 2)$.

Step 3 $3(n + 2) = 40 + [n + (n + 1)]$

Steps 4 and 5 Solve the equation and check the root.

∴ The consecutive integers are 35, 36, and 37.

Suggested Extension Have students find the indicated sums. Challenge them to discover the pattern.

Two terms: $1 + 3 = \underline{\ ?\ }$ 4
Three terms: $1 + 3 + 5 = \underline{\ ?\ }$ 9
Four terms: $1 + 3 + 5 + 7 = \underline{\ ?\ }$ 16
Five terms: $1 + 3 + 5 + 7 + 9 = \underline{\ ?\ }$ 25

and so on.

Note: The sum of the first 2 consecutive odd integers is 2^2, or 4. The sum of the first 3 consecutive odd integers is 3^2, or 9. Continue in this fashion. The sum of the first n consecutive odd integers is n^2.

You can use squared paper to illustrate the relationship between the consecutive odd integers and the perfect squares as follows:

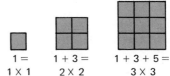

$1 = $ $1 + 3 = $ $1 + 3 + 5 = $ and so on.
1×1 2×2 3×3

Use the pattern to find the following sums:

a. $1 + 3 + 5 + \cdots + 19$ 100

b. $1 + 3 + 5 + \cdots + 25$ 169

c. $1 + 3 + 5 + \cdots + 99$ 2500

4-6 ADDING AND SUBTRACTING POLYNOMIALS

Key Mathematical Ideas   This section introduces the basic vocabulary related to polynomials. Then students are taught to simplify sums and differences of polynomials by combining similar terms as in Section 4-1.

Teaching Suggestions   You may wish to begin the lesson by reviewing the vocabulary and techniques introduced in Section 4-1.

When introducing the terms *monomial, binomial, trinomial,* and *polynomial,* point out the significance of each prefix. Relate *mono*mial to *mono*logue or *mono*poly; *bi*nomial to *bi*cycle or *bi*sect; *tri*nomial to *tri*angle; *poly*nomial to *poly*gon or *Poly*nesia.

Encourage students to use the rule at the foot of text page 117 to express the difference of polynomials as a sum.

Chalkboard Examples

Decide whether each polynomial can be simplified further.

1. $x^2 + y^2$ No

2. $2x^2 + x + 5 + 3x$ Yes

3. $x^2 + 2y^2 + 3x^2 + y^2$ Yes

Simplify. (Use a vertical arrangement if you prefer.)

4. $(x + y + z) + (3x + 2y + 4z)$
$$= (1 + 3)x + (1 + 2)y + (1 + 4)z$$
$$= 4x + 3y + 5z$$

5. $(2xy^2 + x^2 + 4) - (-xy^2 + 6)$
$$= 2xy^2 + x^2 + 4 + xy^2 - 6$$
$$= 3xy^2 + x^2 - 2$$

6. Solve: $(k^2 - 3) - (6 - k^2) = 2k^2 + 3k.$
$$(k^2 - 3) - (6 - k^2) = 2k^2 + 3k$$
$$k^2 - 3 - 6 + k^2 = 2k^2 + 3k$$
$$(1 + 1)k^2 - (3 + 6) = 2k^2 + 3k$$
$$2k^2 - 9 = 2k^2 + 3k$$
$$-9 = 3k$$
$$-3 = k$$

Check to see whether -3 satisfies the original equation.

$\therefore$ the solution set is $\{-3\}$.

4-7 MULTIPLYING MONOMIALS

Key Mathematical Ideas   The key idea of this section is the rule of exponents for a product of powers: $a^m \cdot a^n = a^{m+n}$ where m and n are positive integers. This rule is then used to simplify products of monomials.

Teaching Suggestions   It may be beneficial for you to review the meaning of the terms *factor, power, base* and *exponent* (see text page 7). In addition, you may want to discuss either the Chalkboard Examples or the Oral Exercises to be certain that the students understand the material.

Chalkboard Examples

1. a. How many factors are there in a^4?   Four

b. How many factors are there in a^3?   Three

c. Simplify $a^4 \cdot a^3$.
$$a^4 \cdot a^3 = (a \cdot a \cdot a \cdot a)(a \cdot a \cdot a)$$
$$= a \cdot a \cdot a \cdot a \cdot a \cdot a \cdot a = a^7$$

d. Thus $a^4 \cdot a^3 = \underline{\quad?\quad}$. a^7

2. Use the method of Exercise 1 to simplify these products.

a. $r^2 \cdot r^4 = \underline{\quad?\quad}$ r^6

b. $t^5 \cdot t^3 = \underline{\quad?\quad}$ t^8

c. $z^2 \cdot z^2 = \underline{\quad?\quad}$ z^4

Generalize: $b^m \cdot b^n = \underline{\quad?\quad}$. b^{m+n} for all positive integers m and n. Emphasize that the bases of the powers must be the same in order to use the rule.

Simplify.

3. $(2x^2y^3)(-4xy^5) = 2(-4)(x^2 \cdot x)(y^3 \cdot y^5)$
$$= -8x^3y^8$$
(Remind students that x means x^1.)

4. $(3d^3)(4d^2) - (2d)(d^4) = 12d^5 - 2d^5 = 10d^5$

5. $(s^{n-1})(3s^{n+3}) + (-s^n)(s^n) = 3s^{2n+2} - s^{2n}$

Suggested Extension   Students may be interested in the origin of the notation we use for exponents. If so, refer them to the Historical Note on text page 150.

4-8 POWERS OF MONOMIALS

Key Mathematical Ideas In this section two additional rules of exponents are developed:

$$(ab)^m = a^m b^m \text{ and } (b^m)^n = b^{mn}$$

for all positive integers m and n. The three rules of exponents are then used with the commutative and associative properties of multiplication to multiply monomials.

Teaching Suggestions The two rules for exponents from this section may be introduced by illustrating each with an example:

1. $(3t)^4 = 3t \cdot 3t \cdot 3t \cdot 3t = (3 \cdot 3 \cdot 3 \cdot 3)(t \cdot t \cdot t \cdot t)$
$$= 3^4 t^4 = 81t^4$$

2. $(w^5)^2 = w^5 \cdot w^5 = w^{5+5} = w^{10}$

Be sure students understand why, in general, $a^{m \cdot n} \neq a^{m+n}$.

Chalkboard Examples

1. Simplify $(2r)^4$.
$$(2r)^4 = 2r \cdot 2r \cdot 2r \cdot 2r = (2 \cdot 2 \cdot 2 \cdot 2)(r \cdot r \cdot r \cdot r)$$
$$= 2^4 r^4 = 16r^4$$

2. Use the method of Exercise 1 to simplify.
   a. $(ab)^4 = \underline{}$ $a^4 b^4$
   b. $(xy)^3 = \underline{}$ $x^3 y^3$
   c. $(yz)^5 = \underline{}$ $y^5 z^5$
   Generalize: $(ab)^m = \underline{}$. $a^m b^m$ for every positive integer m

3. Simplify $(2^4)^3$. $(2^4)^3 = 2^4 \cdot 2^4 \cdot 2^4 = 2^{12}$

4. Use the method of Exercise 3 to simplify.
   a. $(j^2)^3 = \underline{}$ j^6
   b. $(j^3)^2 = \underline{}$ j^6
   c. $(k^3)^4 = \underline{}$ k^{12}
   Generalize: $(b^m)^n = \underline{}$. b^{mn} for all positive integers m and n

Simplify.

5. $(-2xy)^3 = (-2)^3 x^3 y^3 = -8x^3 y^3$
   [Students may verify their work by comparing:
   $(-2xy)^3 = (-2xy)(-2xy)(-2xy) = -8x^3 y^3$.]

6. $(st^2)^3(-2s^2 t)^4 = [s^3 t^{2 \cdot 3}][(-2)^4 s^{2 \cdot 4} t^4]$
$$= (s^3 t^6)(16s^8 t^4)$$
$$= 16s^{3+8} t^{6+4} = 16s^{11} t^{10}$$

Suggested Extension Evaluate each expression if $x = 2$ and $y = -3$.

1. $5x^3$; $(5x)^3$ 40; 1000
2. $-2y^2$; $(-2y)^2$; $-(2y)^2$ -18; 36; -36
3. $x^2 + y^2$; $(x + y)^2$ 13; 1
4. $-3xy^2$; $-3(xy)^2$; $(-3xy)^2$ -54; -108; 324

4-9 MULTIPLYING A POLYNOMIAL BY A MONOMIAL

Key Mathematical Ideas In this section students use the laws of exponents and the distributive property to multiply polynomials by monomials.

Teaching Suggestions To multiply a polynomial by a monomial one merely applies the distributive property to obtain an expression of the type found in the previous section. For example,

$$3b(2b^2 + bc) = 3b(2b^2) + 3b(bc) = 6b^3 + 3b^2 c$$

Point out that we can use a vertical arrangement if we wish:

$$\begin{array}{r} 2b^2 + bc \\ 3b \\ \hline 6b^3 + 3b^2 c \end{array}$$

Chalkboard Examples

Multiply.

1. $-6k^2(k^2 - 4k + 12) =$
   $-6k^2(k^2) + (-6k^2)(-4k) + (-6k^2)(12) =$
   $-6k^4 + 24k^3 - 72k^2$

2. $\begin{array}{r} a^3 b^2 - 2a^2 b^3 + 6ab^4 \\ -3a^2 b \\ \hline -3a^5 b^3 + 6a^4 b^4 - 18a^3 b^5 \end{array}$

3. Solve $6(y - 1) - 1 = 2y + 21$.
   $$6(y - 1) - 1 = 2y + 21$$
   $$6y - 6 - 1 = 2y + 21$$
   $$6y - 7 = 2y + 21$$
   $$6y - 2y = 21 + 7$$
   $$4y = 28$$
   $$y = 7$$

   Check: $6(7 - 1) - 1 = 6(6) - 1 = 35$;
   $2(7) + 21 = 14 + 21 = 35$; $35 = 35$ $\checkmark$

   $\therefore$ the solution is 7.

4. Write an equation to represent the following: The product of two consecutive odd numbers is 143.
$n(n + 2) = 143$ or $n(n - 2) = 143$

4-10 MULTIPLYING POLYNOMIALS

Key Mathematical Ideas This section extends the methods of Section 4-9 to products of polynomials. The horizontal and vertical arrangements used to multiply a polynomial by a monomial are used in this section as well.

Teaching Suggestions You may want to illustrate the product $(a + b)(c + d)$ by using a numerical example:

$$27 \times 35 = (20 + 7)(30 + 5)$$
$$= 20(30 + 5) + 7(30 + 5)$$
$$= 600 + 100 + 210 + 35$$
$$= 945$$

$$
\begin{array}{r}
20 + 7 \\
30 + 5 \\
\hline
600 + 210 \\
100 + 35 \\
\hline
600 + 310 + 35 = 945
\end{array}
$$

Chalkboard Examples

Multiply.

1. $(2x^2 - x)(2 - x) = 2x^2(2 - x) - x(2 - x)$
$$= 4x^2 - 2x^3 - 2x + x^2$$
$$= -2x^3 + 5x^2 - 2x$$

2. $(3y + 4)(3y^2 + 5y - 4)$
$$= 3y(3y^2 + 5y - 4) + 4(3y^2 + 5y - 4)$$
$$= 9y^3 + 15y^2 - 12y + 12y^2 + 20y - 16$$
$$= 9y^3 + 27y^2 + 8y - 16$$

3.
$$
\begin{array}{r}
c^2 + 2cd - d^2 \\
c - 4d \\
\hline
c^3 + 2c^2d - cd^2 \\
- 4c^2d - 8cd^2 + 4d^3 \\
\hline
c^3 - 2c^2d - 9cd^2 + 4d^3
\end{array}
$$

Suggested Extension Some students may notice a pattern for multiplying a product of the form $(a + b)(a + c)$:

$(a + b)(a + c) = a^2 + ab + ac + bc$
$= a^2 + (b + c)a + bc$

$(z - 1)(z + 3) = z^2 + (3 - 1)z + 3(-1)$
$= z^2 + 2z - 3$

This pattern allows students to multiply such binomials at sight. Have students apply this method to Written Exercises 1–8 on text page 130. (*Note:* This extension anticipates Section 5-6.)

4-11 SOME APPLICATIONS INVOLVING AREAS

Key Mathematical Ideas In this section all of the skills acquired in Chapter 4 are applied to solving word problems. Students should be encouraged to draw diagrams which will assist them in writing an appropriate equation.

Teaching Suggestions Since many students often have difficulty solving word problems, it may be helpful for you to discuss the example on text page 131.

Chalkboard Examples

1. What is the area of a rectangle if the length of its sides in meters is:

a. $w + 4, w + 5$ $\quad w^2 + 9w + 20\ m^2$

b. $l - 2, l + 6$
$l^2 + 4l - 12\ m^2$

2. Write a polynomial expression for the area of the shaded region.
$(x - 4)(x - 6)$

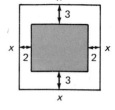

3. The Forands have two cookie sheets, one square and the other rectangular, each having the same surface area. If the length of the rectangular pan is 21 cm greater and the width 14 cm shorter than the length of one side of the square pan, what are the dimensions of each pan? (Use the five-step method to show that the square pan is 42 cm by 42 cm and that the rectangular pan is 63 cm by 28 cm.)

5 Factoring

CHAPTER OVERVIEW

The first part of this chapter covers the factorization of integers, monomials, and polynomials. The next part presents techniques for multiplying binomials and factoring trinomials and other polynomials. The last part of the chapter is devoted to applications of factoring—solving polynomial equations and verbal problems.

SECTION-BY-SECTION COMMENTARY

5-1 FACTORING INTEGERS

Key Mathematical Ideas This section provides a review of the essentials of factoring integers. Included is a method for finding the prime factorization of a positive integer. The prime factorization of two or more integers can be used to determine their greatest common factor.

Teaching Suggestions Students have factored integers in earlier courses. A brief discussion about *integral factors* and *prime factorization of an integer* should suffice. Point out the role that division plays in determining factors (see the bottom of text page 139). You will want to be certain that students notice the definition of *greatest common factor* on text page 142.

Chalkboard Examples

1. Name the positive integral factors of 36.
   $36 = 2 \times 18 = 3 \times 12 = 4 \times 9 = 6 \times 6$

2. Find the prime factorization of each integer.
   - **a.** 54 $2 \cdot 3^3$
   - **b.** 31   31
   - **c.** 240 $2^4 \cdot 3 \cdot 5$
   - **d.** 539 $7^2 \cdot 11$

3. Find the greatest common factor of each pair of integers.
   - **a.** 92, 48   4
   - **b.** 20, 35   5
   - **c.** 30, 75   15
   - **d.** 72, 56   8

Suggested Extension Ask the class to name any three-digit number, say 249. Create a six-digit number by repeating the number: 249,249. Divide the new number by 7; then divide the quotient by 11; and finally divide the resulting quotient by 13. The number obtained is the original number, 249 in this case. Have the class investigate why this "trick" works. The reason, of course, is that $7 \cdot 11 \cdot 13 \cdot 249 = 1001 \cdot 249 = 249{,}249$. (Refer students to the Extra for Experts on text page 142 and to the Computer Activity on text page 144 for additional material on divisibility and factoring.)

5-2 DIVISION AND FACTORING OF MONOMIALS

Key Mathematical Ideas This section uses factoring to simplify quotients. The factoring is based on the property of quotients: $\dfrac{xy}{cd} = \dfrac{x}{c} \cdot \dfrac{y}{d}$ for all real numbers x and y and nonzero real numbers c and d.

In Sections 4-7 and 4-8, three rules of exponents were presented. In this section, an additional rule of exponents, a rule governing the quotient of powers, is presented.

The property of quotients and the rule of exponents for division are then used to simplify quotients of monomials.

Teaching Suggestions Review the rules of exponents introduced in Sections 4-7 and 4-8:

   1. $b^m \cdot b^n = b^{m+n}$
   2. $(ab)^m = a^m b^m$
   3. $(b^m)^n = b^{mn}$

for all positive integers m and n. You may wish to write down an example to illustrate each rule, substituting values for m and n:

1. $a^5 \cdot a^4 = a^{5+4} = a^9$

2. $(rs)^3 = r^3 s^3$

3. $(z^4)^2 = z^{4 \cdot 2} = z^8$

You can use the following examples to develop the rule of exponents for division given on text page 145:

$$\frac{d^5}{d^3} = \frac{d^3 \cdot d^2}{d^3} = \frac{d^3}{d^3} \cdot d^2 = 1 \cdot d^2 = d^2 = d^{5-3}$$

$$\frac{h^6}{h^9} = \frac{h^6}{h^6 \cdot h^3} = \frac{h^6}{h^6} \cdot \frac{1}{h^3} = 1 \cdot \frac{1}{h^3} = \frac{1}{h^{9-6}}$$

Encourage students to simplify expressions mentally when they can.

Chalkboard Examples

Simplify, assuming that divisors are not zero.

(Remind students to simplify coefficients completely and to be sure that no base occurs more than once in the final answer.)

1. $\dfrac{20a^9 b^6}{-4a^2 b^8} = \dfrac{20}{-4} \cdot \dfrac{a^9}{a^2} \cdot \dfrac{b^6}{b^8}$

$$= -5 \cdot a^{9-2} \cdot \frac{1}{b^{8-6}} = -\frac{5a^7}{b^2}$$

2. $\dfrac{-5m^x n^{x+5}}{60mn^{x+1}} = \dfrac{-5}{60} \cdot \dfrac{m^x}{m} \cdot \dfrac{n^{x+5}}{n^{x+1}}$

$$= -\frac{1}{12} \cdot m^{x-1} \cdot n^{(x+5)-(x+1)}$$

$$= -\frac{m^{x-1} n^4}{12}$$

Find the missing factor.

3. $9x^5 y = (3x^3 y)(\underline{})$ $3x^2$

4. $-18a^6 b^2 = (-3a^4 b)(\underline{})$ $6a^2 b$

5. $72mn^3 p^2 = (-6n^2)(\underline{})$ $-12mnp^2$

6. Find the monomial of greatest degree and greatest integral coefficient which is a factor of $63x^4 y^2$ and $105xy^5$. $21xy^2$

Suggested Extensions

1. The *Applications* section on scientific notation (text pages 148–150) provides practical applications of the work with exponents. You may wish to point out that some minicalculators use scientific notation. In addition, if your class has been using the Computer Activity sections, have them compare scientific notation with the exponential notation in BASIC (see text pages 65–66).

2. Refer students to the *Historical Notes* on text page 150 for the origin of the notation used to represent powers.

5-3 MONOMIAL FACTORS OF POLYNOMIALS

Key Mathematical Ideas The theorem that justifies dividing a polynomial by a monomial is given on text page 151: $\dfrac{a+b}{c} = \dfrac{a}{c} + \dfrac{b}{c}$ for all real numbers a and b and all nonzero real numbers c. In addition to simplifying quotients, students learn to find the greatest monomial factor of a polynomial; this skill will prepare them for factoring polynomials.

Teaching Suggestions You may wish to start the lesson with a numerical example of the rule given on text page 151:

$$\frac{9+6}{3} = \frac{15}{3} = 5; \quad \frac{9}{3} + \frac{6}{3} = 3 + 2 = 5;$$

$$\therefore \frac{9+6}{3} = \frac{9}{3} + \frac{6}{3}$$

Generalize to the rule: $\dfrac{a+b}{c} = \dfrac{a}{c} + \dfrac{b}{c}$ for all real numbers a and b and all real numbers c. If we then let a and b represent polynomials and c represent a monomial, we have a method for simplifying quotients. Encourage students to write out intermediate steps to avoid errors (see the Chalkboard Examples).

Chalkboard Examples

Simplify. Assume that divisors are not zero.

1. $\dfrac{6x^2 + 4x}{2x} = \dfrac{6x^2}{2x} + \dfrac{4x}{2x} = 3x + 2$

   (By writing down intermediate steps students will avoid such common errors as

$$\frac{6x^2 + 4x}{2x} = \frac{6x^2}{2x} + 4x = 3x + 4x = 7x.)$$

2. $\dfrac{4y^2 - 2yz + 8}{2y} = \dfrac{4y^2}{2y} - \dfrac{2yz}{2y} + \dfrac{8}{2y} = 2y - z + \dfrac{4}{y}$

3. $\dfrac{g^3 h - 3g^2 h^2}{g^2 h} - \dfrac{4g^4 h^2 - 3g^3 h^3}{g^3 h^2}$

$$= \left(\frac{g^3 h}{g^2 h} - \frac{3g^2 h^2}{g^2 h}\right) - \left(\frac{4g^4 h^2}{g^3 h^2} - \frac{3g^3 h^3}{g^3 h^2}\right)$$

$$= (g - 3h) - (4g - 3h) = -3g$$

4. Find the greatest monomial factor of $35x^2 - 30x^3 + 10x^4$. Express in factored form and check by multiplying.

The greatest monomial factor is $5x^2$.

$$\frac{35x^2 - 30x^3 + 10x^4}{5x^2} = \frac{35x^2}{5x^2} - \frac{30x^3}{5x^2} + \frac{10x^4}{5x^2}$$
$$= 7 - 6x + 2x^2$$

Check: $(5x^2)(7 - 6x + 2x^2)$
$$= 35x^2 - 30x^3 + 10x^4$$
$\therefore 35x^2 - 30x^3 + 10x^4 = (5x^2)(7 - 6x + 2x^2)$

5-4 DIFFERENCES OF SQUARES

Key Mathematical Ideas Sections 5-4 through 5-11 provide a variety of methods for factoring special polynomials. In this section students simplify products of the form $(a + b)(a - b)$ and factor polynomials of the form $a^2 - b^2$.

Teaching Suggestions Ask students to simplify the following products, using either the distributive property or the vertical arrangement shown on text page 156.

$$(y + 6)(y - 6) = y^2 - 36$$
$$(a + b)(a - b) = a^2 - b^2$$
$$(k - 3m)(k + 3m) = k^2 - 9m^2$$

Use these examples to generalize to the rules given on text pages 156 and 157.

Chalkboard Examples

Factor completely.

1. $x^2 - 9 = x^2 - 3^2 = (x + 3)(x - 3)$
(You may want to suggest that students check by computing the product.)
2. $t^2 - 25q^2 = t^2 - (5q)^2 = (t + 5q)(t - 5q)$
3. $4a^2 - 9b^2 = (2a)^2 - (3b)^2 = (2a + 3b)(2a - 3b)$
4. $r^2s^2 - 16z^2 = (rs)^2 - (4z)^2 = (rs + 4z)(rs - 4z)$
5. $2x^2 - 72 = 2(x^2 - 36) = 2(x + 6)(x - 6)$
(Encourage students to check polynomials for their greatest monomial factor.)
6. $2x^6 - 8x^4 = 2x^4(x^2 - 4) = 2x^4(x + 2)(x - 2)$
7. $12a^3 - 48ab^2 = 12a(a^2 - 4b^2)$
$$= 12a(a + 2b)(a - 2b)$$
8. $x^{2m} - y^{4m} = (x^m)^2 - (y^{2m})^2$
$$= (x^m + y^{2m})(x^m - y^{2m})$$

Suggested Extension Challenge students to use the methods of this section to simplify products of numbers mentally. For example, to multiply 101×99:

Think: $101 \times 99 = (100 + 1)(100 - 1) = 100^2 - 1^2$
$$= 10,000 - 1 = 9999$$

Students may enjoy writing similar problems with which to challenge each other.

5-5 FINDING AND FACTORING SQUARES OF BINOMIALS

Key Mathematical Ideas The skills developed in the previous section are extended here to trinomial squares. The rules introduced are $(a + b)^2 = a^2 + 2ab + b^2$ and $(a - b)^2 = a^2 - 2ab + b^2$.

Teaching Suggestions Students may be interested in some numerical applications of the rules given on text page 160:

$$62^2 = (60 + 2)^2 = 60^2 + 2(120) + 2^2$$
$$= 3600 + 240 + 4 = 3844$$
$$36^2 = (40 - 4)^2 = 40^2 - 2(160) + 4^2$$
$$= 1600 - 320 + 16 = 1296$$

Chalkboard Examples

Factor completely.

1. $a^2 - 4ab + 4b^2 = (a - 2b)^2$
2. $9s^2 + 12st + 4t^2 = (3s + 2t)^2$
3. $64x^4 + 80x^2y^3 + 25y^6 = (8x^2 + 5y^3)^2$
4. $294u^2v^3 - 168u^3v^2 + 24u^4v$
$$= 6u^2v(49v^2 - 28uv + 4u^2)$$
$$= 6u^2v(7v - 2u)^2$$
5. $y^2 - 12y + 36 - 25x^2 = (y - 6)^2 - (5x)^2$
$$= (y - 6 + 5x)(y - 6 - 5x)$$

5-6 MULTIPLYING BINOMIALS MENTALLY

Key Mathematical Ideas In this section students learn the general pattern of the polynomial obtained by multiplying two binomials. Understanding this pattern will enable students to find such products at sight.

Teaching Suggestions Point out that the rules introduced in Sections 5-4 and 5-5 illustrate special cases of the quadratic trinomial:

$$(a + b)(a - b) = a^2 + ab - ab - b^2 = a^2 - b^2$$
$$(a + b)^2 = a^2 + ab + ab + b^2 = a^2 + 2ab + b^2$$
$$(a - b)^2 = a^2 - ab - ab + b^2 = a^2 - 2ab + b^2$$

Chalkboard Examples

Simplify.

1. $(a - b)(a - 2b) = a^2 - 3ab + b^2$

2. $(3m^2 - 4n)(5m^2 + 6n) = 15m^4 - 2m^2n - 24n^2$

3. $(2w - 3)^2 - (w - 4)^2$
$$= (4w^2 - 12w + 9) - (w^2 - 8w + 16)$$
$$= 4w^2 - 12w + 9 - w^2 + 8w - 16$$
$$= 3w^2 - 4w - 7$$

4. Solve $(4y + 5)(3y - 2) = (6y + 1)(2y + 3)$.
$$(4y + 5)(3y - 2) = (6y + 1)(2y + 3)$$
$$12y^2 + 7y - 10 = 12y^2 + 20y + 3$$
$$-10 - 3 = 20y - 7y$$
$$-13 = 13y$$
$$-1 = y$$

Suggested Extension The following activity will provide practice with multiplying binomials and experience with searching for mathematical patterns. Have students simplify these products:

$$(x + 1)^1 = x + 1$$
$$(x + 1)^2 = x^2 + 2x + 1$$
$$(x + 1)^3 = (x + 1)(x + 1)^2 = x^3 + 3x^2 + 3x + 1$$
$$(x + 1)^4 = x^4 + 4x^3 + 6x^2 + 4x + 1$$

and so on.

Substituting 1 for x:
$$(1 + 1)^1 = 1 + 1$$
$$(1 + 1)^2 = 1 + 2 + 1$$
$$(1 + 1)^3 = 1 + 3 + 3 + 1$$
$$(1 + 1)^4 = 1 + 4 + 6 + 4 + 1$$

and so on.

Challenge students to discover the pattern in the numbers. The pattern, of course, is Pascal's triangle:

```
        1   1
      1   2   1
    1   3   3   1
  1   4   6   4   1
1   5   10   10   5   1
```

and so on. Each term other than 1 is the sum of the

terms to the right and to the left in the row above. (The "point" of the triangle is omitted because not all students will remember from text page 148 that $a^0 = 1$.) Challenge students to evaluate $(x + 1)^{10}$ without multiplying.

5-7 FACTORING PATTERN FOR $x^2 + bx + c$, c POSITIVE

Key Mathematical Ideas In the previous section students learned to multiply binomials to form quadratic trinomials. Here they learn the reverse process —to express quadratic trinomials as the product of prime polynomials. A polynomial of the form $x^2 + bx + c$ has binomial factors of the form $(x + r)(x + s)$ if and only if $r + s = b$ and $rs = c$.

Teaching Suggestions Be sure that students understand the reasoning used to select trial factors. If rs in $x^2 + (r + s)x + rs$ is positive, then either both r and s are positive or both r and s are negative. (If only one were positive, then the product rs would be negative.) Hence, in Example 1 on text page 167, students need not consider $(-10)(1)$, $(-1)(10)$, $(-2)(5)$, or $(5)(-2)$.

Chalkboard Examples

Factor.

1. $a^2 + 9a + 14 = (a + 2)(a + 7)$
2. $k^2 - 12kt + 11t^2 = (k - t)(k - 11t)$
3. $-c^2 + 17cd - 30d^2 = -(c^2 - 17cd + 30d^2)$
$$= -(c - 2d)(c - 15d)$$
4. $(u + v)^2 + 12(u + v) + 35$
Let $z = u + v$. Then:
$$z^2 + 12z + 35 = (z + 5)(z + 7)$$
$$= (u + v + 5)(u + v + 7)$$

Suggested Extension Discuss the meaning of *irreducible polynomials* and *prime polynomials* as given on text page 168. Ask students to determine whether each of the following polynomials is irreducible.

1. $6w + 12$ Yes (A constant monomial factor does not make a polynomial reducible.)
2. $5x^3 - 25x^2$ No, $5x^3 - 25x^2 = 5x^2(x - 5)$
3. $y^2 + 2y + 1$ No, $y^2 + 2y + 1 = (y + 1)^2$
4. $z^2 + 2z + 2$ Yes

Refer students to Exercises 37–40 on text page 169 for additional practice.

5-8 FACTORING PATTERN FOR $x^2 + bx + c$, c NEGATIVE

Key Mathematical Ideas The same rule applied in the previous section can be applied to factoring $x^2 + bx + c$ where c is negative: the polynomial can be expressed in the form $(x + r)(x + s)$ if and only if $r + s = b$ and $rs = c$.

Teaching Suggestions You may wish to review the method used to factor a polynomial of the form $x^2 + bx + c$, c positive, since the work in this section is a direct extension of that method. Then write a product such as $(x + 4)(x - 2)$ on the chalkboard:

$$(x + 4)(x - 2) = x^2 + 2x - 8$$

with $-2x$ and $4x$ indicated.

Have the class compare this product with $(x + 4)(x + 2)$ and $(x - 4)(x - 2)$.

Now ask the class to factor $x^2 + 2x - 8$. We must look for factors of -8 whose sum is 2. The only ones that work are 4 and -2. Hence $x^2 + 2x - 8 = (x + 4)(x - 2)$.

As in the previous section be certain that students understand how to select appropriate possibilities as factors.

Chalkboard Examples

Factor.

1. $s^2 - s - 12 = (s - 4)(s + 3)$
2. $t^2 + 7t - 18 = (t + 9)(t - 2)$
3. $u^2 + uv - 56v^2 = (u + 8v)(u - 7v)$
4. $(y - 4)^3 - 5(y - 4)^2 - 14(y - 4)$
   $= (y - 4)[(y - 4)^2 - 5(y - 4) - 14]$
   Let $x = y - 4$. Then:
   $x[x^2 - 5x - 14] =$
   $x(x - 7)(x + 2) =$
   $(y - 4)(y - 4 - 7)(y - 4 + 2) =$
   $(y - 4)(y - 11)(y - 2)$

Suggested Extension Show that each polynomial is prime over the set of polynomials with integral coefficients.

1. $a^2 - 5a - 9$ 2. $m^2 + 4m - 11$
3. $k^2 + k - 4$ 4. $j^2 - 3j - 1$

5-9 FACTORING PATTERN FOR $ax^2 + bx + c$, a POSITIVE

Key Mathematical Ideas Students are now ready to factor quadratic trinomials in which the coefficient of the quadratic term is a positive integer. The rule which applies is as follows: $ax^2 + bx + c$ $(a \neq 0)$ can be expressed in the form $(mx + r)(nx + s)$ if and only if $mn = a$, $ms + nr = b$, and $rs = c$.

Teaching Suggestions Point out that quadratic trinomials of the form $ax^2 + bx + c$ introduce many more possibilities for factors. However, if the trinomial is factorable, the methods of this section will always produce the factors.

Chalkboard Examples

Factor.

1. $6a^2 + 31a + 35 = (2a + 7)(3a + 5)$
2. $5b^2 + 19b - 4 = (5b - 1)(b + 4)$
3. $28c^2 - 22c + 4 = (7c - 2)(4c - 2)$
4. $54d^2 + 75cd + 14e^2 = (6d + 7e)(9d + 2e)$
5. $-72d^2 + 48d + 10 = -2(36d^2 - 24d - 5)$
   $\qquad\qquad\qquad\quad = -2(6d + 1)(6d - 5)$

Suggested Extension Show that each polynomial is prime over the set of polynomials with integral coefficients.

1. $2x^2 + x + 3$ 2. $5z^2 - 8z - 1$
3. $7r^2 + 6r - 4$ 4. $11e^2 - e + 1$

5-10 FACTORING BY GROUPING

Key Mathematical Ideas This section develops the last technique for factoring: factoring by grouping. This technique is based on rearranging the terms of a polynomial and using the distributive property to find monomial factors.

Teaching Suggestions The examples that follow review the use of the distributive property:

$$c(x - 4) - d(x - 4) = (c - d)(x - 4)$$
$$(a + b)x + (a + b)y = (a + b)(x + y)$$

Point out that our aim in factoring polynomials in this section is to rearrange and regroup terms so that a common factor can be seen.

Be sure students realize that there is often more than one way to group terms (see the Example on text page 175 and the Chalkboard Examples below).

Chalkboard Examples

Factor.

1. $t^2(t - 1) + (t - 1) = (t^2 + 1)(t - 1)$

2. $2ax + 3ay + 2bx + 3by$
$= a(2x + 3y) + b(2x + 3y) = (a + b)(2x + 3y)$

or

$(2ax + 2bx) + (3ay + 3by)$
$= 2x(a + b) + 3y(a + b) = (2x + 3y)(a + b)$

3. $x^3 + yx^2 - xy^2 - y^3$
$= (x^3 + yx^2) - (xy^2 + y^3)$
$= x^2(x + y) - y^2(x + y) = (x^2 - y^2)(x + y)$
$= (x + y)(x - y)(x + y) = (x + y)^2(x - y)$

or

$(x^3 - xy^2) + (yx^2 - y^3)$
$= x(x^2 - y^2) + y(x^2 - y^2)$
$= (x + y)(x^2 - y^2) = (x + y)^2(x - y)$

The program in the Computer Activity on text page 176 uses "STEP 2" in the FOR step of each loop because prime numbers, except 2, are odd. This program has a loop within a loop (called *nested* loops). The pattern is:

```
┌─ 10 FOR N=3 TO 17 STEP 2
│  . . . . . . . . . . . . . . . . . . . . . . . . . . .
│ ┌─ 20 FOR F=3 TO N/2 STEP 2
│ │  . . . . . . . . . . . . . . . . . . . . . . . . . . .
│ └─ 50 NEXT F
│    . . . . . . . . . . . . . . . . . . . . . . . . . . .
└─ 70 NEXT N
```

Notice that in line 20 it is not necessary to test integers between N/2 and N, since none of them can be a factor (see text page 141). Since N is odd, the last number F to be tried will be the largest odd integer less than N/2. (Actually, it is only necessary to test up to the square root of N.) Since we are testing for prime numbers, the program rejects a number N from the set of primes as soon as one factor is found.

5-11 USING SEVERAL METHODS OF FACTORING

Key Mathematical Ideas This section ties together the various methods for factoring polynomials. These methods are applied in the last part of the chapter to solving equations and problems.

Teaching Suggestions It may be helpful for you to review the checklist given on text page 177. Be sure that students understand the importance of each step.

Chalkboard Examples

Factor completely.

1. $6x^3 + 2x^2 + 2x = 2x(3x^2 + x + 1)$

2. $-3k^2 + 27k - 60 = -3(k^2 - 9k + 20)$
$= -3(k - 5)(k - 4)$

3. $5a^2 - 45b^2 = 5(a^2 - 9b^2) = 5(a + 3b)(a - 3b)$

4. $75t^4 + 60t^3 + 12t^2 = 3t^2(25t^2 + 20t + 4)$
$= 3t^2(5t + 2)(5t + 2)$
$= 3t^2(5t + 2)^2$

Suggested Extension After factoring a given polynomial, students may check their work by evaluating the polynomial and their answer for a particular value of the variable. For example, if $y = 3$, then using the Sample on text page 178:
$2y^4 - 9y^2 + 4 = 2(81) - 9(9) + 4 = 85;$
$(y + 2)(y - 2)(2y^2 - 1) = (5)(1)(2 \cdot 9 - 1) = 85;$
$85 = 85 \checkmark$

5-12 SOLVING EQUATIONS IN FACTORED FORM

Key Mathematical Ideas One important application of factoring is solving polynomial equations by factoring. In this section, the equations are given in factored form so that students may concentrate on the zero-product property.

Teaching Suggestions Ask students to name two numbers neither of which is zero but whose product is zero. When they cannot, introduce the zero-product property given on text page 180.

Encourage students to solve factored equations by inspection. Remind them, however, to set each factor equal to zero and to solve these linear equations if they are unsure of a root.

Chalkboard Examples

Solve.

1. $k(k - 2)(k + 1) = 0$ $\{0, 2, -1\}$
2. $0(x + 1)(x - 7) = 0$ the set of real numbers
3. $(4y - 1)(y - 7) = 0$ $\left\{\frac{1}{4}, 7\right\}$
4. $2(3z - 2)(4z + 9) = 0$ $\left\{\frac{2}{3}, -\frac{9}{4}\right\}$

Suggested Extension The mention in this section of theorems and their converses may be used to stimulate a discussion about converses in general. A statement which can be expressed in the form "*If* clause, *then* clause" is called a conditional. In the statement "If $a = 0$ or $b = 0$, then $ab = 0$," the given assumption "$a = 0$ or $b = 0$" is called the *hypothesis;* the deduction "$ab = 0$" is called the *conclusion.* When the hypothesis and the conclusion are interchanged, the statement formed is called the *converse* of the original statement.

For each statement below, ask students to classify the statement and its converse as true or false. (Point out that if students can find one value of the variable for which a statement is false, then the statement itself is false.)

1. If $t(t - 4)(t + 7) = 0$, then $t = 0$ or $t = 4$ or $t = -7$. True; true
2. If $x = 0$ and $y = 0$, then $x + y = 0$. True; false
3. If $ab = 1$, then $a = 1$ and $b = 1$. False; true
4. If z is a real number, then z^2 is a positive number. False; true

The program in the Computer Activity on text page 182 is designed to give ten practice exercises (see line 40). Notice that:

line 60 selects values of A from $\{-50, \ldots, 50\}$
line 70 selects values of B from $\{-50, \ldots, 50\}$
line 150 selects values of C from $\{-9, \ldots, 9\}$
line 160 selects values of A+B from $\{-100, \ldots, 100\}$

This program is planned to allow practice in speeding up one's mental arithmetic if done at a terminal that types spaces in response to the TAB function. At 10 spaces per second, TAB(50) in line 200 allows 5 seconds. The time can be increased to 6 seconds by using TAB(60) or reduced to 4 seconds by using TAB(40).

5-13 SOLVING POLYNOMIAL EQUATIONS BY FACTORING

Key Mathematical Ideas The goal of solving a polynomial equation is to transform it to an equivalent form in which the roots can be obtained by inspection. In this section, equations are factored using the methods listed in Section 5-11. The zero-product property is then applied to obtain the solutions.

Teaching Suggestion The work in this section is the logical extension of that in the previous section. However, you will want to be certain that students learn the new vocabulary. They should realize that the degree of a polynomial equation gives the maximum number of real roots the equation can have.

When students have factored an equation, they should be encouraged to write the equivalent linear equations side by side (see the Examples in the text). It is also recommended that they check each root in the original equation. (This will prepare them for solving verbal problems in Section 5-14.)

The *Puzzle Time* on text page 185 reinforces the idea that division by zero is not defined in the set of real numbers.

Chalkboard Examples

Solve.

1. $$t^3 - 16t = 0$$
$$t(t^2 - 16) = 0$$
$$t(t + 4)(t - 4) = 0$$
$$\{0, -4, 4\}$$

2. $$4x^2 + 112 = 44x$$
$$4(x^2 - 11x + 28) = 0$$
$$4(x - 7)(x - 4) = 0$$
$$\{7, 4\}$$

3. $$d^3 - d + 2d^2 - 2 = 0$$
$$d(d^2 - 1) + 2(d^2 - 1) = 0$$
$$(d + 2)(d^2 - 1) = 0$$
$$(d + 2)(d + 1)(d - 1) = 0$$
$$\{-2, -1, 1\}$$

4. $(x - 3)(x - 2) = 20$

$\qquad x^2 - 5x + 6 = 20$

$\qquad x^2 - 5x - 14 = 0$

$\qquad (x - 7)(x + 2) = 0$

$\qquad \{7, -2\}$

(In Example 4, be certain that students do not make the common mistake of writing $x - 3 = 20$ and $x - 2 = 20$.)

5-14 USING FACTORING IN SOLVING PROBLEMS

Key Mathematical Ideas The skills developed in this chapter—factoring, multiplying binomials, and solving polynomial equations—are applied in this section to solving verbal problems.

Teaching Suggestions An effective way to deal with verbal problems is to have students work in pairs. If they are permitted to do this, they can correct many of the minor problems by themselves. You will quickly realize which students are having major difficulties and be able to correct their misconceptions.

Stress that not every root of an equation must satisfy the original problem. Thus in Example 1 on text page 186, the root 17 is rejected. Often word problems involve nonnegative numbers; for example, distance, height, and time are measurements that ordinarily are not expressed using negative numbers. If the equation written to solve Example 2 had yielded a negative root, the root would have been rejected.

Chalkboard Examples

Solve using the five-step method.

1. Find two consecutive even integers whose product is 168. (An outline of the solution follows.)

$$n(n + 2) = 168$$
$$n^2 + 2n = 168$$
$$n^2 + 2n - 168 = 0$$
$$(n + 14)(n - 12) = 0$$
$$n = -14 \text{ or } n = 12$$
$$\therefore -14 \text{ and } -12; \ 12 \text{ and } 14$$

2. The number of calories in a baked potato is 20 more than the number in an apple. The product of the numbers is 6300. Find the number of calories in each. (An outline of the solution follows.)

$$c(c + 20) = 6300$$
$$c^2 + 20c = 6300$$
$$c^2 + 20c - 6300 = 0$$
$$(c + 90)(c - 70) = 0$$
$$c = -90 \text{ or } c = 70$$

Reject $c = -90$.

$\therefore$ The number of calories in an apple is 70 and the number in a baked potato is 90.

6 Working with Fractions

CHAPTER OVERVIEW

In this chapter students learn to manipulate fractions, both numerical and algebraic. The key skills developed are the following: reducing fractions and ratios to lowest terms; adding, subtracting, multiplying, and dividing fractions; dividing polynomials; and solving a variety of equations and verbal problems. Throughout the development, algebraic rules for operations with fractions are introduced in terms of numerical examples.

SECTION-BY-SECTION COMMENTARY

6-1 FACTORING AND FRACTIONS

Key Mathematical Ideas Using the methods of factoring developed in Chapter 5, some fractions can be expressed in the form $\dfrac{a \cdot c}{b \cdot c}$ where c is the greatest common factor of the numerator and the denominator. The multiplication property of fractions can then be used to reduce the fractions to lowest terms.

Teaching Suggestions Review the concept of greatest common factor (see text pages 142 and 152). Then write $\dfrac{36}{48}$ on the chalkboard and ask the class what the greatest common factor of 36 and 48 is. Some student should volunteer "12." Thus:

$$\frac{36}{48} = \frac{3 \cdot 12}{4 \cdot 12} = \frac{3}{4} \cdot \frac{12}{12} = \frac{3}{4} \cdot 1 = \frac{3}{4}$$

If students need a reminder of the methods of factoring, refer them to the checklist on text page 177.

Chalkboard Examples

Simplify. (Remind the class that simplifying a fraction means reducing it to lowest terms.)

1. $\dfrac{16x^4}{12x^2} = \dfrac{4x^2 \cdot 4x^2}{3 \cdot 4x^2} = \dfrac{4x^2}{3} \cdot \dfrac{4x^2}{4x^2} = \dfrac{4x^2}{3}; x \neq 0$

   (Be sure that students specify the restrictions on the values of the variable.)

2. $\dfrac{2c^2 + 2c}{c^2 - c} = \dfrac{2c(c + 1)}{c(c - 1)}$

   $= \dfrac{2c + 2}{c - 1}; c \neq 0, c \neq 1$

3. $\dfrac{6 - 5y + y^2}{y^2 - 4} = \dfrac{(3 - y)(2 - y)}{(y + 2)(y - 2)}$

   $= -\dfrac{(3 - y)(y - 2)}{(y + 2)(y - 2)} = -\dfrac{3 - y}{y + 2}$

   $= \dfrac{y - 3}{y + 2}; y \neq 2, y \neq -2$

Suggested Extension Solve: $\dfrac{r - r^3}{3r^2 + 8r + 5} = -1$.

$$\frac{r - r^3}{3r^2 + 8r + 5} = -1$$

$$\frac{r(1 + r)(1 - r)}{(3r + 5)(r + 1)} = -1 \quad \left(r \neq -\frac{5}{3}, r \neq -1\right)$$

$$r - r^2 = -1(3r + 5)$$

$$0 = r^2 - 4r - 5 = (r - 5)(r + 1)$$

$$r = 5 \text{ or } r = -1$$

$$\text{Reject } -1.$$

$\therefore$ the solution set is $\{5\}$.

6-2 RATIOS

Key Mathematical Ideas The key concept of this section is the idea that ratios can be used to compare two quantities *of the same kind*. Students' knowledge of ratios is applied in this section to expressing ratios in lowest terms and to solving verbal problems.

Teaching Suggestions Draw two lengths on the chalkboard: one 1.25 meters long, and the other 65 centimeters long. Point out to the class that in order to compare the lengths meaningfully, they must be written using the same unit. Introduce the *ratio* of two numbers as their quotient. The ratio of the lengths in meters is $\dfrac{1.25}{0.65} = \dfrac{25}{13}$ or $25:13$. In centimeters the ratio is $\dfrac{125}{65} = \dfrac{25}{13}$. Stress that we may choose any unit for comparison; the ratio is the same.

You may wish to draw figures such as that shown below and ask the class to tell you the ratio of the area of the shaded region to the area of the unshaded region.

$$\frac{A_1}{A_2} = \frac{2}{4} = \frac{1}{2}$$

Chalkboard Examples

Write each ratio in its lowest terms.

1. 12 minutes to 60 seconds $1:5$

2. 6 years to 6 months $12:1$

3. 5 cents to 2 dollars $1:40$

4. $\dfrac{xy^2z}{wy}$ $\dfrac{xyz}{w}$, $w \neq 0$, $y \neq 0$

5. Find the ratio of $x:y$ if $\dfrac{3x - y}{2y} = \dfrac{5}{2}$.

$$2y\left(\frac{3x - y}{2y}\right) = 2y\left(\frac{5}{2}\right)$$
$$3x - y = 5y$$
$$3x = 6y$$
$$x = 2y$$
$$\frac{x}{y} = \frac{2}{1} \quad (y \neq 0)$$

Suggested Extensions   Ask one of your students to prepare a report about sports statistics, many of which are based on ratios. Clippings from the sports pages of the newspaper provide ample data for a class discussion.

6-3   MULTIPLYING FRACTIONS

Key Mathematical Ideas   In this section, the study of fractions is extended to expressing a product of fractions as a single fraction in lowest terms. As noted on

text page 205, common factors can be divided from the numerator and the denominator either before or after the expression is written as a single fraction.

Teaching Suggestions   You may wish to discuss Example 2 on text page 206 with the class. Remind them that the procedure for reducing a product of fractions is as follows: factor each numerator and denominator; look for common factors (use slash marks to keep track of factors); regroup the remaining factors in the numerator and the denominator, expressing the product as a single fraction. As in Section 6-2, be sure that students understand that values of the variable for which the denominator is zero are excluded.

Chalkboard Examples

Express as a fraction in lowest terms, noting restrictions on values of the variables.

1. $\dfrac{9s^2 + 6s + 1}{6s + 2} \cdot \dfrac{s^2 - 4}{3s^2 + 7s + 2}$

$$= \frac{(3s + 1)(3s + 1)}{2(3s + 1)} \cdot \frac{(s + 2)(s - 2)}{(3s + 1)(s + 2)}$$

$$= \frac{s - 2}{2}; s \neq -\frac{1}{3}, s \neq -2$$

2. $\dfrac{b^2 - 1}{b^2 + b - 6} \cdot \dfrac{2 - b}{b^2 - 2b + 1}$

$$= \frac{(b + 1)(b - 1)}{(b + 3)(b - 2)} \cdot \frac{-(b - 2)}{(b - 1)(b - 1)}$$

$$= -\frac{b + 1}{(b + 3)(b - 1)}$$

$$= -\frac{b + 1}{b^2 + 2b - 3}; b \neq -3, b \neq 2, b \neq 1$$

(You may wish to show students how to check these answers by using the method outlined on text page 206.)

6-4   DIVIDING FRACTIONS

Key Mathematical Ideas   In this section expressions involving quotients of fractions are simplified using the rule for dividing fractions: $\dfrac{a}{b} \div \dfrac{c}{d} = \dfrac{a}{b} \cdot \dfrac{d}{c} = \dfrac{ad}{bc}$ for any real number a and nonzero real numbers b, c, and d. Using this rule, a quotient of fractions can be written as a product of fractions and then be reduced to lowest terms.

Teaching Suggestions You may wish to review one example from Section 6-3 of the product of two quotients, noting restrictions on the values of the variables. For example, simplify

$$\frac{2a}{3a + 6} \cdot \frac{a^2 - 4}{6a^2} \text{ to } \frac{a - 2}{9a}, a \neq -2, a \neq 0.$$

$$\left(\text{Be certain that students do not write } \frac{\overset{1}{\cancel{a}} - 2}{\cancel{9a}} = \frac{-1}{9}. \right)$$

Now write the quotient $\dfrac{2a}{3a + 6} \div \dfrac{6a^2}{a^2 - 4}$ on the chalkboard. Using the rule for division (text page 78):

$$\frac{2a}{3a + 6} \div \frac{6a^2}{a^2 - 4} = \frac{2a}{3a + 6} \cdot \frac{1}{\dfrac{6a^2}{a^2 - 4}}.$$

Since $\dfrac{6a^2}{a^2 - 4} \cdot \dfrac{a^2 - 4}{6a^2} = 1,$ $\dfrac{6a^2}{a^2 - 4}$ and $\dfrac{a^2 - 4}{6a^2}$ are reciprocals. Then:

$$\frac{2a}{3a + 6} \cdot \frac{1}{\dfrac{6a^2}{a^2 - 4}} = \frac{2a}{3a + 6} \cdot \frac{a^2 - 4}{6a^2}.$$

This product can be simplified by the methods of the previous section.

Chalkboard Examples

Simplify.

1. $\dfrac{x^2 - 9}{x^3} \div \dfrac{x^2 - 6x + 9}{x^4} = \dfrac{x^2 - 9}{x^3} \cdot \dfrac{x^4}{x^2 - 6x + 9}$

$$= \frac{(x + 3)(x - 3) \cdot x^4}{x^3(x - 3)(x - 3)} = \frac{(x + 3)x}{x - 3} = \frac{x^2 + 3x}{x - 3}$$

$$(x \neq 0, x \neq 3)$$

2. $\dfrac{\dfrac{24x^2y^2}{6x}}{\dfrac{8xy}{x^2}} = \dfrac{24x^2y^2}{6x} \div \dfrac{8xy}{x^2} = \dfrac{24x^2y^2}{6x} \cdot \dfrac{x^2}{8xy}$

$$= \frac{24x^4y^2}{48x^2y} = \frac{x^2y}{2}$$

$$(x \neq 0, y \neq 0)$$

6-5 EXPRESSIONS INVOLVING MULTIPLICATION AND DIVISION

Key Mathematical Ideas The work of Sections 6-3 and 6-4 is extended here to simplifying expressions involving both products and quotients of fractions. The rule for order of operations specifies that products and quotients are evaluated in order from left to right.

Teaching Suggestions Review with the class the order of operations. For example:

$$a \div b \div c \text{ means } (a \div b) \div c$$
$$a \cdot b \div c \quad \text{means } (a \cdot b) \div c$$
$$a \div b \cdot c \quad \text{means } (a \div b) \cdot c$$

and so on.

Work through the Chalkboard Examples or a few of the Written Exercises. Remind students to check that their answers cannot be simplified further. Recommend that they check their work by substituting a value other than zero or one that will not make a denominator zero.

Chalkboard Examples

Simplify.

1. $\dfrac{16ab^3}{4a^2b} \cdot \dfrac{20a}{15b} \div \dfrac{4ab}{3a^2} = \dfrac{4b^2}{a} \cdot \dfrac{4a}{3b} \cdot \dfrac{3a^2}{4ab}$

$$= \frac{(4 \cdot 4 \cdot 3)(a^3)(b^2)}{(4 \cdot 3)(a^2)(b^2)}$$

$$= 4a \quad (a \neq 0, b \neq 0)$$

2. $\dfrac{x^2 + 2x + 1}{x^2 + x} \cdot \dfrac{x^2 - x}{x^2 - x - 2} \div \dfrac{x^2 - 1}{x^2 - 5x + 6}$

$$= \frac{(x + 1)(x + 1)}{x(x + 1)} \cdot \frac{x(x - 1)}{(x - 2)(x + 1)} \cdot \frac{(x - 3)(x - 2)}{(x + 1)(x - 1)}$$

$$= \frac{(x + 1)^2 \cdot x \cdot (x - 1)(x - 3)(x - 2)}{(x + 1)^3 \cdot x \cdot (x - 1)(x - 2)}$$

$$= \frac{x - 3}{x + 1} \quad (x \neq 0, x \neq -1, x \neq 2, x \neq 1, x \neq 3)$$

6-6 ADDING AND SUBTRACTING FRACTIONS

Key Mathematical Ideas The key idea of this section is that in order to add or to subtract fractions, the fractions must have equal denominators. The least common denominator is introduced as the most convenient denominator to use.

Teaching Suggestions Write the sum $\dfrac{3}{4} + \dfrac{2}{4}$ on the chalkboard:

$$\frac{3}{4} + \frac{2}{4} = \frac{3 + 2}{4} = \frac{5}{4}$$

Now rewrite the example as $\dfrac{3}{4} + \dfrac{1}{2}$. Ask the class what is needed to find the sum. Some student should volunteer the need for equal denominators:

$$\frac{3}{4} + \frac{1}{2} = \frac{3}{4} + \frac{1}{2} \cdot \frac{2}{2} = \frac{3}{4} + \frac{2}{4} = \frac{5}{4}$$

Finally, discuss the use of the least common denominator (L.C.D.) as the most convenient denominator for simplifying an expression. As illustrated at the bottom of text page 215, the quotient of the L.C.D. and the denominator of a fraction is the number by which the numerator and denominator of the fraction are multiplied.

Chalkboard Examples

Simplify.

1. $\dfrac{1}{2} + \dfrac{5}{8} - \dfrac{3}{16} = \dfrac{1}{2} \cdot \dfrac{8}{8} + \dfrac{5}{8} \cdot \dfrac{2}{2} - \dfrac{3}{16}$

$= \dfrac{8}{16} + \dfrac{10}{16} - \dfrac{3}{16} = \dfrac{8 + 10 - 3}{16} = \dfrac{15}{16}$

2. $\dfrac{3}{x} - \dfrac{8}{x} + \dfrac{2}{x} = \dfrac{3 - 8 + 2}{x} = -\dfrac{3}{x}$

3. $\dfrac{c + 3}{4} + \dfrac{c + 1}{12} = \dfrac{3(c + 3)}{12} + \dfrac{c + 1}{12}$

$= \dfrac{3c + 9 + c + 1}{12}$

$= \dfrac{4c + 10}{12} = \dfrac{2(2c + 5)}{12}$

$= \dfrac{2c + 5}{6}$

4. $\dfrac{3x - y}{x^2 - y^2} - \dfrac{2}{x + y} + \dfrac{4}{x - y}$

$= \dfrac{3x - y}{(x + y)(x - y)} - \dfrac{2}{(x + y)} + \dfrac{4}{(x - y)}$

$= \dfrac{3x - y}{(x + y)(x - y)} - \dfrac{2(x - y)}{(x + y)(x - y)}$

$\qquad\qquad + \dfrac{4(x + y)}{(x + y)(x - y)}$

$= \dfrac{3x - y - (2x - 2y) + (4x + 4y)}{(x + y)(x - y)}$

$= \dfrac{3x - y - 2x + 2y + 4x + 4y}{(x + y)(x - y)}$

$= \dfrac{5x + 5y}{(x + y)(x - y)} = \dfrac{5(x + y)}{(x + y)(x - y)} = \dfrac{5}{x - y}$

Suggested Extension Have the class study these examples and explain why each can be evaluated at sight.

1. $\dfrac{2xy}{x^2 - y^2} \cdot \dfrac{12x^2y^2}{4xy} \cdot \dfrac{x^2 + y^2}{6xy} \cdot 0$

2. $\dfrac{x + y}{y + x} - \dfrac{x - y}{y - x}$

3. $\dfrac{x^2 - y^2}{x + y} \cdot \dfrac{24x^2y}{6xy} \cdot \dfrac{y + x}{y^2 - x^2}$

6-7 MIXED EXPRESSIONS

Key Mathematical Ideas In this section a *mixed expression* is defined as the sum or difference of a polynomial and a fraction. Working with mixed expressions will prepare students for dividing polynomials in the next section.

Teaching Suggestions Review the method for transforming a mixed numeral such as $4\dfrac{2}{3}$ into a fraction:

$$4\frac{2}{3} = 4 + \frac{2}{3} = \frac{4}{1} + \frac{2}{3} = \frac{12}{3} + \frac{2}{3} = \frac{14}{3}$$

$$-3\frac{1}{8} = -\left(\frac{3}{1} + \frac{1}{8}\right) = -\left(\frac{24}{8} + \frac{1}{8}\right) = -\frac{25}{8}$$

Compare mixed numerals with mixed expressions such as $y + \dfrac{5}{y}$. Discuss why $y + \dfrac{5}{y}$ cannot be written as $y\dfrac{5}{y}$. (The implied operation is multiplication, but the intended operation is addition.)

Chalkboard Examples

Express as a fraction in lowest terms.

1. $2 + \dfrac{a - 2b}{a + b} = \dfrac{2(a + b)}{a + b} + \dfrac{a - 2b}{a + b}$

$= \dfrac{2a + 2b + a - 2b}{a + b} = \dfrac{3a}{a + b}$

2. $t + 3 - \dfrac{5t - 5}{t - 1} = \dfrac{(t + 3)(t - 1)}{t - 1} - \dfrac{5t - 5}{t - 1}$

$= \dfrac{t^2 + 2t - 3 - (5t - 5)}{t - 1}$

$= \dfrac{t^2 - 3t + 2}{t - 1}$

$= \dfrac{(t - 2)(t - 1)}{t - 1} = t - 2$

Express as a mixed expression.

3. $\dfrac{36a + 18z^2}{9a} = \dfrac{36a}{9a} + \dfrac{18z^2}{9a} = 4 + \dfrac{2z^2}{a}$

$\left(\text{Be sure that students do not write}\right.$

$$\dfrac{\overset{4}{\cancel{36a}} + 18z^2}{\underset{1}{\cancel{9a}}} = 4 + 18z^2. \Big)$$

4. $\dfrac{12p^2q + 10q^2}{2pq} = \dfrac{12p^2q}{2pq} + \dfrac{10q^2}{2pq} = 6p + \dfrac{5q}{p}$

6-8 DIVIDING A POLYNOMIAL BY A POLYNOMIAL

Key Mathematical Ideas This section develops a technique for dividing a polynomial by a polynomial. The presentation on text page 220 makes it apparent that dividing polynomials is directly analogous to dividing integers.

Teaching Suggestions You may wish to go through Examples 1, 2, and 3 on text pages 220 and 221. Point out that the answer for each example is written in the form

$$\dfrac{dividend}{divisor} = quotient + \dfrac{remainder}{divisor}$$

where the remainder is either 0 or is a term whose degree is less than that of the divisor. (You may wish to review the meaning of *degree,* defined in Section 4-6.) Remind students that a mixed numeral is written with the "+" implied; a mixed expression must have the "+" or "−" explicitly written.

Chalkboard Examples

Divide.

1. $\dfrac{2 + 6t^3 - 8t^2 - 7t}{3t - 1}$

$$\begin{array}{r}
2t^2 - 2t - 3 \\
3t - 1 \overline{)6t^3 - 8t^2 - 7t + 2} \\
\underline{6t^3 - 2t^2 } \\
- 6t^2 - 7t \\
\underline{- 6t^2 + 2t } \\
- 9t + 2 \\
\underline{- 9t + 3} \\
- 1
\end{array}$$

Check: $(3t - 1)(2t^2 - 2t - 3) - 1$
$$= 6t^3 - 8t^2 - 7t + 2 \checkmark$$

(As an alternate check, students may evaluate the expressions for a given value of the variable.)

$$\therefore \dfrac{2 + 6t^3 - 8t^2 - 7t}{3t - 1} = 2t^2 - 2t - 3 - \dfrac{1}{3t - 1}.$$

2. $\dfrac{t^3 + 1}{t + 1}$

$$\begin{array}{r}
t^2 - t + 1 \\
t + 1 \overline{)t^3 + 0t^2 + 0t + 1} \\
\underline{t^3 + t^2 } \\
- t^2 + 0t \\
\underline{- t^2 - t } \\
t + 1 \\
\underline{t + 1} \\
0
\end{array}$$

Check by one of the methods outlined in Exercise 1.

$$\therefore \dfrac{t^3 + 1}{t + 1} = t^2 - t + 1.$$

Suggested Extension Have the class simplify each expression.

1. $\dfrac{6x^3 + 13x^2 + x - 2}{x + 2}$ $6x^2 + x - 1$

2. $\dfrac{y^3 - 125}{y - 5}$ $y^2 + 5y + 25$

3. $\dfrac{z^3 - 2z^2 - z - 6}{z - 3}$ $z^2 + z + 2$

In each case the remainder is zero. Now have the class evaluate the numerator of the fraction:

4. in Exercise 1 for $x = -2$

5. in Exercise 2 for $y = 5$

6. in Exercise 3 for $z = 3$

In each case the expression has the value zero. Ask the class to generalize from these examples to a method for predicting whether an indicated quotient of polynomials has a remainder of zero.

The Egyptian problem shown on text page 223 is from the so-called Rhind Mathematical Papyrus, named after A. Henry Rhind, who took it from Egypt to England in the middle of the nineteenth century. The papyrus is now in the British museum. A couple of translations into English have been made and are available in large libraries.

In the decoration at the right of the page, the top panel shows $\frac{1}{5}$ and 21 as written in the hieratic script, the one in which the papyrus was written. The middle panel shows the corresponding hieroglyphic numerals.

6-9 SOLVING EQUATIONS WITH FRACTIONAL COEFFICIENTS

Key Mathematical Ideas In the previous eight sections students developed the skills related to fractions. In this section these skills are applied to solving equations with fractional coefficients. Using the multiplication property of equality, the members of the equation are multiplied by the L.C.D. of the fractions in the equation. The resulting equation is equivalent to the original one and has integral coefficients.

Teaching Suggestions Students may need some review on solving equations. Remind them that the goal is to transform an equation into an equivalent one whose roots can be seen by inspection. You may wish to write out the solution of an equation such as

$$2(a - 2) + 3(a - 3) + 4(a - 4) = 7.$$

Chalkboard Examples

Solve.

1. $\dfrac{a + 2}{2} = \dfrac{2a}{3}$

$6\left(\dfrac{a + 2}{2}\right) = 6\left(\dfrac{2a}{3}\right)$

$3(a + 2) = 2(2a)$

$3a + 6 = 4a$

$6 = a$

∴ the solution set is {6}.

2. $\dfrac{x - 1}{2} + \dfrac{x - 2}{3} = 3$

$6\left(\dfrac{x - 1}{2} + \dfrac{x - 2}{3}\right) = 6(3)$

$3(x - 1) + 2(x - 2) = 18$

$3x - 3 + 2x - 4 = 18$

$5x - 7 = 18$

$5x = 25$

$x = 5$

∴ the solution is 5.

Suggested Extensions

1. Find the number j for which 2 is a root of the equation $(x + 1)(x + 2) = (x - 4)(x - 5) + j$.

2. Find the number k for which -5 is a root of the equation $\dfrac{y + 1}{4} - \dfrac{y - 1}{3} = 2k$.

Have students create similar exercises and exchange them for additional practice with equations.

6-10 FRACTIONAL EQUATIONS

Key Mathematical Ideas In the previous section students solved equations with fractional coefficients by multiplying both members by the L.C.D. of the fractions. The technique here is similar except that the L.C.D. is a variable expression. The key idea is that multiplying the members of an equation by a variable expression may produce an equation that is not equivalent to the original equation. Hence each possible root must be checked in the original equation.

Teaching Suggestions Some student may suggest the following solution to the Example in the text:

$$\dfrac{2}{x^2 - x} - \dfrac{2}{x - 1} = 1 \quad (x \neq 0, x \neq 1)$$

$$\dfrac{2}{x^2 - x} - \dfrac{2x}{x^2 - x} = \dfrac{x^2 - x}{x^2 - x}$$

$$2 - 2x = x^2 - x$$

$$0 = x^2 + x - 2$$

$$0 = (x + 2)(x - 1)$$

$$x = -2 \text{ or } x = 1$$

The method does produce the possible roots of the equation. However, students must check them in the original equation. If $x = 1$, then the denominator, $x^2 - x$, is zero. Since division by zero is undefined, 1 is not a root of the equation. The solution set is $\{-2\}$.

Chalkboard Examples

Solve.

1. $\dfrac{3 - x}{4 - x} = \dfrac{5 - x}{7 - x} \quad (x \neq 4, x \neq 7)$

$(4 - x)(7 - x)\left(\dfrac{3 - x}{4 - x}\right) = (4 - x)(7 - x)\left(\dfrac{5 - x}{7 - x}\right)$

$(7 - x)(3 - x) = (4 - x)(5 - x)$

$21 - 10x + x^2 = 20 - 9x + x^2$

$1 = x$

Check: $\dfrac{3 - 1}{4 - 1} \stackrel{?}{=} \dfrac{5 - 1}{7 - 1}; \dfrac{2}{3} = \dfrac{4}{6}$ ✓

∴ the solution is 1.

2.
$$\frac{-3}{m+2} - \frac{m+14}{m^2-4} = 0$$

$$(m+2)(m-2)\left[\frac{-3}{m+2} - \frac{m+14}{(m+2)(m-2)}\right]$$
$$= (m+2)(m-2)(0)$$

$$(m-2)(-3) - (m+14) = 0$$
$$-3m + 6 - m - 14 = 0$$
$$-4m - 8 = 0$$
$$-8 = 4m$$
$$-2 = m$$

Note that -2 makes the multiplier zero.

∴ the equation has no solution.

6-11 RATIOS AND PERCENTS; PROPORTIONS

Key Mathematical Ideas Students have previously worked with percents and proportions. However, many students will find a review of this material helpful. The skills acquired in this section are applied to solving verbal problems both in this section and in the remaining sections of the chapter.

Teaching Suggestions Ask students to cut out bank advertisements from the newspaper and bring them in. The interest rates on various kinds of accounts can provide motivation for a class discussion of percents. Some students will find the analogy of *percent* as *per hundred* to be useful.

Chalkboard Examples Use the five-step method to solve each problem.

1. The sales tax on a tennis racket costing $23 was $1.38. What was the rate of the sales tax?
$$\frac{1.38}{23.00} = \frac{x}{100}; \; 6\%$$

2. During a local election in Quincy, 14,690 of the 26,000 registered voters did not vote. What percent of the registered voters did vote?
$$\frac{26,000 - 14,690}{26,000} = \frac{x}{100}; \; 43.5\%$$

6-12 PERCENT-MIXTURE PROBLEMS

Key Mathematical Ideas Percent-mixture problems are a direct application of the percentage formula

$P = RB$. In the example on text page 234, the amount of acid in the 10% solution is expressed as the product of the "rate," 0.1, and the "base," 20 grams. The amount of acid in the 55% solution is similarly obtained. The formula then results from the fact that the amount of acid in the mixture is the sum of the amounts in the two solutions.

Teaching Suggestions To motivate the class, discuss the need to add antifreeze in winter to the radiator of a car. The labels on some brands of antifreeze list the range of temperature over which the car is protected for various solutions of antifreeze. Other brands simply include a table indicating the number of quarts of antifreeze to add. A portion of such a table is shown below.

Cooling System Capacity	44% Anti.	50% Anti.	55% Anti.
6	3 qt.	3 qt.	3 qt.
8	1 gal.	1 gal.	1 gal.
10	1 gal.	5 qt.	6 qt.
12	5 qt.	6 qt.	7 qt.
14	6 qt.	7 qt.	2 gal.
Freezing Protect.	−25°F	−34°F	−45°F
Boiling Protect.	267°F	270°F	273°F

In the table above, the second, third, and fourth columns indicate (to the nearest quart) the number of quarts of 100% antifreeze to add to obtain the desired protection. You may wish to have students calculate the entries for a cooling system capacity of 16, 18, 20, and 24 quarts.

Chalkboard Examples Use the five-step method to solve each problem.

1. How many kilograms of ore containing 5% gold must be melted down with 8 kilograms of 2% ore to produce ore which is 4% gold?
$$(0.05)x + (0.02)(8) = (0.04)(x + 8); \; 16 \text{ kg}$$

2. How much pure alcohol should be added to 8 grams of a 12% solution to produce a 20% solution?
$$1.00x + (0.12)(8) = (0.20)(x + 8); \; 0.8 \text{ gram}$$

6-13 INVESTMENT PROBLEMS

Key Mathematical Ideas The interest formula $I = PRT$ is a special case of the percentage formula $P = RB$. Thus investment problems provide one important application of *percent*.

Teaching Suggestions Review the meaning of *simple interest*. An example such as the following may be helpful: if an individual deposits $100 into an account paying 6% annually, then at the end of the year, the amount of money in the account would be $100 + (0.06)(100) = 106$ dollars. Introduce the interest formula as a special case of the percentage formula.

Chalkboard Examples Use the five-step method to solve each problem.

1. Jean deposited $236 for 3 months at $5\frac{3}{4}\%$. Joan deposited $150 for 4 months at $6\frac{1}{2}\%$. Who earned the greater amount of interest? Jean

2. A company invested part of $6300 at 6% and the rest at 8%. If the annual income from each investment was the same, find the amount invested at each rate. $(0.06)(x) = (0.08)(6300 - x)$; $3600 at 6% and $2700 at 8%

Suggested Extension Refer students to the Consumer Note (text pages 238–239) about how banks compute interest. You may wish to point out that the method of finding compound interest can be reduced to a formula by using factoring:

For the first period: $A = P + RP = P(1 + R)$
For the second period: $A = P(1 + R) + R[P(1 + R)]$
$$= P(1 + R)(1 + R)$$
$$= P(1 + R)^2$$
For the third period verify that: $A = P(1 + R)^3$.

If R is compounded N times a year for T years, the formula becomes:

$$A = P\left(1 + \frac{R}{N}\right)^{NT} \text{and compound interest} = A - P.$$

To find the effective annual yield, let $P = 1$ and $T = 1$ and use this modification:

$$\text{Effective annual yield} = \left(1 + \frac{R}{360}\right)^{365} - 1$$

By using a computer or a minicalculator that can find powers with large exponents, you can determine, for example, that for $R = 0.0775$, the effective annual yield is 0.0817, or 8.17%.

6-14 UNIFORM-MOTION PROBLEMS

Key Mathematical Ideas An object in uniform motion travels a distance equal to the product of the fixed rate and the length of time: $D = RT$. This formula is used to solve verbal problems.

Teaching Suggestions Students may need an explanation of uniform motion and the distance formula. Be certain that students express the distance, rate, and time in corresponding units. For example, if the rate is expressed in kilometers per hour, then the distance is in kilometers and the time is in hours.

Encourage students to use tables such as those in the text to organize the information given in a problem.

Chalkboard Examples

1. What is the distance traveled in 6 hours at 50 km/h? 300 km

2. What is the average rate of speed if 260 km are traveled in 4 hours? 65 km/h

3. How long does it take to travel 330 km at a speed of 55 km/h? 6 h

4. On a cross-country ski trail, Michael and Jennifer average 5 km/h skiing to the end of the trail and 3 km/h back to the beginning. The total time spent skiing was 4 hours. How long is the trail? $3t = 5(4 - t)$; 7.5 km

6-15 RATE-OF-WORK PROBLEMS

Key Mathematical Ideas Rate-of-work problems involve finding how much time it takes to do a particular job if a constant rate of work is assumed.

Teaching Suggestions Point out that rate-of-work problems assume a constant or average rate. The amount of time needed for several people to do a job is clearly less than the time needed for one; thus we add the fractional parts of the job, and not the amounts of time.

Chalkboard Example Working alone, Sean can cultivate a field in 6 hours. However, if his brother Ian helps him, it will only take $3\frac{1}{2}$ hours to cultivate the field. How long would it take Ian to do the job alone? $\frac{1}{6}\left(\frac{7}{2}\right) + \frac{1}{r}\left(\frac{7}{2}\right) = 1$; $8\frac{2}{5}$ h

7 Inequalities

CHAPTER OVERVIEW

This chapter focuses on solving inequalities. The axioms and transformations related to inequalities are introduced as the means to solving open inequalities. As in previous chapters, these skills are then used to solve verbal problems.

In order to specify the solution set of an inequality, some special symbols and vocabulary are introduced. The intersection and union of both finite and infinite sets are discussed and graphed on the number line. All the skills acquired in the chapter are applied in the final section to solving and graphing combined inequalities. The chapter concludes with an *Extra for Experts* section treating equations and inequalities involving absolute value.

SECTION-BY-SECTION COMMENTARY

7-1 ORDER AND BETWEENNESS

Key Mathematical Ideas This section introduces the symbols $<$ and $>$ to express the order of real numbers. An inequality is defined as a sentence including one of these symbols or the symbol $\neq$.

Teaching Suggestions Ask one of your students to draw a number line on the chalkboard. Point out that the arrowhead on the left points in the negative direction and the one on the right points to the positive direction.

Introduce the symbols $<$ and $>$. Point out that if r and s are any real numbers, then exactly one of the following statements is true:

$$r = s \text{ or } r < s \text{ or } s < r.$$

Also be sure that students realize that the statement $r < s$ states not only that r is less than s, but that s is greater than r.

Chalkboard Examples

1. Replace each __?__ with one of the symbols $<$ or $>$ to make a true statement.
   a. -7 __?__ 5 $<$ b. 4 __?__ 3 $>$
   c. $\dfrac{1}{3}$ __?__ $\dfrac{1}{5}$ $>$ d. $\dfrac{1}{100}$ __?__ $-\dfrac{1}{10}$ $>$
   e. $\dfrac{3}{5}$ __?__ $\dfrac{7}{10}$ $<$ f. 0.205 __?__ 0.025 $>$

2. Translate into words.
   a. $-8 < -6 < -4$ b. $2 > 0 > -1$

3. Translate into symbols.
   a. -1 is greater than -2. $-1 > -2$
   b. -3 is less than -1 and 2 is greater than -1. $-3 < -1 < 2$
   c. 7 is greater than 2 and -6 is less than -1. $7 > 2$ and $-6 < -1$

Suggested Extensions

1. The activity that follows provides a useful review of work with fractions and an extension of *betweenness*. Have students find a rational number (see text page 371) between $\frac{1}{2}$ and $\frac{1}{3}$ by finding the average (text page 81) of $\frac{1}{2}$ and $\frac{1}{3}$: $\frac{1}{2}(\frac{1}{2} + \frac{1}{3}) = \frac{1}{2}(\frac{5}{6}) = \frac{5}{12}$. Then have students find a rational number between $\frac{1}{2}$ and $\frac{5}{12}$. Continuing in this fashion, students should recognize that between any two rational numbers there is always another rational number. (See text page 373 for the property of density.) Point out that this property is not true for the set of integers.

2. As an extension of Exercise 1, have students use decimals to find a rational number between two given rational numbers. For example, between 0.125 and 0.126 are 0.1251, 0.1252, and so on.

3. Refer students to the Historical Note (text page 257) on the origin of the symbols for *greater than* and *less than*.

7-2 SUBSETS AND BETWEENNESS

Key Mathematical Ideas In order to specify the solution set of an inequality, one has to understand the meaning of *subset, finite set,* and *infinite set.* This section introduces the concepts and skills related to sets that are required for subsequent work.

Teaching Suggestions You may wish to review the meaning of *natural numbers, whole numbers,* and *integers,* as well as the technique of graphing on the number line (see Section 2-1).

Point out the use of Venn diagrams to picture finite sets and their subsets. You will want to be certain that students distinguish between the symbols ⊂ and ∈. Stress that the empty set is considered a subset of every set, and that a set is its own subset.

Chalkboard Examples

1. Classify each statement as true or false.
   a. Ø is a finite set. True
   b. The set of multiples of seven is a finite set. False
   c. The set of even numbers is a subset of the whole numbers. False

2. Graph {the real numbers less than 4}.

3. Replace each __?__ with one of the symbols =, ≠, ∈, or ⊂ to make a true statement.
   a. 0 __?__ {−1, 0, 1}   ∈
   b. {6, 8, 10} __?__ {10, 8, 6}   =
   c. {1, 4, 7} __?__ {1, 4, 7, 10}   ⊂ or ≠
   d. Ø __?__ {0}   ⊂ or ≠

Suggested Extension Have the students determine a formula for the number of subsets that a set has if the set has n members where $n \in \{1, 2, 3, \ldots\}$. (Remind students that if a set is not empty then the set has itself and the empty set as subsets.) By trial and error, students should produce the following table:

Number of Members	Number of Subsets
1	2
2	4
3	8
4	16
5	32

If a set has n members, then it has 2^n subsets.

7-3 TRANSFORMING INEQUALITIES

Key Mathematical Ideas This section introduces the order axioms of the real numbers. From these axioms result the transformations that produce equivalent inequalities. Except for multiplication (and division), the transformations are similar to those used for equations.

Teaching Suggestions Having solved many types of equations, students should have little difficulty solving inequalities. However, be sure that students realize that multiplying or dividing each member of an inequality by a negative number reverses the direction of the inequality.

Chalkboard Examples

Solve.

1.
$$2t + 3 > 15$$
$$2t + 3 - 3 > 15 - 3$$
$$2t > 12$$
$$t > 6$$
{all real numbers greater than 6}

2.
$$1 - 5y > -9$$
$$-1 + 1 - 5y > -1 + (-9)$$
$$-5y > -10$$
$$y < 2$$
{all real numbers less than 2}

3. $2(1 - k) + 3(1 + k) < 0$
$$2 - 2k + 3 + 3k < 0$$
$$k + 5 < 0$$
$$k + 5 - 5 < -5$$
$$k < -5$$
{all real numbers less than −5}

Suggested Extension Provide the class with various solution sets and have the class create inequalities to fit the solution sets. For example, if you give them {all real numbers greater than −10}, they might write:
$$x > -10$$
$$x + 15 > -10 + 15$$
$$x + 15 > 5$$
$$-\frac{1}{2}(x + 15) < \left(-\frac{1}{2}\right)(5)$$
$$-\frac{x + 15}{2} < -\frac{5}{2}$$

7-4 USING INEQUALITIES TO SOLVE PROBLEMS

Teaching Suggestions You may wish to review how to represent consecutive integers, consecutive even integers, and consecutive odd integers (see Section 4-5). Remind students that n, $n + 2$, $n + 4$ can represent *either* consecutive even or consecutive odd integers, depending on the value of n. Point out that the same is true for $n + 1$, $n + 3$, $n + 5$.

Chalkboard Example Find three consecutive positive odd integers whose sum is less than twice the largest.

Step 1 Find all possible sets of numbers.

Step 2 Let $n =$ the least number.

Step 3 $n + (n + 2) + (n + 4) < 2(n + 4)$

Step 4 $\quad\quad\quad 3n + 6 < 2n + 8$

$\quad\quad\quad\quad\quad\quad n < 2$

Since n is positive, $0 < n < 2$, and $n = 1$.

Step 5 Check: $1 + 3 + 5 \overset{?}{<} 2(5)$; $9 < 10$ ✓

∴ the numbers are 1, 3, and 5.

Suggested Extension Have various members of the class write verbal problems involving inequalities. The problems could then be exchanged and solved.

7-5 INTERSECTION AND UNION OF SETS

Key Mathematical Ideas This section discusses the intersection and union of sets. Venn diagrams and number line graphs are used to represent the relationship between sets of numbers.

Teaching Suggestions To introduce the lesson, choose sets A, B, C:

$$A = \{1, 2, 3, 4, 5\}$$
$$B = \{4, 5, 6, 7, 8\}$$
$$C = \{7, 8\}$$

Draw a Venn diagram to represent the sets:

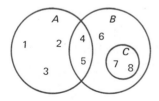

Introduce the *intersection* of two sets as the set whose members belong to both sets:

$$A \cap B = \{4, 5\} \text{ and } B \cap C = \{7, 8\}.$$

Since $A \cap C = \emptyset$, A and C are *disjoint* sets.

Now introduce the *union* of two sets as the set whose members belong to either set:

$$A \cup B = \{1, 2, 3, 4, 5, 6, 7, 8\}$$
$$B \cup C = \{4, 5, 6, 7, 8\}$$
$$A \cup C = \{1, 2, 3, 4, 5, 7, 8\}$$

Remind students that a member of a set should be listed only once.

Chalkboard Examples

1. Draw a Venn diagram to represent the following sets:

$$E = \{-5, -3, -1, 0, 1, 3, 5\};$$
$$F = \{-4, -2, 0, 2, 4\};$$
$$G = \{-5, -2, 0, 1, 4, 7\}.$$

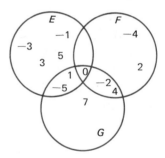

Name:

a. $E \cap F \quad \{0\}$

b. $F \cup G \quad \{-5, -4, -2, 0, 1, 2, 4, 7\}$

c. $E \cap (F \cup G) \quad \{-5, 0, 1\}$

d. $(E \cap F) \cup (F \cap G) \quad \{-5, 0, 1\}$

e. $(E \cap F) \cap G \quad \{0\}$

f. $E \cap (F \cap G) \quad \{0\}$

2. If $A = \{$the negative real numbers less than $-1\}$ and $B = \{$the odd natural numbers between -2 and $2\}$, graph $A \cap B$ and $A \cup B$.

Suggested Extensions

1. **a.** If $R = \{2, 4, 6\}$, $R \cap S = \{4\}$, and $R \cup S = \{2, 3, 4, 5, 6\}$, specify set S. $\{3, 4, 5\}$

    b. If $X = \{-7, -2, 5, 8\}$, $X \cap Y = \emptyset$,   and $X \cup Y = \{-7, -4, -2, 0, 1, 5, 8\}$, specify set Y. $\{-4, 0, 1\}$

2. In Written Exercises 25 and 26, students see that the operations intersection and union are distributive. Have students show that these operations are commutative and associative:

$$A \cap B = B \cap A; \; A \cup B = B \cup A.$$
$$(A \cap B) \cap C = A \cap (B \cap C);$$
$$(A \cup B) \cup C = A \cup (B \cup C)$$

7-6   SOLVING COMBINED INEQUALITIES

Key Mathematical Ideas   In this section the concepts of *intersection* and *union* are used to solve compound open inequalities. The chief skills developed here are solving and graphing conjunctions and disjunctions of inequalities. The symbols $\leq$ and $\geq$ are introduced as examples of disjunctions.

Teaching Suggestions   Suggest some everyday sentences to introduce the use of *and* and *or* to join two sentences: New York is a state *and* France is a country.

Point out that *both* statements must be true for the conjunction to be true. Ask students to suggest examples of conjunctions that are false. Now discuss how to find the solution set of a mathematical conjunction such as $x > -3$ and $x < 2$. Point out that the solution set consists of those values of x that satisfy both sentences, that is, the intersection of the two solution sets. Use a similar development to relate *disjunction* and *union*.

Chalkboard Examples

Solve.

1. $-5 \leq 3r + 4 < r - 6$

    $-5 \leq 3r + 4$ and $3r + 4 < r - 6$
    $\quad -9 \leq 3r$ $\quad$ and $\quad$ $2r < -10$
    $\quad -3 \leq r$ $\quad$ and $\quad$ $r < -5$

    Since there is no value of r that is both greater than or equal to -3 and less than -5, the solution set is $\emptyset$.

2. $2r + 5 \geq 6$ or $25 < -5r$

    $\quad 2r \geq 1$ or $-5 > r$

    $\quad r \geq \dfrac{1}{2}$ or $-5 > r$

    The solution set is $\Big\{$all real numbers that are less than -5, or greater than or equal to $\dfrac{1}{2}\Big\}$.

8 Functions and Relations

CHAPTER OVERVIEW

In this chapter the important concepts of *functions* and *relations* are developed. A function or relation can be specified by a table or graph, by a rule, or by an equation. Open sentences in two variables are solved to obtain ordered pairs (functions and relations). The ordered pairs are then graphed as points on a coordinate plane. Several sections are devoted to the properties related to linear equations and their graphs. The chapter concludes with an application of linear functions: direct variation and proportion.

SECTION-BY-SECTION COMMENTARY

8-1 FUNCTIONS DEFINED BY EQUATIONS

Key Mathematical Ideas This section introduces the important concept of *function* as a special correspondence between elements of the domain and those of the range. Various ways of specifying a function are introduced. These include equations, arrow notation, and function notation. It is emphasized that a rule *and a domain* are needed to specify a function.

Teaching Suggestions To introduce the concept of *correspondence,* relate the length of a side of a square to the area of the square.

s	A
1 cm	1 cm²
2 cm	4 cm²
3 cm	9 cm²

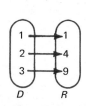

Alternatively, the distance traveled at a constant speed of 5 km/h is related to the time elapsed.

t	d
1 h	5 km
2 h	10 km
3 h	15 km
4 h	20 km

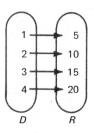

In the first example, the function A can be defined as $A = s^2$, $A: s \rightarrow s^2$, or $A(s) = s^2$. In the second example, the function d can be defined as $d = 5t$, $d: t \rightarrow 5t$, or $d(t) = 5t$.

Chalkboard Examples

1. If $h(y) = 2y - 5$ and the domain $D = \{1, 2, 3, 4\}$, find the range R. $R = \{-3, -1, 1, 3\}$

2. Given that $f: w \rightarrow w^2$, $g: s \rightarrow s^2 + 1$, and $k: n \rightarrow n^2 + 2n - 3$, find:
   a. $f(2) + g(1) = (2^2) + (1^2 + 1) = 4 + 2 = 6$
   b. $k(1) + g(-1) = (1^2 + 2 \cdot 1 - 3) + [(-1)^2 + 1]$
      $= 0 + 2 = 2$
   c. $k(-2) - f(3) = [(-2)^2 + 2(-2) - 3] - (3^2)$
      $= -3 - 9 = -12$

Suggested Extension Written Exercises 41–44 introduce the *composition of two functions*. Exercises 43 and 44 show that, in general, $f(g(x)) \neq g(f(x))$ where f and g are any two functions. However, have students show that if we use $j(x) = x + 1$ and $k(x) = x + 3$, then $j(k(x)) = k(j(x))$ for every value of x. Challenge students to find functions whose composition is commutative and others whose composition is not. In general, the composition of two functions f and g is commutative if the functions are either of the form: a. $f(x) = x + c$, $g(x) = x + d$; or b. $f(x) = cx$, $g(x) = dx$, where c and d are constants.

8-2 FUNCTIONS DEFINED BY DIFFERENT RULES

Key Mathematical Ideas Some functions are best defined by explicitly stating assignments between the members of the domain and the range. The text and teaching suggestions provide examples of functions that are often defined by a table, a correspondence, a list of ordered pairs, or a graph.

Teaching Suggestions Point out that not every function can be named by the methods of the previous section. The following example can be used to illustrate this. In a science experiment, the temperature of a liquid was recorded every half minute, as the liquid was heated. The results are shown in the chart.

Time elapsed (minutes)	Temperature
0	6°C
0.5	7°C
1.0	8°C
1.5	10°C
2.0	12°C
2.5	15°C
3.0	20°C

The data in the chart cannot be expressed by a rule; for this reason, a table, a correspondence, or a list of ordered pairs is an appropriate way of expressing the data. You may wish to draw a broken-line graph for the data; ask students to estimate "in-between" times and to predict the temperature after 4 minutes.

Chalkboard Examples The table below shows the ten teams in the National Hockey League that acquired the greatest number of penalty minutes in a particular season.

Teams in the N.H.L.	Total Number of Penalty Minutes
Boston	1097
Buffalo	943
Detroit	893
Los Angeles	888
Minnesota	881
N.Y. Islanders	881
Philadelphia	1756
Pittsburgh	866
St. Louis	1195
Vancouver	943

1. Why does the table describe a function? **Each member of the domain is paired with exactly one member of the range.**
2. List the domain and the range.
3. Express the data as ordered pairs, for example, (Boston, 1097).
4. Make a bar graph for the data. (Point out that a broken-line graph would not be a useful way to organize this data.)

Suggested Extension Have students collect the weather report column from the newspaper over a two-week period. (The information below was taken from an actual newspaper clipping.)

TEMPERATURES
(CELSIUS)
Overseas
Temperatures (Celsius) at noon yesterday and midnight Greenwich Mean Time:

Aberdeen 24, 13, clear; Amsterdam 16, 10, clear; Ankara 26, 16, cloudy; Antigua 28, 27, clear; Athens 31, 23, clear; Auckland 24, 10, clear; Berlin 22, 16, clear; Birmingham 19, 11, clear; Brussels 17, 13, clear; Cairo 32, 25, clear; Casablanca 22, 18, partly cloudy; Copenhagen 20, 12, clear; Dublin 19, 16, clear; Geneva 24, 17, clear; Hong Kong 29, 29, partly cloudy; Lisbon 21, 17, partly cloudy; London 19, 13, clear;

U.S. Points
Chicago	21	27
Detroit	17	25
Boston	23	26
New York	23	27
Washington	26	34
Jacksonville	23	28
Tampa	23	32
Miami	23	31
St. Louis	24	30
Denver	14	33
Los Angeles	13	22
San Francisco	10	20

Have students make some broken-line graphs, comparing the temperature changes in various cities. Based on their graphs, students may enjoy predicting the temperature and checking their predictions in the newspaper.

8-3 COORDINATES IN A PLANE

Key Mathematical Ideas This section introduces the vocabulary and skills related to plotting points in a coordinate plane. The key idea is that the arrangement of the axes and units is a useful convention which allows us to picture relationships realistically.

Teaching Suggestions You may want to review how a function such as

$$f: x \longrightarrow x + 2 \qquad D = \{-2, -1, 0, 1\}$$

generates a set of ordered pairs:

$$\{(-2, 0), (-1, 1), (0, 2), (1, 3)\}.$$

The ordered pairs may then be graphed on a chalk-board grid. A set of axes made of masking tape might prove useful throughout the study of this chapter. Point out that using the same scale on both axes avoids distorting the graph.

Chalkboard Examples

1. To give students practice with plotting points, make two sets of 21 cards, each with a number from -10 to 10 on it. Put the cards in a box and have a student draw two cards at random. The student uses the numbers as coordinates and plots the point on a chalkboard grid.

2. Draw the graph shown below on the chalkboard.

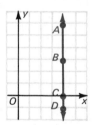

Ask the class to name the coordinates of points A, B, C, and D. Point out that the x-coordinate of each point is constant, and that the line is parallel to the y-axis.

3. Repeat Exercise 2 for a straight line parallel to the x-axis. Point out that the y-coordinate of each point on the line is constant.

4. Have students locate points that satisfy the given condition.

   a. The ordinate is -3.

   b. The abscissa is twice the ordinate.

   c. The ordinate is one more than the abscissa.

   d. The sum of the ordinate and the abscissa is 5.

Suggested Extension Have students decode the "message" by plotting the points and joining them.

Join $(-8, 9)$ to $(-8, 3)$.
Join $(-8, 6)$ to $(-5, 6)$.
Join $(-5, 3)$ to $(-5, 9)$.
Join $(-3, 3)$ to $(-3, 9)$.

The message is "HI." Have students create other such messages and exchange them.

8-4 RELATIONS

Key Mathematical Ideas In this section a *relation* is defined as any set of ordered pairs. Then a *function* is defined as a special kind of relation—one such that each member of the domain is paired with exactly one member of the range.

Teaching Suggestions Copy the diagrams below on the chalkboard.

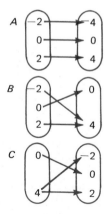

Discuss how diagram C differs from diagram A and B. Point out that although all three diagrams represent relations, only diagrams A and B represent functions.

Chalkboard Examples

State the domain and the range for each relation. Is the relation a function?

1. $\{(1, 1), (2, 2), (3, 1), (4, 2), (5, 1)\}$
   $D = \{1, 2, 3, 4, 5\}$; $R = \{1, 2\}$; yes

2. $\{(1, 1), (2, 2), (2, 3), (3, 3), (3, 2)\}$
   $D = \{1, 2, 3\}$; $R = \{1, 2, 3\}$; no

3.

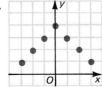

$D = \{-3, -2, -1, 0, 1, 2, 3\}; \ R = \{1, 2, 3, 4\};$
yes

4.

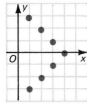

$D = \{1, 2, 3, 4\}; \ R = \{-3, -2, -1, 0, 1, 2, 3\};$
no

5. Graph $\{(-3, -1), \ (-3, 0), \ (-2, 1), \ (-1, -2),$
$(0, 1), (1, 0), (1, -1)\}$. Is this relation a function?

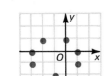

No

6. In order to make the relation named in Exercise
5 a function, which point(s) would have to be eliminated? Two points—either $(-3, -1)$ or $(-3, 0)$;
and either $(1, 0)$ or $(1, -1)$.

8-5 OPEN SENTENCES IN TWO VARIABLES

Key Mathematical Ideas In this section students find
the solution sets of open sentences in two variables
—sets of ordered pairs of numbers. The open sentences
that students solve here have finite solution sets.

Teaching Suggestions You may wish to review the
meaning of *open sentence* and *solution* of an open
sentence. For example, if the replacement set of x is
the set of real numbers, then the open sentence

$$6(x + 1) - 2 = 11x - 4(2x - 3)$$

has one solution, $\frac{8}{3}$. However, if the replacement set is
the set of whole numbers, then the equation has no
solution.

Chalkboard Examples

1. Find the solution set of $x + 4y = 10$ given that the
replacement set of both x and y is the set of whole
numbers.

$$x + 4y = 10$$
$$x = 10 - 4y$$

y	$10 - 4y$	Solutions
0	10	(10, 0)
1	6	(6, 1)
2	2	(2, 2)
3	-2	

Values of y greater than 2 produce negative values
of x.

$\therefore$ the solution set is $\{(10, 0), (6, 1), (2, 2)\}$.

$\left(\text{Point out that one can use } y = \dfrac{10 - x}{4} \text{ to deter-}\right.$
mine the solution set, but the calculations are easier
using $x = 10 - 4y.\Big)$

2. Graph the solution set of $y \leq -x + 2$ given that
$\{-1, 0, 1, 2\}$ is the replacement set of x and y.

8-6 THE GRAPH OF A LINEAR EQUATION IN TWO VARIABLES

Key Mathematical Ideas The key idea in this section
is that the graph of a linear equation in two variables is
a line in the coordinate plane. Conversely, a line in the
plane is the graph of some linear equation in two
variables.

T88

Teaching Suggestions Find and graph the solution set of $x + 2y = 6$ if the replacement set of x and y is the set of integers.

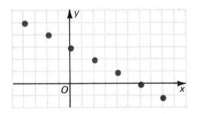

Have students use a ruler to determine other points that seem to lie on the line passing through the points. Emphasize that any ordered pair that satisfies the equation $x + 2y = 6$ lies on the line and *vice versa*.

Remind students that a line extends indefinitely in both directions. This is indicated by using arrowheads. In this book, the axes are differentiated from other lines by a single arrowhead in the positive direction.

Chalkboard Examples

1. Find the coordinates of the points where the graph of $3x + 8y = 27$ crosses the x-axis and the y-axis. $(9, 0)$; $(0, \frac{27}{8})$

2. Graph the equations $x + 2y = -3$ and $3x - y = 5$ on the same set of axes. Name the coordinates of the point of intersection and show that the coordinates satisfy both equations.

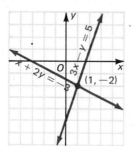

$$1 + 2(-2) = -3 \checkmark; \; 3(1) - (-2) = 5 \checkmark$$

8-7 SLOPE OF A LINE

Key Mathematical Ideas Students should have an intuitive feeling for steepness or slope. This section deals with the slope of a straight line, and prepares students for their work with the slope-intercept form of an equation in the next section.

Teaching Suggestions A simple classroom model can be used to illustrate the concept of *slope*. Place a stack of books on a table and prop a ruler up on the books as shown below.

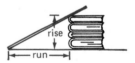

Point out that the steepness of the ruler depends on the number of books in the pile. The speed of a marble rolling down the ruler increases as the number of books increases.

By drawing several lines, help students realize that the slope of a straight line is constant—positive if the line rises from left to right, negative if it falls from left to right. They should also understand that any two points on a line may be used to determine the slope of the line.

Chalkboard Examples

Find the slope of the line.

1.
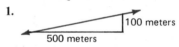

$$\text{slope} = \frac{100}{500} = 0.2$$

2. The line has equation $4x + 3y = 12$.
   Solution 1: Graph the line.

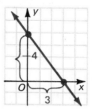

Count the number of units in the rise and the run:
$$\text{slope} = -\frac{4}{3}.$$

Solution 2: Find two points on the line, say $(3, 0)$ and $(0, 4)$. The slope $= \frac{4 - 0}{0 - 3} = -\frac{4}{3}$.

3. The slope of a line passing through point $(5, 0)$ is $\frac{1}{2}$. If point $(x, 4)$ lies on the line, find the value of x. $\frac{4 - 0}{x - 5} = \frac{1}{2}$; $4(2) = (x - 5)(1)$; $13 = x$

8-8 THE SLOPE-INTERCEPT FORM OF A LINEAR EQUATION

Key Mathematical Ideas In Section 8-6 students learned the standard form of a linear equation: $Ax + By = C$ where A, B, and C are integers, and A and B are not both zero. In this section students work with the slope-intercept form of a linear equation: $y = mx + b$ where m is the slope and b is the y-intercept. This form is sometimes a useful one for sketching the graph.

Teaching Suggestions On the same set of axes, graph the following equations: $y = x$, $y = 2x$ and $y = 3x$. Point out that each of these equations passes through the origin, and that in each case, the coefficient of x is the slope of the line.

Now graph these equations on a second set of axes: $y = -2x - 1$, $y = -2x$, $y = -2x + 1$, and $y = -2x + 2$. Point out that these lines are parallel and each has slope -2. The line with equation $y = -2x - 1$ passes through $(0, -1)$; the line with equation $y = -2x$ passes through $(0, 0)$; in general, the line with equation $y = mx + b$ has slope m and passes through $(0, b)$.

Chalkboard Examples

Write the slope-intercept form of each equation and sketch the graph.

1. $m = -\dfrac{1}{2}$, $b = 3$ $y = -\dfrac{1}{2}x + 3$

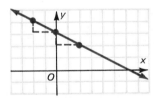

2. $5x - 3y = 15$
$-3y = -5x + 15$
$y = \dfrac{5}{3}x - 5$

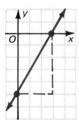

Suggested Extension In Exercise 30 on text page 323, students are asked to derive the formula

$y = -\dfrac{A}{B}x + \dfrac{C}{B}$ from $Ax + By = C$. Point out that if an equation is expressed in standard form, we can name its slope and y-intercept at sight: its slope is $-\dfrac{A}{B}$ and its y-intercept is $\dfrac{C}{B}$. Challenge students to name the slope and y-intercept of the lines whose equations are given in Exercises 13–24.

8-9 FINDING AN EQUATION OF A LINE, Y-INTERCEPT NOT GIVEN

Key Mathematical Ideas In this section students learn to write an equation for a line, given either a point on the line and the slope or two points on the line. In the latter case, the slope m is computed; then the coordinates of either point are substituted in the equation $y = mx + b$, producing the value of b.

Teaching Suggestions Given two points (x_1, y_1) and (x_2, y_2) on a line, $m = \dfrac{y_2 - y_1}{x_2 - x_1} = \dfrac{y_1 - y_2}{x_1 - x_2}$. Thus point out that in Example 2, the slope can equally well be computed as $\dfrac{1 - 3}{-3 - 5} = \dfrac{1}{4}$. Also, either point may be substituted to find the value of b. Thus in Example 2, the same result is obtained by substituting $(-3, 1)$ as by substituting $(5, 3)$:

$$1 = \frac{1}{4}(-3) + b$$

$$\frac{4}{4} + \frac{3}{4} = b$$

$$\frac{7}{4} = b$$

Chalkboard Examples

Write an equation in standard form for the line described.

1. The line passes through point $(2, 3)$ and has slope -4.

$$y = -4x + b$$
$$3 = -4(2) + b$$
$$11 = b$$
$$y = -4x + 11$$
$$4x + y = 11$$

2. The line passes through points $(0, 1)$ and $(4, 7)$. (Students should note that using the point $(0, 1)$ rather than the point $(4, 7)$ results in simpler calculations.)

$$m = \frac{7 - 1}{4 - 0} = \frac{6}{4} = \frac{3}{2}$$

$$y = \frac{3}{2}x + b$$

$$1 = \frac{3}{2}(0) + b$$

$$1 = b$$

$$y = \frac{3}{2}x + 1$$

$$-\frac{3}{2}x + y = 1$$

$$-3x + 2y = 2$$

Suggested Extension In the Suggested Extension for the previous section it was pointed out that the slope-intercept form of $Ax + By = C$ is $y = -\frac{A}{B}x + \frac{C}{B}$. Write an equation in standard form for the line that passes through point $(-2, -3)$ and has y-intercept $\frac{1}{2}$.

Solution 1:

$$y = mx + \frac{1}{2}$$

$$-3 = m(-2) + \frac{1}{2}$$

$$-\frac{7}{2} = -2m$$

$$\frac{7}{4} = m$$

$$y = \frac{7}{4}x + \frac{1}{2}$$

$$-7x + 4y = 2$$

Solution 2:

$$\frac{C}{B} = \frac{1}{2}$$

$$y = -\frac{A}{B}x + \frac{1}{2}$$

$$-3 = -\frac{A}{B}(-2) + \frac{1}{2}$$

$$-\frac{7}{4} = \frac{A}{B}$$

$$y = -\left(-\frac{7}{4}\right)x + \frac{1}{2}$$

$$-7x + 4y = 2$$

Students may wish to create other such problems and exchange them. Point out that the formula $y = -\frac{A}{B}x + \frac{C}{B}$ may be used as an alternate method of finding equations in standard form.

8-10 DIRECT VARIATION AND PROPORTIONS

Key Mathematical Ideas The slope-intercept form of an equation, $y = mx + b$, has a special application when $b = 0$. For then the equation defines a linear direct variation, a function whose coordinates are proportional.

The importance of direct variation lies in the fact that many of the mathematical relationships encountered in science courses and in everyday calculations are direct variations. For example, the circumference of a circle is directly proportional to its radius. (Work with variations is continued in the first part of Chapter 11.)

Teaching Suggestions You may wish to explain the use of subscripts on text pages 327 and 328. Stress that each variable with a subscript represents a particular or constant value of the variable. Point out, too, that although the definition of a linear direct variation specifies only that the constant $k \neq 0$, in most practical situations, the constant is a positive number.

Chalkboard Examples

1. The amount of money collected at the school musical varies directly with the number of tickets sold. The total amount collected on the first night was $412.50 for 275 admissions. How much was collected on the second night if 320 tickets were sold?

$$\frac{412.50}{275} = \frac{d_2}{320}; \ d_2 = 480; \ \$480$$

2. A length on a map is directly proportional to the distance it represents. A distance of 20 kilometers is represented by 10 centimeters. What is the area of the actual region represented on the map as a square region 5 cm on a side?

$$\frac{20}{10} = \frac{k_2}{5}; \ k_2 = 10; \ (10)(10) = 100 \ (km^2)$$

9 Systems of Open Sentences in Two Variables

CHAPTER OVERVIEW

This chapter deals with the solutions of systems of equations and inequalities. The graphic method of solving a system of linear equations is related, in the first section, to the possible number of solutions the system may have. Two additional methods, the substitution method and the addition-or-subtraction method, are introduced and used in two sections to solve a variety of verbal problems. The chapter concludes with a section on graphing systems of linear inequalities.

SECTION-BY-SECTION COMMENTARY

9-1 SOLUTION BY THE GRAPHIC METHOD

Key Mathematical Ideas This section introduces the meaning of a *system* of two linear equations. The solution set of such a system is one of the following: Ø, one number, or an infinite set of numbers. Systems are sometimes characterized as *consistent* and *inconsistent:* a consistent system has at least one solution, whereas an inconsistent system has no solution.

Teaching Suggestions Be sure that students realize that the graphic method may provide only an estimate of the solution. To verify their results students should substitute the coordinates of the intersection point in both of the original equations.

Chalkboard Examples

Solve each system by graphing.

1. $x + 2y = 3$
    $2x + 3y = 6$

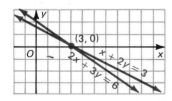

Check: $3 + 2(0) = 3$ ✓
           $2(3) + 3(0) = 6$ ✓
$\{(3, 0)\}$

2. $3x - 5y = -6$
    $x - \dfrac{5}{3} y = -2$

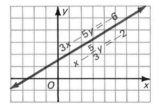

An infinite set of solutions (You may wish to show that the equations are equivalent.)

3. $3y + x = 9$
    $2x + 6y = 5$

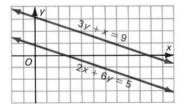

Ø

(To verify that the lines are parallel, write each equation in slope-intercept form:

$$3y + x = 9 \longrightarrow y = -\frac{1}{3}x + 3$$

$$2x + 6y = 5 \longrightarrow y = -\frac{1}{3}x + \frac{5}{6}$$

Since the slopes are equal and the y-intercepts are different, the lines are parallel.)

Suggested Extension As preparation for the next section, have students write pairs of equations that have the same solution set. Then ask students to graph several of the pairs on a set of axes. For example, the following pairs of equations have the same solution set, $\{(4, 3)\}$.

$$3x - 4y = 0 \qquad x + y = 7$$
$$x - 4y = -8 \qquad y = 3$$

$$x = 4 \qquad x - 4y = -8$$
$$x + y = 7 \qquad x = 4$$

9-2 SOLUTION BY THE SUBSTITUTION METHOD

Key Mathematical Ideas The graphic method is not, in general, an accurate way of determining the solution of a system of equations. Thus, in this section, a more systematic method, the substitution method, is introduced. In this book, the substitution method is presented before the addition-or-subtraction method because: (*1*) it follows easily from the work on writing equations in slope-intercept form; and (*2*) it can be applied more generally, for example, to any pair of equations in which one is linear.

Teaching Suggestions To introduce the need for a systematic method for solving two equations in two variables, ask the class to solve this system graphically:

$$3x + 9y = -1$$
$$x - y = 1$$

The solution, $(\frac{2}{3}, -\frac{1}{3})$ is difficult to determine from the graph of the equations. Discuss how easily the above system can be solved using substitution. Point out that the substitution method is most easily applied when the coefficient of one of the variables in one of the equations is either 1 or -1.

Chalkboard Example

Solve: $\begin{cases} 1. & 2x - y = -9 \\ 2. & 7x + 3y = 1 \end{cases}$

1. $2x + 9 = y$

2. $7x + 3(2x + 9) = 1$
$$7x + 6x + 27 = 1$$
$$13x = -26$$
$$x = -2$$

1. $y = 2x + 9 = 2(-2) + 9 = 5$

Check: $\qquad 2x - y = -9$
$$2(-2) - 5 \overset{?}{=} -9$$
$$-9 = -9 \checkmark$$

$$7x + 3y = 1$$
$$7(-2) + 3(5) \overset{?}{=} 1$$
$$1 = 1 \checkmark$$

$$\{(-2, 5)\}$$

Suggested Extension Have each student select one written exercise and relate their algebraic solution to the changes in the graph. An example follows.

$$x + 2y = 4$$
$$x - 3y = -1$$

$$x = 4 - 2y$$
$$x - 3y = -1$$

Substituting for x, we obtain

$$y = 1$$
$$x - 3y = -1$$

Substituting for y, we obtain

$$y = 1$$
$$x = 2$$

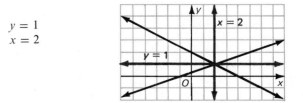

9-3 SOLVING PROBLEMS WITH TWO VARIABLES

Key Mathematical Ideas In this section students write and solve systems of linear equations to solve verbal problems.

Teaching Suggestions You may wish to point out that although the verbal problems in this section could be solved using just one variable, students should use two variables to gain experience in writing and solving systems of simultaneous equations.

Chalkboard Example Solve, using the five-step method: A science museum charges $2 admission for adults and $1 admission for children. On a particular day, 295 tickets were sold and $402 was collected. How many adults and how many children were admitted that day? (An outline of the solution follows.)

$a + c = 295$

$2a + c = 402$

$c = 295 - a$

$2a + (295 - a) = 402$

$\qquad a = 107$

$\qquad c = 295 - 107 = 188$

107 adults and 188 children

9-4 SOLUTION BY THE ADDITION-OR-SUBTRACTION METHOD

Key Mathematical Ideas The basis for the addition-or-subtraction method is the addition property of equality. The method is used in this section to solve equations in which the coefficients of one of the variables have the same absolute value. In the next section the method is extended to include linear combinations of equations.

Teaching Suggestions To convince students of the validity of the addition-or-subtraction method, graph the system $2x + y = 10$ and $x - 2y = -5$. On the same set of axes, graph the equation obtained by adding the given equations $(3x - y = 5)$ and the equation obtained by subtracting the given equations $(x + 3y = 15)$. Stress that since the graph of each equation passes through the point $(3, 4)$, the original system is equivalent to a system formed by selecting any two of the following equations:

$$2x + y = 10 \qquad x + 3y = 15$$
$$x - 2y = -5 \qquad x = 3$$
$$3x - y = 5 \qquad y = 4$$

Chalkboard Examples

Solve.

1. $x + y = 7$

   $\underline{x - y = 1}$

   $2x \quad\;\; = 8; \; x = 4$

   $\qquad 2y = 6; \; y = 3$

   $\{(4, 3)\}$

2. $-15x + 10y = 17$

   $\underline{15x - 10y = 50}$

   $\qquad\qquad 0 = 67$

   $\emptyset$

3. $\dfrac{4}{3}x - \dfrac{2}{3}y = 0 \longrightarrow 4x - 2y = 0$

   $\dfrac{1}{2}(x + 2y) = 2 \longrightarrow \underline{x + 2y = 4}$

   $\qquad\qquad\qquad\qquad\quad 5x \qquad = 4$

   $\qquad\qquad\qquad\qquad\qquad x = \dfrac{4}{5}$

   $\qquad\qquad\qquad \dfrac{4}{5} + 2y = 4$

   $\qquad\qquad\qquad\qquad 2y = \dfrac{16}{5}$

   $\qquad\qquad\qquad\qquad\; y = \dfrac{8}{5}$

   $\left\{\left(\dfrac{4}{5}, \dfrac{8}{5}\right)\right\}$

9-5 MULTIPLICATION IN THE ADDITION-OR-SUBTRACTION METHOD

Key Mathematical Ideas In this section the multiplication property of equality is used to transform a given system of equations into one which can be solved by the methods of the previous section.

Teaching Suggestions Remind students that multiplying both members of an equation by a nonzero constant produces an equation whose graph is identical to that of the original equation (see text page 338). For this reason, an equation $ax + by = c$ in a system may be substituted by an equivalent one of the form $kax + kby = kc \; (k \neq 0)$.

Chalkboard Examples

Solve.

1.
$$2x + 5y = 4$$
$$-3x + 2y = 13$$

$$6x + 15y = 12$$
$$\underline{-6x + 4y = 26}$$
$$19y = 38$$
$$y = 2$$
$$2x + 5(2) = 4$$
$$2x = -6$$
$$x = -3$$
$$\{(-3, 2)\}$$

2. $\dfrac{1}{3}x + \dfrac{1}{2}y = 2 \longrightarrow 2x + 3y = 12$

$\ 4x + 6y = 24 \longrightarrow 2x + 3y = 12$

Infinite set of solutions

Suggested Extension Have students trace the step-by-step solution of the system
$$2x - 3y = 11$$
$$x - 2y = 6$$
by drawing the graph of each equation used in solving the system. (The solution set is $\{(4, -1)\}$.)

9-6 PUZZLE PROBLEMS

Key Mathematical Ideas In this section students write systems of equations in two variables to solve problems about numbers, age, and fractions.

Teaching Suggestions You will probably want to work through a problem of each type before assigning homework. Remind students to check each answer with the words of the problem.

Chalkboard Examples

Solve, using the five-step method. (An outline of each solution is given.)

1. A two-digit number is 6 times the sum of its digits. If the digits are reversed, the number is decreased by 9. Find the original number.

1. $10t + u = 6(t + u)$
2. $10u + t = (10t + u) - 9$
1. $4t - 5u = 0$
2. $\ \ t - u = 1$

Solving, the original number is 54.

2. Three years ago, John's age was half Susan's present age. In 7 years, the sum of their ages will be 77 years. Find the present age of each.

1. $\qquad\qquad j - 3 = \dfrac{1}{2}s$

2. $(j + 7) + (s + 7) = 77$
1. $2j - s = 6$
2. $\ j + s = 63$

Solving, John is now 23 and Susan is 40.

3. The numerator of a fraction is 3 less than the denominator. If 4 is added to the numerator and the denominator, the resulting fraction is equal to $\dfrac{3}{4}$. Find the original fraction.

1. $\qquad\quad n = d - 3$

2. $\dfrac{n + 4}{d + 4} = \dfrac{3}{4}$

1. $\quad n - d = -3$
2. $4n - 3d = -4$

Solving, the original fraction is $\dfrac{5}{8}$.

9-7 UNIFORM-MOTION PROBLEMS

Teaching Suggestions It may be helpful to review the material of Section 6-14. Remind students that the rate per unit of time is an *average* rate.

Chalkboard Example The Chang family traveled a total distance of 840 km. Part of the trip was by car at a rate of 80 km/h. The remainder of the trip was by private plane at a rate of 320 km/h. If the entire trip took 3 hours, what was the distance traveled by car and the distance traveled by plane? (An outline of the solution follows.)

1. $\qquad c + p = 840$

2. $\dfrac{c}{80} + \dfrac{p}{320} = 3$

1. $\ \ c + p = 840$
2. $4c + p = 960$

Solving, the distance traveled by car was 40 km, and the distance by plane was 800 km.

9-8 GRAPHS OF LINEAR INEQUALITIES IN TWO VARIABLES

Key Mathematical Ideas The key idea of this section is that the graph of a linear inequality in two variables is a half-plane. The graph of a system of linear inequalities is the intersection of half-planes.

Teaching Suggestions You will want to be certain that students note the difference between a dashed and a solid line in a graph. Point out that once the associated equation of an inequality is graphed, any point not on the graph may be selected as a "test" point to determine appropriate shading. For example, in Example 1 on text page 361, one can test the point $(0, 0)$:

$$0 \overset{?}{\geq} 3(0) - 6$$
$$0 \geq -6 \checkmark$$

Therefore, the half-plane containing point $(0, 0)$ is the one to shade.

Chalkboard Examples

Graph.

1. $y < 2x + 1$

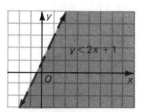

2. $2x - 5y \geq -2$
$\quad\ x < 3$

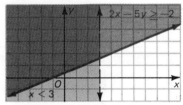

(The doubly-shaded region is the graph.)

10 Rational and Irrational Numbers

CHAPTER OVERVIEW

This chapter begins with an introduction to the rational numbers, including the properties of rational numbers and their forms. A section on rational square roots leads naturally into the study of irrational numbers, and, in particular, irrational square roots. Work with radicals leads to the solution of quadratic equations. The Pythagorean theorem provides students with the opportunity to solve new kinds of verbal problems. The chapter concludes with operations on radical expressions and the solution of radical equations.

SECTION-BY-SECTION COMMENTARY

10-1 PROPERTIES OF RATIONAL NUMBERS

Key Mathematical Ideas This section defines *rational numbers* and outlines the key property of the rational numbers, the property of density.

Teaching Suggestions Stress that the set of integers is a subset of the set of rational numbers; the set of rational numbers is a subset of the set of real numbers.

Chalkboard Examples

Arrange in order, from least to greatest.

1. $\dfrac{2}{3}, \dfrac{5}{8}, \dfrac{3}{4}$

   $\dfrac{5}{8} = \dfrac{15}{24}, \dfrac{2}{3} = \dfrac{16}{24}, \dfrac{3}{4} = \dfrac{18}{24}$

2. $-\dfrac{4}{5}, -\dfrac{2}{3}, -\dfrac{3}{4}$

   $-\dfrac{4}{5} = -\dfrac{48}{60}, -\dfrac{3}{4} = -\dfrac{45}{60}, -\dfrac{2}{3} = -\dfrac{40}{60}$

3. Find the number halfway between $\dfrac{1}{2}$ and $\dfrac{3}{4}$.

   $\dfrac{1}{2}\left(\dfrac{1}{2} + \dfrac{3}{4}\right) = \dfrac{1}{2}\left(\dfrac{2+3}{4}\right) = \dfrac{5}{8}$

Suggested Extension The axioms of closure for the addition and multiplication of real numbers are listed on text page 88. You may wish to have students investigate the closure of the rational numbers with respect to addition and subtraction. (The set of rational numbers is closed with respect to both operations.) Refer students to the Extra for Experts on text pages 376 and 377 for additional work with closure.

10-2 DECIMAL FORMS FOR RATIONAL NUMBERS

Key Mathematical Ideas The key idea of the section is that every rational number can be expressed both as a common fraction and as a terminating or repeating decimal. The section covers the techniques used to convert from one form to another.

Teaching Suggestions Ask the class to perform the indicated divisions in order to find the decimal form of each fraction:

$\dfrac{1}{2}$	$\dfrac{5}{8}$	$-\dfrac{3}{4}$	$\dfrac{1}{4}$	$-\dfrac{1}{8}$	$-\dfrac{2}{5}$
$\dfrac{4}{7}$	$-\dfrac{7}{9}$	$\dfrac{5}{6}$	$\dfrac{1}{3}$	$-\dfrac{2}{9}$	$-\dfrac{8}{7}$

After a brief time, write the decimal equivalent of each fraction on the chalkboard. Challenge students to generalize about the decimal form of a fraction. If students do not believe that the decimal form of every fraction either terminates or repeats, let them choose rational numbers and express them as decimals.

Most students will not be familiar with the method of converting a repeating decimal to a fraction. Be certain they understand how to determine the correct power of ten to use as a multiplier.

Chalkboard Examples

1. Round to the nearest tenth.

    a. 3.83 3.8   **b.** 28.684 28.7

    c. 0.491 0.5   **d.** $-1.2\overline{2}$ -1.2

2. Express each number as a terminating or repeating decimal.

    a. $\dfrac{13}{48}$ $0.2708\overline{3}$ **b.** $\dfrac{7}{80}$ 0.0875

3. Express each number as a fraction in lowest terms.

    a. 0.385 $\dfrac{385}{1000} = \dfrac{77}{200}$

    b. $0.\overline{63}$

$$100N = 63.\overline{63}$$
$$\underline{N = 0.\overline{63}}$$
$$99N = 63$$
$$N = \frac{63}{99} = \frac{7}{11}$$

Suggested Extensions

1. Students may be surprised by the results they obtain when expressing $0.4\overline{9}$ and $3.\overline{9}$ as common fractions. (In lowest terms, the fractions are $\frac{1}{2}$ and $\frac{4}{1}$.) Ask students to predict the value of any repeating decimal of the form $d.e\overline{9}$ or $d.\overline{9}$ where d and e are whole numbers.

2. **a.** Have students find the decimal form for $\frac{1}{9}$ and $\frac{2}{9}$:

    $\frac{1}{9}$ is equivalent to $0.\overline{1}$;

    $\frac{2}{9}$ is equivalent to $0.\overline{2}$.

    Then ask students to predict the decimal form of $\frac{3}{9}, \frac{4}{9}, \frac{5}{9}, \ldots$

    b. Repeat Exercise 2a for $\frac{1}{11}, \frac{2}{11}, \ldots$

    $\frac{1}{11}$ is equivalent to $0.\overline{09}$;

    $\frac{2}{11}$ is equivalent to $0.\overline{18}$;

    and so on.

10-3 RATIONAL SQUARE ROOTS

Key Mathematical Ideas The principal idea of this section is that every positive real number b has two square roots, $\sqrt{b}$ and $-\sqrt{b}$. The product and the quotient properties of square roots are used to simplify radicals.

Teaching Suggestions Encourage students to read "$\sqrt{x}$" as "the *positive* square root of x." This will help them remember that the principal square root of a number is nonnegative.

You may wish to show students that there is sometimes more than one way to find the square root of a number. For example:

$$\sqrt{64} = \sqrt{8^2} = 8$$
$$\sqrt{64} = \sqrt{2^2 \cdot 4^2} = \sqrt{2^2} \cdot \sqrt{4^2} = 2(4) = 8$$

Chalkboard Examples

Simplify each expression.

1. $\sqrt{121} = \sqrt{11^2} = 11$

2. $-\sqrt{576} = -\sqrt{2^6 \cdot 3^2} = -(2^3 \cdot 3) = -24$

3. $\sqrt{\dfrac{50}{72}} = \sqrt{\dfrac{25}{36}} = \dfrac{\sqrt{25}}{\sqrt{36}} = \dfrac{5}{6}$

4. $\pm\sqrt{0.0484} = \pm\sqrt{\dfrac{484}{10,000}}$

$$= \pm\sqrt{\dfrac{121}{2500}}$$

$$= \pm\dfrac{\sqrt{121}}{\sqrt{2500}} = \pm\dfrac{11}{50}$$

10-4 IRRATIONAL SQUARE ROOTS

Key Mathematical Ideas This section introduces the set of irrational numbers, those real numbers that cannot be expressed as common fractions. The section also presents an iterative method for calculating an irrational square root. The method rapidly produces an accurate approximation to the square root. Refer students to the table of square roots on text page 487.

Teaching Suggestions To introduce this lesson, review the definition of *rational number*. Remind students that the decimal form of a rational number either terminates or eventually repeats. Write the following numeral on the chalkboard:

$$0.01001000100001\ldots$$

Since this decimal neither terminates nor repeats, the real number represented by the decimal is *irrational*. Be sure students realize that every real number is either rational or irrational.

Chalkboard Examples

Compute to the nearest hundredth.

1. $\sqrt{13.7}$

From the table on text page 487: Since $13 < 13.7 < 14$, $\sqrt{13} < \sqrt{13.7} < \sqrt{14}$.

a. $\dfrac{3.6 + 3.7}{2} = 3.65$

b. $13.7 \div 3.65 \doteq 3.75$

c. $\dfrac{3.65 + 3.75}{2} = 3.70$

d. $13.7 \div 3.70 \doteq 3.7027$

$\therefore \sqrt{13.2} \doteq 3.70$

2. $\sqrt{175} = \sqrt{5^2 \cdot 7} = 5\sqrt{7}$

From the table, $5\sqrt{7} \doteq 5(2.646) = 13.23$

3. $\sqrt{0.63} = \sqrt{\dfrac{63}{100}} = \dfrac{\sqrt{63}}{\sqrt{100}} \doteq \dfrac{7.937}{10} \doteq 0.79$

10-5 SQUARE ROOTS OF VARIABLE EXPRESSIONS

Key Mathematical Ideas In this section students solve equations of the form $ax^2 = b$ where a and b are real numbers. They then apply the skills of this section to solving verbal problems.

Teaching Suggestions Be sure students understand that since $\sqrt{x^2}$ denotes a nonnegative number, $\sqrt{x^2} = |x|$. In Example 3 on text page 391, stress that $4a^2$ is an acceptable answer since $4a^2 = |4a^2|$ for every real number a.

Before assigning the problems on text page 393, you may wish to review the formula for the area of a circle. Point out that problems 5 and 6 do not require the use of $\frac{22}{7}$ as an approximation for π.

Chalkboard Examples

Simplify.

1. $\sqrt{64x^2} = \sqrt{8^2 \cdot x^2} = 8|x|$

2. $\sqrt{25r^2 - 30rs + 9s^2} = \sqrt{(5r - 3s)^2} = |5r - 3s|$

3. $\sqrt{225z^6} = \sqrt{3^2 \cdot 5^2 \cdot (z^3)^2} = 15|z^3|$

Solve.

4. $3x^2 - 192 = 0$

$3x^2 = 192$

$x^2 = 64$

$x = \pm\sqrt{64} = \pm 8$

$\therefore$ the solution set is $\{8, -8\}$.

5. $2k^2 = 686$

$k^2 = 343$

$k = \pm\sqrt{343} = \pm\sqrt{7^2 \cdot 7} = \pm 7\sqrt{7}$

From the table on text page 487:

$k \doteq \pm 7(2.646) \doteq \pm 18.5$

$\therefore$ the solution set is $\{18.5, -18.5\}$.

Suggested Extension Problem 6 on text page 393 can be extended as follows: How many pipes each with a radius of 5 cm are needed to supply the same amount of water as one pipe with a radius of 50 cm? Ask students to guess the answer and then solve the problem. (The answer is 100 pipes.) Have students vary the radius of the smaller pipe to create additional problems.

10-6 GEOMETRIC INTERPRETATIONS OF SQUARE ROOTS

Key Mathematical Ideas This section introduces the Pythagorean theorem and its converse, both of which are used to solve verbal problems.

Teaching Suggestions Students have probably used the Pythagorean theorem previously. Nevertheless, some explanation may be helpful. Draw the diagram shown below on the chalkboard:

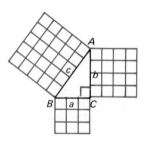

Have students count the squares to verify that $c^2 = a^2 + b^2$.

Chalkboard Examples

In Exercises 1–3, a, b, and c represent the lengths of the sides of a right triangle, with c representing the length of the hypotenuse. Complete the chart.

	a	b	c	
1.	9	12	_?_	15
2.	8	_?_	17	15
3.	_?_	$\sqrt{6}$	$\sqrt{26}$	$2\sqrt{5}$

4. Find the length of a side of a square whose diagonal is 6 cm long. (An outline of the solution follows.)

$$s^2 + s^2 = 6^2$$
$$s^2 = 18$$
$$s = 3\sqrt{2} \doteq 3(1.414) \doteq 4.2 \text{ (cm)}$$

Suggested Extension Most students have, upon occasion, taken a short cut through a lot rather than walked around its perimeter.

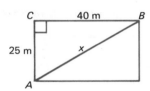

Have students estimate and then calculate how much further they walk when they take the path $A \rightarrow C \rightarrow B$ rather than walking directly from A to B. $x = 5\sqrt{89} \doteq 47.2$; thus the distance covered is about 17.8 m longer.

10-7 MULTIPLICATION, DIVISION, AND SIMPLIFICATION OF RADICALS

Key Mathematical Ideas The key idea is that the product and quotient properties of square roots can be used with the axioms of real numbers to simplify products and quotients of radicals. Rationalizing the denominator of radical expressions is used to facilitate the evaluation of radical expressions.

Teaching Suggestions Remind students to be sure that the radicand is in lowest terms before applying either of the properties of square roots (text page 383). For example, to simplify $\sqrt{\dfrac{10}{12}}$, one would first write $\sqrt{\dfrac{10}{12}} = \sqrt{\dfrac{5}{6}}$ and then proceed as in Example 3 on text page 398.

Chalkboard Examples

Simplify. All radicands are nonnegative real numbers.

1. $4\sqrt{50} = 4\sqrt{5^2 \cdot 2} = 4 \cdot 5\sqrt{2} = 20\sqrt{2}$

2. $\sqrt{\dfrac{36}{20}} = \sqrt{\dfrac{9}{5}} = \dfrac{\sqrt{9}}{\sqrt{5}} \cdot \dfrac{\sqrt{5}}{\sqrt{5}} = \dfrac{3\sqrt{5}}{5}$

3. $\dfrac{2\sqrt{15}}{5\sqrt{50}} = \dfrac{2\sqrt{15}}{25\sqrt{2}} = \dfrac{2\sqrt{15}}{25\sqrt{2}} \cdot \dfrac{\sqrt{2}}{\sqrt{2}} = \dfrac{2\sqrt{30}}{50} = \dfrac{\sqrt{30}}{25}$

$\left(\text{or } \dfrac{2\sqrt{15}}{5\sqrt{50}} = \dfrac{2}{5}\sqrt{\dfrac{15}{50}} = \dfrac{2}{5}\sqrt{\dfrac{3}{10}} = \dfrac{2\sqrt{3}}{5\sqrt{10}} \cdot \dfrac{\sqrt{10}}{\sqrt{10}}\right.$
$$\left. = \dfrac{2\sqrt{30}}{50} = \dfrac{\sqrt{30}}{25}\right)$$

4. $3\sqrt{2} \cdot \sqrt{12} \cdot \sqrt{6} = 3\sqrt{2} \cdot 2\sqrt{3} \cdot \sqrt{6}$
$$= 6\sqrt{36} = 6 \cdot 6 = 36$$

5. $\sqrt{x}(\sqrt{xy} + \sqrt{y}) = x\sqrt{y} + \sqrt{xy}$

10-8 ADDITION AND SUBTRACTION OF RADICALS

Key Mathematical Ideas In this section work with radicals is extended to include simplifying sums and differences of radical expressions.

Teaching Suggestions Be sure that students realize that in order to apply the distributive axiom to a sum or difference of radicals, the radicands must be the same. Thus an expression such as $4\sqrt{5} + 5\sqrt{4}$ cannot be simplified further.

Chalkboard Examples

Simplify.

1. $\sqrt{72} + \sqrt{50} = \sqrt{6^2 \cdot 2} + \sqrt{5^2 \cdot 2}$
$$= 6\sqrt{2} + 5\sqrt{2} = 11\sqrt{2}$$

2. $\sqrt{98} + \sqrt{75} - \sqrt{32} - \sqrt{27}$
$$= \sqrt{7^2 \cdot 2} + \sqrt{5^2 \cdot 3} - \sqrt{4^2 \cdot 2} - \sqrt{3^2 \cdot 3}$$
$$= 7\sqrt{2} + 5\sqrt{3} - 4\sqrt{2} - 3\sqrt{3} = 3\sqrt{2} + 2\sqrt{3}$$

3. $4\sqrt{20} - \dfrac{1}{2}\sqrt{80} + 10\sqrt{\dfrac{1}{20}}$
$$= 4\sqrt{2^2 \cdot 5} - \frac{1}{2}\sqrt{4^2 \cdot 5} + 10 \cdot \frac{1}{\sqrt{2^2 \cdot 5}}$$
$$= 4 \cdot 2\sqrt{5} - \frac{1}{2} \cdot 4\sqrt{5} + \frac{10}{2\sqrt{5}}$$
$$= 8\sqrt{5} - 2\sqrt{5} + \frac{5}{\sqrt{5}} \cdot \frac{\sqrt{5}}{\sqrt{5}}$$
$$= (8 - 2 + 1)\sqrt{5} = 7\sqrt{5}$$

Suggested Extension Students frequently make the following error:
$$\sqrt{16} + \sqrt{9} = \sqrt{25}$$
To indicate that the above statement is false, write:
$$\sqrt{16} + \sqrt{9} = \sqrt{4^2} + \sqrt{3^2} = 4 + 3 = 7$$
$$\sqrt{25} = \sqrt{5^2} = 5$$
Since $7 \neq 5$, $\sqrt{16} + \sqrt{9} \neq \sqrt{25}$. Ask students to determine whether each statement below is true or false.

1. $\sqrt{64} + \sqrt{36} = \sqrt{100}$ False
2. $\sqrt{28} + \sqrt{8} = \sqrt{36}$ False
3. $\sqrt{18} + \sqrt{8} = \sqrt{50}$ True
4. $3\sqrt{24} - 2\sqrt{6} = \sqrt{96}$ True

For additional practice, have students write other statements involving sums and differences of radicals, some true and others false. The statements could then be exchanged or assigned to the class.

10-9 MULTIPLICATION OF BINOMIALS CONTAINING RADICALS

Key Mathematical Ideas This section develops the skills of multiplying binomials containing radicals and simplifying fractions whose denominators are binomials containing radicals.

Teaching Suggestions Encourage students to apply the distributive axiom mentally in products such as $2\sqrt{2}(\sqrt{2} + \sqrt{3})$:
$$2\sqrt{2}(\sqrt{2} + \sqrt{3}) = 4 + 2\sqrt{6}$$
If necessary, refer students to Section 5-6 for review.

The technique of multiplying binomials involving radicals is the same as that outlined for the general binomial.

Chalkboard Examples

Simplify.

1. $(2 + \sqrt{2})(2 - \sqrt{2}) = 2^2 - (\sqrt{2})^2 = 4 - 2 = 2$
2. $(3 + 5\sqrt{3})^2 = 3^2 + 2(3)(5\sqrt{3}) + (5\sqrt{3})^2$
$$= 9 + 30\sqrt{3} + 75 = 84 + 30\sqrt{3}$$
3. $(7 + 6\sqrt{3})(4 - 2\sqrt{3})$
$$= 28 - 14\sqrt{3} + 24\sqrt{3} - 12(3)$$
$$= -8 + 10\sqrt{3}$$
4. $\dfrac{3}{2 - \sqrt{3}} = \dfrac{3}{2 - \sqrt{3}} \cdot \dfrac{2 + \sqrt{3}}{2 + \sqrt{3}}$
$$= \frac{3(2 + \sqrt{3})}{2^2 - (\sqrt{3})^2}$$
$$= \frac{6 + 3\sqrt{3}}{4 - 3} = 6 + 3\sqrt{3}$$

10-10 SIMPLE RADICAL EQUATIONS

Key Mathematical Ideas The skills acquired throughout the chapter are applied in this section to solving radical equations. In solving a radical equation, the process of squaring often introduces values of the variable that are not roots. Thus, it is important that every possible root is verified in the original equation.

Teaching Suggestions Point out to students that in solving a radical equation, they should first transform the equation so that one member contains just the radical. For example, to solve Written Exercise 5 one writes:
$$\sqrt{r} - 3 = 1$$
$$\sqrt{r} = 4$$
$$r = 16$$

Chalkboard Examples

Solve. (An outline of each solution is given.)

1. $\sqrt{s} = 8$
$$s = 64$$
Check: $\sqrt{64} = 8$ ✓
$\therefore$ the solution is 64.

2. $\sqrt{2y^2 - 7} = 5$

$\quad 2y^2 - 7 = 25$

$\quad\quad 2y^2 = 32$

$\quad\quad\quad y = \pm 4$

Since both roots check, the solutions are 4 and -4.

3. $\sqrt{2t^2 - 49} = t$

$\quad 2t^2 - 49 = t^2$

$\quad\quad t^2 = 49$

$\quad\quad\quad t = \pm 7$

Since 7 checks but -7 does not, the solution is 7.

4. $\sqrt{4a^2 - 3} = 2a + 1$

$\quad 4a^2 - 3 = 4a^2 + 4a + 1$

$\quad\quad -4 = 4a$

$\quad\quad -1 = a$

Since -1 does not check, the solution set is Ø.

Suggested Extension Students may enjoy finding the error in the following "proof" that $\sqrt{2} = 1$:

$$\text{Let } a = b.$$
$$\text{Then } a^2 = ab.$$
$$a^2 - b^2 = ab - b^2$$
$$(a + b)(a - b) = b(a - b)$$
$$a + b = b*$$
$$2b = b \text{ (from Step 1)}$$
$$\sqrt{2b} = \sqrt{b}$$
$$\sqrt{2} \cdot \sqrt{b} = \sqrt{b}$$
$$\sqrt{2} = 1$$

(The error occurs in the starred step. Since $a = b$, $a - b = 0$. Thus dividing both members of the equation by $a - b$ is prohibited.)

11 Quadratic Functions and Equations

CHAPTER OVERVIEW

This chapter deals with nonlinear functions and equations. Quadratic direct variation, inverse variation, and variation inversely as the square are used to solve verbal problems. Quadratic functions and their properties are introduced. Several sections focus on various methods of solving quadratic equations. The chapter concludes with a section in which quadratic equations are used to solve verbal problems.

SECTION-BY-SECTION COMMENTARY

11-1 QUADRATIC DIRECT VARIATION

Key Mathematical Ideas This section introduces quadratic direct variation. Students are given the opportunity to graph quadratic functions and to solve problems involving quadratic direct variation. (Note, however, that a complete discussion about quadratic functions is postponed until Section 11-4.)

Teaching Suggestions You may wish to review *linear direct variation* (Section 8-10). It may be helpful to use the following example: The perimeter of an equilateral triangle varies directly as the length of one of its sides.

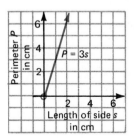

Next, use the following example of *quadratic* direct variation: The area of a square varies directly as the square of the length of one of its sides.

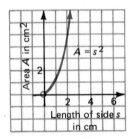

Compare the two functions and their corresponding graphs. Students should notice that the first graph is linear and the second is not.

Chalkboard Examples

If y is directly proportional to x^2, find the missing values.

1. $x_1 = 3$, $y_1 = 9$, $x_2 = 4$, $y_2 = $ ___?___

$$\frac{9}{3^2} = \frac{y_2}{4^2}; \ 1 = \frac{y_2}{16}; \ y_2 = 16$$

2. $x_2 = 6$, $y_2 = 144$, $x_1 = $ ___?___ , $y_1 = 256$

$$\frac{256}{x_1{}^2} = \frac{144}{6^2}; \ \frac{256}{x_1{}^2} = \frac{144}{36} = 4;$$

$$x_1{}^2 = \frac{256}{4} = 64; \ x_1 = \pm 8$$

3. The resistance, R, of air to a moving object varies directly as the square of its speed, s. If the air resistance to a car traveling at a speed of 25 km/h is 100 units, what is the resistance to a car traveling at the rate of 50 km/h?

$$\frac{R_1}{s_1{}^2} = \frac{R_2}{s_2{}^2}; \ \frac{100}{25^2} = \frac{R_2}{50^2}; \ R_2 = 400$$

(Other methods of solving are possible.)

You may wish to point out that faster traveling speed results in greater air resistance and, in turn, to greater gas consumption.

Suggested Extension A simple experiment may be used to illustrate a quadratic relationship. Form a ramp by resting a slotted drapery rod against a stack of books. Roll a marble or a small ball down the ramp and use a stopwatch to time the descent. Vary the length of the rod and time each descent. The data obtained will depend on the inclination of the rod and on the mass of the marble or ball used. A representative set of data follows.

distance (d) in cm	time (t) in sec	$\dfrac{d}{t^2}$
24	1	24.00
95	2	23.75
215 ·	3	23.89
390	4	24.38

The above data seems to agree with the formula $d = kt^2$ where $k \doteq 24$.

11-2 INVERSE VARIATION

Key Mathematical Ideas The key idea of this section is that a function defined by an equation of the form $xy = k$, $k \neq 0$, is an inverse variation.

Teaching Suggestions To introduce inverse variation, use the distance formula, $d = rt$. Suppose we are to travel a distance of 100 km. If we assume that we can travel as fast or as slow as we wish, then the following table can be prepared.

rate (r) in km/h	time (t) in h
100	1
50	2
25	4
20	5
10	10
5	20
2	50
1	100

Plot the data on a set of chalkboard axes and connect the points to form one branch of the hyperbola having equation $rt = 100$.

Chalkboard Examples

1. If a varies inversely as b and $a = 4$ when $b = 20$, find the equation specifying the variation.
$ab = k$; $(4)(20) = k$; $80 = k$; $ab = 80$

2. If x varies inversely as y, $x_1 = 9$, $y_1 = 36$, and $x_2 = 27$, then $y_2 = \underline{\ ?\ }$.
$x_1 y_1 = x_2 y_2$; $9(36) = 27 y_2$; $y_2 = 12$

3. A triangle has an altitude of 2 cm and a base of 6 cm. Find the altitude of another triangle of equal area whose base is 8 cm.
$\frac{1}{2} b_1 h_1 = \frac{1}{2} b_2 h_2$; $6(2) = 8 h_2$; $h_2 = \frac{3}{2}$ (cm)

11-3 VARIATION INVERSELY AS THE SQUARE

Teaching Suggestions A flashlight or another light source may be used to illustrate that illumination decreases as one moves away from the light source. Students may be surprised to learn that, in fact, illumination varies inversely as the square of the distance from the light source. Other examples of variation inversely as the square include the following: *1.* the weight of an object at or above the earth's surface varies inversely as the square of the object's distance from the center of the earth; and *2.* the electrical resistance of a wire of fixed length varies inversely as the square of the diameter of the wire.

Chalkboard Examples

1. If y varies inversely as x^2, and $x = 4$ when $y = 8$, find y when $x = 8$.
$\dfrac{y_1}{x_2^2} = \dfrac{y_2}{x_1^2}$; $\dfrac{8}{8^2} = \dfrac{y_2}{4^2}$; $y_2 = 2$

2. The intensity of sound varies inversely as the square of the distance from the source. What is the effect on the intensity of the music if you sit twice as far away from the stage as someone else? $I_1 d_1^2 = I_2 d_2^2$; $I_1 d_1^2 = I_2 (2d_1)^2$; $\frac{1}{4} I_1 = I_2$; the intensity is one-fourth as great.

3. The attraction between a magnet and an iron object is inversely proportional to the square of the distance between them. What happens to the attraction if a magnet 6 cm from an iron object is moved 4 cm closer to the object? $A_1 d_1^2 = A_2 d_2^2$; $A_1 \cdot 6^2 = A_2 \cdot 2^2$; $9 A_1 = A_2$; the attraction is nine times greater.

11-4 QUADRATIC FUNCTIONS

Key Mathematical Ideas In Section 11-1 quadratic direct variations were graphed and used to solve problems. In this section students explore the more general group of quadratic functions, those defined by equations of the form $y = ax^2 + bx + c$, $a \neq 0$.

Teaching Suggestions You may wish to begin the lesson by reviewing the work from Section 11-1. For example, graph the parabolas having equations $y = x^2$ and $y = -x^2$. Discuss why the graphs represent functions. Remind students that the coefficient of x^2 determines whether the graph of the function opens upward or downward, and thus whether the function has a minimum or a maximum value. Stress that the parabolas are symmetric about a line passing through the vertex, that is, that the points occur in pairs. Extend the discussion to quadratic equations of the form $y = ax^2 + bx + c$.

Chalkboard Examples

Graph each equation. Use the graph to determine the vertex and check by using the formula.

1. $y = 2x^2 - 4x - 1$

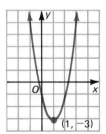

$$-\frac{b}{2a} = -\frac{-4}{2(2)} = 1;$$

$$y = 2 \cdot 1^2 - 4 \cdot 1 - 1$$
$$= -3;$$

∴ the vertex is $(1, -3)$.

2. $y = -x^2 + 4x + 1$

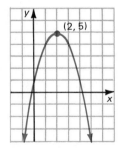

$$-\frac{b}{2a} = -\frac{4}{2(-1)} = 2;$$

$$y = -2^2 + 4(2) + 1 = 5;$$

∴ the vertex is $(2, 5)$.

Suggested Extension In Section 8-8 students explored the role of m and b in the slope-intercept form of a linear equation $y = mx + b$. Have the students

consider the role of a and c in the quadratic equation $y = ax^2 + c$. Students should graph each set of equations on one set of axes.

1. $y = x^2$ **2.** $y = -x^2$
  $y = 2x^2$ $y = -2x^2$
  $y = \frac{1}{2}x^2$ $y = -\frac{1}{2}x^2$

3. $y = x^2$ **4.** $y = -2x^2$
  $y = x^2 + 1$ $y = -2x^2 + 1$
  $y = x^2 - 1$ $y = -2x^2 - 1$

Have students generalize from Exercises 1–4 about the role of a and c in the equation $y = ax^2 + c$. (The greater the absolute value of a, the "narrower" the parabola is; c is the y-intercept of the parabola.)

11-5 QUADRATIC FUNCTIONS AND QUADRATIC EQUATIONS

Key Mathematical Ideas Given a function $f: x \rightarrow ax^2 + bx + c$, one can select values of the function and determine the corresponding values of x. A useful value of a quadratic function is zero, for that value produces the x-intercepts or roots of the associated quadratic equation. In this section, the roots are obtained by factoring; subsequent sections cover other methods.

Teaching Suggestions An effective way of introducing this lesson is to draw an analogy between a linear and a quadratic equation. For example, draw the graph of the linear function with equation $y = x - 6$. Review how to find the x-intercept and the y-intercept. Extend the discussion to a quadratic equation such as $y = x^2 - 5x - 6$.

Chalkboard Examples

1. Find the intersection of the line with the given equation and the parabola with equation $y = x^2 - 1$.

 (**a**) $x = -2$
     $y = (-2)^2 - 1 = 3$; $(-2, 3)$
 (**b**) $y = 8$
     $8 = x^2 - 1$; $9 = x^2$; $\pm 3 = x$;
     $(3, 8)$ and $(-3, 8)$

2. Graph the parabola of Exercise 1. Use the graph to name (**a**) a horizontal line which intersects the parabola in just one point; **(b)** a horizontal line which does not intersect the parabola; and **(c)** the roots of the associated quadratic equation.

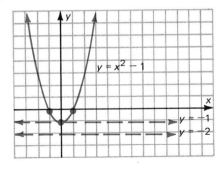

(a) $y = -1$

(b) Answers may vary. For example, $y = -2$.

(c) $(-1, 0)$ and $(1, 0)$

11-6 MORE ABOUT QUADRATIC EQUATIONS

Key Mathematical Ideas In the previous section, quadratic equations were solved by factoring. In this section the method of solving is based on writing the quadratic equations in the form

"perfect square = constant."

Teaching Suggestions You may wish to review the property of square roots of equal numbers (text page 392). Remind students that an equation such as $x^2 = k$, $k > 0$, has two real roots: $\sqrt{k}$ and $-\sqrt{k}$. An equation such as $\sqrt{x} = k$, $k > 0$, has just one real root: k^2.

Chalkboard Examples

Solve.

1. $x^2 - 28 = 0$
$$x^2 = 28$$
$$x = \pm\sqrt{28}$$
$$= \pm 2\sqrt{7}$$

2. $6t^2 - 100 = 0$
$$6t^2 = 100$$
$$t^2 = \frac{50}{3}$$
$$t = \pm\sqrt{\frac{50}{3}} = \pm\frac{5\sqrt{6}}{3}$$

3. $(x + 4)^2 + 2 = 0$
$$(x + 4)^2 = -2$$
No real solution

4. $2(d + 5)^2 - 1 = 9$
$$2(d + 5)^2 = 10$$
$$(d + 5)^2 = 5$$
$$d + 5 = \pm\sqrt{5}$$
$$d = -5 \pm \sqrt{5}$$

Suggested Extension Example 5 on text page 433 and Chalkboard Example 3 involve equations which have no real-number solutions. Have students graph the associated quadratic functions: $y = 8x^2 + 1$ and $y = (x + 4)^2 + 2$. They should see that an equation whose graph lies entirely above or entirely below the x-axis has no real-number solution. (The number of real roots a quadratic equation has depends on the discriminant, dealt with in Section 11-8.)

11-7 COMPLETING THE SQUARE

Key Mathematical Ideas The quadratic equations solved in the previous section were all easily written in the form "perfect square = constant." In this section the quadratic equations are not factorable. They are solved by adding a constant to both members, transforming the equation into one which can be solved by the methods of Section 11-6.

Teaching Suggestions You may wish to introduce the lesson with an example which can be solved either by factoring or by completing the square. The quadratic equation $x^2 - 4x - 5 = 0$ is such an example:

$$x^2 - 4x - 5 = 0 \qquad\qquad x^2 - 4x = 5$$
$$(x - 5)(x + 1) = 0 \qquad x^2 - 4x + 4 = 5 + 4$$
$$x = 5 \text{ or } x = -1 \qquad\qquad (x - 2)^2 = 3^2$$
$$x - 2 = \pm 3$$
$$x = 2 \pm 3$$
$$x = 5 \text{ or } x = -1$$

Be sure students realize that many of the equations they will solve in this section are *not* factorable.

The Oral Exercises on text page 437 can help students understand the form of a perfect square. You may wish to provide some similar exercises in which the missing term is the linear one.

Chalkboard Examples

Solve.

1. $x^2 + 12x + 12 = 0$

$$x^2 + 12x = -12$$
$$x^2 + 12x + 36 = -12 + 36$$
$$(x + 6)^2 = 24$$
$$x + 6 = \pm\sqrt{24}$$
$$x = -6 \pm 2\sqrt{6}$$

Check the roots. $\{-6 + 2\sqrt{6}, -6 - 2\sqrt{6}\}$

2. $2x^2 + 8x - 13 = 0$

$$x^2 + 4x - \frac{13}{2} = 0$$
$$x^2 + 4x + 4 = \frac{13}{2} + 4$$
$$(x + 2)^2 = \frac{21}{2}$$
$$x + 2 = \pm\sqrt{\frac{21}{2}}$$
$$x = -2 \pm \frac{\sqrt{42}}{2}$$

Check the roots.

$$\left\{-2 + \frac{1}{2}\sqrt{42}, -2 - \frac{1}{2}\sqrt{42}\right\}$$

Chalkboard Examples

Find the solution set.

1. $x^2 + 3x - 9 = 0$

$$a = 1, b = 3, c = -9$$
$$x = \frac{-b \pm \sqrt{b^2 - 4ac}}{2a}$$
$$= \frac{-3 \pm \sqrt{3^2 - 4(1)(-9)}}{2(1)}$$
$$= \frac{-3 \pm \sqrt{45}}{2} = \frac{-3 \pm 3\sqrt{5}}{2}$$
$$\left\{\frac{-3 + 3\sqrt{5}}{2}, \frac{-3 - 3\sqrt{5}}{2}\right\}$$

2. $3x^2 - 6x + 5 = 0$

$$a = 3, b = -6, c = 5$$
$$x = \frac{-b \pm \sqrt{b^2 - 4ac}}{2a}$$
$$= \frac{-(-6) \pm \sqrt{(-6)^2 - 4(3)(5)}}{2(3)}$$
$$= \frac{6 \pm \sqrt{36 - 60}}{6} = \frac{6 \pm \sqrt{-34}}{6}$$

Since the radicand is negative, the roots are not real numbers.

∴ the equation has no real roots.

11-8 THE QUADRATIC FORMULA

Key Mathematical Ideas This section introduces a formula for finding the roots of a quadratic equation. The real roots of $ax^2 + bx + c = 0$ are given by the formula $\dfrac{-b \pm \sqrt{b^2 - 4ac}}{2a}$ if $a \neq 0$ and if $b^2 - 4ac \geq 0$. The value of the discriminant, $b^2 - 4ac$, can be used to determine the number of real roots a quadratic equation has. Similarly $b^2 - 4ac$ can be used to determine the number of x-intercepts that the graph of a quadratic function has. (See text pages 440 and 441.)

Teaching Suggestions Students should realize that the quadratic formula is obtained by completing the square for the standard quadratic equation. While students should not be expected to derive the formula, they should know the formula and be encouraged to write the formula every time they use it.

11-9 USING QUADRATIC EQUATIONS TO SOLVE PROBLEMS

Key Mathematical Ideas Students now have the following methods for solving quadratic equations:

1. factoring
2. using the property of square roots of equal numbers
3. completing the square
4. using the quadratic formula

This section discusses how to choose an appropriate method and provides applications of quadratic equations.

Teaching Suggestions Be sure students realize that more than one method may be suitable for solving a particular quadratic equation. However, encourage them to select the one involving the least complicated calculations.

Recommend that students check their answers to each verbal problem with the words of the problem and reject inappropriate roots.

Chalkboard Examples

Solve, using the five-step method. (Partial solutions are provided to facilitate class discussion.)

1. The difference between two numbers is 8 and the sum of their squares is 104. Find the numbers.

$$x^2 + (x + 8)^2 = 104$$
$$x^2 + x^2 + 16x + 64 = 104$$
$$2x^2 + 16x - 40 = 0$$
$$x^2 + 8x - 20 = 0$$
$$(x - 2)(x + 10) = 0$$
$$x = 2 \text{ or } x = -10$$

The numbers are 2 and 10, or -10 and -2.

2. The sum of the first n positive integers is represented by the formula $\dfrac{n(n + 1)}{2}$. How many positive integers yield a sum of 153?

$$\frac{n(n + 1)}{2} = 153$$
$$n^2 + n = 306$$
$$n^2 + n - 306 = 0$$
$$n = \frac{-1 \pm \sqrt{1 - 4(1)(-306)}}{2(1)}$$
$$= \frac{-1 \pm \sqrt{1 + 1224}}{2} = \frac{-1 \pm 35}{2}$$
$$n = 17 \text{ or } n = -18$$

Reject -18.

$\therefore$ 17 positive integers yield a sum of 153.

12 Geometry and Trigonometry

CHAPTER OVERVIEW

This chapter offers an introduction to geometry. The first few sections explore the properties of lines, rays, and angles. The subsequent sections are devoted to the properties of general triangles and special triangles such as right, isosceles, equilateral, and similar triangles. The final three sections introduce the trigonometric ratios, the use of trigonometric tables, and applications of trigonometry.

SECTION-BY-SECTION COMMENTARY

12-1 LINES AND ANGLES

Key Mathematical Ideas This section centers on the vocabulary relating to lines and angles. The use of the protractor to find the degree measure of an angle is also reviewed.

Teaching Suggestions Most students will have previously used the vocabulary introduced in this section. A helpful way to review the geometric concepts of *point, line,* and *plane* is to have the class identify representations of each in the classroom. For example, a point can be represented by the tip of a pencil or by a corner of the classroom; a line or a line segment can be represented by an edge of a book or by an edge of the door; a plane can be represented by the floor or by a desktop. Be sure that students realize that points, lines, and planes are abstract concepts. Remind them that lines and planes extend indefinitely, although their representations do not.

Students should be able to differentiate between $\overleftrightarrow{AB}$, $\overline{AB}$, AB, and $\overrightarrow{AB}$. A flashlight or a pointer can be used to illustrate a *ray*.

When introducing the notation used for angles, emphasize that the middle letter names the vertex. A chalkboard compass or a pair of flashlights can provide a physical model of an *angle*.

Chalkboard Examples

1. Draw the following diagram on the chalkboard.

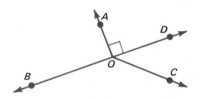

Ask students to measure each angle shown and to classify it as acute, right, or obtuse.

Acute: $\angle DOC$; right: $\angle AOB$, $\angle AOD$; obtuse: $\angle AOC$, $\angle COB$

2. Name the geometric figure which corresponds to each mathematical sentence.

a. $x = 1$ point B
b. $x \geq 1$ $\overrightarrow{BC}$
c. $-3 \leq x \leq 1$ $\overline{AB}$
d. the entire number line $\overleftrightarrow{AB}$, $\overleftrightarrow{BC}$, or $\overleftrightarrow{AC}$

12-2 PAIRS OF ANGLES

Key Mathematical Ideas This section introduces the properties of vertical angles, adjacent angles, complementary angles, and supplementary angles. These properties form the basis of numerical and verbal problems.

Teaching Suggestions One effective way to reinforce the concepts of this section is to provide each student with a duplicated sheet of many angles to measure. If you distribute the sheets at the beginning of the lesson, students can themselves discover the relationships between the measures of the special angles. An added benefit is that students gain practice using a protractor.

Chalkboard Examples

1. Find the measure of the complement of an angle having the given measure.
   a. 36°   54°   **b.** 3°   87°
   c. $x°$ $(90 - x)°$ **d.** 120°   no complement

2. Find the measure of the supplement of an angle having the given measure.
   a. 36°   144°   **b.** 3°   177°
   c. $x°$ $(180 - x)°$ **d.** 120°   60°

3. The product of the measures of two vertical angles is twenty times the measure of one vertical angle. Find the measure of each. (An outline of the solution is given.)

$$n \cdot n = 20 \cdot n$$
$$n^2 - 20n = 0$$
$$n(n - 20) = 0$$
$$n = 0 \quad \text{or} \quad n = 20$$

Reject $n = 0$.
∴ The measure of each angle is 20°.

Suggested Extension Challenge students to solve the following problems:

1. The measure of the supplement of an angle is 10° more than two times the measure of its complement. What is the measure of the angle?   10°

2. Have students find the measure of the angle described in Problem 1 if "20°" is substituted for "10°."   20°

3. Have the students use their results from Problems 1 and 2 to make a generalization. Ask students to prove that if $k°$ represents the measure of an angle, then:
$$180 - k = k + 2(90 - k).$$

12-3   TRIANGLES

Key Mathematical Ideas The key idea of this section is that the sum of the measures of the angles of a triangle is equal to 180°. This property is used to solve problems involving general and special triangles.

Teaching Suggestions You may wish to ask students for examples of triangles in the classroom. Triangles are often used in construction to lend rigidity to structures.

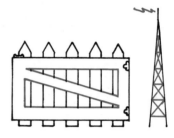

Ask students to suggest other examples in which triangles occur.

Chalkboard Examples

Find the value of x.

1.

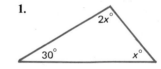

$$30 + x + 2x = 180$$
$$3x = 150$$
$$x = 50$$

2.

$$x + (x + 10) + 90 = 180$$
$$2x = 80$$
$$x = 40$$

3.

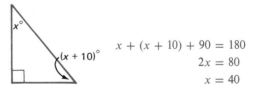

$$(\tfrac{1}{2}x + 5) + x + x = 180$$
$$\tfrac{5}{2}x = 175$$
$$x = 70$$

T110

4. The measures of two angles of a triangle are equal and the measure of the third angle is one-fourth the sum of the other two. Find the measure of each angle. (An outline of the solution is given.)

$$x + x + \frac{1}{4}(x + x) = 180$$

$$2x + \frac{x}{2} = 180$$

$$\frac{5x}{2} = 180$$

$$x = 72$$

∴ the measures are 72°, 72°, and 36°.

12-4 SIMILAR TRIANGLES

Key Mathematical Ideas Two similar triangles have the following properties: the measures of corresponding angles are equal and the lengths of corresponding sides are proportional. These properties are used to solve numerical and verbal problems.

Teaching Suggestions On a sunny day, mark a spot on a windowsill and set a pencil upright on the spot so that it casts a shadow. Measure the pencil and its shadow. Repeat the procedure with a pencil of a different length. Have the class compute $\frac{AB}{DE}$ and $\frac{AC}{DF}$.

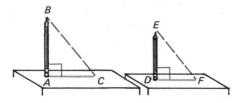

Since $\triangle ABC \sim \triangle DEF, \frac{AB}{DE} \doteq \frac{AC}{DF}$.

Chalkboard Examples

1. If $\triangle MNP \sim \triangle XYZ$, find YZ and ZX.

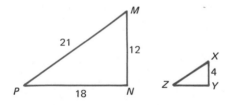

$$\frac{MN}{XY} = \frac{NP}{YZ}; \frac{12}{4} = \frac{18}{YZ}; YZ = 6$$

$$\frac{MN}{XY} = \frac{PM}{ZX}; \frac{12}{4} = \frac{21}{ZX}; ZX = 7$$

2. To measure the width of a park, similar triangles were formed as shown below. What is the width of the park?

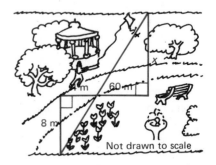

Not drawn to scale

(A partial solution is given.)

$$\frac{x}{60} = \frac{8}{4}; x = 2(60) = 120$$

The park is 120 m wide.

3. If $\triangle ABC \sim \triangle DEF$, $m\angle B = 35°$, and $m\angle E = (5x^2 - 18x)°$, then what is the value of x? (A partial solution is given.)

$35 = 5x^2 - 18x; 0 = 5x^2 - 18x - 35 = (5x + 7)(x - 5); x = -\frac{7}{5}$ or $x = 5$

Suggested Extensions

1. Have students use the methods shown in Example 2 and Problems 3 and 7 (all on text page 462) to indirectly measure lengths such as the height of the school or the flagpole.

2. You may wish to initiate a class discussion about the Historical Note on text page 463. Students may want to try the method outlined in the section to make indirect measurements.

12-5 TRIGONOMETRIC RATIOS AND FUNCTIONS

Key Mathematical Ideas This section uses similar right triangles to introduce the sine, cosine, and tangent ratios. The sections dealing with trigonometry are intended to be introductory rather than rigorous; this glimpse should suffice at this stage.

Teaching Suggestions This section can be introduced by having each student draw a figure like the one shown below. (Point out that $\triangle ABG$, $\triangle ACF$, and $\triangle ADE$ are similar triangles.)

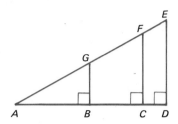

Have each student complete the following chart by making the appropriate measurements.

AB	BG	GA
AC	CF	FA
AD	DE	EA

Ask the students to use their charts to compute $\dfrac{AB}{GA}$, $\dfrac{AC}{FA}$, and $\dfrac{AD}{EA}$ (to the nearest tenth). For each diagram, the values obtained are approximately the same. Introduce the meaning of *sine*. The other trigonometric ratios may be introduced in a similar fashion.

Chalkboard Examples

Find the sine, cosine, and tangent of $\angle A$.

1.

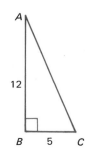

$$AC = \sqrt{12^2 + 5^2}$$
$$= \sqrt{144 + 25}$$
$$= 13$$

$$\sin A = \frac{5}{13}$$

$$\cos A = \frac{12}{13}$$

$$\tan A = \frac{5}{12}$$

2.

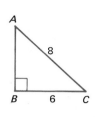

$$AB = \sqrt{8^2 - 6^2}$$
$$= \sqrt{64 - 36}$$
$$= 2\sqrt{7}$$

$$\sin A = \frac{6}{8} = \frac{3}{4}$$

$$\cos A = \frac{2\sqrt{7}}{8} = \frac{\sqrt{7}}{4}$$

$$\tan A = \frac{6}{2\sqrt{7}} = \frac{3\sqrt{7}}{7}$$

Suggested Extension You may wish to refer students to the trigonometric table on text page 488. If coordinate axes are marked off with the x-axis in units of 5°, and the y-axis in tenths, then partial graphs of the sine, cosine and tangent functions can be drawn.

12-6 USING TRIGONOMETRIC TABLES

Key Mathematical Ideas In this section the values of the trigonometric ratios are calculated for an isosceles right triangle and for an equilateral triangle. The rest of the section focuses on the way to read and use trigonometric tables.

Teaching Suggestions Draw a right triangle containing an angle of measure 39°. Point out that in order to compute cos 39°, for example, one has to measure two lengths to the nearest unit and compute the quotient. Turning to text page 488, students can use the table to find sin 39°, cos 39°, and tan 39°, each correct to four decimal places.

Chalkboard Examples

1. Use the table to find the values of the trigonometric functions for angles of degree measure 45°, 30°, and 60°. Compare the answers to those on text page 467.

2. Find the measure of angle $\angle A$ to the nearest degree.
   a. $\sin A = 0.9175$ 67°
   b. $\tan A = 1.8045$ 61°
   c. $\cos A = 0.9710$ 14°
   d. $\sin A = 0.9932$ 83°
   e. $\cos A = 0.6611$ 49°

12-7 NUMERICAL TRIGONOMETRY

Key Mathematical Ideas In this section trigonometric ratios are used to solve a variety of problems. The methods introduced for indirect measurement may be applied in classroom experiments, if time permits.

Teaching Suggestions Introduce this section by finding JL to the nearest meter.

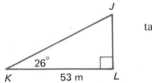

$$\tan 26° = \frac{JL}{LK};$$

$$JL \doteq (0.4877)(53)$$

$$\doteq 26$$

Discuss how JL in the diagram might represent, for example, the height of an airborne kite. Encourage students to draw a diagram to solve a trigonometric problem if one is not given.

You may wish to point out that sometimes one trigonometric ratio is more helpful than another. For example, to find x in Example 1 on text page **469**, one might write:

$$\sin B = \frac{50}{x}$$

$$\sin 85° = \frac{50}{x}$$

$$x = \frac{50}{\sin 85°}$$

Note that the computation needed here is the quotient $50 \div 0.9962$. Most students will agree that the product $50(0.0875)$ is easier to compute.

Chalkboard Examples

1. Find x to the nearest cm.

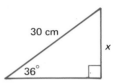

$\sin 36° = \frac{x}{30}$; $x \doteq 30(0.5878) \doteq 18$; 18 cm

2. Find $m\angle A$ to the nearest degree.

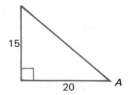

$\tan A = \frac{15}{20} = 0.75$; $m\angle A \doteq 37°$

3. Find the height of the tree to the nearest meter.

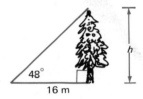

$\tan 48° = \frac{h}{16}$; $h \doteq (1.1106)(16) \doteq 18$; 18 m

Algebra
STRUCTURE and METHOD
Book 1

Mary P. Dolciani

William Wooton

Robert H. Sorgenfrey

Richard G. Brown

Editorial Advisers
Andrew M. Gleason
Albert E. Meder, Jr.

Houghton Mifflin Company · Boston

Atlanta   Dallas   Geneva, Illinois
Hopewell, New Jersey   Palo Alto

Algebra

STRUCTURE and METHOD

Book 1

ABOUT THE AUTHORS

Mary P. Dolciani, University Dean for Academic Development and Professor of Mathematics, Hunter College, City University of New York. Dr. Dolciani has been a director and teacher in numerous National Science Foundation and New York State Education Department institutes for mathematics teachers, and also Visiting Secondary School Lecturer for the Mathematical Association of America.

William Wooton, Mathematics Consultant, Vista, California, Unified School District. Mr. Wooton was formerly a professor of mathematics at Los Angeles Pierce College and has taught mathematics at both the junior and senior high school levels. He has also been a team member of the National Council of Teachers of Mathematics (NCTM) summer writing projects.

Robert H. Sorgenfrey, Professor of Mathematics, University of California, Los Angeles. Dr. Sorgenfrey, a topologist, has won the Distinguished Teaching Award at U.C.L.A. and has been Chairman of the Committee on Teaching there. He has been a team member of the NCTM summer writing projects.

Richard G. Brown, Mathematics Teacher, The Phillips Exeter Academy, Exeter, New Hampshire. An experienced teacher and author, Mr. Brown has taught a wide range of mathematics courses for both students and teachers at several schools and universities, including Newton, Massachusetts, High School and the University of New Hampshire.

ABOUT THE EDITORIAL ADVISERS

Andrew M. Gleason, Hollis Professor of Mathematics and Natural Philosophy, Harvard University. Professor Gleason is a well-known research mathematician. His many affiliations include membership in the National Academy of Sciences.

Albert E. Meder, Jr., Dean and Vice Provost and Professor of Mathematics, Emeritus, Rutgers, The State University of New Jersey.

ISBN: 0-395-20489-5

Contents

v

4 Working with Polynomials

5 Factoring

6 Working with Fractions

7 Inequalities

8 Functions and Relations

9 Systems of Open Sentences in Two Variables

10 Rational and Irrational Numbers

11 Quadratic Functions and Equations

12 Geometry and Trigonometry

Symbols

		Page				Page
·	x (times)	1	⊂	is a subset of		258
=	equals, is equal to	1	∩	the intersection of		270
( )	parentheses—a grouping symbol	2	∪	the union of		271
			≥	is greater than or equal to		275
[ ]	brackets—a grouping symbol	2	≤	is less than or equal to		275
π	pi, a number approximately equal to $\frac{22}{7}$	12	$f(x)$	f of x, the value of f at x		288
			(a, b)	ordered pair whose first component is a and second component is b		291
≐	is approximately equal to	12				
∈	is a member of, belongs to	17	$\sqrt{}$	principal square root		382
∴	therefore	17	$\overleftrightarrow{AB}$	line AB		453
≠	is not equal to	17	$\overline{AB}$	segment AB		453
⁻	negative	32	AB	the length of AB		453
⁺	positive	32	$\overrightarrow{AB}$	ray AB		454
$\overset{?}{=}$	is this statement true?	37	°	degrees		454
$-a$	opposite of a, additive inverse of a, negative of a	38	∠	angle		454
			$m\angle A$	measure of angle A		454
$|a|$	absolute value of a	39	△	triangle		459
$\frac{1}{b}$	reciprocal or multiplicative inverse of b	70	~	is similar to		461
			cos A	cosine of A		464
∅	empty set, null set	107	sin A	sine of A		464
$a:b$	ratio of a to b	201	tan A	tangent of A		464
<	is less than	255				
>	is greater than	255				

Metric system symbols

cm	centimeter	h	hour	
g	gram	min	minute	
kg	kilogram	s	second	
km	kilometer	°C	degrees Celsius	
km/h	kilometers per hour	ℓ	liter	
m	meter	kl	kiloliter	
m/s	meters per second			

Diagnostic Tests in Arithmetic*

1. Whole Numbers—Addition

1. $\begin{array}{r} 6 \\ +9 \\ \hline 15 \end{array}$	2. $\begin{array}{r} 2 \\ 2 \\ +3 \\ \hline 7 \end{array}$	3. $\begin{array}{r} 4 \\ 6 \\ +7 \\ \hline 17 \end{array}$	4. $\begin{array}{r} 55 \\ +25 \\ \hline 80 \end{array}$	5. $\begin{array}{r} 68 \\ +15 \\ \hline 83 \end{array}$
6. $\begin{array}{r} 575 \\ +371 \\ \hline 946 \end{array}$	7. $\begin{array}{r} 778 \\ +177 \\ \hline 955 \end{array}$	8. $\begin{array}{r} 814 \\ 857 \\ +311 \\ \hline 1982 \end{array}$	9. $\begin{array}{r} 7456 \\ 3701 \\ 6101 \\ +5592 \\ \hline 22{,}850 \end{array}$	

2. Whole Numbers—Subtraction

1. $\begin{array}{r} 7 \\ -2 \\ \hline 5 \end{array}$	2. $\begin{array}{r} 11 \\ -9 \\ \hline 2 \end{array}$	3. $\begin{array}{r} 97 \\ -54 \\ \hline 43 \end{array}$	4. $\begin{array}{r} 769 \\ -608 \\ \hline 161 \end{array}$	5. $\begin{array}{r} 684 \\ -308 \\ \hline 376 \end{array}$
6. $\begin{array}{r} 736 \\ -365 \\ \hline 371 \end{array}$	7. $\begin{array}{r} 6508 \\ -4395 \\ \hline 2113 \end{array}$	8. $\begin{array}{r} 643 \\ -177 \\ \hline 466 \end{array}$	9. $\begin{array}{r} 4220 \\ -3686 \\ \hline 534 \end{array}$	10. $\begin{array}{r} 40{,}704 \\ -27{,}978 \\ \hline 12{,}726 \end{array}$

3. Whole Numbers—Multiplication

1. $\begin{array}{r} 6 \\ \times 6 \\ \hline 36 \end{array}$	2. $\begin{array}{r} 21 \\ \times 4 \\ \hline 84 \end{array}$	3. $\begin{array}{r} 28 \\ \times 3 \\ \hline 84 \end{array}$	4. $\begin{array}{r} 66 \\ \times 8 \\ \hline 528 \end{array}$	5. $\begin{array}{r} 375 \\ \times 3 \\ \hline 1125 \end{array}$	6. $\begin{array}{r} 69 \\ \times 20 \\ \hline 1380 \end{array}$
7. $\begin{array}{r} 125 \\ \times 200 \\ \hline 25{,}000 \end{array}$	8. $\begin{array}{r} 1291 \\ \times 2000 \\ \hline 2{,}582{,}000 \end{array}$	9. $\begin{array}{r} 96 \\ \times 65 \\ \hline 6240 \end{array}$	10. $\begin{array}{r} 734 \\ \times 29 \\ \hline 21{,}286 \end{array}$	11. $\begin{array}{r} 825 \\ \times 955 \\ \hline 787{,}875 \end{array}$	12. $\begin{array}{r} 801 \\ \times 203 \\ \hline 162{,}603 \end{array}$

4. Whole Numbers—Division

1. $9\overline{)54}$ $\quad^{6}$
2. $2\overline{)42}$ $\quad^{21}$
3. $8\overline{)448}$ $\quad^{56}$
4. $5\overline{)2285}$ $\quad^{457}$
5. $13\overline{)455}$ $\quad^{35}$
6. $16\overline{)216}$ $\quad^{13\ R8}$

7. $568\overline{)416090}$ $\quad^{732\ R314}$

8. Express the quotient as a mixed numeral: $482\overline{)285385}$ $\quad^{592\ R41}$

9. Express the quotient to the nearest hundredth: $6\overline{)38}$ 6.33

5. Fractions—Basic Skills

1. Identify by letter the figure that is divided into thirds. A

A   B   C

---

* Used by permission from INDIVIDUALIZED COMPUTATIONAL SKILLS PROGRAM, COMPUTER VERSION by Bryce R. Shaw, Miriam M. Schaefer, and Petronella M.W. Hiehle. Copyright © 1973 by Houghton Mifflin Company.

2. What is the denominator in $\frac{1}{3}$? 3

3. The area shaded in figure D is represented by which fraction in row E? $\frac{1}{5}$

D  E $\frac{2}{5}, \frac{3}{5}, \frac{1}{5}, \frac{5}{1}$

4. Which of the figures below represents the fraction $\frac{1}{3}$? G

F

G   H

5. Write the fraction represented by the set diagram shown below. $\frac{2}{3}$

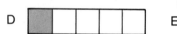

6. Identify by letter the set diagram at the right that represents the fraction $\frac{2}{6}$. M

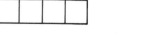
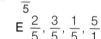
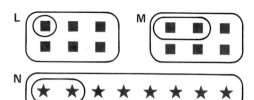

7. Which fraction represents the number 1? $\frac{4}{1}, \frac{4}{4}, \frac{4}{8}, \frac{1}{4}, \frac{4}{4}$

8. Which fraction represents C on the number line? $\frac{5}{3}, \frac{3}{2}, \frac{3}{3}, \frac{5}{2}, \frac{3}{2}$

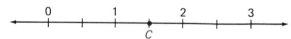

9. Write the consecutive multiples of 6: 6, __?__, __?__, __?__   12; 18; 24

10. Find the least common multiple of 3, 4, and 6. 12

11. Write 36 as the product of prime factors. $2 \times 2 \times 3 \times 3$ or $2^2 \times 3^2$

12. Find the greatest common factor of 12 and 28. 4

13. Find the fraction in row Y that is equal to each fraction or mixed numeral in row X.
    (a) $\frac{4}{6} = \frac{6}{9}$ (b) $\frac{3}{5} = \frac{9}{15}$ (c) $2\frac{3}{4} = \frac{11}{4}$

    X: (a) $\frac{4}{6}$ (b) $\frac{3}{5}$ (c) $2\frac{3}{4}$

    Y: $\frac{2}{2}, \frac{6}{4}, \frac{11}{4}, \frac{3}{4}, \frac{9}{15}, \frac{6}{9}$

14. Find the least common denominator for the fractions $\frac{2}{4}, \frac{1}{6}$, and $\frac{7}{8}$ 24

15. Find the fraction or mixed numeral in row Y that is equal to each fraction or mixed numeral in row X.
    (a) $\frac{5}{4} = 1\frac{1}{4}$ (b) $2\frac{3}{5} = \frac{13}{5}$

    X: (a) $\frac{5}{4}$ (b) $2\frac{3}{5}$

    Y: $\frac{1}{4}, 1\frac{1}{4}, \frac{13}{5}, \frac{5}{13}$

6. Fractions—Addition

1. $\dfrac{1}{5} + \dfrac{2}{5} = $ __?__ $\dfrac{3}{5}$

2. $3\dfrac{1}{8} + 4\dfrac{1}{8} = $ __?__ $7\dfrac{1}{4}$

3. $\begin{aligned}3\dfrac{7}{12}\\+4\dfrac{11}{12}\\\hline 8\dfrac{1}{2}\end{aligned}$

4. $\dfrac{1}{5} + \dfrac{1}{4} = $ __?__ $\dfrac{9}{20}$

5. $\begin{aligned}4\dfrac{2}{3}\\+3\dfrac{4}{7}\\\hline 8\dfrac{5}{21}\end{aligned}$

7. Fractions—Subtraction

1. $\begin{aligned}\dfrac{2}{4}\\-\dfrac{1}{4}\\\hline \dfrac{1}{4}\end{aligned}$
2. $\begin{aligned}3\dfrac{3}{8}\\-1\dfrac{1}{8}\\\hline 2\dfrac{1}{4}\end{aligned}$
3. $\begin{aligned}7\\-5\dfrac{1}{6}\\\hline 1\dfrac{5}{6}\end{aligned}$
4. $\begin{aligned}7\dfrac{1}{9}\\-1\dfrac{7}{9}\\\hline 5\dfrac{1}{3}\end{aligned}$
5. $\begin{aligned}\dfrac{2}{3}\\-\dfrac{1}{7}\\\hline \dfrac{11}{21}\end{aligned}$
6. $\begin{aligned}14\dfrac{4}{6}\\-3\dfrac{4}{5}\\\hline 10\dfrac{13}{15}\end{aligned}$

8. Fractions—Multiplication

1. $\dfrac{1}{3} \times \dfrac{1}{9} = $ __?__ $\dfrac{1}{27}$

2. $\dfrac{7}{8} \times \dfrac{6}{7} = $ __?__ $\dfrac{3}{4}$

3. $\dfrac{1}{2} \times 4 = $ __?__ 2

4. $4\dfrac{5}{6} \times \dfrac{3}{5} = $ __?__ $2\dfrac{9}{10}$

5. $1\dfrac{3}{5} \times 2\dfrac{1}{2} = $ __?__ 4

9. Fractions—Division

1. $5 \div \dfrac{1}{9} = $ __?__ 45

2. $6 \div \dfrac{3}{4} = $ __?__ 8

3. $\dfrac{1}{6} \div \dfrac{1}{2} = $ __?__ $\dfrac{1}{3}$

4. $5\dfrac{5}{9} \div \dfrac{2}{7} = $ __?__ $19\dfrac{4}{9}$

5. $5\dfrac{1}{8} \div 4 = $ __?__ $1\dfrac{9}{32}$

6. $5\dfrac{5}{8} \div 5\dfrac{5}{6} = $ __?__ $\dfrac{27}{28}$

10. Decimals

1. Write the decimal which represents "two and six thousandths." 2.006

2. $\dfrac{5}{1000} = $ __?__ (Decimal) 0.005

3. $0.206 = $ __?__ (Fraction) $\dfrac{103}{500}$

4. $3\dfrac{4}{5} = $ __?__ (Decimal) 3.8

5. Round 40.5656 to the nearest tenth. 40.6

6. $1.033 + 0.1 + 10.066 = $ __?__ 11.199

7. $856.175 - 20.05 = $ __?__ 836.125

8. $\begin{aligned}71.60\\500.42\\+53.96\\\hline 625.98\end{aligned}$

9. $\begin{aligned}735.02\\-7.709\\\hline 727.311\end{aligned}$

10. $\begin{aligned}6639\\\times.0031\\\hline 20.5809\end{aligned}$

11. $.07\overline{)21.707}$ 310.1

11. Percents

1. $\dfrac{7}{4} = \dfrac{?}{100}$ 175

2. $0.69 = $ __?__ % 69

3. $\dfrac{1}{3} = $ __?__ % $33\dfrac{1}{3}$

4. $6\dfrac{1}{2} = $ __?__ % 650

5. $2.405 = $ __?__ % 240.5

6. $289\% = $ __?__ (Mixed numeral in simplest form) $2\dfrac{89}{100}$

7. $38\dfrac{1}{2}\% = $ __?__ (Decimal) 0.385

8. 25% of 23 = __?__ 5.75

9. __?__ % of 20 = 8 40

10. 20% of __?__ = 340 1700

Why Study Algebra?

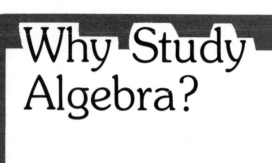

Why should *you* study algebra?

Will *you* use algebra in *your* daily life?

The study of algebra may help you in two ways:
(1) It will prepare you to continue your studies in mathematics if you wish.
(2) It will help you to organize your thoughts to solve mathematical problems that everyone meets from day to day.

You may feel that calculators and computers will take care of all your problem solving. Of course, that is impossible because machines do not think. *You* must do the thinking. If you know what steps to take—what numbers and operations to use—then calculators and computers can be made to do a great deal of the work for you.

Mathematics is like a large tree with many branches. Arithmetic is at the root of the tree, and algebra and geometry may be thought of as forming the trunk.

For any future work in mathematics, you will need the ideas developed in this course. Also, many of these ideas will find useful application in your future career.

As you look through this book, you will find a photograph facing the first page of each chapter. These photographs have been selected to suggest several fields of human activity. The photographs for Chapters 1–3 suggest the arts, and those for Chapters 4–6 deal with the physical sciences. The photographs for Chapters 7–9 relate to the life sciences, and those for Chapters 9–12 are connected with the social sciences.

Whatever you choose to do in the future—from running a household to running a business to doing scientific research—you will need to use some mathematics.

Information about some particular career opportunities are given in the Career Notes: Computer Service Technician, page 25; Optician, page 41; Market Researcher, page 69; Environmental Health Technician, page 126; Technical Writer, page 155; Pharmacist, page 232; Statistician, page 278; Photographer, page 310; Landscape Architect, page 354; Livestock Production Technician, page 385; Airline Dispatcher, page 423.

Introduction to Algebra

1

The Language of Algebra

1-1 Numerals and Expressions

OBJECTIVE To learn how to simplify numerical expressions.

The numerical expressions

$$5 - 1, \quad 3.5 + 0.5, \quad 36 \div 9,$$
$$1 + 1 + 1 + 1, \quad 34 - 30,$$
$$2 \times 2 \text{ or } 2 \cdot 2 \quad [\cdot \text{ means } \times]$$

all have the *value four*. A **numeral**, or **numerical expression**, is a *name* for a number. The **number** is the **value of the expression**.

To say that any two of the expressions, such as "36 ÷ 9" and "4", name the same number, you use the **equality symbol**, =. You write

$$36 \div 9 = 4$$

and say, "thirty-six divided by nine **equals** (or **is equal to**) four." Of course, "4" is the *simplest* name for *four*.

Whenever you replace a numerical expression by the simplest, or most common, name of its value, you say that you have **simplified the expression.**

In simplifying a numerical expression, you use the following:

> **Substitution Principle**
>
> Changing the numeral by which a number is named in an expression does not change the value of the expression.

Example 1 Simplify $(50 - 14) + 1$.

Solution The pair of parentheses ( ) show how the numerals in the expression are to be grouped. Thus:

$(50 - 14) + 1 = 36 + 1 = 37$ *Answer*

A **grouping symbol** is a device, such as a pair of parentheses, used to enclose an expression. Brackets [ ] may also be used.

Multiplication symbols need not be used with grouping symbols. Thus:

$7 \cdot (3 + 2) = 7(3 + 2)$ and $7 \cdot 5 = 7(5) = (7)5 = (7)(5)$.

In a fraction such as "$\dfrac{5 + 16}{3}$" the bar is a grouping symbol as well as a division symbol. Thus:

$$\frac{5 + 16}{3} = \frac{21}{3} = 21 \div 3 = 7.$$

> **Grouping Symbols**
>
> | Parentheses | Brackets | Fraction Bar |
> |---|---|---|
> | $7(3 + 2)$ | $7[3 + 2]$ | $\dfrac{5 + 16}{3}$ |

You first simplify the numeral in the innermost grouping symbol and continue until the simplest expression is found as shown here:

Example 2 Simplify $3 + [5 + (7 - 2)]$.

Solution $3 + [5 + (7 - 2)] = 3 + [5 + 5] = 3 + 10 = 13$ *Answer*

Example 3 Simplify $\dfrac{6(7 - 2)}{5}$.

Solution $\dfrac{6(7 - 2)}{5} = \dfrac{6(5)}{5} = \dfrac{30}{5} = 6$ *Answer*

Oral Exercises

Simplify each expression.

1. $6 + (5 \times 2)$ 16
2. $(8 \times 3) + 1$ 25
3. $(12 - 3) \div 4$ $\frac{9}{4}$
4. $12 - (3 + 4)$ 5
5. $6 \cdot (3 + 1)$ 24
6. $(4 + 2) \cdot 3$ 18
7. $(10 - 2)3$ 24
8. $2(8 - 3)$ 10
9. $12 \div (3 - 1)$ 6
10. $14 \div (5 + 2)$ 2
11. $(8 - 5) \times (3 - 2)$ 3
12. $(12 + 4) \div (10 - 2)$ 2

Written Exercises

Simplify each expression.

A
1. $(8 - 3) + 7$ 12
2. $6 + (18 - 2)$ 22
3. $3 \times (12 + 2)$ 42
4. $(15 - 6) \times 8$ 72
5. $(3 + 12) \div 5$ 3
6. $6 + (15 \div 3)$ 11
7. $6(15 \div 3)$ 30
8. $(15 \div 3)6$ 30
9. $(12 \cdot 2) - (6 \cdot 3)$ 6
10. $[12 - (3 \cdot 2)] \div 3$ 2
11. $8 - [2 \div (3 - 1)]$ 7
12. $[6 + (5 - 1)] + 8$ 18

13. $\dfrac{60 - 5}{10 + 1} + 2$ 7
14. $3 + \dfrac{20 + 6}{16 - 3}$ 5
15. $4 \times \left(\dfrac{8 - 2}{3 - 1}\right)$ 12
16. $64 \div \left(\dfrac{19 + 5}{2 \times 3}\right)$ 16

Simplify the expression on each side of the __?__ . If the expressions name the same number, write "equal." If the expressions do not name the same number, write "not equal."

B
17. $3[5(3 - 1)]$ __?__ $6(4 + 1)$ equal

18. $\dfrac{8 - [2(5 - 2)]}{4 - 2}$ __?__ $8 \div (10 - 2)$ equal

19. $6 \times 3[2 + (8 - 3)]$ __?__ $\dfrac{12 + 6}{9 - 3} + 100$ not equal

20. $(36 \div 2) \times (4 + 2)$ __?__ $\dfrac{18 + 6}{10 - 2}$ not equal

21. $\dfrac{10 - [3(3 - 1)]}{8 + 2}$ __?__ $[2(5 - 4)] \div 8$ not equal

22. $\dfrac{15 - 5}{4 + 1} + 24$ __?__ $(6 \times 4) + 3(7 - 4)$ not equal

23. $8[12 - 3(6 - 3)]$ __?__ $3(2 + 4) + (42 \div 7)$ equal

24. $\dfrac{6 + [3(7 + 2)]}{5 - 2}$ __?__ $(63 \div 9) + (16 \div 4)$ equal

1-2 Variables and Expressions

OBJECTIVE To learn how to evaluate variable expressions.

The Ecology Club is having a car wash to raise money for a field trip. They can wash 10 automobiles in one hour. Therefore, they can wash

in one hour: 10×1
in two hours: 10×2
in three hours: 10×3

Each of these numerical expressions fits the pattern

$$10 \times n,$$

where the letter n may stand for "1", "2", or "3". n is called a *variable*. The *domain* of n here is

$\{1, 2, 3\}$ (read "the set whose members are one, two, and three").

The *values* of n are 1, 2, and 3. The symbols { } are called braces.
  In general:

> A **variable** is a symbol used to represent one or more numbers. The **set,** or collection, of numbers that the variable may represent is the **domain,** or **replacement set,** of the variable. The numbers in the domain are called the **values of the variable.**

An expression, such as "$10 \times n$", which contains a variable is called a variable expression or an open expression.
  When you write a product that contains a variable, you usually omit the multiplication symbol. Thus,

"$10 \times n$" is usually written "$10n$",
"$y \times z$" is usually written "yz".

Such a product is considered to be *grouped*. Thus,

"$10n + 6$" means "$(10 \times n) + 6$"

and

"$yz \div 10n$" means "$(y \times z) \div (10 \cdot n)$".

But notice that in writing "10 × 2" or 10(2), you must use symbols such as "×", or "•", or "( )" in order to avoid confusion.

> The process of replacing each variable in an expression by the numeral for a given value of the variable and simplifying the result is known as **evaluating the expression** or **finding its value.**

Example If the value of x is 6 and the value of y is 2, find the value of $\dfrac{4x + 3y}{x - 2y}$.

Solution

1. Replace "x" with "6" and "y" with "2", and insert the necessary multiplication and grouping symbols:

$$\frac{4x + 3y}{x - 2y} = \frac{(4 \times 6) + (3 \times 2)}{6 - (2 \times 2)}$$

2. Simplify:

$$= \frac{24 + 6}{6 - 4} = \frac{30}{2} = 15 \quad Answer$$

It is a useful shortcut to write

"If $x = 6$" for "If x has the value 6".

Here "$=$" means "has the value".

Oral Exercises

In each of Exercises 1–12, the given expression indicates one or more operations to be performed. Describe the operation(s) for each expression. (More than one answer may be possible.) A. = add, S. = subt., M. = mult., D. = divide

Sample $5 + 3c$ *Solution* "Multiply 3 and c, and then add the product to 5."

or "Add to 5 the product of 3 and c."

M. 3 and a M. 7 and b S. 2 from b S. c from 8 D. 20 by c D. 46 by a

1. $3a$ 2. $7b$ 3. $b - 2$ 4. $8 - c$ 5. $\dfrac{20}{c}$ 6. $\dfrac{46}{a}$

D. 16 by prod. of a and c D. 24 by prod. of b and c M. 3 and sum S. 1 from a; D. sum of a S. a from b;

7. $\dfrac{16}{ac}$ 8. $\dfrac{24}{bc}$ 9. $3(c + 1)$ of c and 1 10. $5(a - 1)$ M. 5 by this diff. 11. $\dfrac{a + c}{b}$ and c by b 12. $\dfrac{c}{b - a}$ D. c by this diff.

13–24. In Exercises 1–12, if $a = 2$, $b = 3$, and $c = 4$, find the value of each expression. **13.** 6 **14.** 21 **15.** 1 **16.** 4 **17.** 5 **18.** 23 **19.** 2 **20.** 2 **21.** 15 **22.** 5 **23.** 2 **24.** 4

Written Exercises

Evaluate if $r = 1$, $s = 2$, $t = 3$, $w = 10$, $x = 1$, and $y = 0$:

Sample $\dfrac{st + 4}{w - y}$ *Solution* $\dfrac{(2 \cdot 3) + 4}{10 - 0} = \dfrac{6 + 4}{10} = \dfrac{10}{10} = 1$ *Answer*

A 1. xy 0

2. rs 2

3. $w - st$ 4

4. $rt - y$ 3

5. $st + wx$ 16

6. $tw - sx$ 28

7. $r(w - y)$ 10

8. $s(w - t)$ 14

9. $(r)(st)$ 6

10. $(xw)(y)$ 0

11. $st(r - y)$ 6

12. $xy(t + s)$ 0

13. $rstwx$ 60

14. $rstxy$ 0

15. $(w - 3r)(3t - y)$ 63

16. $(2w - s)(4x - r)$ 5

17. $\dfrac{w - st}{r}$ 4

18. $\dfrac{sw + x}{t}$ 7

19. $\dfrac{wx - s}{3t - r}$ 1

20. $\dfrac{w - rs}{t - x}$ 4

B 21. $w(t - s) + \dfrac{st}{r}$ 16

22. $x(s + w) - rt$ 9

23. $\dfrac{4(rs + rt)}{s}$ 10

24. $\dfrac{5(swx + wx)}{rt}$ 50

25. $\dfrac{20xy + 3w}{t + 2st} + \dfrac{w - rt}{x + st}$ 3

26. $\dfrac{r(w + st)}{x(w - s)} - \dfrac{x(t + r)}{2t - s}$ 1

★ Self-Test 1

Be sure that you understand these terms:

numeral (p. 1)

numerical expression (p. 1)

number (p. 1)

value of an expression (p. 1)

equals (p. 1)

simplify (p. 1)

substitution principle (p. 2)

grouping symbol (p. 2)

variable (p. 4)

set (p. 4)

domain (p. 4)

replacement set (p. 4)

values of a variable (p. 4)

variable expression (p. 4)

open expression (p. 4)

evaluate (p. 5)

Be sure that you understand these symbols:

$\cdot$ (p. 1) $=$ (p. 1)   ( ) (p. 2)   [ ] (p. 2)   { } (p. 5)

Simplify.

1. $7 + 2(11 - 4)$

2. $\dfrac{8(17 - 11)}{4}$

Objective 1-1, p. 1

Evaluate if $m = 2$, $n = 3$, $p = 1$:

3. $\dfrac{m + n + p}{pm}$

4. $\dfrac{mn - p}{m + n}$

Objective 1-2, p. 5

Check your answers with those printed at the back of the book.

1-3 Factors and Exponents

> **OBJECTIVE** To learn how to write exponential expressions.

When two or more numbers are multiplied, each of the numbers is called a **factor** of the product. Thus, 3 and 4 are factors of 12; other pairs of factors of 12 are 2 and 6; 1 and 12. That is,

$$12 = 3 \cdot 4 = 2 \cdot 6 = 1 \cdot 12; \quad \text{also, } 12 = 2 \cdot 2 \cdot 3.$$

When a number can be expressed as a product of equal factors, except 1, the number is called a **power** of the repeated factor. Here is how the powers of 5 are defined:

First Power: $5 = 5^1$

Second Power: $25 = 5 \cdot 5 = 5^2$ (read "five squared" or "the square of five" or "the second power of five")

Third Power: $125 = 5 \cdot 5 \cdot 5 = 5^3$ (read "five cubed" or "the cube of five" or "the third power of five")

Fourth Power: $625 = 5 \cdot 5 \cdot 5 \cdot 5 = 5^4$ (read "five to the fourth power" or "the fourth power of five")

and so on.

In general:

> If x denotes any number and n denotes any member of the set $\{1, 2, 3, 4, \ldots\}$, then:
>
> $$x^n = \underbrace{x \cdot x \cdot \cdots \cdot x}_{n \text{ factors}}$$
>
> You call x^n the **nth power** of x. In x^n, the value of x is called the **base** and the value of the small raised symbol n is called the **exponent** (*ek*-spo-nent).

The exponent tells the number of times the base x occurs as a factor in the product. Thus:

Exponent ⟶
$$x^n = \text{the } n\text{th power of } x$$
Base ⟶

8 *Chapter 1*

In writing the power "x^3" in the form "$x \cdot x \cdot x$", you say that you have written the power in **factored form**. The expression "x^3" is called the **exponential** (ek-spo-*nen*-chal) **form**.

Example 1 If the value of r is 6, find the value of r^3.

Solution Replace r by "6" and simplify the resulting expression:

$$r^3 = r \cdot r \cdot r = (r \cdot r) \cdot r$$
$$= (6 \cdot 6) \cdot 6$$
$$= 36 \cdot 6 = 216 \quad Answer$$

Example 2 If the value of r is 6, find the value of $3r$.

Solution Replace r by "6" and simplify the resulting expression:

$$3r = 3 \cdot r$$
$$= 3 \cdot 6$$
$$= 18 \quad Answer$$

In the expression "$5y^2$", 2 is the exponent of the base y. On the other hand, "$(5y)^2$" stands for "$5y \cdot 5y$". In this case, the parentheses show that the base is $5y$. Consider the following examples:

$4 \cdot 3^2 = 4(3 \cdot 3) = 36,$ but $(4 \cdot 3)^2 = (4 \cdot 3)(4 \cdot 3) = 144.$
$yz^3 = y(z \cdot z \cdot z),$ but $(yz)^3 = (yz)(yz)(yz).$
$6 + x^2 = 6 + (x \cdot x),$ but $(6 + x)^2 = (6 + x)(6 + x).$

Oral Exercises

For each expression, state the power, the base of that power, and the exponent. Then read the expression with the power in factored form.

P = power
B = base
E = exponent

Sample $5a^3$ *Solution* Power, a^3; base, a; exponent, 3.
Factored form, $5 \cdot a \cdot a \cdot a$, read "five times a times a times a."

1. $3a^2$ P = a^2 B = a E = 2
2. $2b^3$ P = b^3 B = b E = 3
3. c^4 P = c^4 B = c E = 4
4. $3(xy)^2$ P = $(xy)^2$ B = xy E = 2
5. $(c + d)^3$ P = $(c + d)^3$ B = $c + d$ E = 3
6. $4(a - b)^2$ P = $(a - b)^2$ B = $a - b$ E = 2

Evaluate each expression for the given value of the variable.

7. a^2; $a = 1$ 1
8. x^3; $x = 2$ 8
9. $3b$; $b = 3$ 9
10. $5b$; $b = 4$ 20
11. $(2a)^2$; $a = 3$ 36
12. $2a^2$; $a = 3$ 18
13. $(a - 3)^2$; $a = 5$ 4
14. $b^2 - 4$; $b = 3$ 5

Written Exercises

Write each expression in exponential form.

A 1. $a \cdot a \cdot a$ a^3 2. $c \cdot c \cdot c \cdot c$ c^4 3. b squared b^2 4. x cubed x^3

5. $5 \cdot a \cdot a$ $5a^2$ 6. $7 \cdot b \cdot b \cdot b$ $7b^3$ 7. $8 \cdot a \cdot a \cdot b$ $8a^2b$ 8. $2 \cdot a \cdot c \cdot c \cdot c$ $2ac^3$

9. $12 \cdot c \cdot c \cdot c \cdot d \cdot d$ $12c^3d^2$ 10. $9 \cdot r \cdot r \cdot s \cdot s \cdot s$ $9r^2s^3$ 11. $(a + b)(a + b)(a + b)$ $(a + b)^3$

12. $(x + y)(m - n)(m - n)$ 13. The square of $y - 1$ $(y - 1)^2$ 14. The fifth power of $a + 3$

$\quad (x + y)(m - n)^2$ $(a + 3)^5$

15. The quotient of 32 and the cube of $(c + d)$ **15.** $\dfrac{32}{(c + d)^3}$ **16.** $7(x - 6)^3$

16. The product of 7 and the cube of $x - 6$

17. The fourth power of the sum of x and y **17.** $(x + y)^4$ **18.** $((z + 8)^2)^5$

18. The fifth power of the square of $(z + 8)$

Evaluate each expression for the given value of the variable.

19. a^2; 7   49   20. f^2; 12   144   21. $5x^3$; 1   5   22. $3x^3$; 0   0   23. $2c^2$; 3   18   24. $2a^4$; 2   32

25. $(3a)^2$; 2   36 26. $(4y)^2$; 3   144   27. $(8m)^3$; 1   512 28. $(4p)^4$; 2   29. 2^3x^2; 3   72 30. 3^2y^3; 2   72

$\qquad\qquad\qquad\qquad\qquad\qquad\qquad\qquad\qquad\qquad\qquad$ 4096

31. $(r + 1)^2(r - 1)$; 4   75   32. $3(x + 1)(x + 1)^2$; 5   648   33. $(y + 2)(2y - 3)^2$; 3   45

34. $(3m - 1)(m + 1)^3$; 2   135   35. $2(2p - 3)^2(3p - 1)$; 2   10   36. $3(q + 2)^3(5q - 3)$; 2   1344

In Exercises 37–44, if $a = 3$, $b = 4$, and $c = 5$, evaluate the given expression.

B 37. $\dfrac{a^2 + b^2}{c}$ 5   38. $\dfrac{c^2 - b^2}{a}$ 3   39. $\dfrac{(a^2 + 2b) - 2}{c}$ 3   40. $\dfrac{3b + 4c}{b^2}$ 2

41. $\dfrac{a^3 - 3c}{ab}$ 1   42. $\dfrac{(a^4 + b^2) + 3}{c^2}$ 4   43. $\dfrac{a^2 + bc + 11}{bc}$ 2   44. $\dfrac{ac + b^2 + 5}{a^2}$ 4

Historical Note
The Equality Symbol

Robert Recorde wrote a mathematics book called *Whetstone of Witte*, which was published in London in 1557 (the year before Elizabeth I became queen). In that book "to avoid the tedious repetition of the words 'is equal to'" he used instead the symbol ====.

He chose a pair of line segments of the same length because "no two things could be more equal." With the passage of time, the segments were shortened until the symbol became =.

1-4 Order of Operations

OBJECTIVE To learn how to evaluate expressions involving powers and other operations.

What does the expression

$$3 \times 8 + 3^2$$

mean? You might insert grouping symbols to make it mean

$$(3 \times 8) + 3^2, \text{ or else}$$
$$3 \times (8 + 3^2), \text{ or even}$$
$$3 \times (8 + 3)^2.$$

When grouping symbols have been omitted, you take the following steps.

> To simplify numerical expressions:
>
> 1. Simplify the names of powers.
>
> 2. Then simplify the names of products and quotients in order from left to right.
>
> 3. Then simplify the names of sums and differences in order from left to right.

Example If $m = 3$ and $k = 1$, evaluate $25k^3 - 2m^2 \div 6$.

Solution $25k^3 - 2m^2 \div 6$

$$25 \cdot 1^3 - 2 \cdot 3^2 \div 6$$

(1) $= \underline{25 \cdot 1} - \underline{2 \cdot 9} \div 6$

(2) $= 25 - \underline{18 \div 6}$

     $= 25 - 3$

(3) $= 22$ *Answer*

Oral Exercises

Simplify each expression.

1. $12 - 6 - 3$ 3
2. $25 - 1 - 0$ 24
3. $82 \div 2 \div 41$ 1
4. $30 \div 2 \div 3$ 5
5. $8 - 6 \cdot 0$ 8
6. $8 \cdot 2 + 4$ 20
7. $16 \div 8 \cdot 7$ 14
8. $10 \cdot 4 \div 10$ 4
9. $15 - 2^2 + 4 \cdot 3$ 23
10. $20 \div 4 + 2^3$ 13
11. $0 \div 3^2 \div 2$ 0
12. $63 \cdot 2 \cdot 0 + 5$ 5

Written Exercises

Simplify each expression.

A
1. $2 + 4 + 6 \div 2 - 1$ 8
2. $2 + (4 + 6) \div 2 - 1$ 6
3. $(2 + 4 + 6) \div 2 - 1$ 5
4. $(2 + 4 + 6) \div (2 - 1)$ 12
5. $8 + 2 - (2 - 1)$ 9
6. $8 + 2 - 2 + 1$ 9
7. $3 \cdot 2^2 - 5 \cdot 1 - 4$ 3
8. $6 \cdot 3 - 1^2 + 3^2$ 26
9. $(6^2 - 14 + 3) \div (5^2 + 0)$ 1
10. $4^3 \div (2^2 + 4 - 6)$ 32
11. $\dfrac{19 \cdot 3 - 10 \cdot 3}{2^2 + 5}$ 3
12. $\dfrac{9^2 - 11}{(3 + 4) \cdot 10}$ 1

Evaluate each expression if $a = 2$ and $b = 3$.

13. $a^2 + 2ab + b^2$ 25
14. $(a + b)^2$ 25
15. $(a + b + 1)/2$ 3
16. $(a + 2b)/2$ 4
17. $\dfrac{3a + 2b}{6}$ 2
18. $3a \div 6 + 2b \div 6$ 2

Simplify each expression.

B
19. $6(9 - 4) \div 3 - 1$ 9
20. $7(6 + 2) - 48 \div 12$ 52
21. $11 \times 6 \div 3 \cdot 2 \div 11$ 4
22. $25 \div 5 \cdot 6 - 15 - 6$ 9
23. $3^5 \div 3^2 \div 3^2 \div 3$ 1
24. $2^4 - 2^2 \div 2^2 - 2$ 13
25. $\dfrac{33 - 5(4 - 3)}{2 \cdot 6 + 2}$ 2
26. $\dfrac{5(3 + 4) - 3}{2 \cdot 5 - 2}$ 4
27. $\dfrac{36 - 5 + 6 \div 2}{6 \div 3}$ 17
28. $\dfrac{10(5 - 2) - 25}{6 - 1}$ 1
29. $\dfrac{2^2 + 3 - 12 \div 2}{3^2 - 2^3}$ 1
30. $\dfrac{5^2 - 2 \cdot 2^2 - 6 \div 6}{3^2 - 1}$ 2

Evaluate each expression if $a = 3$, $b = 2$, $c = 1$.

31. $abc - c^2$ 5
32. $a^2 + b^2 + c^2$ 14
33. $a + b \div c$ 5
34. $2a \div b \div c$ 3
35. $a^2b \div 3c$ 6
36. $3b^2c \div ab$ 2

1-5 Formulas from Geometry

> **OBJECTIVE** To learn how to evaluate formulas, particularly geometric formulas.

Formulas express relationships between quantities such as physical or other measurements. They contain variable expressions that can be evaluated for given values of the variables.

> The **perimeter,** *P*, of a geometric figure is the distance around it.
>
> The **area,** *A*, of a region is the number of unit squares it contains.
>
> The **volume,** *V*, of a solid is the number of unit cubes it contains.
>
> Perimeter is 20.
> Area is 24.
> Volume is 30.

The perimeter of a circle is given a special name, **circumference,** *C*, and

$$C = \pi d,$$

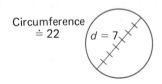

Circumference ≐ 22   *d* = 7

where π stands for a number that *is approximately equal to* ($\doteq$) $\frac{22}{7}$ and *d* is the measure of the *diameter*.

Written Exercises

Using the values and formulas given, find the perimeter of each figure.

Sample $C = 2\pi r$, *r* is the measure of the *radius*. $r = 14$

Solution   Since $d = 2r$, the formulas $C = \pi d$ and $C = 2\pi r$ are equivalent.

$C = 2\pi r$ $C \doteq 2 \cdot \dfrac{22}{7} \cdot 14 = 88$ *Answer*

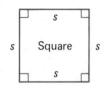

s Square s

s

$P = 4s$

A
1. $s = 3$ 12
2. $s = 2$ 8

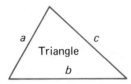

a c Triangle

b

$P = a + b + c$

3. $a = 2, b = 5, c = 4$ 11
4. $a = 3, b = 4, c = 5$ 12

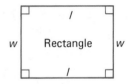

l

w Rectangle w

l

$P = 2l + 2w$

5. $l = 4, w = 3$ 14
6. $l = 5, w = 4$ 18

f Parallelogram

b

$P = 2b + 2f$

7. $b = 3, f = 2$ 10
8. $b = 4, f = 1$ 10

m

General
quadrilateral n

q

p

$P = p + q + m + n$

9. $p = 2, q = 1, m = 2, n = 1$ 6
10. $p = 3, q = 2, m = 1, n = 2$ 8

d

$C = \pi d$

11. $d = 21$ 66
12. $d = 35$ 110

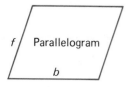

r

$P = \pi r$

13. $r = 14$ 44
14. $r = 28$ 88

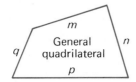

t

s s

t

$P = 2s + t + \dfrac{1}{2}\pi t$

15. $s = 6, t = 7$ 30
16. $s = 10, t = 14$ 56

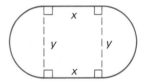

x

y y

x

$P = 2x + \pi y$

17. $x = 3, y = 7$ 28
18. $x = 8, y = 14$ 60

Using the values and formulas given, find the area of the region bounded
by each figure.

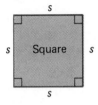

s

s Square s

s

$A = s^2$

19. $s = 8$ 64
20. $s = 6$ 36

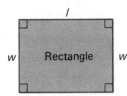

l

w Rectangle w

l

$A = lw$

21. $l = 4, w = 3$ 12
22. $l = 6, w = 4$ 24

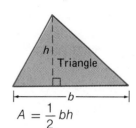

h Triangle

b

$A = \dfrac{1}{2}bh$

23. $b = 11, h = 8$ 44
24. $b = 12, h = 7$ 42

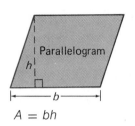

Parallelogram

$$A = bh$$

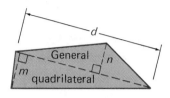

General quadrilateral

$$A = \frac{1}{2}d(m + n)$$

$$A = \pi r^2$$

25. $b = 10, h = 6$ 60   27. $d = 10, m = 6, n = 5$ 55   29. $r = 7$ 154
26. $b = 12, h = 5$ 60   28. $d = 14, m = 4, n = 3$ 49   30. $r = 14$ 616

Using the values and formulas given, find the volume of each solid.

Cube

Rectangular solid

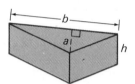

$$V = s^3$$

$$V = lwh$$

$$V = \frac{1}{2}abh$$

31. $s = 3$ 27   33. $l = 5, w = 3, h = 1$ 15   35. $a = 6, b = 5, h = 2$ 30
32. $s = 4$ 64   34. $l = 6, w = 2, h = 3$ 36   36. $a = 7, b = 10, h = 3$ 105

Cylinder

$$V = s^2h$$

$$V = \pi r^2h$$

$$V = \pi r^3$$

37. $s = 5, h = 4$ 100   39. $r = 7, h = 11$ 1694   41. $r = 14$ 8624
38. $s = 6, h = 10$ 360   40. $r = 5, h = 14$ 1100   42. $r = 7$ 1078

Since perimeter is a linear measure, it is measured in the same units as the given lengths.

B 43. Find the perimeter of a square if each side measures 10 centimeters.   40 cm

44. Find the circumference of a circle if the diameter measures 14 meters.   44 m

45. Find the perimeter of a rectangle if the length is 12 meters and the width is 8 meters.   40 m

46. Find the perimeter of a triangle if the sides measure 8 centimeters, 10 centimeters, and 12 centimeters.   30 cm

Area is measured in square units. Volume is measured in cubic units.

Sample Find the volume of a cube if each edge measures 3 meters.

Solution $V = s^3$; $s = 3$
$V = 3 \cdot 3 \cdot 3 = 27$
The volume is 27 cubic meters. *Answer*

47. Find the area of a rectangle if the length is 6 centimeters and the width is 4 centimeters. **24 cm²**

48. Find the area of a circle if the radius measures 7 meters. **154 m²**

49. Find the volume of a rectangular solid that is 10 centimeters long, 8 centimeters wide, and 2 centimeters high. **160 cm³**

50. Find the volume of a cylinder with radius measuring 7 centimeters and height 10 centimeters. **1540 cm³**

Write a formula for the perimeter of each of these figures.

C 51.

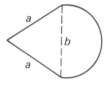

$P = 2a + \frac{1}{2}\pi b$

52.

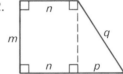

$P = m + 2n + p + q$

Biographical Note
Maria and Henry Mitchell

Maria and Henry Mitchell, two of the ten children in a family, were born and grew up on the island of Nantucket, located off the southern coast of Massachusetts. Their father, William, was interested in navigation and astronomy and encouraged his children to explore the skies with him.

Maria (1818–1889) did excellent work in arithmetic and was able to help her father with astronomical calculations. She went on to study and explore on her own. In 1847 she discovered a new comet, for which she was awarded a gold medal by the King of Denmark. Some years later, Matthew Vassar invited her to be the first professor of astronomy at his new college at Poughkeepsie, New York.

Henry (1830–1902) went into the Coast Survey and studied the tides. He was considered to be the leading hydrographer in America in his day.

★ *Self-Test 2*

Be sure that you understand these terms:

factor (p. 7)	power (p. 7)	base (p. 7)
exponent (p. 7)	factored form (p. 8)	exponential form (p. 8)
formula (p. 12)	perimeter (p. 12)	area (p. 12)
volume (p. 12)	circumference (p. 12)	

Be sure that you understand these symbols:

π (p. 12) $\doteq$ (p. 12)

1. Write $2 \cdot 2 \cdot a \cdot a \cdot a$ in exponential form.   Objective 1-3, p. 7

Evaluate if $x = 3$, $y = 4$, $z = 2$:

2. $xy \div 3 + 7$ 3. $3y \div z \div x$ Objective 1-4, p. 10

4. Find the perimeter and the area of a square with each side measuring   Objective 1-5, p. 12
8 centimeters.

Check your answers with those printed at the back of the book.

Just for Fun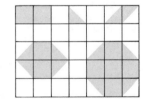

Some overall patterns can be made by drawing geometric shapes on squared paper. Some possible units that can be used repeatedly are shown at the right. Some ways of fitting them together are shown below. Such overall, repetitive patterns are called **tessellations**. Now make up some patterns of your own.

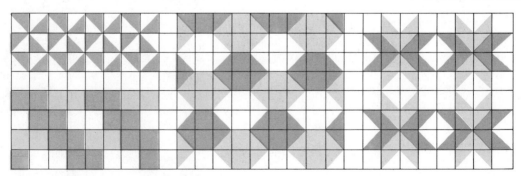

Solving Simple Equations and Problems

1-6 Equations and Inequalities

OBJECTIVE To learn how to find solution sets of open sentences.

Here are three *equations:*

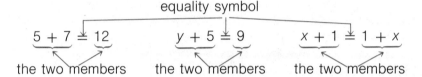

$$5 + 7 \overset{=}{=} 12 \qquad y + 5 \overset{=}{=} 9 \qquad x + 1 \overset{=}{=} 1 + x$$

the two members   the two members   the two members

> An **equation** is formed by placing an equality symbol between two numerical or variable expressions, called the **members** of the equation.

Example 1 If

$y \in \{2, 4, 6\}$ (read "y is a **member of** or **belongs to** the set whose members are two, four, and six"),

find any values that convert $y + 5 = 9$ into a true statement.

Solution In the given equation, replace y by each of its values:

$$\begin{aligned} y + 5 &= 9 \\ 2 + 5 &= 9 \quad \text{False} \\ 4 + 5 &= 9 \quad \text{True} \\ 6 + 5 &= 9 \quad \text{False} \end{aligned}$$

∴ (read "therefore") the required value is 4.   *Answer*

You can change the false statement "$2 + 5 = 9$" to a true statement by using the "not" symbol "/" together with the symbol "$=$". Thus,

$2 + 5 \neq 9$ (read, "two plus five **is not equal to** nine")

The sign $\neq$ is called an **inequality symbol**.

Placing an inequality symbol between two numerical or variable expressions produces an **inequality** having the joined expressions as its members.

Equations and inequalities containing variables are called open sentences. An open sentence is a pattern for the different statements, which you obtain by replacing each variable by the names for the different values in the replacement set of the variable. Some of these statements may be true. Some may be false.

Any value of a variable that converts an open sentence into a true statement is called a **solution** or **root** of the sentence, and is said to **satisfy** the sentence.

The set of all solutions of a sentence from a given domain of the variable is called the solution set of the sentence *over* that domain. Finding the solution set is called solving the sentence.

Example 2 If $a \in \{2, 3, 5, 7, 11\}$, what is the solution set of

$18 - a \neq 11$?

Solution Replace a by each of its values:

$18 - a \neq 11$
$18 - 2 \neq 11$ True
$18 - 3 \neq 11$ True
$18 - 5 \neq 11$ True
$18 - 7 \neq 11$ False
$18 - 11 \neq 11$ True

∴ the solution set is $\{2, 3, 5, 11\}$. *Answer*

Oral Exercises

If $x \in \{1, 2, 3, 4, 5\}$, is there a value of x that converts the open sentence into a true statement? Which value(s)?

1. $x + 1 = 4$ yes; 3
2. $x - 1 = 4$ yes; 5
3. $2x = 4$ yes; 2
4. $x \div 2 = 2$ yes; 4
5. $x + 2 \neq 6$ yes; 1, 2, 3, 5
6. $x - 3 \neq 2$ yes; 1, 2, 3, 4
7. $x + 1 = 7$ no
8. $2x = 12$ no

Written Exercises

If $x \in \{1, 2, 3, 4, 5, 6\}$, write the solution set of each open sentence.

A
1. $x + 2 = 8$ $\{6\}$
2. $3 + x = 7$ $\{4\}$
3. $12 \div x = 4$ $\{3\}$
4. $5x = 15$ $\{3\}$
5. $6 - x = 1$ $\{5\}$
6. $x - 2 = 4$ $\{6\}$
7. $4x = 8$ $\{2\}$
8. $x \div 2 = 3$ $\{6\}$
9. $x + 3 \neq 4$
   $\{2, 3, 4, 5, 6\}$
10. $2x \neq 8$
    $\{1, 2, 3, 5, 6\}$
11. $x^2 = 4$ $\{2\}$
12. $x^3 \neq 8$
    $\{1, 3, 4, 5, 6\}$

B
13. $2x + 1 = 9$ $\{4\}$
14. $3x - 1 = 14$ $\{5\}$
15. $2x + 3 \neq 7$
    $\{1, 3, 4, 5, 6\}$
16. $13 - 2x \neq 3$
    $\{1, 2, 3, 4, 6\}$

Historical Note
Why We Call It "Algebra"

At the court of Caliph al-Mamun in ninth-century Baghdad, there were many scholars. One of these was Muhammad ibn Musa al-Khwarizmi, who was a great mathematician and astronomer. He wrote a mathematical treatise with the title "hisab al-jabr wa'l muqabalah," which means "the science of reduction and comparison."

When the Moors moved into Spain, they took their books with them. In the twelfth century this mathematics book was translated into Latin, the common language of European scholars. As it was studied throughout Europe, the word "al-jabr" in its title grew into "algebra," which is what we call this branch of mathematics today.

The photograph at the right shows a courtyard of the Alhambra, a palace built by the Moors in Spain.

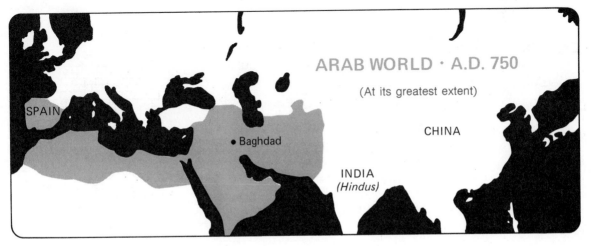

SPAIN

ARAB WORLD · A.D. 750

(At its greatest extent)

• Baghdad

CHINA

INDIA
(Hindus)

1-7 Converting Words into Symbols

> **OBJECTIVE** To learn how to convert words into symbols.

In applying algebra, you often convert word phrases into numerical or variable expressions and word sentences into equations.

Example 1 Convert this word sentence into an equation: The sum of the number *n* and three is eight.

Solution $n + 3 = 8$ *Answer*

Example 2 Convert this word sentence into an equation: The sum of four and the product three times the number *x* is equal to nineteen.

Solution $4 + 3x = 19$ *Answer*

Example 3 below shows how you can choose a variable to use in representing numbers (part a) and then write an equation based on the additional information (part b).

Example 3 The Brodys have a wall at the back of their lot. They want to fence off a space for a rectangular garden 8 meters (m) long.

   a. Choose a variable for the width.

   b. The Brodys have 14 m of fencing on hand and plan to use all of it. Write an equation.

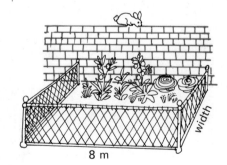

Solution

   a. Let *w* meters = width. *Answer*

   b. $2w + 8 = 14$ *Answer*

Oral Exercises

Convert each word expression into a variable expression.
Use *n* to represent the given number.

Sample   Ten more than the number   *Solution* $10 + n$ (or $n + 10$)   *Answer*

1. Twice the number $2n$

2. Two less than the number $n - 2$

3. Three greater than the number $n + 3$

4. The product of seven and the number $7n$

5. Four less than twice the number $2n - 4$

6. Three greater than three times the number $3n + 3$

Convert each sentence into an equation. Use *x* to represent the number.

7. Three more than the number is twenty-one. $x + 3 = 21$

8. Four less than the number is seven. $x - 4 = 7$

9. The sum of six and three times the number is twelve. $6 + 3x = 12$

10. If three is subtracted from four times the number, the difference is nine. $4x - 3 = 9$

Written Exercises

For each of the following:
a. Choose a variable to represent the number indicated.
b. Write an equation.

A   1. The perimeter of a square is 20. (Measure of a side) s; $4s = 20$

2. The three sides of a triangle have equal lengths, and the perimeter is 24. (Measure of a side) s; $3s = 24$

3. The circumference of a circle is 35. (Measure of the radius) r; $2\pi r = 35$

4. The perimeter of a square is 48. (Measure of a side) s; $4s = 48$

5. Six cans of vegetables cost $1.20. (Cost of 1 can) c; $6c = 1.20$

6. A dozen pencils cost $2.40. (Cost of 1 pencil) c; $12c = 2.40$

7. Senior citizens were given a dollar off the admission price for an amateur play. Anne Polsky, a senior citizen, paid $1.50. (Admission price) p; $1.50 = p - 1.00$

8. A store charges 75¢ for postage and handling on a coat ordered by mail. Josefa sent a check for $30.75. (Price of the coat) p; $30.75 = p + .75$

B   9. Jake and Rose took a bus to Fernwood and then a taxi to their aunt's house. They spent $2 for the taxi and had $4 left from the $10 they had started out with. (Single bus fare) f; $2f + 2 = 10 - 4$

10. Carol and Mark O'Brien went to a movie and paid $2 for parking. They had dinner, for which the total cost was $8. They had $6 left from a $20 bill. (Price of a single movie ticket) p; $2p + 2 + 8 = 20 - 6$

1-8 Using Equations to Solve Problems

> **OBJECTIVE** To learn a method for solving problems.

In a "word problem" you are told how certain numbers relate to one another. If you can convert the relationship into an equation, then you can solve the problem by solving the equation.

We illustrate the method first with a very simple "problem."

Example 1 An average tangerine contains 35 calories, which is 7 times as many as a large stalk of celery. How many calories are in the celery stalk?

Solution

Step 1. Read the problem carefully. What numbers are asked for?	This problem asks for the number of calories in the stalk of celery.
Step 2. Choose a variable. Use it to represent the number(s) asked for and other given facts.	Let n = the number of calories in the celery stalk. Then $7n$ = the number of calories in the tangerine.
Step 3. Write an equation based on the given facts.	The number of calories in the tangerine is 35. $$7n \quad\quad = 35$$
Step 4. Solve the equation.	The one and only number whose product with 7 is 35 is 5: $$n = 5$$
Step 5. Check your results with the words of the problem.	Is the number of calories in the tangerine (35) seven times the number in the celery stalk (5)? $35 \overset{?}{=} 7 \cdot 5$ $35 = 35 \checkmark$

∴ there are 5 calories in the celery stalk. *Answer*

Diagrams picturing the facts of a problem may help you to see relationships. Notice how a diagram helps in the next example.

Example 2   Theresa practices diving from a platform that is 10 meters above the water. Michael dives from a springboard. If the height of the platform is 1 meter more than 3 times the height of the springboard, what is the height of the springboard?

Solution

Step 1   The problem asks for the number of meters in the height of the springboard.

Step 2   Let x = the number of meters in the height of the spring-board.
Then $1 + 3x$ = the number of meters in the height of the platform.

Step 3   The height of the platform is 10 meters.

$$1 + 3x = 10$$

Step 4   The diagram at the right shows that $3x = 9$.
The one and only number whose product with 3 is 9 is 3.

Step 5   Checking the result of Step 4 is left to you. $1 + 3x = 1 + 3 \cdot 3$
$= 1 + 9 = 10 \checkmark$
∴ the height of the springboard is 3 meters.   *Answer*

The five steps used to solve the problems in Examples 1 and 2 form a plan that usually helps in solving any word problem.

Plan for Solving a Word Problem

Step 1. Read the problem carefully and decide what numbers are asked for. A sketch may be helpful.

Step 2. Choose a variable and, with the given facts, use it to represent the number(s) asked for.

Step 3. Write an equation based on the given facts.

Step 4. Solve the equation and find the required numbers.

Step 5. Check your results with the words of the problem.

Written Exercises

Write out the five steps for each of these problems.

A 1. The Bears scored twice as many points as the Bulls. If the Bears scored 28 points, how many points did the Bulls score? **14 points**

2. Kenneth, Linda, Rita, and Manuel are on the committee to redecorate the Teen Center. They have found a remnant of adhesive-backed paper 3 meters (300 centimeters) long. They plan to decorate the walls with panels 60 centimeters long. How many panels can they make? **5 panels**

3. Opal said, "It takes me 20 minutes to walk to school." Philip said, "It takes me 5 minutes less." How long does it take Philip to walk to school? **15 minutes**

4. The charge for a scarf gift-wrapped was $4.25. The price of the scarf was $3.50. How much did the gift-wrapping cost? **$.75**

5. Lucia's father weighs 20 kilograms less than twice what Lucia weighs. If her father weighs 100 kilograms, how much does Lucia weigh? **60 kilograms**

6. The total height of the Sutherland Falls in New Zealand is 580 meters. That is 20 meters less than ten times the approximate height of Niagara Falls (between New York State and Ontario, Canada). What is the approximate height of Niagara Falls? **60 meters**

Metric System
Measures of Length

In this book, metric measures of length are used. The metric system originated in France in the 1790's. It is easy to use because the units are related to each other by powers of ten.

The base unit of length is the **meter**, which is a little longer than a yard. For longer distance a **kilometer** is used:

> 1 kilometer (km) = 1000 meters (m)

A kilometer is shorter than a mile:

> 100 kilometers = about 62 miles

For shorter distances, a **centimeter** is used:

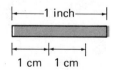

> 100 centimeters (cm) = 1 meter

About 2.5 centimeters make up an inch.

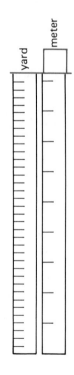

★ *Self-Test 3*

Be sure that you understand these terms:

equation (p. 17)
inequality (p. 18)
root (p. 18)
solving (p. 18)

member of an equation (p. 17)
open sentence (p. 18)
satisfy (p. 18)

member of a set (p. 17)
solution (p. 18)
solution set (p. 18)

Be sure that you understand these symbols:

$\in$ (p. 17) $\therefore$ (p. 17) $\neq$ (p. 17)

If $d \in \{1, 2, 5, 10\}$, find the solution set of:

1. $2d \neq 10$ 2. $d + 3 = 8$ Objective 1-6, p. 17

3. Convert this word sentence into an equation: If three is subtracted from   Objective 1-7, p. 20
the number n, the difference is seven.

4. Use the 5-step method to solve this problem: Al scored twice as many   Objective 1-8, p. 22
points as Sal. If Al scored 16 points, how many points did Sal score?

Check your answers with those printed at the back of the book.

Career Note
Computer Service Technician

Computer service technicians install, repair, and service computer systems. This means that such technicians must be familiar with how computer systems work. They must be able to diagnose failures, using such instruments as voltmeters, ohmmeters, and oscilloscopes.

The educational requirements are one to two years of training after high school with emphasis on electronics or electrical engineering. High school courses should include mathematics and physics; electronics and computer programming are also helpful. Hobbies which involve electronics, such as building radios, can provide a good background for a career in this field.

Since computer technology is changing rapidly from year to year, technicians use technical journals and repair manuals to keep up with new maintenance procedures.

Computer Activity

Throughout the book there will be optional Computer Activities suggesting ways in which you may broaden your experiences by using a computer.

If you have access to a computer that will accept BASIC, type in the following program and RUN it to see how a computer handles grouping symbols. [Remember to press the RETURN key after each line or command that you type.]

```
10  PRINT  (((2*9+3)*9+4)*9+5)*9+7  [* means "times"]
20  END
```

Compute the result by hand and check your answer against the one found by the computer. The multiplication symbol * can *never* be omitted.

You can use the computer to evaluate expressions. For example, try this program:

```
10  LET R=1
20  LET S=2
30  LET T=3
40  LET W=10
50  LET X=1
60  LET Y=0
70  PRINT (S*T+4)/(W-Y)
80  END
```

The result will be 1, the answer to the sample on page 6. Notice that in BASIC when a fraction bar is replaced by /, its grouping function must be taken care of by using parentheses.

By changing line 70, you can check the results of any of the Written Exercises on page 6. For example, by changing line 70 to

```
70  PRINT X*Y
```

you can check the result of Exercise 1.

To investigate how the computer handles operations when no grouping symbols are used, try this program:

```
10  LET X=9
20  PRINT 2*X↑4+3*X↑3+4*X↑2+5*X+7  [↑ means "to the power"]
30  END
```

Does the computer follow the rules for order of operations given on page 10? Compare this result with the one you found in the first program above.

Chapter Summary

1. The language of algebra consists of numerals, variables, expressions, and symbols connecting them.
2. A variable expression is evaluated by replacing each variable with a numeral for the value of the variable and simplifying the resulting numerical expression.
3. Grouping symbols should be used to show the order in which operations are to be performed to simplify an expression. If no grouping symbols are shown, you follow the steps listed on page 10.
4. A method of solving a problem is to set up an equation from the facts given and then solve the equation.

Chapter Test

1-1   1. Simplify $\dfrac{7(10 + 2)}{6}$.   14

1-2   2. If $x = 2$ and $y = 3$, evaluate $\dfrac{xy + 4}{5}$.   2

1-3   3. Write $11a^2b^3$ in factored form. $11 \cdot a \cdot a \cdot b \cdot b \cdot b$

4. Write $p \cdot p \cdot p \cdot p \cdot q \cdot q$ in exponential form. p^4q^2

1-4   5. If $d = 2$ and $e = 1$, evaluate $4d^2 + 3e^3$.   19

1-5   6. A rectangle is 10 centimeters long and 5 centimeters wide. Find:
a. its perimeter 30 cm b. its area   50 cm²

If $y \in \{2, 3, 5, 11\}$ find the solution set of:

1-6   7. $2y + 1 = 11$ {5}   8. $y + 8 \neq 11$ {2, 5, 11}

1-7   9. Convert this word sentence into an equation: Six more than twice the number w is 14. $2w + 6 = 14$

1-8   10. Use the 5-step method to solve this problem: An average serving of vanilla ice cream contains three times as many calories as a small orange. If the serving of ice cream contains 150 calories, how many calories are in the orange?   50 calories

Programmed Chapter Review

1-1   1. The value of the expression $2(4 + 3)$ is __?__ .   14

   2. ( ) and [ ] are called __?__ symbols.   grouping

1-2   3. The set of values that a variable may represent is called   domain
        the __?__ or the __?__ set.   replacement

   4. Evaluating an expression means to find its __?__ .   value

1-3   5. In the expression a^m, the number represented by a is called   base
        the __?__ , and the number represented by m is called the __?__ .   exponent

   6. $2 \cdot 3^3 \cdot 5^2 = $ __?__   1350

1-4   7. $2 \cdot 3 + 4 \cdot 2 - 3 \cdot 4 = $ __?__   2

1-5   8. If $l = 8$ and $w = 3$, then $A = lw = $ __?__ and $P = 2l + 2w = $ 24
        __?__ .   22

1-6   9. In $x + 2 = 7$, "$x + 2$" is called a __?__ of the equation.   member

   10. If $y = 3$ and $y + 2 = 5$, then 3 is a __?__ or a __?__ of the   root, solution
       equation.

1-7 11. "Six more than a number is 8" in symbols is "__?__ = 8." $n + 6$

1-8 12. The first step in solving a problem is to read it and de-   what numbers are
         cide __?__ .   asked for

   13. After variables have been chosen, they are used to write an __?__ .   equation

   14. To solve the problem, you __?__ the equation.   solve

Looking
Ahead

Section 1–8 has given you a sample of some of the things that you
can do with algebra. You prepared to solve a problem by writing
an equation. Then you had to solve the equation.

Up to now, you have had to solve an equation by trying various
values of the variable until you found one that made a true statement. You surely realize that there must be a better way!

The next few chapters will help you to develop a systematic
method for solving equations and so make it easier for you to solve
problems.

Maintaining Skills

Remember how?
```
   342
  1617
    21
 + 305
  2285
```

Now practice:

1.
```
   314
    21
  1623
 + 150
  2108
```

2.
```
   625
  1421
  3012
 + 105
  5163
```

3.
```
   723
    41
  3516
 + 812
  5092
```

4.
```
  6132
   157
    91
 +   6
  6386
```

5.
```
     4
   203
  1027
 +6143
  7377
```

6.
```
  2021
   103
  2005
 + 892
  5021
```

Remember how?
```
  6124
 -3215
  2909
```

Now practice:

7.
```
  3165
 -2154
  1011
```

8.
```
  3829
 -1418
  2411
```

9.
```
  6251
 -3143
  3108
```

10.
```
  8021
 -3131
  4890
```

11.
```
  2146
 -1387
   759
```

12.
```
  6003
 -5914
    89
```

Remember how?
```
   214
  x 35
  1070
   642
  7490
```

Now practice:

13.
```
   132
  x 21
  2772
```

14.
```
   234
  x 42
  9828
```

15.
```
  3126
  x 53
165,678
```

16.
```
  2159
  x 67
144,653
```

17.
```
     8123
     x 304
2,469,392
```

18.
```
     6712
     x 278
1,865,936
```

Remember how?
```
        124
  26)3224
        26
        62
        52
       104
       104
         0
```

Now practice:

19.
```
      28
 31)868
```

20.
```
        62
 53)3286
```

21.
```
        54
 37)1998
```

22.
```
         126
 62)7812
```

23.
```
         243
 85)20655
```

24.
```
          1005
 71)71355
```

29

Addition and Subtraction

Fine Arts   Weaving is an art among the Navajo Indians of Arizona and New Mexico. They are known for the bold geometric designs in their rugs and blankets.

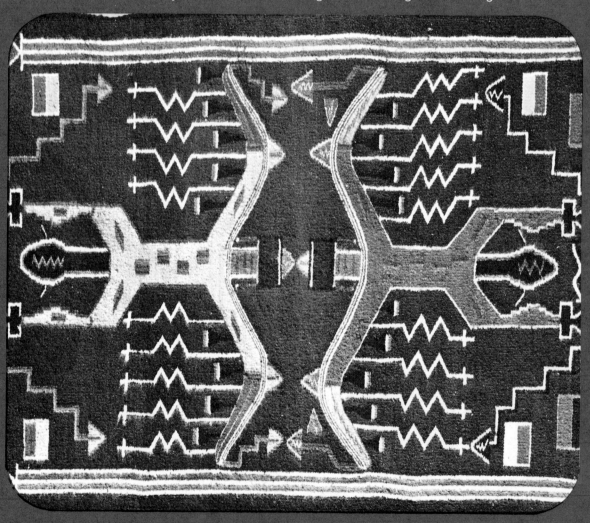

2

Adding Real Numbers

2-1 Graphing Sets of Real Numbers

OBJECTIVE To learn how to graph sets of real numbers on a number line and how to read such graphs.

To construct a number line:

1. Choose a starting point on a line, and label it "0" (zero). This point is called the **origin**.

2. Choose a second point on the line, and label it "1" (one). The distance between "0" and "1" is the **unit distance**. The direction from "0" to "1" is the **positive direction**. (If the line is horizontal, the positive direction is usually chosen to the right.)

3. Mark off unit distances on the line beyond "1," labeling them

$$2, 3, 4, 5, \ldots$$

and on the other side of "0" (in the **negative direction**), labeling them

$$^-1, ^-2, ^-3, ^-4, \ldots$$

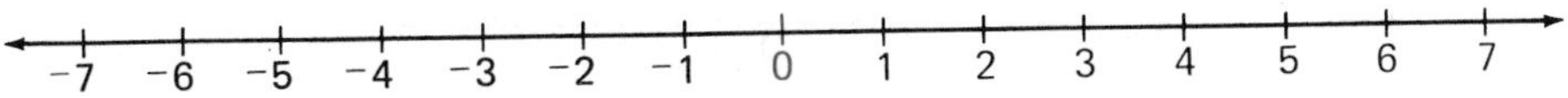

Figure 2-1

31

You read "⁻1" as "negative one." You usually read "1" as "one." You may also read "1" as "positive one," and you may write it as "⁺1."

Each point on a number line is called the **graph** of the number assigned to it, and the assigned number is called the **coordinate** of the point.

You can use number lines to graph sets of numbers:

{the **natural (counting) numbers**} or {1, 2, 3, 4, . . .} has the graph:

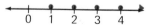

{the **whole numbers**} or {0, 1, 2, 3, . . .} has the graph:

{the **integers**} or {. . . , ⁻3, ⁻2, ⁻1, 0, 1, 2, 3, . . .} has the graph:

The large colored arrowheads show that the graphs can be extended indefinitely in the direction the arrowheads point.

You can see from Figure 2-1 that there are many points on a number line that are not paired with *the positive or negative integers or 0.* Do these points also have coordinates? The answer to this question is *yes.* Each point has a coordinate called a **real number.** In fact, in working with the number line, you take for granted that:

> 1. There is exactly one point on a number line paired with any real number.
>
> 2. There is exactly one real number paired with any given point on a number line.

The graph of the **set of real numbers** is the entire number line:

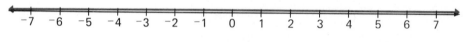

Figure 2-2

Such a pairing of points and numbers is an example of a **one-to-one correspondence.** Each member of one set (numbers) is paired with one and only one member of the other set (points), and each member of the second set (points) is paired with one and only one member of the first set (numbers).

Example 1 Graph {the first five natural numbers}.

Solution

Example 2 Graph $\{-3, -1, 0, \frac{1}{2}, 1, 2\}$.

Solution

Example 3 Name the set represented by this graph.

Solution $\{-2, 1, 4, 5\}$

Oral Exercises

Exercises 1–24 refer to the number line below.

Name the point that is the graph of the given number.

Sample 1 -4 *Solution* The graph is point *C*.

1. 2 *I*	2. 5 *L*	3. -1 *F*	4. -4 *C*	5. 6 *M*	6. -6 *A*
7. -3 *D*	8. 0 *G*	9. -5 *B*	10. 4 *K*	11. 1 *H*	12. -2 *E*

State the coordinate of the given point.

Sample 2 *E*   *Solution* The coordinate is -2.

13. *D* -3	14. *J* 3	15. *G* 0	16. *B* -5	17. *C* -4	18. *F* -1
19. *N* 7	20. *K* 4	21. *H* 1	22. *L* 5	23. *A* -6	24. *E* -2

Written Exercises

Name the set represented by each graph.

A 1. 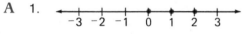 {0, 1, 2} 2. 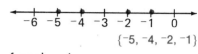 {⁻2, ⁻1, 0

3. 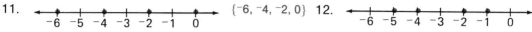 {⁻1, 1, 3} 4. 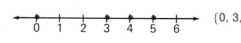 {⁻3, ⁻1, ⁻1

5. {⁻3, ⁻2, 0} 6. {⁻1, 0, 3}

7. {⁻3, ⁻1, 1} 8. {⁻2, 0, 1,

9. {1, 2, 4, 6} 10. {0, 3, 4,

11. {⁻6, ⁻4, ⁻2, 0} 12.

{⁻5, ⁻4, ⁻2, ⁻1}

List the letters for the points that would make a graph of each set.

P   Q   R   S   T   U M V   W   X N Y   Z
⁻6 ⁻5 ⁻4 ⁻3 ⁻2 ⁻1   0   1   2   3   4

13. {1, 3, 4} *W, Y, Z* 14. {⁻5, ⁻3, ⁻1} *Q, S, U* 15. {0, ⁻2, ⁻4} *V, T, R* 16. {0, 1, 2} *V, W, X*

17. {⁻6, ⁻5, ⁻4} *P, Q, R* 18. {⁻2, ⁻1, 0} *T, U, V* 19. {⁻1, 1, 3} *U, W, Y* 20. {⁻4, 0, 4} *R, V, Z*

Graph on a number line. Draw a separate line for each exercise.

B 21. {3, 8, 12} 22. {⁻4, ⁻1, 2} 23. {2, 4, 6, 8, . . .} 24. {1, 4, 7, 10, . . .}

Historical Note
Plus and Minus

You have used + and − in addition and subtraction since your earliest work in arithmetic. These symbols are the result of experimentation over several centuries with various abbreviations and symbols and came into common use in Europe at about the time Columbus discovered America. Robert Recorde used them along with his equality symbol in 1557 (see page 9).

During the nineteenth century, as mathematicians turned to the foundations of algebra, they tried various ways of differentiating between "plus and minus" and "positive and negative." At about the beginning of the twentieth century, the small raised symbols, ⁺ for positive and ⁻ for negative, that are used in this book came into general use in America.

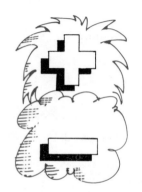

2-2 Addition on the Number Line

> **OBJECTIVE** To learn how to add real numbers, using the number line as a guide.

You can use arrows along a number line to help you find the sum of two real numbers. Positive numbers are represented by arrows in the positive direction (to the right). For example, you can represent the sum of 4 and 5 as pictured in Figure 2-3.

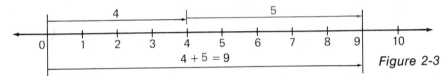

Figure 2-3

Arrows pointing in the negative direction (to the left) represent negative numbers. Thus, to represent ⁻6 + 2, you move 6 units to the left from the origin and then move 2 units to the right as shown in Figure 2-4.

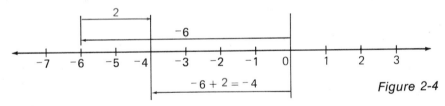

Figure 2-4

Now look at Figure 2-5. Do you see that it pictures the sum

$$2 + {}^-6 = {}^-4?$$

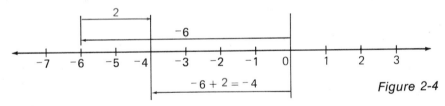

Figure 2-5

Together, Figures 2-4 and 2-5 illustrate the fact that

$${}^-6 + 2 = 2 + {}^-6.$$

You can use the method illustrated in Figures 2-4 and 2-5 to find the sum of any two real numbers.

Can you visualize $^-4 + 0$ on the number line? Interpreting "add 0" to mean "move no distance," you can see that

$$^-4 + 0 = {^-4} \quad \text{and} \quad 0 + {^-4} = {^-4}.$$

Oral Exercises

Give an addition statement pictured by each diagram.

1.
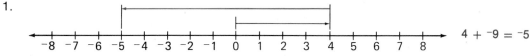
$4 + {^-9} = {^-5}$

2.
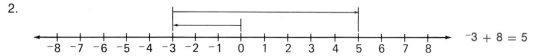
$^-3 + 8 = 5$

3.
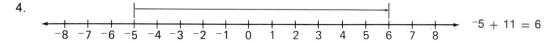
$3 + {^-9} = {^-6}$

4.
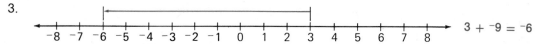
$^-5 + 11 = 6$

Simplify each expression. Think of arrows along the number line.

5. $^-8 + 0$ $^-8$
6. $0 + {^-3}$ $^-3$
7. $^-2 + 2$ 0
8. $5 + {^-5}$ 0
9. $^-6 + {^-4}$ $^-10$
10. $^-8 + {^-1}$ $^-9$
11. $3 + {^-2}$ 1
12. $^-5 + 6$ 1
13. $^-7 + {^-9}$ $^-16$
14. $^-10 + 11$ 1
15. $17 + {^-20}$ $^-3$
16. $^-1 + {^-99}$ $^-100$
17. $52 + {^-52}$ 0
18. $^-46 + 46$ 0
19. $0 + {^-6}$ $^-6$
20. $^-8 + 0$ $^-8$
21. $^-6 + (2 + {^-7})$ $^-11$
22. $(^-11 + 3) + 4$ $^-4$
23. $(^-2 + {^-1}) + 5$ 2
24. $^-6 + (3 + 5)$ 2

Written Exercises

Simplify each expression using the number line if necessary.

A 1. $(^-2 + 3) + {^-1}$ 0
2. $(5 + {^-4}) + {^-9}$ $^-8$
3. $(13 + {^-24}) + 6$ $^-5$
4. $(^-10 + {^-16}) + 32$ 6
5. $27 + (^-5 + 30)$ 52
6. $46 + (3 + {^-11})$ 38
7. $^-61 + (12 + 21)$ $^-28$
8. $(32 + {^-8}) + 0$ 24
9. $(^-35 + {^-25}) + 2$ $^-58$
10. $(^-2 + {^-7}) + 57$ 48
11. $[(^-3 + 2) + {^-7}] + {^-6}$ $^-14$
12. $[5 + (^-13 + {^-2})] + {^-36}$ $^-46$

Solve each of the following equations given that the replacement set of the variable is the set of real numbers. Use the number line as needed.

Sample $-2 + x = 6$ *Solution* To arrive at 6 from -2, you move 8 units to the right.

Check: $-2 + 8 \overset{?}{=} 6$ ($\overset{?}{=}$ means "Is this statement true?")
$$6 = 6 \checkmark \quad (\checkmark \text{ means "Yes, it is."})$$
∴ the solution is 8. *Answer*

13. $a + 2 = 5$ 3
14. $3 + b = 7$ 4
15. $x + {}^-2 = {}^-6$ ⁻4
16. $5 + y = {}^-7$ ⁻12
17. $6 + r = {}^-2$ ⁻8
18. ${}^-8 + s = {}^-5$ 3
19. $t + {}^-1 = {}^-8$ ⁻7
20. $a + {}^-10 = {}^-10$ 0
21. $0 = {}^-9 + d$ 9
22. $y + 37 = 0$ ⁻37
23. $7 + n = 7$ 0
24. $x + x = 0$ 0

Problems

Solve.

Sample An elevator starts at the ground floor and goes up to the 8th floor. It then goes down 4 floors and up 2 floors. At what floor is the elevator then located?

Solution

Step 1. The problem asks for the number of the floor where the elevator is located.

Step 2. Let x = number of floor.

Step 3. $x = (8 + {}^-4) + 2$

Step 4. $x = 4 + 2 = 6$

Step 5. The check is left to you.

∴ the elevator is at the 6th floor. *Answer*

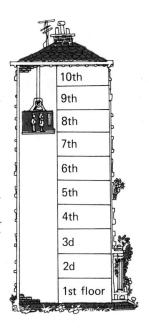

A 1. A jet plane flying at an altitude of 8000 meters dropped 1000 meters and then rose 600 meters. What was the new altitude?   7600 m

2. A submarine dove to a level 250 meters below the surface of the ocean. Later it climbed 70 meters and then dove another 30 meters. What was the new depth of the submarine? ⁻210 m

3. George had $103 in his checking account. He deposited $35 and then wrote a check for $17. How much was left in the checking account? $121

4. The temperature was 10 °C (Celsius) in the morning and then rose 5 °C by noon. The temperature then fell 8 °C during the afternoon. What was the temperature then?   7 °C

5. Janet flew from Chicago to Denver, leaving Chicago at noon. The flight took 3 hours, but the time in Denver is 1 hour earlier than it is in Chicago. What time was it in Denver when she landed?   2:00 P.M.

6. The stock of a company opened in the morning at $24 a share. By noon it had lost $3, but during the afternoon it gained $5. What was its closing value? $26

2-3 Opposites and Absolute Values

OBJECTIVE To learn the meaning of opposites and absolute values and how to use them.

In Figure 2-6 the origin is paired with itself and the other paired points are at the same distance from the origin.

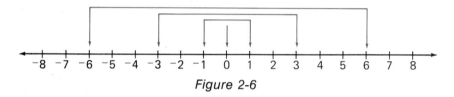

Figure 2-6

The coordinates of the paired points can also be paired:

$^-1$ with 1
$^-3$ with 3
$^-6$ with 6
and so on.

You can check that adding two such paired numbers on the number line gives 0. As shown in Figure 2-7:

$$^-6 + 6 = 0$$

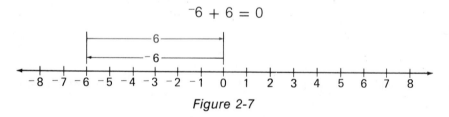

Figure 2-7

Each number in such a pair is called the *opposite* or the *additive inverse* or the *negative* of the other number.

The symbol $-a$ (note the lowered position of the minus sign) denotes the **opposite of a** or the **additive inverse of a** or the **negative of a,** and

$$a + (-a) = 0 \quad \text{and} \quad -a + a = 0.$$

Every real number has an opposite. For example:

$$-6 = {}^-6,\text{ read ``the opposite of six equals negative six'';}$$
$$-({}^-5) = 5,\text{ read ``the opposite of negative five equals five'';}$$
$$-0 = 0,\text{ read ``the opposite of zero equals zero.''}$$

Since $-6 = {}^-6$, you can use the numeral "-6" (lowered minus sign) in place of the numeral "${}^-6$" (raised minus sign). Thus,

$$-6 \text{ can mean } \begin{cases} \text{negative 6 or} \\ \text{the opposite of 6} \end{cases}$$

Throughout the rest of this book, lowered minus signs will be used in the numerals for negative numbers.

In general:

$$-(-a) = a$$

CAUTION! Be careful about reading variable expressions like $-a$. This should be read "the opposite of a" or "the additive inverse of a" or "the negative of a" or "minus a." Never call it "negative a," because $-a$ may denote a negative number, a positive number, or zero, depending on the value of a. Thus, if a denotes -3, $-a$ is positive, that is, 3.

Example 1 Simplify: a. $-(6 + 8)$ b. $-(-5)$ c. -0

Solution a. -14 b. 5 c. 0 *Answer*

Example 2 $-(-7) + (-9) = 7 + (-9) = -2$ *Answer*

In any pair of nonzero opposites, like 5 and -5, one number is a positive number, while the other is a negative number.

> The positive number of any pair of opposite real numbers is called the **absolute value** of each of the numbers.

The absolute value of a number is denoted by writing a name of the number between a pair of vertical bars $|\ |$. For example,

$$|5| = 5 \quad \text{and} \quad |-5| = 5.$$

The absolute value of 0 is defined to be 0 itself: $|0| = 0$.

The absolute value of a number may be thought of as the length of the arrow representing the number, as in Figure 2-8.

Figure 2-8

Example 3 $4|2| + (-|-3|) = 4 \cdot 2 + [-(3)]$
$$= 8 + (-3) = 5 \quad Answer$$

Oral Exercises

Name the opposite (additive inverse) of each.

Sample -18 *Solution*   18

1. 7 -7 2. 3 -3 3. -1 1   4. -8 8   5. 100 -100 6. -1001 1001

7. 0 0   8. $\frac{1}{2}$ $-\frac{1}{2}$ 9. $2\frac{1}{2}$ $-2\frac{1}{2}$ 10. $-1\frac{1}{2}$ $1\frac{1}{2}$ 11. $-(2 + 19)$ $2 + 19$ or 21   12. $6 + (-2)$ $-(6 + (-2))$ or -4

Simplify.

13. $-(-10)$ 10   14. $-(-23)$ 23   15. $-[-(-8)]$ -8 16. $-[-(-0)]$ 0

17. $(-6 + 6) + (-3)$ -3 18. $10 + [5 + (-5)]$ 10   19. $3 + [-(-2)]$ 5   20. $-(-6) + 6$ 12

21. $|14|$ 14   22. $|-22|$ 22   23. $2 + |2|$ 4   24. $2 + |-2|$ 4

25. $-5 + |-5|$ 0   26. $-|5| + |-5|$ 0   27. $-(-|3| + |1|)$ 2   28. $-(-|-6| + |-6|)$ 0

Written Exercises

Simplify.

A   1. $-(-3) + 9$ 12   2. $-(-6) + 2$ 8   3. $-9 + [-(-1)]$ -8 4. $8 + [-(-3)]$ 11

5. $-(10 + 1)$ -11 6. $-(-3 + 4)$ -1 7. $-(-5) + 5$ 10   8. $-(41 + 39)$ -80

9. $-21 + [-(-13)]$ -8 10. $-[57 + (-25)]$ -32 11. $-[-2 + (-2)]$ 4   12. $-[8 + (-7)]$ -1

13. $7 + |-3|$ 10   14. $|-6| + |1|$ 7   15. $|-8| + |10|$ 18   16. $|7| + |-7|$ 14

17. $|2 + (-1)| + 5$ 6   18. $|-3 + 9| - 6$ 0   19. $-|-3 + 5|$ -2 20. $-|7 + (-9)|$ -2

21. $2|-1| + |4|$ 6   22. $6|-3| + |-2|$ 20   23. $-(3|5|) + (-|5|)$ -20 24. $-[4|-2| + (-8)]$ 0

Career Note
Optician

An optician supplies eyeglasses and other optical goods. Having seen an optometrist and obtained a prescription, a customer consults an optician who assists in selecting a proper frame. In some cases, the optician prepares the lenses. When the lenses are available, the optician fits the lenses to the frame and adjusts the frame to the customer's face.

There are about a dozen schools in the United States offering courses for opticians. Such a school provides courses in mechanical optics, theoretical optics, geometric optics, and applied mathematics. A high school diploma is required for admission to a two-year course in opticianry. High school courses in algebra, geometry, trigonometry, physics, and English are useful preparation for the training in opticianry.

Opticians are usually required to be licensed, which involves passing an examination. They may work in optical laboratories or independently, making regular lenses or contact lenses.

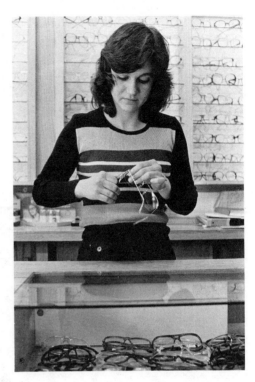

Just for Fun

Copy the diagram and write the products in the boxes. Do you see a pattern in the results?

$142857 \times 1 =$ ___?___

$142857 \times 2 =$ ___?___

$142857 \times 3 =$ ___?___

$142857 \times 4 =$ ___?___

$142857 \times 5 =$ ___?___

$142857 \times 6 =$ ___?___

		1	4	2	8	5	7		
			2	8	5	7	1	4	
		4	2	8	5	7	1		
	5	7	1	4	2	8			
	7	1	4	2	8	5			
8	5	7	1	4	2				

2-4 Rules for Addition

> **OBJECTIVE** To learn how to add real numbers without using a number line.

The diagrams below suggest rules for addition.

$5 + 2 = 7$

$(-5) + (-2) = -7 = -(5 + 2)$

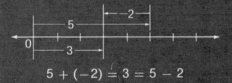

$5 + (-2) = 3 = 5 - 2$

$-5 + 2 = -3 = -(5 - 2)$

Rules for Addition

If a and b are positive numbers, then $a + b$ is a positive number and

$$a + b = |a| + |b|.$$

If a and b are negative numbers, then $a + b$ is a negative number and

$$a + b = -(|a| + |b|).$$

If a is a positive number and b is a negative number and the arrow representing a is longer than the arrow representing b, then $a + b$ is a positive number and

$$a + b = |a| - |b|.$$

If a is a negative number and b is a positive number and the arrow representing a is longer than the arrow representing b, then $a + b$ is a negative number and

$$a + b = -(|a| - |b|).$$

Using these rules along with the addition and subtraction facts of arithmetic, we can add any pair of real numbers.

Example 1 Simplify $7 + 16$.

Solution $7 + 16 = 23$ *Answer*

Example 2 Simplify $-12 + (-4)$.

Solution $-12 + (-4) = -(12 + 4)$
$= -16$ *Answer*

Example 3 Simplify $17 + (-6)$.

Solution $17 + (-6) = 17 - 6$
$$= 11 \quad Answer$$

Example 4 Simplify $-21 + 6$.

Solution $-21 + 6 = -(21 - 6)$
$$= -15 \quad Answer$$

Note that when we add two real numbers, the sum is the same no matter what order we use in adding them. Thus,

$$2 + 5 = 5 + 2, \quad -2 + 5 = 5 + (-2), \quad \text{and so on.}$$

This fact is called the commutative (kuh-*myu*-tuh-tiv) property for addition.

To find the sum of several numbers, such as

$$6 + 10 + (-4),$$

you must decide how to begin. You can find

$$(6 + 10) + (-4) = 16 + (-4) = 12$$

or

$$6 + [10 + (-4)] = 6 + 6 = 12.$$

Thus,

$$(6 + 10) + (-4) = 6 + [10 + (-4)].$$

This example suggests that the way that you group, or *associate,* real numbers in a sum of three (or more) numbers makes no difference in the result. This fact is called the associative (a-*so*-shia-tiv) property for addition.

These properties allow us to add numbers in any order or grouping.

Example 5 Simplify $-7 + 15 + 6 + (-11)$.

Solution 1

Step 1	Step 2	Step 3
$-7 + 15 = 8$	$8 + 6 = 14$	$14 + (-11) = 3 \quad Answer$

Solution 2

Step 1	Step 2	Step 3
-7	15	21
-11	6	-18
$\overline{-18}$	$\overline{21}$	$\overline{3} \quad Answer$

Example 6 Add.

	Solution	Step 1	Step 2	Step 3
243		243	-167	306
-167		63	-218	-385
-218		306	-385	$-$ 79 *Answer*
63				

Oral Exercises

Add.

1. 5	2. -2	3. -8	4. 7	5. -21	6. -1
5	-3	5	-10	-33	9
10	-5	-3	-3	-54	8
7. -13	8. -11	9. -13	10. 57	11. -85	12. 45
6	$-$ 3	32	-75	23	-19
-7	-14	19	-18	-62	26

Simplify.

13. $-8 + (-1)$ -9

14. $-11 + 5$ -6

15. $4 + (-4)$ 0

16. $6 + (-3)$ 3

17. $6 + (-1) + (-5)$ 0

18. $-2 + (-7) + 9$ 0

Written Exercises

Add.

A	1. 6	2. -3	3. 33	4. -25	5. 182	6. -123
	5	-7	-13	41	-64	231
	-1	4	42	38	-38	$-$ 75
	4	2	$-$ 6	-60	$-$ 9	$-$ 56
	14	-4	56	-6	71	-23

Simplify.

7. $-3 + 7 + (-2) + 5$ 7

8. $-11 + (-12) + 6 + 10$ -7

9. $21 + (-11) + (-9) + (-1)$ 0

10. $74 + 6 + (-7) + (-2)$ 71

11. $(-54) + (-16) + (-3) + 42$ -31

12. $29 + (-47) + (-3) + 11$ -10

13. $-[35 + (-1)] + [-(-3 + 6)]$ -37

14. $[-2 + (-4)] + [-(2 + 6)]$ -14

15. $23 + (-54) + (-23) + 0 + 54 + 123$ 123

16. $-60 + 124 + (-31) + (-90) + 4$ $-$

17. $31 + 42 + (-13) + 12 + (-51) + 5 + (-31) + (-13)$ -18

18. $38 + (-21) + 12 + 0 + (-45) + (-4) + (-18)$ -38

Problems

Solve.

A 1. Juan had $135 in his checking account. He made deposits of $10, $25, and $50 and then wrote checks for $5, $7, $26, and $15. How much money remained in his checking account? **$167**

2. Monique owned 820 shares of stock in the Aztec Corporation. On Monday she sold 65 shares, on Tuesday she sold 40 shares, on Wednesday she purchased 110 shares, and on Thursday sold 135 shares. How many shares of the stock did she then own? **690 shares**

3. During its first year of operation, the Helix Corporation had a net loss of $152,000. During its second and third years, it had net gains of $60,000 and $121,000. What was the corporation's net gain or loss over the three-year period? **net gain of $29,000**

4. During a 4-day period, Tri-City Hospital received 15 new patients and discharged 2, received 10 and discharged 11, received 6 and discharged 21, and received 8 and discharged 9. How did the number of patients in the hospital then compare with the number at the start of the 4-day period? **4 fewer patients**

5. On a revolving charge account, Marilyn purchased $58.20 worth of clothing, and $260.40 worth of furniture. She then made two monthly payments of $25.00 each. If the interest charges for the period of two months totaled $3.50, what did Marilyn then owe the account? **$272.10**

6. David had a balance of $233.41 in his checking account. During the next week, he wrote checks for $52.60, $19.23, $5.25, and $10.20. He then made a deposit of $78.00. What was his balance after the deposit? **$224.13**

7. A submarine 70 meters below sea level, climbed 16 meters and then fired a rocket which rose 270 meters. How far above sea level did the rocket rise? **216 meters**

8. During a ten-year period, the population of Reedville increased by 6700 people. During the following decade, the population grew by 2600. It decreased by 1820 during the succeeding decade, and during the next ten years it decreased again by 3000. What was the net change in population during the 40-year period? **increase of 4480 people**

★ Self-Test 1

Be sure that you understand these terms:

origin (p. 31)
negative direction (p. 31)
natural numbers (p. 32)
integers (p. 32)

unit distance (p. 31)
graph (p. 32)
counting numbers (p. 32)
real numbers (p. 32)

positive direction (p. 31)
coordinate (p. 32)
whole numbers (p. 32)
one-to-one
   correspondence (p. 33)

opposite (p. 38)
absolute value (p. 39)

additive inverse (p. 38)
commutative property
   for addition (p. 43)

negative (p. 38)
associative property
   for addition (p. 43)

Be sure that you understand these symbols:

$^-$ (p. 32) $^+$ (p. 32) $\stackrel{?}{=}$ (p. 37) $\sqrt{}$ (p. 37) $-a$ (p. 38) $|\ |$ (p. 39)

1. Graph $\{^-5, ^-1, 0, 2\}$ on a number line.   Objective 2-1, p. 31
2. Draw arrows on a number line to represent   Objective 2-2, p. 35
   $6 + ^-4 = 2$ and $^-6 + 4 = ^-2$.
3. Write the opposite of $^-5$.   Objective 2-3, p. 38
4. Simplify $|5|$.
5. Simplify $|4 + (-7)|$.
6. $-3 + 2 = 2 + (-3)$ is an illustration of the __?__ property for addition.   Objective 2-4, p. 42

Simplify.

7. $3 + (-7)$ 8. $-8 + 11$
9. $-9 + (-2)$ 10. $3 + 11 + (-7) + 6 + (-2)$

Check your answers with those printed at the back of the book.

Computer Activity

If you have access to a computer that will accept BASIC, type in this program to add any two numbers that you give it.

```
10   PRINT "TYPE IN TWO NUMBERS TO BE ADDED."
20   INPUT A
30   INPUT B
40   PRINT "SUM =";A+B
50   END
```

When the computer prints a question mark, you type in any positive or negative integer or decimal and then press the RETURN key.

To add more than two numbers (except zero), try this program.

```
10   PRINT "TYPE IN A NUMBER AFTER EACH QUESTION MARK."
20   PRINT "TO END INPUT AND PRINT SUM, TYPE ZERO."
30   LET S=0
40   INPUT N
50   IF N=0 THEN 80
60   LET S=S+N
70   GOTO 40
80   PRINT "SUM =";S
90   END
```

This program uses zero to indicate the end of your list of numbers to be added.

Consumer Note $$$$$$$$$$$$$$$$$$$$$$$$$$$$$$$$$$$$$$$
Balancing a Checkbook

Whenever a check is written, the writer should make a record of the amount (usually on the check "stub"). This amount is then subtracted from the previous balance.

When the monthly statement comes from the bank, the canceled checks are included. The steps for "balancing the checkbook" for a simple checking account are as follows:

1. Mark off on the records the checks that have been returned canceled.

2. Note the checks that have not yet been canceled, and find the total of these "outstanding" checks.

3. Subtract the total of outstanding checks from the bank balance and compare this result (called the corrected bank balance) with the checkbook balance. (If there are bank charges, these must be subtracted from the checkbook balance.)

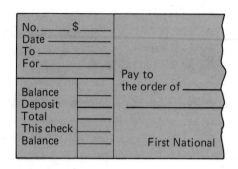

4. BIG QUESTION—DO THE BALANCES AGREE?

If the balances do not agree, search for the error. First, go over the arithmetic so far. If no error appears, go back to the previous correct balance and:

1. Add the sum of the deposits.
2. Subtract the total of the amounts of the checks written.

If this result agrees with the corrected bank balance, then there is simply an error in computing the running balances, which must be located. If this result does not agree, then find the difference between the balances. Does it suggest a check or a deposit that was not recorded?

Balance this checkbook:

Previous balance	$243.52
Check No. 19	2.43
	241.09
Check No. 20	11.75
	229.34
Check No. 21	20.00
	209.34
Deposit	50.00
	259.34
Check No. 22	17.95
	241.39

Bank Statement

Checks	Deposits	Balance
		$243.52
11.75		231.77
20.00		211.77
	50.00	261.77

Bank balance		$261.77
Outstanding checks	?	$20.38
Corrected balance	?	$241.39

Transforming Equations

2-5 Transforming Equations by Addition

> **OBJECTIVE** To learn how to use "transformation by addition" to solve simple equations.

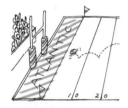

Suppose that the Atlantic and Bayville football teams are tied 21 to 21 at the end of the third quarter. If the Atlantic team scores *a* points in the fourth quarter, and the Bayville team scores *b* points, then the final score will be $21 + a$ to $21 + b$. Now suppose that the teams score the *same* number of fourth-quarter points. Then

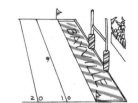

$a = b$, and therefore $21 + a = 21 + b$;

the game will end in a tie.

This example illustrates the following property.

> **Addition Property of Equality**
>
> If $a = b$, then $a + c = b + c$ and $c + a = c + b$.

Now study the following sequences of equations in which the addition property of equality is used:

(1) $x + 8 = 2$ (3) $x = -6$

(2) $x + 8 + (-8) = 2 + (-8)$ (2') $x + 8 = -6 + 8$

(3) $x = -6$ (1) $x + 8 = 2$

To obtain the third equation, you add -8 to each member of the first equation (Step 2) and simplify the resulting expressions (Step 3). On the other hand, when you add 8 to each member of the third equation, you obtain the first equation. The solution (root) of (3) is clearly -6.

The addition property of equality guarantees that any root of (1) will also satisfy (3), and any root of (3) will also satisfy (1). Therefore, the two equations have the same solution, namely -6.

> Equations having the same solution set over a given domain (page 18) are called **equivalent equations** over that domain.

To *solve* an equation, you usually try to change, or *transform,* it into an equivalent equation whose solution set can be found by inspection.

> Each of the following transformations produces an equivalent equation.
>
> **Transformation by Substitution:** Replacing either member of an equation by an expression equivalent to it.
>
> **Transformation by Addition:** Adding the same number to each member of an equation.

Example 1   Solve $z + (-9) = -5$.

Solution
$$z + (-9) = -5$$
$$z + (-9) + 9 = -5 + 9$$
$$z = 4$$

To obtain z alone in the left member, add to both members the opposite of -9, namely 9.

Check: If $z = 4$, then
$$z + (-9) = 4 + (-9) = -5. \checkmark$$
$\therefore$ the solution is 4.   *Answer*

Check your work by verifying that each root of the transformed equation satisfies the original equation.

Example 2   Solve $-14 = 16 + t$.

Solution
$$-14 = 16 + t$$
$$-16 + (-14) = -16 + 16 + t$$
$$-30 = t$$

To obtain t alone in the right member, add the opposite of 16, namely -16, to both members.

Check: If $t = -30$, then
$$16 + t = 16 + (-30) = -14. \checkmark$$
$\therefore$ the solution is -30.   *Answer*

When you replace

$$\text{``}z + (-9) + 9\text{''} \quad \text{by} \quad \text{``}z\text{''}$$

in Example 1 you use a very helpful idea: to "undo" addition of a number, add to the sum the opposite of that number.
   In general:

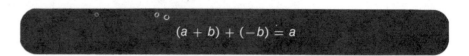

$$(a + b) + (-b) = a$$

Oral Exercises

Tell the number which must be added to each member of the first equation to produce the second equation. Then state the root of the first equation.

Sample $s + (-7) = 4; s = 11$ *Solution* 7; 11 *Answer*

1. $x + 2 = 7; x = 5$ **−2; 5**
2. $t + 4 = 5; t = 1$ **−4; 1**
3. $u + (-2) = 7; u = 9$ **2; 9**
4. $y + (-10) = 2; y = 12$ **10; 12**
5. $z + 11 = 1; z = -10$ **−11; −10**
6. $r + 9 = 8; r = -1$ **−9; −1**
7. $6 + s = -6; s = -12$ **−6; −12**
8. $-2 + t = 2; t = 4$ **2; 4**
9. $-2 + x = -2; x = 0$ **2; 0**
10. $10 + r = 10; r = 0$ **−10; 0**
11. $2 = z + (-5); 7 = z$ **5; 7**
12. $-6 = y + (-10); 4 = y$ **1**
13. $-9 = -2 + w; -7 = w$ **2; −7**
14. $5 = -1 + v; 6 = v$ **1; 6**
15. $0 = \frac{3}{4} + t; -\frac{3}{4} = t$ **$-\frac{3}{4}$;**
16. $\frac{5}{7} = \frac{1}{7} + u; \frac{4}{7} = u$ **$-\frac{1}{7}; \frac{4}{7}$**
17. $9 + s = -2; s = -11$ **−9; −11**
18. $-7 + x = -13; x = -6$ **7; −6**

Written Exercises

Use transformation by addition to solve each equation.

A
1. $y + (-10) = 15$ **25**
2. $x + (-7) = 13$ **20**
3. $t + 6 = 24$ **18**
4. $u + 17 = 20$ **3**
5. $-16 + x = 14$ **30**
6. $-49 + m = 51$ **100**
7. $z + (-2) = -18$ **−16**
8. $k + (-24) = -16$ **8**
9. $x + 15 = -22$ **−37**
10. $v + 70 = -25$ **−95**
11. $18 + k = 0$ **−18**
12. $0 = x + (-15)$ **15**
13. $x + (-21) = -42$ **−21**
14. $y + (-72) = -100$ **−28**
15. $7 + p = -14$ **−21**
16. $16 + q = -34$ **−50**
17. $45 = t + 7$ **38**
18. $36 = s + 5$ **31**
19. $-14 + z = -17$ **−3**
20. $-20 + k = -80$ **−60**
21. $r + 4 = |-16|$ **12**
22. $u + (-4) = |18|$ **22**
23. $v + 3 = |4 - 7|$ **0**
24. $w + (-5) = |8 - 13|$ **10**

Sample $-x + 15 = 6$

Solution

$$-x + 15 = 6$$
$$-x + 15 + (-15) = 6 + (-15)$$
$$-x = -9$$

By inspection:
$$x = 9$$
(Now do the check.) $-x + 15 = -9 + 15 = 6$ ✓

B 25. $-t + 10 = 4$ **6**

26. $-x + 1 = 17$ **−16**

27. $10 + (-z) = 16$ **−6**

28. $-3 + (-s) = 12$ **−15**

29. $6 = 9 + (-v)$ **3**

30. $7 = -v + 1$ **−6**

31. $(y + 1) + 5 = 3$ **−3**

32. $(r + 2) + 7 = 1$ **−8**

33. $1 = 9 + (1 + x)$ **−9**

34. $3 = 15 + (t + 1)$ **−13**

35. $(x + 1) + (-2) = 8$ **9**

36. $(y + 1) + (-3) = 7$ **9**

Problems

Solve by using an equation.

Sample Seven more than a number is 25. Find the number.

Solution

Step 1. The problem asks us to find the number described.

Step 2. Let $n =$ the number.

Step 3. $n + 7 = 25$

Step 4. $(n + 7) + (-7) = 25 + (-7)$
$$n = 18$$

Step 5. The check is left to you. $n + 7 = 18 + 7 = 25$ ✓

∴ the number is 18. *Answer*

A 1. Six more than a number is 11. Find the number. **5**

2. Eight more than a number is 10. Find the number. **2**

3. Four more than a number is −2. Find the number. **−6**

4. Three more than a number is −6. Find the number. **−9**

5. It was decided to increase the price of the tickets to the school play by $1.50. If the new price is $3.50, what was the previous price? **$2.00**

6. Sandra arrived at school at 8:15 A.M. This was 12 minutes later than her usual time of arrival. At what time did she usually arrive? **8:03**

7. Anthony brought a dozen bottles of soft drink to a party. There were then 36 bottles on hand. How many bottles had been brought by others? **24 bottles**

8. After the spring vacation, three new students enrolled in the social studies class, making a total of 32 students. How many students had been in the class previously? **29 students**

9. Ted hit a grand-slam home run, scoring 4 runs and making the score for his team 7. What had been the score before that? **3**

10. Madeline's time down a ski slope was 90 seconds. This was 10 seconds longer than her previous time. What was her previous time? **80 seconds**

2-6 Subtraction of Real Numbers

> **OBJECTIVE** To learn how to express differences and how to simplify expressions containing differences.

If you buy a 20-cent candy bar and give the clerk a quarter, he may hand you a nickel and say

"20 and 5 is 25."

The clerk uses addition,

$$20 + 5 = 25,$$

to do subtraction,

$$25 - 20 = 5.$$

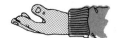

In general:

> The **difference** $a - b$ is defined to be the number whose sum with b is a. Thus, the equations
> $$b + x = a \quad \text{and} \quad a - b = x$$
> are equivalent equations.

Example 1 State an equation involving x to fit the diagram below, and solve the equation.

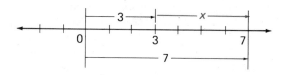

Solution Each of the following equations fits the diagram:

      (1) $3 + x = 7$ (2) $x = 7 - 3$

The solution of each equation is 4. *Answer*

Example 2 State an equation involving y to fit the diagram below, and solve the equation.

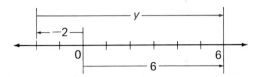

Solution Each of the following equations fits the diagram:

(1) $-2 + y = 6$ (2) $y = 6 - (-2)$

The solution of each equation is 8. *Answer*

You can find a simple expression for $a - b$ by transforming the equation "$b + x = a$" by addition.

Solve the equation:	Check the root:
$b + x \qquad = a$	$b + x \qquad\qquad = a$
$x + b \qquad = a$	$b + [a + (-b)] \overset{?}{=} a$
$(x + b) + (-b) = a + (-b)$	$b + [(-b) + a] \overset{?}{=} a$
$x + [b + (-b)] = a + (-b)$	$[b + (-b)] + a \overset{?}{=} a$
$x + \qquad 0 \qquad = a + (-b)$	$0 \qquad + a \overset{?}{=} a$
$\therefore x = a + (-b)$	$a = a \ \checkmark$

Since the one and only root of "$b + x = a$" is $a + (-b)$, we have discovered the following:

> **Rule for Subtraction**
>
> $$a - b = a + (-b)$$

Using this rule, you may replace any difference by a sum; for example,

$$5 - 3 = 5 + (-3) = 2.$$

Moreover, the expression

$$9 - 6 - 5 + 4$$

means

$$9 + (-6) + (-5) + 4.$$

You may evaluate the expression by grouping from left to right:

$$9 - 6 - 5 + 4$$
$$\underline{3}$$
$$\underline{-2}$$
$$2$$

This method is convenient if you are doing the work mentally or with a small calculator. For pencil and paper work, you may group positive terms and negative terms:

$$9 - 6 - 5 + 4 = (9 + 4) - (6 + 5) = 13 - 11 = 2.$$

On the other hand, you may replace sums by differences as in

$$4 + (-t) = 4 - t \quad \text{and} \quad -b + a = a - b.$$

Is subtraction commutative? You can see that

$$9 - 3 = 6 \quad \text{but} \quad 3 - 9 = -6,$$

and so *subtraction is not commutative.*
Is subtraction associative? You can see that

$$7 - (2 - 3) = 8 \quad \text{but} \quad (7 - 2) - 3 = 2,$$

and so *subtraction is not associative.*

Summary for Addition and Subtraction

Commutative Property for Addition — For all real numbers a and b:
$$a + b = b + a$$

Associative Property for Addition — For all real numbers a, b, and c:
$$(a + b) + c = a + (b + c)$$

Subtraction is neither commutative nor associative.

Oral Exercises

Simplify.

1. $27 - 9$ **18**
2. $16 - 11$ **5**
3. $7 - 11$ **−4**
4. $8 - 28$ **−20**

5. $0 - 7$ $^{-7}$ 6. $0 - (-3)$ 3 7. $-14 - 0$ $^{-14}$ 8. $-9 - 6$ $^{-15}$

9. $2 - (-5)$ 7 10. $7 - (-1)$ 8 11. $-5 - (-8)$ 3 12. $-7 - (-3)$ $^{-4}$

Written Exercises

Simplify.

A 1. $32 - 212$ $^{-180}$ 2. $124 - 241$ $^{-117}$ 3. $19 - (-12)$ 31 4. $17 - (-19)$ 36

5. $-15 - (-3)$ $^{-12}$ 6. $-23 - (-9)$ $^{-14}$ 7. $-28 - 42$ $^{-70}$ 8. $-31 - 47$ $^{-78}$

9. $-143 - (-23)$ $^{-120}$ 10. $-201 - (-42)$ $^{-159}$ 11. $172 - (-103)$ 275 12. $185 - (-145)$ 330

13. $113 - (55 - 49)$ 107 14. $250 - (75 - 60)$ 235 15. $242 - (62 - 75)$ 255

16. $193 - (25 - 70)$ 238 17. $(22 - 33) - (55 - 66)$ 0 18. $(43 - 50) - (72 - 80)$ 1

19. $(12 - 17) - (-4 + 7)$ $^{-8}$ 20. $(22 - 13) - (-7 + 9)$ 7 21. $1066 - 1492 + 1776$ 1350

22. $1914 - 1860 + 1892$ 1946 23. $7 - (-5) - [6 - (-7)]$ $^{-1}$ 24. $-8 - 6 - [-5 - (-7)]$ $^{-16}$

25. $2 - 4 + 8 - 16 + 32$ 22 26. $18 - 14 + 13 + 4 - 21$ 0

27. $33 - 14 - 42 + 16 - 26$ $^{-33}$ 28. $42 - 18 + 10 - 21 - 33$ $^{-20}$

29. $124 - 15 + 21 - 89 + 41 - 37$ 45 30. $225 - 125 + 72 - 65 + 14 - 33$ 88

Problems

Solve.

A 1. George walked on Second Street from 4 blocks east of Main Street to 3 blocks west of Main Street. How many blocks did he walk?   **7 blocks**

2. Ramona rode her bicycle along Second Street from 4 blocks west of Main Street to 2 blocks east of Main Street. How many blocks did she ride?   **6 blocks**

3. The temperature dropped from 5 °C (Celsius) to −5 °C. How many degrees did the temperature drop?   **10 °C**

4. The highest temperature recorded in Nova Scotia was about 38 °C and the lowest was about −41 °C. What was the difference in temperatures?   **79 °C**

5. The top of Mount Whitney in California is about 4418 meters above sea level. Death Valley, California is about 86 meters below sea level. About how many meters is the top of Mount Whitney above Death Valley?   **4504 m**

6. The Dead Sea, between Israel and Jordan, is about 396 meters below sea level. The top of Mount Everest, between Nepal and Tibet, is about 8848 meters above sea level. About how many meters higher is Mount Everest?   **9244 m**

2-7 Transforming Equations Involving Subtraction

> **OBJECTIVE** To learn how to solve equations involving subtraction.

Example 1 Solve $t - 2 = 7$.

Solution
$$t - 2 = 7$$
$$t + (-2) = 7$$
$$t + (-2) + 2 = 7 + 2$$
$$t = 9$$

Condensed Solution
$$t - 2 = 7$$
$$t - 2 + 2 = 7 + 2$$
$$t = 9$$

Check: If $t = 9$, then
$$t - 2 = 9 - 2 = 7. \checkmark$$

∴ the solution is 9. *Answer*

Example 2 Solve $z + 9 = 17$.

Solution
$$z + 9 = 17$$
$$z + 9 - 9 = 17 - 9$$
$$z = 8$$

Check: If $z = 8$, then
$$z + 9 = 8 + 9 = 17. \checkmark$$

∴ the solution is 8. *Answer*

You may call the method used in Example 2 **transformation by subtraction** because we *subtracted* 9 from each member of the equation. Of course, transformation by subtraction is just a special case of transformation by addition, since we could equally well have added -9.

Oral Exercises

Tell the number which must be added to or subtracted from each member of the first equation to produce the second equation. Then state the root of the first equation. A. = add, S. = subtract

Sample 1 $x + 7 = -2; x = -9$

Solution Subtract 7; -9 *Answer*

Sample 2 $x - 5 = 4; x = 9$

Solution Add 5; 9 *Answer*

1. $x + 2 = 10; x = 8$ S. 2; 8
2. $u + 4 = -2; u = -6$ S. 4; -6
3. $v + 7 = 22; v = 15$ S. 7; 15
4. $t + 5 = 6; t = 1$ S. 5; 1
5. $z + 1 = 5; z = 4$ S. 1; 4
6. $y + 7 = 1; y = -6$ S. 7; -6

7. $x - 2 = 4$; $x = 6$ A. 2; 6   8. $y - 7 = 2$; $y = 9$ A. 7; 9   9. $j - 6 = -4$; $j = 2$ A. 6; 2
10. $k - 4 = -8$; $k = -4$ 11. $p - 10 = -12$; $p = -2$ 12. $q - 12 = 10$; $q = 22$
          A. 4; -4 A. 10; -2 A. 12; 22

Written Exercises

Solve.

A 1. $u + 18 = 42$ **24**   2. $x + 21 = 69$ **48**   3. $-1 = w + 21$ **-22**
   4. $z + 8 = -22$ **-30**   5. $10 + s = 10$ **0**   6. $1.6 + k = 1.6$ **0**
   7. $x - 3 = 14$ **17**   8. $y - 2 = 5$ **7**   9. $r - 3 = 7$ **10**
   10. $t - 5 = 4$ **9**   11. $14 = s - 2$ **16**   12. $16 = q - 10$ **26**

B 13. $24 - x = 10$ **14**   14. $17 - t = -5$ **22**   15. $(s + 7) - 2 = -3$ **-8**
   16. $(z - 4) + 16 = 120$ **108**   17. $(u - 3) + 5 = 11$ **9**   18. $(v + 1) + 7 = 10$ **2**
   19. $w - 4 = |6 - 10|$ **8**   20. $y - 6 = |7 - 16|$ **15**   21. $p + |6 - 8| = -7$ **-9**
   22. $q + |2 - 4| = -1$ **-3**   23. $x - 5 = \big||-4| - |2|\big|$ **7**   24. $y - 7 = \big||-3| - |-7|\big|$ **11**

Problems

Solve by using an equation.

Sample Six less than a number is 10. Find the number.

Solution
   Step 1. The problem asks us to find the   **Step 4.** $(n - 6) + 6 = 10 + 6$
      number described. $n = 16$

   Step 2. Let n = the number.   **Step 5.** The check is left to you. $n - 6 = 16 - 6$
                                                           $= 10$ √
   Step 3. $n - 6 = 10$ ∴ the number is 16.   *Answer*

A 1. Thirteen less than a number is 17. Find the number. **30**
   2. Eight less than a number is 18. Find the number. **26**
   3. Five less than a number is -10. Find the number. **-5**
   4. Seven less than a number is -13. Find the number. **-6**
   5. Four less than a number is -3. Find the number. **1**
   6. Nine less than a number is -6. Find the number. **3**
   7. A store is offering record albums at $1 off the regular price. If the sale price is $3, what is the regular price? **$4**
   8. Joyce said, "I have lost 5 kilograms and now weigh 60 kilograms." What did she weigh before she lost weight? **65 kilograms**
   9. Rosalie swam the length of a pool in 21 seconds. This was 2 seconds less than her previous time. What was her previous time? **23 sec**
   10. Eduardo played a round of golf in 89 strokes. This was 3 less than his previous record. What was his previous record? **92 strokes**

Biographical Note
John Von Neumann

John Von Neumann (1903–1957) made contributions to several fields of mathematics, including mathematical logic and set theory. One of his most important achievements was the development of the theory of games. The basic proof in his theory is that in any game of strategy (such as chess, ticktacktoe, or bridge), there is at least one method of play or choice of moves which results in the least possible loss. The theory of games has been applied to economics, warfare, and many of the social sciences. Von Neumann also developed many of the basic ideas of modern computer design and served on the United States Atomic Energy Commission.

 Self-Test 2

Be sure that you understand these terms:

equivalent equations (p. 49)
transformation by addition (p. 49)
transformation by subtraction (p. 56)

transformation by substitution (p. 49)
difference (p. 52)

Solve.

1. $3 + x = 4$ 2. $q + (-2) = 3$ Objective 2-5, p. 48

Simplify.

3. $21 - 32$ 4. $-4 - 5$ Objective 2-6, p. 52
5. $12 - (-2)$ 6. $-17 - (-5)$

Solve.

7. $y - 7 = 2$ 8. $w + 7 = 2$ Objective 2-7, p. 56

9. Anna scored 20 baskets in a game and reported to her parents that she had made 3 more baskets than in the preceding game. Find how many baskets she had made in the preceding game by writing an equation and solving it.

Check your answers with those printed at the back of the book.

Chapter Summary

1. Addition and subtraction of real numbers can be illustrated by drawing arrows on a number line.

2. Opposites and absolute values are used in rules for adding and subtracting real numbers.

3. Transforming an equation by substitution, by addition, or by subtraction produces an equivalent equation. These transformations are used in solving equations.

Chapter Test

2-1   1. Graph $\{-3, 0, 1, 3\}$ on a number line.

2-2   2. Draw a diagram showing $7 + (^-10)$.

2-3   3. Simplify $-[21 + |-8|]$.   **−29**

2-4   4. $2 + (-3 + 4) = [2 + (-3)] + 4$ is an illustration of the __?__   **associative** property for addition.

     5. Simplify $7 + (-3) + 8 + (-10)$.   **2**

2-5   6. Solve $y + (-3) = -7$.   **−4**   7. Solve $z + 5 = 21$.   **16**

2-6   8. Simplify $7 - (-4)$.   **11**   9. Simplify $107 - (15 - 38)$.   **130**

2-7   10. Solve $x - 5 = 11$.   **16**   11. Solve $w + 5 = -10$.   **−15**

     12. The Cranston hockey team made 5 goals in a game against the Danville team. This was 3 more goals than the Danville team made. Use an equation to find how many goals the Danville team made.   **2 goals**

Historical Note
François Vieta

François Vieta (or Viète)* (1540–1603) was a French lawyer and mathematician, who worked in the service of King Henry IV (Henry of Navarre). In 1591 he published a mathematics book in which he used letters to represent variables and numbers, giving his algebra a nearly modern appearance. During the war between France and Spain, he broke the Spanish code, making it possible for the French to read messages that the Spanish thought were secret.

* Pronounced Fron-swah Vee-ay-*tah* (or Vee-*yet*).

Programmed Chapter Review

2-1 1. Each point on a number line is called the __?__ of the number assigned to it, and the assigned number is called the __?__ of the point. | graph coordinate

2. {..., ⁻3, ⁻2, ⁻1, 0, 1, 2, 3, ...} = {the __?__} | integers

3. There is a __?__ correspondence between the real numbers and the points of the number line. | one-to-one

2-2 4. Arrows pointing in the positive direction along a number line represent __?__ numbers. | positive

5. ⁻5 + 3 = 3 + (__?__) | ⁻5

2-3 6. The opposite of 7 is __?__, the opposite of ⁻6 is __?__, and the opposite of 0 is __?__. | −7, 6 ; 0

7. |42| = __?__; |−13| = __?__ | 42, 13

2-4 8. The sum of two positive numbers is __?__. | positive

9. The sum of two negative numbers is __?__. | negative

10. If one number is positive and another number is negative, and on the number line the arrow representing the negative number is longer than the arrow representing the positive number, then the sum is a __?__ number. | negative

2-5 11. The addition property of equality states that if $a = b$, then $a + c = b +$ __?__. | c

12. Equations having the same solution set over a given domain are called __?__ equations. | equivalent

13. To solve an equation, you __?__ it into one whose solution set can be found by inspection. | transform

14. To solve $x + 1 = 2$, you add __?__ to both members. | −1

15. The solution of $x + 1 = 2$ is __?__. | 1

2-6 16. The rule for subtraction states that $a - b = a + ($ __?__ $)$. | −b

17. $16 - (-4) =$ __?__ | 20

2-7 18. To solve $y - 3 = -1$, you add __?__ to both members. | 3

19. To solve $w + 7 = 6$, you may subtract __?__ from both members. | 7

20. The solution of $w + 7 = 6$ is __?__. | −1

Maintaining Skills

Remember how? $\underline{3.12 + 6.1 + 2.106} = 11.326$

$$
\begin{array}{r}
3.12 \\
6.1 \\
+\ 2.106 \\
\hline
11.326
\end{array}
$$

Now practice:

1. $7.82 + 12.15 + 2.103$ **22.073**
2. $6.021 + 11.15 + 18.3$ **35.471**
3. $13.2 + 6.81 + 21.099$ **41.109**
4. $81.63 + 210.97 + 1821.03$
   2113.63

5.
$$
\begin{array}{r}
243.2 \\
15.07 \\
+161.39 \\
\hline
419.66
\end{array}
$$

6.
$$
\begin{array}{r}
281.6 \\
5.021 \\
+\ 13.952 \\
\hline
300.573
\end{array}
$$

7.
$$
\begin{array}{r}
47.8 \\
500.37 \\
+\ 61.83 \\
\hline
610.00
\end{array}
$$

8.
$$
\begin{array}{r}
213.61 \\
1923.82 \\
+5037.612 \\
\hline
7175.042
\end{array}
$$

Remember how? $\underline{21.291 - 8.062} = 13.229$

$$
\begin{array}{r}
21.291 \\
-\ 8.062 \\
\hline
13.229
\end{array}
$$

Now practice:

9. $12.95 - 6.86$ **6.09**
10. $18.36 - 16.08$ **2.28**
11. $12.031 - 9.285$ **2.746**
12. $182.6 - 63.52$ **119.08**

13.
$$
\begin{array}{r}
182.65 \\
-\ 84.82 \\
\hline
97.83
\end{array}
$$

14.
$$
\begin{array}{r}
321.032 \\
-\ 86.917 \\
\hline
234.115
\end{array}
$$

15.
$$
\begin{array}{r}
18.6 \\
-\ 7.3821 \\
\hline
11.2179
\end{array}
$$

16.
$$
\begin{array}{r}
623.851 \\
-586.293 \\
\hline
37.558
\end{array}
$$

Remember how? $\underline{32.7 \times 6.13} = 200.451$

$$
\begin{array}{r}
32.7 \\
\times 6.13 \\
\hline
981 \\
327 \\
1962 \\
\hline
200.451
\end{array}
$$

Now practice:

17. 6.21×3.5 **21.735**
18. 8.1×3.25 **26.325**
19. 70.2×0.81 **56.862**
20. 691.2×0.23 **158.976**
21. 21.32×0.14 **2.9848**
22. 6.021×0.32 **1.92672**

23.
$$
\begin{array}{r}
62.31 \\
\times\ 1.42 \\
\hline
88.4802
\end{array}
$$

24.
$$
\begin{array}{r}
81.9 \\
\times\ 623 \\
\hline
51{,}023.7
\end{array}
$$

25.
$$
\begin{array}{r}
21.63 \\
\times\ 1.05 \\
\hline
22.7115
\end{array}
$$

26.
$$
\begin{array}{r}
30.14 \\
\times\ 2.031 \\
\hline
61.21434
\end{array}
$$

Multiplication and Division

Fine Arts This mask was carved by members of the Baluba tribe, who live in what is now the African country of Zaire. African art has had a great influence on modern painting and sculpture.

3

Multiplying Real Numbers

3-1 Rules for Multiplication

OBJECTIVE To learn how to multiply real numbers.

Corresponding to the commutative and associative properties for addition (page 54) are the **commutative property for multiplication**, illustrated by

$$2 \cdot 5 = 5 \cdot 2,$$

and the **associative property for multiplication**, illustrated by

$$(2 \cdot 5) \cdot 4 = 2 \cdot (5 \cdot 4).$$

To learn how to multiply negative numbers, notice that

$$2 \times (-1) = -1 + (-1) = -2$$
$$3 \times (-1) = -1 + (-1) + (-1) = -3$$

and so on.

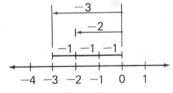

Figure 3-1

Notice that in each case the product of the given number and -1 is the opposite of the given number. In general:

Multiplicative Property of -1

$$a(-1) = -a \quad \text{and} \quad (-1)a = -a$$

63

A special case of this property occurs when the value of a is -1; we have $(-1)(-1) = 1$.

You can use the multiplicative property of -1 together with the multiplication facts of arithmetic to compute the product of any two real numbers. For example:

1. $3 \cdot 4 = 12$

2. $(-3)4 = (-1 \cdot 3)4 = -1(3 \cdot 4) = -1(12) = -12$

3. $3(-4) = 3[4(-1)] = (3 \cdot 4)(-1) = 12(-1) = -12$

4. $(-3)(-4) = (-1 \cdot 3)(-1 \cdot 4) = [-1(-1)](3 \cdot 4) = 1 \cdot 12 = 12$

Practice in computing products will lead you to discover the following rules.

Rules for Multiplication

1. The absolute value of the product of two real numbers is the product of the absolute values of the numbers:

$$|ab| = |a| \times |b|$$

2. The product of two positive numbers or of two negative numbers is a positive number.
3. The product of a positive number and a negative number is a negative number.

Oral Exercises

Simplify.

Sample 1 $(5)(-6) = -30$

Sample 2 $(-2)^3 = [(-2)(-2)](-2) = 4(-2) = -8$

1. $(-1)6$ **−6**
2. $(-3)(-2)$ **6**
3. $-5(-20)$ **100**
4. $7(-10)$ **−70**
5. $(-4)(6)(-1)$ **24**
6. $7(-4)(-5)$ **140**
7. $(-10)(-3)(-4)$ **−120**
8. $(-6)(-1)(-8)$ **−4**
9. $-42 \cdot 11 \cdot 0$ **0**
10. $-21 \cdot 0 \cdot (-4)$ **0**
11. $(-1)^4$ **1**
12. $(-2)^4$ **16**
13. $3(-2)^2$ **12**
14. $-1(-3)^3$ **27**
15. $|(-2)^3|$ **8**
16. $|(-5)^2|$ **25**

Complete.

17. The product of an even number of negative numbers is __?__. **a positive number**
18. The product of an odd number of negative numbers is __?__. **a negative number**

Written Exercises

Simplify.

A 1. $(-20)(-4)(12)$ **960** 2. $(5)(-4)(16)$ **−320** 3. $(4)(12)(-10)$ **−480** 4. $(-6)(12)(-20)$ **1440**

5. $(-6)(-3)(-5)$ **−90** 6. $(-7)(-4)(-10)$ **−280** 7. $(3)(-4)(5)(0)$ **0** 8. $(1700)(4)(0)$ **0**

9. $(-400)(-5000)$ 10. $(-1200)(-500)$ 11. $(1600)(-5)$ **−8000** 12. $(-7)(900)$ **−6300**
        2,000,000   **600,000**

13. $(-1)^2(4)(5)$ **20** 14. $(4)(7)(-1)^3$ **−28** 15. $(-4)(2)(3)(-5)$ **120** 16. $(-3)(5)(6)(-2)$ **180**

17. $(-2)^3(-5)(6)$ **240** 18. $(2)(-8)(-1)^4$ **−16** 19. $(-5)(20)(-4)(25)$ 20. $(16)(-5)(-2)(15)$
                                                          10,000   **2400**

21. $(4)(-2)(-10)(-5)$ **−400** 22. $(-5)(15)(-2)(-10)$ **−1500**

23. $(-4)(-1)(-7)(-10)$ **280** 24. $(-8)(-5)(-3)(-4)$ **480**

25. $(-1)^3(-3)^2$ **−9** 26. $(-2)^4(-1)^2$ **16**

27. $(-7)(-5)^2(-2)$ **350** 28. $(-3)^2(-10)(-6)$ **540**

Problems

Solve.

A 1. The O'Briens had $400 in a special checking account for installment payments. After paying $40 a month for three months and $20 a month for two months, how much was left in the account? **$240**

2. Loretta earns $10 a week and puts $7.50 a week into a savings account and spends the rest. How much does she spend in six weeks? **$15**

3. Lynne Goodman commutes from a suburb to the city to work. Each day she pays 50¢ bus fare and 25¢ subway fare each way. She budgets $20 a 5-day week for expenses. How much does she have left for other expenses after paying for her transportation? **$12.50**

4. José budgets $5 a week for entertainment. Out of this he buys a 20¢ newspaper six days a week and a 60¢ magazine once a week. How much does he have for other entertainment over a four-week period? **$12.80**

Computer Activity

If you have access to a computer that will accept BASIC, type in this program to multiply any two numbers that you give it.

```
10  PRINT "TYPE IN TWO NUMBERS TO BE MULTIPLIED."
20  INPUT A
30  INPUT B
40  PRINT "PRODUCT =";A*B
50  END
```

If the absolute value of the product is greater than 999999, it will be printed in an exponential notation. For example, if you multiply 3452 by 675, the answer will be printed in this form:

$$2.33010E+06$$

The "E+06" means "times 10^6," and so

$$2.33010E+06 \quad \text{means} \quad 2.33010 \times 10^6 \quad \text{or} \quad 2,330,100.$$

This happens to be the exact answer. However, if you multiply 67892 by 543, the answer may be printed as:

$$3.68654E+07$$

This is not an exact answer. It gives *six significant digits* of the answer, 36,865,400, although the exact answer would be 36,865,356. Computers using BASIC commonly give such answers rounded to six significant digits.

Verify that 999×999 is less than 999999. Then add 1 successively to one factor until the product is greater than 999999.

Verify that 9999×99 is less than 999999. Then keep one factor fixed and add 1 successively to the other factor until the product is greater than 999999. Do this with each factor.

To find the product of several numbers, change the second program on page 46 as follows:

```
30   LET P = 1
60   LET P = P*N
```

and the words in lines 20 and 80.

Just for Fun

Find the sum of each row, column, and diagonal in the table at the right.

For example: $[3 + (-4)] + 1 = \underline{\quad ? \quad}$

The sum of each row, column, and diagonal is zero.

3	−4	1	?
−2	0	2	?
−1	4	−3	?
?	?	?	?

3-2 The Distributive Property

> **OBJECTIVE** To learn how to use the distributive property in computation.

Mr. Costa's truck will carry 3 metric tons of gravel while his trailer carries another 2 metric tons. Since in a single trip Mr. Costa can carry $3 + 2$ metric tons, in four trips he can carry

$$4(3 + 2) = 4(5) = 20 \text{ metric tons.}$$

His total tonnage in 4 trips is also the sum of the tons carried by the truck and those of the trailer:

$$(4 \times 3) + (4 \times 2) = 12 + 8 = 20 \text{ tons.}$$

Either way you compute it, the tonnage is the same. That is,

$$4(3 + 2) = (4 \times 3) + (4 \times 2).$$

Note that 4 is *distributed* as a multiplier of each term of $3 + 2$. This example illustrates a fact that we will use in working with real numbers: multiplication is *distributive* (dis-*trib*-u-tiv) *with respect to addition*.
The distributive property can be illustrated as in Figure 3-2.

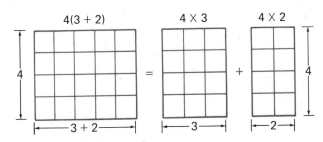

Figure 3-2

> **Distributive Property of Multiplication with Respect to Addition**
>
> $a(b + c) = ab + ac$ and $(b + c)a = ba + ca.$

You can also state the distributive property in the following form.

$$ab + ac = a(b + c) \quad \text{and} \quad ba + ca = (b + c)a.$$

The following examples show some uses of the distributive property.

Example 1 $12(27) = 12(20 + 7) = 12(20) + 12(7) = 240 + 84 = 324$

Example 2 $8(3.5) = 8(3 + 0.5) = 8(3) + 8(0.5) = 24 + 4 = 28$

Oral Exercises

Use the distributive property to simplify each expression.

1. $2(40 + 3)$ 86
2. $3(50 + 4)$ 162
3. $5(20 + 4)$ 120
4. $4(30 + 5)$ 140
5. $2(20 - 4)$ 32
6. $3(40 - 3)$ 111
7. $4(500 - 1)$ 1996
8. $5(300 - 2)$ 149
9. $8(2.5)$ 20
10. $6(5.5)$ 33
11. $6(7.5)$ 45
12. $4(9.5)$ 38

Written Exercises

Evaluate each of the following expressions in two ways.

Sample $(-2)[4 + (-1)]$

Solution

1. Simplify the sum $[4 + (-1)]$ and then multiply it by -2:
$$(-2)[4 + (-1)] = (-2)(3) = -6 \quad \textit{Answer}$$

2. Apply the distributive property to $(-2)[4 + (-1)]$ and then simplify the resulting expression:
$$(-2)[4 + (-1)] = (-2)(4) + (-2)(-1)$$
$$= -8 + 2 = -6 \quad \textit{Answer}$$

A
1. $(-6)(6 + 4)$ −60
2. $(-3)[(-1) + (-7)]$ 24
3. $[18 + (-5)](-2)$ −26
4. $(-5 + 20)(0)$ 0
5. $0[-3 + (-21)]$ 0
6. $27[2 + (-2)]$ 0

7. $7 \cdot 1 + 7(-5)$ −28

8. $-6 \cdot 12 + (-6) \cdot 2$ −84

9. $-8(-9) + (-8)$ 64

10. $21 + 21(-15)$ −294

11. $32(88) + 32(-88)$ 0

12. $(-13)(-2) + (-2)(13)$ 0

13. $-7 + 7(-56)$ −399

14. $-99(5) + (-5)$ −500

15. $-(-3 + 15)$ −12

16. $-[-2 + (-19)]$ 21

17. $(-18)[7 + (-2)]$ −90

18. $36(-8 + 19)$ 396

19. $0 \cdot 4[16 + (-41)]$ 0

20. $20(-14 + 2 \cdot 0) \cdot 0$ 0

21. $-30 - [-51 + (-55)]$ 76

22. $16 - [7 + (-10)]$ 19

23. $-[4 + (-2)] - 13$ −15

24. $-[-7 + (-11)] + 20$ 38

Evaluate in the simplest way.

25. $275(-200 + 200)$ 0

26. $1243[750 + (-750)]$ 0

27. $84 \cdot 36 + 16 \cdot 36$ 3600

28. $33 \cdot 21 + 67 \cdot 21$ 2100

29. $327 \cdot 10 + 327 \cdot 3$ 4251

30. $22 \cdot 195 + 3 \cdot 195$ 4875

31. $553 \cdot 1001$ 553,553

32. $437 \cdot 1010$ 441,370

33. $600(25 \cdot 10 + 40 \cdot 10)$ 390,000

34. $350(20 \cdot 4 + 20 \cdot 6)$ 70,000

35. $36(50 \cdot 4 - 50 \cdot 6)$ −3600

36. $47(25 \cdot 8 - 25 \cdot 10)$ −2350

37. $3 \cdot 37 + 6 \cdot 37 + 5 \cdot 37$ 518

38. $8 \cdot 26 + 1 \cdot 26 + 2 \cdot 26$ 286

39. $15 \cdot 3 + 15 \cdot 5 - 15 \cdot 7$ 15

40. $23 \cdot 17 - 23 \cdot 18 + 23 \cdot 2$ 23

Career Note
Market Researcher

A market researcher obtains information about consumer demand and opinion and about a company's advertising and sales strategy. This kind of information helps management make decisions about such problems as what quantities of an item should be produced and where certain products are most likely to be sold. The sources of a market researcher's information include company records, population and income statistics, and opinion surveys, which the researcher may design and direct. The researcher is responsible for gathering data and compiling it in reports.

A bachelor's degree with a major in economics or business administration is usually required for jobs at the entry levels in the field. Courses in sociology, psychology, statistics, or engineering are necessary for specialized areas of market research. Knowledge of data processing is helpful because of the wide use of computers in the field of market research.

3-3 The Reciprocal of a Real Number

> **OBJECTIVE** To learn how to use the reciprocal, or multiplicative inverse, of a number.

Numbers whose product is 1 are called *reciprocals* or *multiplicative inverses* of each other. For example:

1. -4 and $-\frac{1}{4}$ are reciprocals because $-4(-\frac{1}{4}) = 1$.
2. 1 is its own reciprocal because $1 \cdot 1 = 1$.
3. -1 is its own reciprocal because $(-1)(-1) = 1$.
4. 0 has no reciprocal because the product of 0 and any real number is 0, *not* 1.

> If $b \neq 0$, the symbol $\frac{1}{b}$ denotes the **reciprocal,** or **multiplicative inverse,** of b, and
> $$b \cdot \frac{1}{b} = 1 \quad \text{and} \quad \frac{1}{b} \cdot b = 1.$$

It is also true that

$$\frac{1}{-b} = -\frac{1}{b}$$

for every nonzero real number b.
  That every real number except 0 has a reciprocal is a basic fact.

Example Simplify $(3 \cdot 5)\left(\frac{1}{3} \cdot \frac{1}{5}\right)$.

Solution $(3 \cdot 5)\left(\frac{1}{3} \cdot \frac{1}{5}\right) = \left(3 \cdot \frac{1}{3}\right) \cdot \left(5 \cdot \frac{1}{5}\right)$

$= 1 \cdot 1 = 1$ *Answer*

Since $\dfrac{5}{7} \times \dfrac{7}{5} = 1$, $\dfrac{5}{7}$ and $\dfrac{7}{5}$ are reciprocals:

$$\dfrac{5}{7} = \dfrac{1}{\frac{7}{5}} \quad \text{and} \quad \dfrac{7}{5} = \dfrac{1}{\frac{5}{7}}.$$

Oral Exercises

State the reciprocal, or multiplicative inverse, of each number.

1. $2\dfrac{1}{2}$

2. -3 $-\dfrac{1}{3}$

3. 1 1

4. $\dfrac{1}{6}$ 6

5. -5 $-\dfrac{1}{5}$

6. $\dfrac{7}{6}$ $\dfrac{6}{7}$

7. $-\dfrac{1}{10}$ -10

8. $-\dfrac{2}{5}$ $-\dfrac{5}{2}$

9. $\dfrac{x}{2}$, $x \neq 0$ $\dfrac{2}{x}$

10. $\dfrac{a}{4}$, $a \neq 0$ $\dfrac{4}{a}$

11. $\dfrac{7}{b}$, $b \neq 0$ $\dfrac{b}{7}$

12. $-\dfrac{1}{d}$, $d \neq 0$ $-d$

Written Exercises

Simplify each expression.

Sample 1 $-72xy\left(-\dfrac{1}{9}\right) = \left[-72\left(-\dfrac{1}{9}\right)\right]xy$

$$= [(-1)(-1)]\left(72 \cdot \dfrac{1}{9}\right)xy$$

$$= 1 \cdot 8 \cdot xy$$

$$= 8xy \quad Answer$$

A 1. $\dfrac{1}{6}(12)$ 2

2. $\dfrac{1}{13}(26)$ 2

3. $100\left(-\dfrac{1}{10}\right)$ -10

4. $\left(-\dfrac{1}{4}\right)(-40)$ 10

5. $72\left(-\dfrac{1}{6}\right)\left(-\dfrac{1}{12}\right)$ 1

6. $(-51)\left(-\dfrac{1}{3}\right)$ 17

7. $\dfrac{1}{-3} \cdot 39 \cdot \dfrac{1}{2}$ $-\dfrac{13}{2}$

8. $(-54)\left(\dfrac{1}{9}\right)\left(\dfrac{1}{-3}\right)$ 2

9. $3ab\left(-\dfrac{1}{3}\right)$ $-ab$

10. $11xy\left(-\dfrac{1}{11}\right)$ $-xy$

11. $\dfrac{1}{a}(6ab)$, $a \neq 0$ $6b$

12. $(2rs)\dfrac{1}{r}$, $r \neq 0$ $2s$

13. $(-14a^2)\left(-\dfrac{1}{2}\right)$ $7a^2$

14. $(-60c^3)\left(\dfrac{1}{10}\right)$ $-6c^3$

15. $-\dfrac{1}{7}(28c^4)$ $-4c^4$

Sample 2 $\frac{1}{2}[12r + (-8s)] = \frac{1}{2}(12r) + \frac{1}{2}(-8s)$

$$= \left(\frac{1}{2} \cdot 12\right)r + \left[\frac{1}{2}(-8)\right]s$$
$$= 6r + (-4)s$$
$$= 6r - 4s \quad Answer$$

16. $-\frac{1}{13}(-130c^7)$ **10c⁷** 17. $\frac{1}{2}(6x + 10)$ **3x + 5**   18. $\frac{1}{4}(12a + 16)$ **3a + 4**

19. $-\frac{1}{3}(-21a + 36b)$ 20. $[8r + (-8s)]\left(-\frac{1}{2}\right)$ 21. $[-25x + (-5)y]\left(-\frac{1}{5}\right)$ **5x + y**
    7a − 12b   **−4r + 4s**

22. $-\frac{1}{7}(49u + 84v)$ 23. $\frac{1}{6}(-6b^2 + 6c^2)$ 24. $\frac{1}{8}[16a^4 + (-16)b^4]$ **2a⁴ − 2b⁴**
    −7u − 12v   **−b² + c²**

★ Self-Test 1

Be sure that you understand these terms:

commutative property for multiplication (p. 63)
associative property for multiplication (p. 63)
distributive property of multiplication with respect to addition (p. 67)
reciprocal (p. 70)
multiplicative inverse (p. 70)

Be sure that you understand this symbol:

$\frac{1}{b}$ (p. 70)

Simplify.

1. $(4)(12)$ 2. $(-4)(-12)$ Objective 3-1, p. 63
3. $4(-12)$ 4. $(-4)(12)$
5. $(-2)^3$ 6. $(-1)^{16}$
7. $-7(6 + 5)$ 8. $6[2 + (-7)]$ Objective 3-2, p. 67
9. $4(70 + 5)$ 10. $3[80 + (-1)]$
11. $\frac{1}{5}(5x)$ 12. $\frac{1}{9}(-18y)$ Objective 3-3, p. 70

13. $\frac{1}{3}(6a + 9)$ 14. $\frac{1}{5}(10 - 15b)$

Check your answers with those printed at the back of the book.

Consumer Note $$$$$$$$$$$$$$$$$$$$$$$$$$$$$$$$$$$
Unit Pricing

On the market shelves you often see two prices: a price for the item and a "unit price" giving the price per unit of weight or volume.

For example, a 12-ounce jar of jam is marked:

77¢, $1.03 per pound

Since 12 ounces $= \frac{3}{4}$ pound, the unit price per pound is found as follows:

$$\frac{0.77}{\frac{3}{4}} = \frac{4}{3} \times 0.77 \doteq 1.03$$

[The jar is also marked with the weight as 340 grams. The unit price per kilogram could be found as

$$\frac{0.77}{0.34} \doteq 2.26$$

or $2.26 per kilogram.]

You can compare prices by looking at the unit prices. The article with the lowest unit price is the least expensive provided you can use the entire amount. (It is not economical to buy a large size if you cannot use it up in a reasonable time. *Your* unit price is the price per unit that you *used*.) Also you have to consider whether the amount is the significant feature. For example, does the box of detergent with the lowest price per pound give you the best cleaning power?

1. A can of corn chowder gives the weight of the contents as 15 ounces, and the price is 45¢. What is the unit price per pound? **$.48 per pound**

2. A 12-ounce can of vegetable juice costs 23¢ and a 24-ounce can costs 43¢. Is it cheaper to buy two 12-ounce cans or one 24-ounce can? **one 24-ounce can**

Watch for the unit prices as you shop and look to see how the unit prices are computed.

Puzzle Time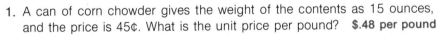

Find at least three numbers such that:

there is a remainder of 1 when the number is divided by 2.
there is a remainder of 2 when the number is divided by 3.
there is a remainder of 3 when the number is divided by 4.

Three possible numbers are 11, 23, and 35.

Transforming Equations

$\mathbf{3\text{-}4}$ Transforming Equations by Multiplication

OBJECTIVE To learn how to use "transformation by multiplication" to solve simple equations.

Bob said: "I am the same age as my sister Ann. My mother is three times as old as Ann, and my father is three times as old as I." From this information you can conclude that Bob's parents are the same age: If Ann's age is a and Bob's age is b, then

$$a = b \text{ and therefore } 3a = 3b.$$

Bob's mother's age is $3a$, and his father's age is $3b$. This example illustrates the following property:

> **Multiplication Property of Equality**
>
> If $a = b$, then $ac = bc$ and $ca = cb$.

This property guarantees that:

> The following transformation produces an equivalent equation.
>
> **Transformation by Multiplication.** Multiplying each member of a given equation by the same *nonzero* number.

What happens if you multiply each member of an equation by zero? Look at this example:

$$2x = 8 \rightarrow \text{Solution is 4.}$$

Multiply each member by 0: $0(2x) = 0 \cdot 8$

$$(0 \cdot 2)x = 0$$

$$0 \cdot x = 0 \rightarrow \text{Solution set is the set of real numbers.}$$

The first equation has 4 as its *only* root, but *any* real number will satisfy $0 \cdot x = 0$. *Multiplication by 0 cannot be used* because it does not, in general, produce an equivalent equation.

Example 1 Solve $5x = 35$.

Solution

$$5x = 35$$
$$\frac{1}{5}(5x) = \frac{1}{5} \cdot 35$$
$$x = 7$$

To obtain x alone in the left member, multiply the product $5x$ by $\frac{1}{5}$, the reciprocal of 5.

Check: If $x = 7$, then
$$5x = 5 \cdot 7 = 35. \checkmark$$
∴ the solution is 7. *Answer*

Example 2 Solve $\frac{1}{4}t = -6$.

Solution

$$\frac{1}{4}t = -6$$
$$4 \cdot \frac{1}{4}t = 4 \cdot (-6)$$
$$t = -24$$

To obtain t alone in the left member, multiply the product $\frac{1}{4}t$ by 4, the reciprocal of $\frac{1}{4}$.

Check: If $t = -24$, then
$$\frac{1}{4}t = \frac{1}{4}(-24) = -6. \checkmark$$
∴ the solution is -24. *Answer*

When you replace

$$\text{``}\frac{1}{5}(5x)\text{''} \text{ by ``}x\text{''},\quad \text{or ``}4 \cdot \frac{1}{4}t\text{'' by ``}t\text{''},$$

you use a very helpful idea: to "undo" multiplication by a number, multiply the product by the reciprocal of that number. In general:

If $b \neq 0$, then $\frac{1}{b}(ba) = a$.

Example 3 Solve $-3z = 51$.

Solution

$$-3z = 51$$
$$-\frac{1}{3}(-3z) = -\frac{1}{3} \cdot 51$$
$$z = -17$$

Check: If $z = -17$, then
$$-3z = -3(-17) = 51. \checkmark$$
$\therefore$ the solution is -17. *Answer*

Oral Exercises

Tell the number by which each member of the first equation must be multiplied to produce the second equation. Then tell the root of the first equation.

1. $\frac{1}{3}x = 2$; $x = 6$ 3; 6

2. $\frac{1}{2}z = 6$; $z = 12$ 2; 12

3. $\frac{1}{10}t = 3$; $t = 30$ 10; 30

4. $\frac{1}{7}s = \frac{1}{7}$; $s = 1$ 7; 1

5. $3v = 15$; $v = 5$ $\frac{1}{3}$; 5

6. $6y = 18$; $y = 3$ $\frac{1}{6}$; 3

7. $-2r = 12$; $r = -6$ $-\frac{1}{2}$; -6

8. $-6x = -18$; $x = 3$ $-\frac{1}{6}$; 3

9. $\frac{1}{3}s = \frac{4}{3}$; $s = 4$ 3; 4

10. $\frac{1}{4}z = 6$; $z = 24$ 4; 24

11. $-\frac{1}{5}t = -3$; $t = 15$ -5; 15

12. $\frac{1}{3}u = 15$; $u = 45$ 3; 45

Written Exercises

Solve each equation.

A 1. $\frac{1}{7}u = 18$ 126

2. $\frac{1}{9}s = 12$ 108

3. $\frac{1}{6}x = -123$ -738

4. $\frac{1}{11}z = -111$

5. $7t = 91$ 13

6. $8v = -104$ -13

7. $-5y = 750$ -150

8. $-11w = 154$

9. $-5 = -\frac{1}{21}x$ 105

10. $-\frac{1}{5}z = -25$ 125

11. $12r = -60$ -5

12. $-25t = 625$

B 13. $\frac{1}{2}w = \frac{3}{2}$ 3

14. $\frac{1}{3}v = \frac{5}{3}$ 5

15. $-\frac{7}{5} = \frac{1}{5}s$ -7

16. $-\frac{2}{7} = -\frac{1}{7}x$

17. $-\frac{3}{4} = -\frac{1}{8}t$ 6

18. $\frac{2}{5} = -\frac{1}{20}z$ -8

19. $-2y = \frac{2}{5}$ $-\frac{1}{5}$

20. $-3u = -\frac{3}{2}$ $\frac{1}{2}$

21. $4t = \frac{16}{5}$ $\frac{4}{5}$

22. $2x = -\frac{14}{3}$ $-\frac{7}{3}$

23. $-5s = \frac{1}{2}$ $-\frac{1}{10}$

24. $10z = -\frac{1}{2}$

Problems

Solve.

A 1. The perimeter of a square is 84 meters. How long is each side of the square?   **21 m**

2. The perimeter of an equilateral triangle (all sides of the same length) is 84 meters. What is the length of each side of the triangle?   **28 m**

3. Twelve-year-old Jenny is one fourth as old as her father. How old is he?   **48 years old**

4. One eighth of a pie is sold for 25¢. How much will be received when all the pieces have been sold?   **$2.00**

5. Six pencils cost 96¢. How much did each pencil cost?   **16¢**

6. Twelve eggs cost 84¢. How much is one egg worth?   **7¢**

7. The area of a rectangle is 72 square kilometers. Its width is 6 kilometers. What is its length?   **12 km**

8. A triangular region has base 16 centimeters long and area 16 square centimeters. Find its height.   **2 cm**

Historical Note
Multiplication Sign

The diagram below has lines to show the pattern for finding the product 25 × 43:

$$5 \times 3 = 15$$

$$5 \times 40 = 200$$

$$20 \times 3 = 60$$

$$20 \times 40 = \underline{800}$$

$$1075$$

Perhaps this pattern suggested using the × as a symbol for multiplication. William Oughtred (pronounced *Ott*-red), an English clergyman, used a small raised cross to indicate multiplication in a mathematics book published in 1631. On the other hand, a French mathematician, Adrien M. Legendre (Le-*zhondre*) used a large cross in his book on geometry, published in 1794.

In 1698, the dot for multiplication was introduced by Gottfried W. von Leibniz (pronounced *Lyp*-nits), a German mathematician. He thought that the × sign could be mistaken too easily for the letter *x*. In the United States, the multiplication dot is raised and the decimal point is on the line of writing. In some other countries, the usage is reversed.

3-5 Division of Real Numbers

> **OBJECTIVE** To learn how to express quotients and how to simplify expressions involving quotients.

Because $4 \times 7 = 28$ is a true statement, you know that $28 \div 4 = 7$ is true as well. In general:

> If b is not zero, the **quotient** $a \div b$ is defined to be the number x whose product with b is a. That is,
>
> $$bx = a \quad \text{and} \quad a \div b = x$$
>
> are equivalent equations.

Quotients are often represented by fractions:

$$a \div b = \frac{a}{b}.$$

When you studied fractions, you learned facts like these:

$$\frac{5}{8} = 5 \times \frac{1}{8}; \quad \frac{7}{3} = 7 \times \frac{1}{3}; \quad \frac{12}{4} = 12 \times \frac{1}{4}.$$

These equations suggest the following rule.

> ### Rule for Division
>
> $$a \div b = a \cdot \frac{1}{b} \quad \text{or} \quad \frac{a}{b} = a \cdot \frac{1}{b} \quad (b \neq 0)$$
>
> Thus, dividing by a nonzero number b gives the same result as multiplying by the reciprocal of b.

You can show that this rule is correct by transforming the equation "$bx = a$" by multiplication as follows on page 79.

Solve the equation:

$$bx = a$$
$$xb = a$$
$$xb \cdot \frac{1}{b} = a \cdot \frac{1}{b} \quad (b \neq 0)$$
$$x \left(b \cdot \frac{1}{b} \right) = a \cdot \frac{1}{b}$$
$$x \cdot 1 = a \cdot \frac{1}{b}$$
$$\therefore x = a \cdot \frac{1}{b}.$$

Check the root:

$$bx = a$$
$$b \left(a \cdot \frac{1}{b} \right) \stackrel{?}{=} a$$
$$b \left(\frac{1}{b} \cdot a \right) \stackrel{?}{=} a$$
$$\left(b \cdot \frac{1}{b} \right) \cdot a \stackrel{?}{=} a$$
$$1 \cdot a \stackrel{?}{=} a$$
$$a = a \; \checkmark$$

You can use the rule to replace any quotient by a product; for example,

$$-28 \div 4 = -28 \times \frac{1}{4} = -7$$

or

$$\frac{-28}{4} = -28 \times \frac{1}{4} = -7.$$

Why must you never divide by zero? For any number a, $\frac{a}{0} = x$ would mean that $0 \cdot x = a$. If $a \neq 0$, no value of x can satisfy this equation because $0 \cdot x = 0$ for each value of x. But if $a = 0$, then every value of x would satisfy $0 \cdot x = a$. Therefore a "quotient" $\frac{a}{0}$ either would have *no* value or would have *many* values. Thus:

> Division by zero has no meaning in the set of real numbers.

But can you divide zero by any other number? Consider these examples:

$$\frac{0}{8} = 0 \cdot \frac{1}{8} = 0; \quad 0 \div (-3) = 0 \cdot \left(-\frac{1}{3} \right) = 0$$

Thus, *the quotient of zero divided by any nonzero number is zero.*

Is division commutative? You can see that

$$8 \div 2 = 4 \quad \text{but} \quad 2 \div 8 \neq 4,$$

and so *division is not commutative.*

Is division associative? You can see that

$$(12 \div 4) \div 2 = 3 \div 2 \quad \text{but} \quad 12 \div (4 \div 2) = 12 \div 2 = 6,$$

and so *division is not associative.*

> **Summary for Multiplication and Division**
>
> | Commutative Property for Multiplication | For all real numbers a and b: $a \cdot b = b \cdot a$ |
> | Associative Property for Multiplication | For all real numbers a, b, and c: $(a \cdot b) \cdot c = a \cdot (b \cdot c)$ |
>
> Division is neither commutative nor associative.

Oral Exercises

Simplify.

Sample 1 $\dfrac{-48}{6} = -8$　　**Sample 2** $\dfrac{16x}{-8} = -2x$

1. $\dfrac{18}{-3}$ -6　2. $\dfrac{35}{7}$ 5　3. $\dfrac{-15}{15}$ -1　4. $\dfrac{14}{-1}$ -14　5. $0 \div 9$ 0　6. $-6 \div (-6)$ 1

7. $\dfrac{36}{-6}$ -6　8. $\dfrac{-49}{7}$ -7　9. $\dfrac{64}{-8}$ -8　10. $\dfrac{-32}{-16}$ 2　11. $(-1) \div (-1)$ 1　12. $-16 \div 1$ -16

13. $\dfrac{x}{1}$ x　14. $\dfrac{y}{-1}$ $-y$　15. $\dfrac{15t}{-3}$ $-5t$　16. $\dfrac{-18a}{-6}$ $3a$　17. $\dfrac{b}{-b}$ $(b \neq 0)$ -1　18. $\dfrac{-c}{-c}$ $(c \neq 0)$ 1

Read each quotient as a product. Then state the value of the quotient.

Sample 3 $12 \div \left(-\dfrac{1}{3}\right) = 12 \cdot (-3) = -36$

$6 \cdot 2 = 12$　　　　$-10 \cdot 5 = -50$　　　　$8 \cdot (-2) = -16$　　　　$-1 \cdot (-10) = 10$

19. $6 \div \dfrac{1}{2}$　　　20. $-10 \div \dfrac{1}{5}$　　　21. $8 \div \left(-\dfrac{1}{2}\right)$　　　22. $-1 \div \left(-\dfrac{1}{10}\right)$

23. $60 \div (-10)$　　24. $36 \div (-4)$　　25. $-5 \div \dfrac{1}{x}$ $(x \neq 0)$　　26. $-1 \div \left(-\dfrac{1}{z}\right)$ $(z \neq 0)$

$60 \cdot \left(-\dfrac{1}{10}\right) = -6$　　$36 \cdot \left(-\dfrac{1}{4}\right) = -9$　　$-5 \cdot x = -5x$　　$-1 \cdot (-z) = z$

Written Exercises

Simplify each quotient.

A 1. $-128 \div 32$ -4 2. $102 \div (-17)$ -6 3. $27 \div \left(-\dfrac{1}{3}\right)$ -81 4. $0 \div (-19)$ 0

5. $\dfrac{-16}{-\frac{1}{4}}$ 64 6. $\dfrac{3}{-\frac{1}{2}}$ -6 7. $\dfrac{-10}{\frac{1}{3}}$ -30 8. $\dfrac{0}{-\frac{1}{5}}$ 0

9. $\dfrac{75x}{-15}$ $-5x$ 10. $\dfrac{84z}{-7}$ $-12z$ 11. $\dfrac{-105a}{3a}$ $(a \neq 0)$ -35 12. $\dfrac{-96c}{-12c}$ $(c \neq 0)$ 8

Find the average of the numbers in each set. The **average** is the sum of the numbers divided by the number of numbers.

Sample 1 $\{14, -8, -15, 1\}$

Solution $\dfrac{14 + (-8) + (-15) + 1}{4} = \dfrac{15 - 23}{4}$

$$= \dfrac{-8}{4} = -2 \ Answer$$

13. $\{-16, 7, -8, 5\}$ -3 14. $\{12, -17, -1, 14\}$ 2
15. $\{20, -3, -18, 2, -16\}$ -3 16. $\{21, -16, 0, -23, 13\}$ -1

Evaluate each expression if $x = 2$, $y = -1$, $z = -3$, $u = 6$.

Sample 2 $\dfrac{xz^2}{x - y}$

Solution $\dfrac{xz^2}{x - y} = \dfrac{2 \cdot (-3)^2}{2 - (-1)}$

$$= \dfrac{2 \cdot 9}{3} = 6 \ \ Answer$$

B 17. $\dfrac{xz}{u}$ -1 18. $\dfrac{2z}{xy}$ 3 19. $\dfrac{xz^2}{u}$ 3 20. $\dfrac{uz}{xy}$ 9

21. $\dfrac{x^2u}{yz}$ 8 22. $\dfrac{uy^2}{z}$ -2 23. $\dfrac{z}{x + y}$ -3 24. $\dfrac{u}{x + z}$ -6

25. $\dfrac{u + z}{y}$ -3 26. $\dfrac{x - y}{u + z}$ 1 27. $\dfrac{z - u}{x - y}$ -3 28. $\dfrac{z^2 - x^2}{z + x}$ -5

29. $\dfrac{u^2 - y^2}{u - y}$ 5 30. $\dfrac{x^2 + u^2}{y + z}$ -10 31. $\dfrac{(x + u)^2}{y + z}$ -16 32. $\dfrac{x^2}{y} + \dfrac{u^2}{z}$ -16

3-6 Transforming Equations Involving Division

> **OBJECTIVE** To learn how to solve equations involving division.

Example 1 Solve $-13 = -\dfrac{z}{3}$.

Solution

$$-13 = -\frac{z}{3}$$

$$-13 = -\left(\frac{1}{3}z\right)$$

$$-13 = \left(-\frac{1}{3}\right)z$$

$$(-3)(-13) = (-3)\left(-\frac{1}{3}\right)z$$

$$39 = z$$

Condensed Solution

$$-13 = -\frac{z}{3}$$

$$-3(-13) = -3 \cdot \frac{z}{-3}$$

$$39 = z$$

Check: If $z = 39$, then

$$-\frac{z}{3} = -\frac{39}{3} = -13. \checkmark$$

∴ the solution is 39. *Answer*

Example 2 Solve $6x = -54$.

Solution

$$6x = -54$$

$$\frac{6x}{6} = \frac{-54}{6}$$

$$x = -9$$

Check: If $x = -9$, then

$$6x = 6(-9) = -54. \checkmark$$

∴ the solution is -9. *Answer*

Because you can describe the method used in Example 2 as *dividing* each member of the equation by 6 $\Big($ rather than *multiplying* each member by $\dfrac{1}{6}\Big)$, you may call the method **transformation by division**.

Of course, transformation by division is just a special case of transformation by multiplication.

Oral Exercises

Tell the number by which each member of the first equation must be divided to obtain the second.

1. $6x = 12$; $x = 2$ 6
2. $7t = -7$; $t = -1$ 7
3. $5u = -15$; $u = -3$ 5
4. $-4z = 20$; $z = -5$ -4
5. $-9y = -9$; $y = 1$ -9
6. $-25s = -75$; $s = 3$ -25

Find the root of each equation.

7. $3z = 12$ 4
8. $2x = -14$ -7
9. $-5t = 20$ -4
10. $-7 = 7u$ -1
11. $0 = -3s$ 0
12. $-9r = -27$ 3
13. $x \div 3 = 12$ 36
14. $\frac{1}{2}y = -8$ -16
15. $10 = x \div 2$ 20
16. $4 = -\frac{1}{3}w$ -12
17. $-6v = -6$ 1
18. $11s = 110$ 10

Written Exercises

Solve.

A
1. $15t = 450$ 30
2. $30x = 510$ 17
3. $-243 = 27z$ -9
4. $-338 = -13u$ 26
5. $-7w = 119$ -17
6. $15y = -195$ -13
7. $-14z = -196$ 14
8. $-5u = 125$ -25
9. $-9a = -108$ 12
10. $12b = -288$ -24
11. $8s = -248$ -31
12. $-11t = 132$ -12
13. $6d = 222$ 37
14. $680 = 40v$ 17
15. $-187 = 11g$ -17
16. $-16k = 176$ -11
17. $5 = \frac{1}{84}j$ 420
18. $0 = -\frac{1}{99}m$ 0
19. $-\frac{1}{10}r = -71$ 710
20. $-33 = -\frac{1}{9}w$ 297
21. $27h = -648$ -24
22. $608 = -32q$ -19
23. $-39c = -507$ 13
24. $-22f = -924$ 42

Problems

Solve.

A
1. Seven times a number is -105. Find the number. -15

2. Eight times a number is -256. Find the number. -32

3. A 12-ride commuter ticket costs $12.96. How much does one ride cost?   **$1.08**

4. A season ticket for a series of six concerts costs $27. How much is that for each concert? $4.50

5. Six oranges cost 90¢. How much does one orange cost?   15¢

6. A box of 24 packets of tissues costs $2.40. How much does each packet cost? $ .10

7. A box of 12 greeting cards costs $1.80. How much does one card cost? $ .15

8. A box of 6 muffins costs 72¢. How much does each muffin cost?   12¢

Computer Activity

If you have access to a computer that will accept BASIC, type in this program for division.

```
10  PRINT "WHAT IS THE DIVIDEND";
20  INPUT D
30  PRINT "WHAT IS THE DIVISOR";
40  INPUT E
50  PRINT "QUOTIENT = ";D/E
60  END
```

The quotient will be given in decimal form, rounded to a number of significant digits, usually six.

Some small numbers will be given in exponential form with negative exponents. For example, 1/128 will be printed as:

$$7.81250E-03$$

This means 7.81250×10^{-3} or $7.81250/1000$ or 0.00781250.

(For more information about negative exponents, see pages 148–150.)

Biographical Note
Doris Margaret Wills

Doris Margaret Wills (1902–1963) was born in Maryland. She received her bachelor's degree from Cornell University and did graduate work at George Washington University. At first her interests were in astronomy. She worked at the Harvard Observatory and became acting director of the Maria Mitchell Observatory in 1928. In 1942 she became a research engineer for Brown Instruments Division of Minneapolis-Honeywell Regulator Company, which later became Honeywell, Incorporated. There she achieved recognition as an authority on the theory of control system engineering. Control systems may be used to regulate things such as the temperature of the rooms in an office building or the voltage of an automobile battery. The human body is equipped with complex control systems, one of which maintains body temperature. In 1959, Doris Wills and George K. Tucker published *A Simplified Technique of Control System Engineering*, which became the standard reference work in the field.

3-7 Using Several Transformations

> **OBJECTIVE** To learn how to use several transformations to solve equations.

If you watched someone build an equation, it would be easy for you to solve it: You would simply undo what the builder had done, as in the following example.

Building an Equation
$$x = 6$$
$$4 \cdot x = 4 \cdot 6 \quad \text{Multiply by 4}$$
$$4x = 24$$
$$4x - 9 = 24 - 9 \quad \text{Subtract 9}$$
$$4x - 9 = 15$$

Solving the Equation
$$4x - 9 = 15$$
$$4x - 9 + 9 = 15 + 9 \quad \text{Add 9}$$
$$4x = 24$$
$$\frac{4x}{4} = \frac{24}{4} \quad \text{Divide by 4}$$
$$x = 6$$

Notice that to "undo" the *subtraction* of a given number, you use the *addition* of that number. We call addition and subtraction **inverse operations**. Multiplication and division are also inverse operations.

The following steps are usually helpful in transforming an equation into an equivalent equation which can be solved by inspection.

> 1. Simplify each member of the equation.
>
> 2. If there are indicated additions or subtractions, use the inverse operations to undo them.
>
> 3. If there are indicated multiplications or divisions involving the variable, use the inverse operations to undo them.
>
> 4. If you can now solve the transformed equation by inspection, check its root in the given equation.

Example Solve $16 - 3(2t - 1) = -11$.

Solution

1. Copy the equation; use the distributive property and simplify the left member.
2. Subtract 19 from each member.

$$16 - 3(2t - 1) = -11$$
$$16 - 6t + 3 = -11$$
$$-6t + 19 = -11$$
$$-6t + 19 - 19 = -11 - 19$$
$$-6t = -30$$

3. Divide each member by -6.

$$\frac{-6t}{-6} = \frac{-30}{-6}$$
$$t = 5$$

Check: If $t = 5$, then $16 - 3(2t - 1) = 16 - 3(2 \cdot 5 - 1)$
$$= 16 - 3(10 - 1)$$
$$= 16 - 3 \cdot 9 = -11 \checkmark$$

$\therefore$ the solution is 5. *Answer*

Oral Exercises

1. To solve "$3x + 4 = 7$," you first __?__ and then you __?__. subtract 4; divide by 3
2. To solve "$5x - 3 = 7$," you first __?__ and then you __?__. add 3; divide by 5
3. To solve "$\frac{1}{4}x - 5 = -3$," you first __?__ and then you __?__. add 5; multiply by 4
4. To solve "$\frac{1}{3}x + 4 = 6$," you first __?__ and then you __?__. subtract 4; multiply by 3

Written Exercises

Solve.

A 1. $2t + 3 = 11$ 4
2. $3y - 1 = 14$ 5
3. $5x - 11 = -16$ -1
4. $4w + 2 = -10$ -3

5. $\frac{z}{2} - 2 = 5$ 14
6. $\frac{u}{3} + 1 = 7$ 18
7. $\frac{t}{5} + 2 = -10$ -60
8. $\frac{-r}{4} - 6 = -1$ -20

9. $16 = 2 - 2x$ -7
10. $14 = -1 - 5n$ -3
11. $8 - 3x = 20$ -4
12. $1 - 5y = -9$ 2

13. $3z + 12 = 0$ -4
14. $5s - 55 = 0$ 11
15. $\frac{1}{2}t - 7 = -3$ 8
16. $\frac{1}{4}r + 6 = 5$ -4

17. $2(x + 1) = 0$ -1
18. $3(y - 1) = 0$ 1
19. $4(r - 2) = 12$ 5
20. $3(w + 3) = -15$ —

21. $2(s - 2) = 6$ 5
22. $3(t + 2) = 15$ 3
23. $4(a - 2) = -20$ -3
24. $5(b + 3) = -30$ -9

B 25. $3(x - 1) + 4 = -5$ -2
28. $5(z - 1) + 6 = 1$ 0
31. $7 - 3(x - 1) = 1$ 3
34. $3(5s + 1) + 2 = 50$ 3

26. $2(y + 1) - 5 = 7$ 5
29. $11 + 3(a - 1) = -1$ -3
32. $5 - 4(y + 1) = -3$ 1
35. $7 - 3(2r + 1) = -2$ 1

27. $4(w + 2) - 11 = -3$ 0
30. $13 + 4(b + 1) = -3$ -5
33. $2(3t - 2) - 3 = 11$ 3
36. $5 + 4(3v - 6) = 17$ 3

Problems

Solve.

Sample 1 Three times a number, increased by 20, is 41. Find the number.

Solution **Step 1** The problem asks us to find the specified number.

Step 2 Let n = the number. Then $3n$ = 3 times the number.

Step 3 $3n + 20 = 41$ **Step 4:** $3n = 41 - 20$; $3n = 21$; $n = 7$

Complete the solution. **Step 5:** $3n + 20 = 3 \cdot 7 + 20 = 21 + 20 = 41$ $\checkmark$

Sample 2 Four times a number, diminished by 3, is 13. Find the number.

Solution **Step 1** The problem asks us to find the specified number.

Step 2 Let n = the number.

Step 3 $4n - 3 = 13$ **Step 4:** $4n = 13 + 3$; $4n = 16$; $n = 4$

Complete the solution. **Step 5:** $4n - 3 = 4 \cdot 4 - 3 = 16 - 3 = 13$ $\checkmark$

A 1. The sum of twice a number and 21 is 83. Find the number. 31

2. The sum of three times a number and 7 is 40. Find the number. 11

3. Twice a number, diminished by 17, is -3. Find the number. 7

4. Forty diminished by twice a number is 6. Find the number. 17

5. Twenty-three increased by twice a number is 5. Find the number. -9

6. Six times a number, increased by 3, is 27. Find the number. 4

7. If you add to 7 the product of 4 and a number, you get 23. Find the number. 4

8. If you subtract 10 from the product of 3 and a number, you get -1. Find the number. 3

9. Team A's score of 39 points was one point less than twice team B's score. Find team B's score. 20 points

10. Team C's score of 92 points was 2 points more than twice team D's score. Find team D's score. 45 points

11. The perimeter of a rectangle is 24 and the width is 4. Find the length. 8

12. The perimeter of a rectangle is 36 and the length is 12. Find the width. 6

13. Add 5 to a number, multiply the sum by 2 and you get 4. Find the number. -3

14. Multiply by 3 the difference of 5 minus a number and the result is 27. Find the number. -4

3-8 Axioms of Algebra

> **OBJECTIVE** To learn the basic axioms of algebra and how these are used to form the structure of algebra.

Many rules or number properties have been stated earlier in this book. Some of these are *axioms*. Others are *theorems*. An **axiom** is a statement that is *assumed* to be true. A **theorem** is a statement that is *shown* to be true by using axioms, definitions, and other theorems in a logical development. The axioms that account for the rules or properties used in working with real numbers are listed below.

The domain of each variable is the set of real numbers except as noted.		
Axioms of Equality		
	Reflexive property $\quad a = a$ Symmetric property $\quad$ If $a = b$, then $b = a$. Transitive property $\quad$ If $a = b$ and $b = c$, then $a = c$.	
	Addition	Multiplication
Axiom of closure	$a + b$ is a real number. The set of real numbers is closed with respect to addition.	ab is a real number. The set of real numbers is closed with respect to multiplication.
Commutative axiom	$a + b = b + a$	$ab = ba$
Associative axiom	$(a + b) + c = a + (b + c)$	$(ab)c = a(bc)$
Identity axiom	0 is the identity element for addition: $a + 0 = 0 + a = a$	1 is the identity element for multiplication: $a \cdot 1 = 1 \cdot a = a$
Axiom of inverses	$-a$ is the opposite, or additive inverse, of a: $a + (-a) = (-a) + a = 0$	$\dfrac{1}{a}$ $(a \neq 0)$ is the reciprocal, or multiplicative inverse, of a: $a \cdot \dfrac{1}{a} = \dfrac{1}{a} \cdot a = 1$
Distributive axiom	$a(b + c) = ab + ac$ or $(b + c)a = ba + ca$	

Logical reasoning from known facts and axioms to a theorem is called a proof. The following examples show how theorems are proved in algebra.

Example 1 Prove: For all real numbers a and b, $(a + b) + (-b) = a$.

Proof

$(a + b) + (-b) = a + [b + (-b)]$	Associative axiom for addition
$b + (-b) = 0$	Axiom of inverses for addition
$a + [b + (-b)] = a + 0$	Substitution principle
$a + 0 = a$	Identity axiom for addition
$(a + b) + (-b) = a$	Transitive property of equality

We shall generally give a shortened form of proof, in which only the *key reasons* are stated. (The substitution principle and axioms of equality are not stated.)

$(a + b) + (-b) = a + [b + (-b)]$	Associative axiom for addition
$= a + 0$	Axiom of inverses for addition
$= a$	Identity axiom for addition

Similarly, $-b + (b + a) = a$.

Example 2 Prove: For all real numbers a and b such that $a \neq 0$ and $b \neq 0$,

$$\frac{1}{ab} = \frac{1}{a} \cdot \frac{1}{b}.$$

Proof Since $\dfrac{1}{ab}$ is the reciprocal of ab, we can prove that

$$\frac{1}{ab} = \frac{1}{a} \cdot \frac{1}{b}$$

by showing that the product of ab and $\dfrac{1}{a} \cdot \dfrac{1}{b}$ is 1:

$(ab)\left(\dfrac{1}{a} \cdot \dfrac{1}{b}\right) = \left(a \cdot \dfrac{1}{a}\right)\left(b \cdot \dfrac{1}{b}\right)$	Commutative and associative axioms for multiplication
$= 1 \cdot 1$	Axiom of inverses for multiplication
$= 1$	Identity axiom for multiplication

Oral Exercises

1. Which property of equality permits us to interchange the members of an equation?   **symmetric property**

2. Which two properties of equality would be used to prove the following?   **symmetric transitive**

$$\text{If } m = n \text{ and } p = n, \text{ then } m = p.$$

Give the key reasons.

3. $6 + (15 + 4) = 6 + (4 + 15)$ __?__   Commutative axiom for addition
   $= (6 + 4) + 15$ __?__   Associative axiom for addition
   $= 10 + 15 = 25$ Substitution principle

4. $(17 + 10) + 3 = (10 + 17) + 3$ __?__   Commutative axiom for addition
   $= 10 + (17 + 3)$ __?__   Associative axiom for addition
   $= 10 + 20 = 30$ Substitution principle

5. $20 + (-4) = (16 + 4) + (-4)$ Substitution principle
   $= 16 + [4 + (-4)]$ __?__   Associative axiom for addition
   $= 16 + 0$ __?__   Axiom of inverses for addition
   $= 16$ __?__   Identity axiom for addition

Note: Exercise 5 is an illustration of the theorem that was proved in Example 1 on page 89. However, it is not necessary to go through the steps again. Once a theorem has been proved, it can be used in other proofs. Thus:

$20 + (-4) = (16 + 4) + (-4)$ Substitution principle
$= 16$ Example 1, page 89,
        with $a = 16, b = 4$.

6. $-7 + 19 = 19 + (-7)$ __?__   Commutative axiom for addition
   $= (12 + 7) + (-7)$ Substitution principle
   $= 12$ __?__   Example 1, page 89,
           with $a = 12, b = 7$

Written Exercises

Give the values of the variables in the application of the theorem of Example 1, page 89.

Sample 1 $[6 + (-2)] + 2 = 6$

Solution $(a + b) + (-b)$ with $a = 6$ and $b = -2$

A   1. $(11 + 4) + (-4) = 11$ $a = 11, b = 4$ 2. $[6 + (-5)] + 5 = 6$ $a = 6, b = -5$

    3. $(-4 + 3) + (-3) = -4$ $a = -4, b = 3$ 4. $[-10 + (-3)] + 3 = -10$ $a = -10, b = -3$

    5. $[-12 + (-4)] + 4 = -12$ $a = -12$ 6. $(-7 + 9) + (-9) = -7$ $a = -7, b = 9$
                                $b = -4$

In the following exercises notice the cases in which

addition and opposite (additive inverse)

correspond to

multiplication and reciprocal (multiplicative inverse).

Give the missing reasons. Any theorem that has been proved can be used in later proofs.

7. **Prove:**   If $b \neq 0$, $\frac{1}{b}(ba) = a$.

   Proof:

   $$\frac{1}{b}(ba) = \left(\frac{1}{b} \cdot b\right)a \qquad \underline{\ ?\ } \quad \text{Assoc. axiom for mult.}$$
   $$= 1 \cdot a \qquad\qquad \underline{\ ?\ } \quad \text{Axiom of inverses for mult.}$$
   $$= a \qquad\qquad\quad \underline{\ ?\ } \quad \text{Identity axiom for mult.}$$

   Notice that this statement corresponds to $-b + (b + a) = a$. Compare this proof with the one given in Example 1, page 89.

   Similarly, $ab\left(\frac{1}{b}\right) = a$.

8. Prove the *property of the opposite of a sum:*

   $$-(a + b) = (-a) + (-b).$$

   Proof:

   Since $-(a + b)$ is the opposite of $a + b$, we can prove that

   $$-(a + b) = (-a) + (-b)$$

   by showing that $a + b + [(-a) + (-b)] = 0$.

   $$a + b + [(-a) + (-b)] = [a + (-a)] + [b + (-b)] \qquad \underline{\ ?\ } \quad \text{Comm., Assoc. axioms for add.}$$
   $$= 0 + 0 \qquad\qquad\qquad\qquad \underline{\ ?\ } \quad \text{Axiom of inverses for add.}$$
   $$= 0 \qquad\qquad\qquad\qquad\quad \underline{\ ?\ } \quad \text{Identity axiom for add.}$$

   Notice that this proof corresponds to that given in Example 2, page 89.

Sample 2   Prove the *addition property of equality:*

If $a = b$, then $a + c = b + c$ and $c + a = c + b$.

Proof

$a + c = a + c$; $c + a = c + a$ Reflexive property of equality

$a + c = b + c$; $c + a = c + b$ Substitution principle (substituting b for a in the right member)

9. Prove the *multiplication property of equality:*

$$\text{If } a = b, \text{ then } ac = bc \text{ and } ca = cb.$$

Proof: $ac = ac; ca = ca$ __?__   Reflexive property of equality

$ac = bc; ca = cb$ __?__   Substitution principle

Compare this proof with that in Sample 2.

10. Prove: If $a + c = b + c$, then $a = b$.

Proof: $a + c \qquad\qquad = b + c$ Given

$(a + c) + (-c) = (b + c) + (-c)$ __?__   Addition prop. of equality

$a = b$ __?__   Example 1, page 89

Similarly, if $c + a = c + b$, then $a = b$.

11. Prove: If $ac = bc$ and $c \neq 0$, then $a = b$.

Proof: $ac = bc$ Given

$(ac) \cdot \dfrac{1}{c} = (bc) \cdot \dfrac{1}{c}$ __?__   Mult. prop. of equality

$a = b$ __?__   Exercise 7, page 91

Similarly, if $ca = cb$ and $c \neq 0$, then $a = b$.
Compare this exercise with Exercise 10.

B 12. Prove the *multiplicative property of zero:*

$$a \cdot 0 = 0 \quad \text{and} \quad 0 \cdot a = 0.$$

Proof: $0 = 0 + 0$ Identity axiom for addition

$a \cdot 0 = a(0 + 0)$ __?__   Mult. prop. of equality

$a \cdot 0 = a \cdot 0 + a \cdot 0$ __?__   Distributive axiom

But $a \cdot 0 = a \cdot 0 + 0$.   Identity axiom for addition

$\therefore a \cdot 0 + a \cdot 0 = a \cdot 0 + 0$.   Transitive property of equality

$a \cdot 0 = 0$ __?__   Exercise 10, page 92

$0 \cdot a = 0$ __?__   Comm. axiom for add.

13. Prove the *multiplicative property of -1:*

$$a(-1) = -a \quad \text{and} \quad (-1)a = -a.$$

Proof: $a = a \cdot 1$ __?__   Identity axiom for mult.

$a + a(-1) = a \cdot 1 + a(-1)$ __?__   Add. prop. of equality

$= a[1 + (-1)]$ __?__   Distributive axiom

$= a \cdot 0$ __?__   Axiom of inverses for add.

$= 0$ __?__   Mult. prop. of zero

$= a + (-a)$ __?__   Axiom of inverses for add.

$\therefore a(-1) = -a.$ __?__   Exercise 10, page 92

$(-1)a = -a$ __?__   Comm. axiom for mult.

14. Prove: $\dfrac{1}{-b} = -\dfrac{1}{b}$

Proof: Proceed as in Example 2, page 89.

Show that $-b \cdot \left(-\dfrac{1}{b}\right) = 1$:

$$-b \cdot \left(-\dfrac{1}{b}\right) = (-1)(-1)\left(b \cdot \dfrac{1}{b}\right)$$ $\underline{\quad?\quad}$ Mult. prop. of -1; Comm., Assoc. axioms for add.

$$= 1 \cdot 1$$ $\underline{\quad?\quad}$ Substitution prin.; Axiom of inverses for mult.

$$= 1$$ $\underline{\quad?\quad}$ Identity axiom for mult.

15. Give the reason for each step in the solution of the equation on page 53 and prove the *rule for subtraction*. Given; Comm. axiom for add.; Add. prop. of equality; Assoc. axiom for add.; Axiom of inverses for add.; Identity axiom for add.

16. Give the reason for each step in the solution of the equation on page 79 and prove the *rule for division*. Given; Comm. axiom for mult.; Mult. prop. of equality; Assoc. axiom for mult.; Axiom of inverses for mult.; Identity axiom for mult.

17. Prove the property of the opposite of a difference:
$$-(a - b) = -a + b = b - a.$$

Proof: Proceed as in Exercise 8, page 91.

Show that $(a - b) + (-a + b) = 0$:

$$(a - b) + (-a + b) = [a + (-b)] + (-a + b)$$ $\underline{\quad?\quad}$ Rule for subtraction

$$= [a + (-a)] + [b + (-b)]$$ $\underline{\quad?\quad}$ Comm., Assoc. axioms for add.

$$= 0 + 0$$ $\underline{\quad?\quad}$ Axiom of inverses for add.

$$= 0$$ $\underline{\quad?\quad}$ Identity axiom for add.

$$-a + b = b - a$$ $\underline{\quad?\quad}$ Comm. axiom for add. and Rule for subtraction

18. Prove: $\dfrac{1}{\frac{a}{b}} = \dfrac{b}{a}$

Proof:

Show that $\dfrac{a}{b} \cdot \dfrac{b}{a} = 1$:

$$\dfrac{a}{b} \cdot \dfrac{b}{a} = \left(a \cdot \dfrac{1}{b}\right)\left(b \cdot \dfrac{1}{a}\right)$$ $\underline{\quad?\quad}$ Rule for division

$$= \left(a \cdot \dfrac{1}{a}\right)\left(b \cdot \dfrac{1}{b}\right)$$ $\underline{\quad?\quad}$ Comm., Assoc. axioms for mult.

$$= 1 \cdot 1$$ $\underline{\quad?\quad}$ Axiom of inverses for mult.

$$= 1$$ $\underline{\quad?\quad}$ Identity axiom for mult.

Compare this exercise with Exercise 17.

C 19. Prove that multiplication is distributive with respect to subtraction:

$$a(b - c) = ab - ac.$$

20. Prove that division is distributive with respect to addition:

$$\frac{a + b}{c} = \frac{a}{c} + \frac{b}{c}.$$

★ Self-Test 2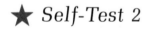

Be sure that you understand these terms:

transformation by multiplication (p. 74)
average (p. 81)
inverse operations (p. 85)
theorem (p. 88)

quotient (p. 78)
transformation by division (p. 82)
axiom (p. 88)
proof (p. 89)

Solve.

1. $\frac{1}{2}x = 13$ 2. $\frac{1}{5}x = 10$ Objective 3-4, p. 74

Simplify.

3. $\frac{-24}{8}$ 4. $35 \div (-7)$ Objective 3-5, p. 78

5. $-16 \div -4$ 6. $-25 \div \frac{1}{5}$

Solve.

7. $12x = -36$ 8. $-4x = 24$ Objective 3-6, p. 82

9. $2x - 3 = -5$ 10. $-3x + 4 = -5$ Objective 3-7, p. 85

11. The length of a sofa is 232 centimeters. That is 32 centimeters more than twice the width of the matching easy chair. How wide is the chair?

12. Give the key reason for each step: Objective 3-8, p. 88

$$4x + 5 = 29$$
$$(4x + 5) + (-5) = 29 + (-5) \qquad \underline{\quad ? \quad}$$
$$4x = 24 \qquad \underline{\quad ? \quad}$$

$$\frac{1}{4} \cdot 4x = \frac{1}{4} \cdot 24 \qquad \underline{\quad ? \quad}$$

$$x = 6 \qquad \underline{\quad ? \quad}$$

Check your answers with those printed at the back of the book.

Computer Activity

If you have access to a computer that will accept BASIC, try this program for practice in adding, subtracting, and multiplying integers. You should check the use of RND with your own system. [INT(17*RND(1)) would give a random selection from the set {0, 1, 2, . . . , 16}. INT(17*RND(1)−8) gives a random selection from the set {−8, −7, . . . , 0, 1, 2, . . . , 8}.]

This program will keep repeating the exercise until you get the right answer!

```
10   PRINT "HOW MANY EXERCISES WOULD YOU LIKE";
20   INPUT N
30   PRINT
40   FOR I=1 TO N
50   LET A=INT(3*RND(1)+1)
60   LET B=INT(17*RND(1)-8)
70   LET C=INT(17*RND(1)-8)
80   PRINT I;"."
90   GOTO A OF 100,150,200
100  PRINT "(";B;") + (";C;") = ";
110  INPUT R
120  IF R=B+C THEN 250
130  PRINT "SORRY; TRY AGAIN!"
140  GOTO 100
150  PRINT "(";B") - (";C;") = ";
160  INPUT R
170  IF R=B-C THEN 250
180  PRINT "OOPS; TRY AGAIN!"
190  GOTO 150
200  PRINT "(";B;") × (";C;") = ";
210  INPUT R
220  IF R=B*C THEN 250
230  PRINT "TRY AGAIN--BE CAREFUL!"
240  GOTO 200
250  PRINT
260  NEXT I
270  END
```

Looking Ahead

You have now learned the basic methods for solving simple equations. In order to be able to solve more complicated equations, you need to learn how to operate with expressions called *polynomials*. You will also need to learn how to work with *fractions*. The next three chapters are devoted to these topics.

Chapter Summary

1. Rules for multiplication of real numbers are based on the fact that $a(-1) = -a$.
2. The distributive property of multiplication with respect to addition is fundamental in computation in arithmetic and algebra.
3. Transforming an equation by multiplication or division (not by zero) produces an equivalent equation.
4. Inverse operations are used in solving equations.
5. The structure of algebra is built up of axioms and theorems proved by using the axioms in a logical development.

Chapter Test

Simplify.

3-1 1. $(-2)(3)(-3)$ 18   2. $(-2)^3(4)(-5)$ 160

3-2 3. $3[24 - (-4)]$ 84   4. $3 \cdot 20 + 7 \cdot 20$ 200

3-3 5. $\frac{1}{4}(16c^2)$ $4c^2$ 6. $\frac{1}{3}(6a + 3b)$ $2a + b$

Solve.

3-4 7. $\frac{1}{2}x = -12$ -24 8. $-\frac{1}{4}y = -7$ 28

Simplify.

3-5 9. $14 \div (-7)$ -2 10. $(-30) \div (-3)$ 10

Solve.

3-6 11. $3w = -33$ -11 12. $-5r = 125$ -25

3-7 13. $2a + 3 = 11$ 4   14. $-3 - 5b = 17$ -4

Give the reason.

3-8 15. $\quad\quad 3x - 4 = 26$
$\quad\quad\quad (3x - 4) + 4 = 26 + 4$ $\quad\quad$ _?_ $\quad$ Add. prop. of equality

16. $\quad\quad\quad\quad 3x = 30$
$\quad\quad\quad 3x \div 3 = 30 \div 3$ $\quad\quad$ _?_ $\quad$ Exercise 11, page 92

Programmed Chapter Review

3-1	1. The multiplicative property of -1 tells you that $(-1)(7) = \underline{\ ?\ }$.	-7
	2. $(-5)(7) = (-1)(\underline{\ ?\ })(7) = \underline{\ ?\ }$	$5,\ -35$
	3. $(-2)^3(5) = \underline{\ ?\ }$	-40
3-2	4. $3(7 + 14) = 3(\underline{\ ?\ }) + 3(\underline{\ ?\ })$	$7,\ 14$
	5. $3 \cdot 111 + 4 \cdot 111 = (3 + 4)(\underline{\ ?\ })$	111
3-3	6. $\frac{1}{5}(\underline{\ ?\ }) = 1$ 7. $7(\underline{\ ?\ }) = 1$	$5 \qquad \frac{1}{7}$
3-4	8. The multiplication property of equality states that if $a = b$, then $ac = b(\underline{\ ?\ })$.	c
	9. To solve $\frac{1}{3}x = 7$, you multiply both members by $\underline{\ ?\ }$.	3
3-5	10. The rule for division states that $a \div b = a \cdot (\underline{\ ?\ })$.	$\frac{1}{b}$
	11. $24 \div 8 = 24 \cdot (\underline{\ ?\ })$	$\frac{1}{8}$
3-6	12. To solve $6y = -30$, you may divide both members by $\underline{\ ?\ }$.	6
	13. The solution of $6y = -30$ is $\underline{\ ?\ }$.	-5
3-7	14. Addition and subtraction are $\underline{\ ?\ }$ operations.	inverse
	15. To undo a multiplication, you use $\underline{\ ?\ }$.	division
	16. To solve $-2x + 7 = 11$, you first subtract $\underline{\ ?\ }$ from both members; then you divide both members by $\underline{\ ?\ }$.	7 -2
3-8	17. A statement assumed to be true is called an $\underline{\ ?\ }$.	axiom
	18. Statements that can be proved are called $\underline{\ ?\ }$.	theorems
	19. The transitive property of equality states that if $a = b$ and $b = \underline{\ ?\ }$, then $a = c$.	c
	20. The identity element for addition is $\underline{\ ?\ }$.	0
	21. The identity element for multiplication is $\underline{\ ?\ }$.	1
	22. The additive inverse of 7 is $\underline{\ ?\ }$.	-7

Cumulative Review, Chapters 1-3

Simplify each expression.

1. $(15 + 3)5$ **90**   2. $24 \div (2 + 6)$ **3**   3. $12 + [3 + (5 - 1)]$ **19** 4. $\left(\dfrac{16 - 4}{3}\right) \div 4$ **1**

5. $8 + (-7)$ **1**   6. $-(21 - 12)$ **−9** 7. $-(4 - 14)$ **10**   8. $-2 + 8 + (-16)$ **−10**

9. $4 + |-3|$ **7**   10. $|6 + (-8)|$ **2**   11. $-|-3 + 5| + |-1|$ **−1**   12. $[4 + (-8)] + (-3 + 4)$ **−**

13. $(-5)(6)$ **−30**   14. $(-8)(-10)$ **80**   15. $-8(4)(-1)^3$ **32**   16. $3(-2) + 4$ **−2**

17. $3(a + 2b)$ **3a + 6b** 18. $\dfrac{1}{5}(25x^2)$ **5x²**   19. $38 \div (-9)$ **−4$\frac{2}{9}$**   20. $-18 \div (-6)$ **3**

Given $x = 5$, $y = 8$, $z = 1$, and $t = 0$, evaluate each expression.

21. xyz **40**   22. $(x + y)xt$ **0**   23. $\dfrac{3y}{2x - 2z}$ **3**   24. $4z^3 + 3t^2$ **4**

If $x \in \{1, 2, 3, 4, 5, 6\}$, find the solution set of:

25. $3x - 4 = 8$ **{4}** 26. $7 - 2x = 1$ **{3}**

Graph each set on a number line.

27. $\{6, 8, 12\}$ 28. $\{-4, -1, 0, 3\}$

Solve.

29. $t + 4 = 8$ **4**   30. $x - 3 = 12$ **15** 31. $14 = y + 12$ **2**   32. $25 = -18 + x$ **43**

33. $-14 = m - 12$ **−2** 34. $4 + r = -8$ **−12** 35. $-8 + t = -8$ **0**   36. $a + (-2) = -7$ **−5**

37. $\dfrac{1}{6}y = 3$ **18**   38. $-\dfrac{1}{3}m = -2$ **6** 39. $6y = -4$ **−$\frac{2}{3}$**   40. $-7t = -21$ **3**

41. $3x - 2 = 10$ **4** 42. $4y + 3 = 19$ **4** 43. $-4 - 3b = 11$ **−5** 44. $-3z + 5 = -22$ **9**

45. Eight more than twice a number is 14. Find the number. **3**

46. A house costs 7 times as much as the lot it stands on, and together the house and lot cost $40,000. What is the cost of the lot? **$5000**

47. Twelve less than a number is 14. What is the number? **26**

48. Lee drives 30 kilometers north from the office to see a customer. Lee then drives 50 kilometers south to see another customer. How far is Lee then from the office? **20 kilometers south**

Maintaining Skills

Remember how? $8.947 \div 2.3 = 3.89$

$$
\begin{array}{r}
3.89 \\
2.3\overline{)8.947} \\
6\,9 \\
\hline
2\,04 \\
1\,84 \\
\hline
207 \\
207 \\
\hline
0
\end{array}
$$

Now practice: 1. $6.36 \div 1.2$ 2. $7.20 \div 0.15$
                            5.3   48

3. $17.16 \div 1.3$ 4. $53.13 \div 0.21$ 5. $16.224 \div 0.26$
            13.2   253   62.4

6. $40.32 \div 24$ 7. $6.2\overline{)0.19468}$ 8. $0.83\overline{)2.0833}$
            1.68   0.0314   2.51

To **round** a number to a specified place:
If the succeeding digit is 5 or more, add 1 to the digit in the specified place (and replace succeeding digits with 0). If the succeeding digit is less than 5, do not change the digit in that place.

Examples
To hundreds: $2470 \rightarrow 2500$
To hundredths: $0.247 \rightarrow 0.25$
To thousandths: $1.2245 \rightarrow 1.225$
To thousands: $24,376 \rightarrow 24,000$
To tenths: $1.24 \rightarrow 1.2$

9–16. Round each answer to Exercises 1–8 to an integer.
   9. 5   10. 48   11. 13   12. 253   13. 62   14. 2   15. 0   16. 3

Remember how? $28\% = \underline{\ ?\ }$ (decimal)
$28\% = 0.28$

Now practice: 17. $25\% = \underline{\ ?\ }$ 18. $15\% = \underline{\ ?\ }$
                            0.25   0.15
19. $1\% = \underline{\ ?\ }$ 20. $2.5\% = \underline{\ ?\ }$
         0.01   0.025

Remember how?
$$\frac{2}{5} = \frac{40}{100} = 0.40 = 40\%$$

Now practice: 21. $0.25 = \underline{\ ?\ }\%$ 25
22. $0.6 = \underline{\ ?\ }\%$ 60   23. $\frac{3}{5} = \underline{\ ?\ }\%$ 60

Remember how? $20 = n\%$ of 84

$$\frac{n}{100} = \frac{20}{84}$$
$$n = \frac{20 \times 100}{84} = \frac{2000}{84}$$
$$n \doteq 23.8$$
$$20 \doteq 24\% \text{ of } 84$$

$$
\begin{array}{r}
0.238 \\
84\overline{)20.000} \\
16\,8 \\
\hline
3\,20 \\
2\,52 \\
\hline
680 \\
672
\end{array}
$$

Remember how? 28% of $80 = n$

$$\frac{28}{100} = \frac{n}{80}$$
$$n = \frac{28 \times 80}{100} = \frac{2240}{100}$$
$$n = 22.4$$
$$28\% \text{ of } 80 = 22.4$$

$$
\begin{array}{r}
80 \\
0.28 \\
\hline
640 \\
160 \\
\hline
22.40
\end{array}
$$

Now practice:
24. $15 = n\%$ of 25 60   25. $18 = n\%$ of 360   5
26. $28 = n\%$ of 35 80   27. $110 = n\%$ of 100 110

Now practice: 11.16   71
28. 18% of $62 = n$ 29. 71% of $100 = n$
30. 8% of $240 = n$ 31. 110% of $180 = n$
            19.2   198

Working with Polynomials

Physical Science The Royal Observatory in Jaipur, India, was built in 1734. The shafts with steps cast shadows from which astronomers calculated the sun's distance from the equator.

4

Addition and Subtraction

4-1 Similar Terms

OBJECTIVE To learn how to use the distributive axiom to simplify expressions containing similar terms.

A mathematical expression using numerals or variables or both to indicate a product or a quotient is called a **term**. The expressions

$$4x, 2xy, 7, \text{ and } \frac{m}{m + n}$$

are all terms.

In such an expression as $5xy$, each factor is the **coefficient** (ko-e-*fish*-ent) of the product of the other factors. Thus, in the product

$$5xy,$$

5 is the coefficient of xy,
$5x$ is the coefficient of y,
$5y$ is the coefficient of x,
xy is the coefficient of 5.

However, when "coefficient" is used alone, it usually refers to the *numerical* coefficient. For example:

In the term $5xy$, the coefficient is 5.

Also, the coefficient of x is 1, since $x = 1 \cdot x$.

Example 1 Show that for every real number y,

$$2y + 8y = 10y.$$

Solution $2y + 8y = (2 + 8)y$ Distributive axiom
$\qquad\qquad\; = 10y \qquad$ Substitution principle

Because properties of real numbers guarantee that for *all* values of the variable, each of the expressions

$$2y + 8y \quad \text{and} \quad 10y$$

represents the same number as the other expression, we call them **equivalent expressions.** When you replace an expression containing a variable by an equivalent expression with as few terms as possible, you say that you have **simplified** the expression.

Terms such as "$2y$" and "$8y$" are called *similar terms* or *like terms*.

> Two terms are **similar** if they are exactly alike or if they differ only in their numerical coefficients.

For example:

$2x^2$ and $5x^2$ are similar terms.
$7xy$ and $-4xy$ are similar terms.

Example 1 shows how the distributive axiom enables you to replace a sum of similar terms by a single term. Notice that an expression, like "$2z^2 - 3$," in which the terms are unlike cannot be replaced by a single term.

Example 2 Simplify $2x + 3y + 4x + (-5y)$.

Solution

$\begin{aligned}
2x + 3y + 4x + (-5y) &= 2x + 4x + 3y + (-5y) &&\text{Commutative axiom for addition}\\
&= (2 + 4)x + [3 + (-5)]y &&\text{Distributive axiom}\\
&= 6x + (-2)y &&\text{Substitution principle}\\
&= 6x - 2y &&\text{Rule for subtraction}
\end{aligned}$

Oral Exercises

Pick out the similar terms.

1. 2m, 3mn, −2n, −5m, 7n, −3mn
2. 3ab, −4b, −3a, 7ab, 6ba, −2a
3. 3x², −4x²y, −2x, 5y, 7x², −2xy², 6x²y, 7y
4. 7r²s², −6r², 5s², 6r²s, −4r²s², −3r², 5r²s, 3r²

Simplify.

5. 2a + 3a   5a   6. 7m + 4m   11m   7. 6d + (−4)d   2d   8. −11p + 3p   −8p

9. a + b + 2b + (−3)a   −2a + 3b   10. 3x + 4x + y + 2z + 3y + z   7x + 4y + 3z

11. r + s + 2s − 3r   −2r + 3s   12. 7p − 8q + 6q + 3p − 2q   10p − 4q

Written Exercises

Simplify.

A 1. x + 2y + (−x)   2y
3. 4a + (−2b) + (−2a) + b   2a − b
5. −15s + 12 + 20s + (−29)   5s − 17
7. 17x + 3y + 30x + (−5y)   47x − 2y
9. 4p − 6q + 6q − 10p + q   −6p + q
11. −r + 7 + 3r − 9 − 2r   −2

2. 3a + 2c + (−a)   2a + 2c
4. 5c + (−6d) + (−7c) + d   −2c − 5d
6. −11t + (−31) + 7t + (−9)   −4t − 40
8. −13m + 26n + (−19m) + 14n   −32m + 40n
10. 3a + 7b − 3a − 9b   −2b
12. 6 − a + 5a − 8 − 6a   −2a − 2

B 13. 3(a + 2b) + (−1)(b + 2a)   a + 5b
15. 6[h + (−m)] + (−3)(3h + m)   −3h − 9m
17. 2(−2a² − 4d) + [−(−3a² + 17d)]−a² − 25d
19. 2[3(−x² + x) − 1] − 5x − 6x²−12x² + x − 2
21. 5[−2 + 6(−4rp + 1)] + 4(12 − 7rp)
−148rp + 68

14. 5[c + (−d)] + 6(2c + d)   17c + d
16. −3(−7c + d) + 12[c + (−d)]   33c − 15d
18. [−(−6r³ + s³)] + 10(−r³ − 2s³)   −4r³ − 21s³
20. −7[2(−1 + 4mn) − 2] + 5(−mn + 7)   (below)
22. −4[x + 5(−3xy + x)] + (−1)(10 + 15xy)
45xy − 24x − 10

20. −61mn + 63

Just for Fun

Suppose that you earned 2¢ for each problem that you solved correctly, but had to pay back 1¢ for each problem that you failed to solve correctly. Suppose that after doing 45 problems, you were 15¢ ahead. How many problems had you solved correctly?   **20 problems**

4-2 Equations with Similar Terms

OBJECTIVE   To learn how to solve equations containing similar terms.

Example 1   Solve $2x + 3x - 3 = 22$.

Solution $2x + 3x - 3 = 22$ *Check:* If $x = 5$, then
$(2 + 3)x - 3 = 22$ $2x + 3x - 3 = 2 \cdot 5 + 3 \cdot 5 - 3$
$5x = 25$ $= 10 + 15 - 3$
$x = 5$ $= 22 \checkmark$

$\therefore$ the solution is 5.   *Answer*

Example 2   During a three-hour period, Val watched television for a number of hours and then listened to the stereo for twice as long. How long did Val watch television?

Solution

  Step 1 The problem asks how long Val watched television.

  Step 2 Let n = number of hours Val watched television.

  Then $2n$ = number of hours Val listened to the stereo.

  Then $n + 2n$ = total number of hours.

  Step 3 $n + 2n = 3$ **Step 4:** $3n = 3$; $n = 1$

  Complete the solution.   **Step 5:** $n + 2n = 1 + 2 \cdot 1 = 1 + 2 = 3 \checkmark$

Oral Exercises

Solve.

1. $2x + x = 12$ 4

2. $5y - y = 16$ 4

3. $2a - 5a = 6$ -2

4. $-5c + 7c = 42$ 21

5. $-5w + 2w = 21$ -7

6. $3z - z = -4$ -2

7. $5u + 3u = -16$ -2

8. $6v - 3v = -15$ -5

9. $6p + 5p = 22$ 2

10. $-5q - 3q = 88$ -11

11. $-2r + 5r = -9$ -3

12. $7s - 11s = -8$ 2

Written Exercises

Solve.

A 1. $3v - v = 12$ 6
2. $5r - 3r = 18$ 9
3. $3w - 2 - w = 8$ 5

4. $4t - 4 - 3t = 3$ 7
5. $y + 1 - 4y = 4$ −1
6. $r - 4 - 4r = -1$ −1

7. $0 = m - 16 - 3m$ −8
8. $7x - 2 + x = 14$ 2
9. $3t - 1 - t = -11$ −5

10. $0 = z + 5 + 4z$ −1
11. $x + 2x + 3x = 18$ 3
12. $3r - 2r + r = 30$ 15

B 13. $(k - 2) + (k - 1) + k = 0$ 1
14. $(1 - t) + (2 - t) + (3 - t) = 0$ 2

15. $3(z + 1) - 2z = -5$ −8
16. $2(y - 1) - y = -2$ 0

17. $2(1 - x) + x = 10$ −8
18. $2(2 - z) - 2z = 16$ −3

19. $3(2 - t) + 2t - 1 = 3$ 2
20. $4(3 - s) - 5 + 2s = 13$ −3

21. $2(r - 3) + (r + 3) = 9$ 4
22. $3(u + 2) + 2(u - 3) = -5$ −1

23. $3(x + 2) - (x - 1) = 17$ 5
24. $5(z - 3) - (5 - z) = 0$ $\frac{10}{3}$

C 25. $4(t + 2) - 2(1 - t) - 4t = 0$ −3
26. $5(v - 2) - 2(v + 4) = 6$ 8

27. $6 - [y + 2(y - 1)] = -1$ 3
28. $x - 2[4 - (1 - 2x)] = 0$ −2

29. $5z + 2[3(1 - z) - 2(1 + z)] = 12$ −2
30. $\frac{1}{2}[3(t + 2) - (2 - t)] + 1 = 7$ 2

Problems

Solve.

A 1. Joy Chen weighs eight times as much as her baby boy. When she stepped on the scale holding him, it registered 54 kilograms. How much does she weigh?   48 kg

2. Jane bought a soft drink and a sandwich for 75 cents. What was the price of each if the sandwich cost four times as much as the drink?   drink: 15¢; sandwich: 60¢

3. Matt beat his opponent by seven points in a game which ends when a total of 101 points have been scored. How many points did Matt have?   54 points

B 7. One number is 15 greater than a second number. When the lesser number is subtracted from twice the greater number, the difference is 75. Find the lesser number.   45

4. Jan rented a boat for 90 minutes to go scuba diving. She was under water for 12 minutes longer than she was in the boat. How long was she under water?   51 minutes

5. The side of one square is twice as long as that of a second square, and the perimeters of the squares differ by 36 cm. Find the lengths of their sides.   18 cm and 9 cm

6. Dr. Johnson took one hour to drive from her home to Mercy Hospital and back. The return drive took 8 minutes less than the trip to the hospital. How long did it take her each way?   34 and 26 minutes

8. Two numbers differ by 2, and 5 times the lesser diminished by twice the greater is 8. Find the numbers.   6 and 4

9. Joe: 68 kg; sister: 32 kg **10.** sofa: $274; chair: $142

9. Joe's weight is four kilograms greater than twice his sister's. Together they weigh 100 kilograms. What are their weights? *(above)*

10. Together a chair and sofa cost $416. If the sofa costs $10 less than twice the price of the chair, what is the price of each? *(above)*

11. Jan is twice as old as Pam and Rick is 3 years older than Pam. How old is Pam if the sum of Jan's and Rick's ages is 30? **9 years old**

C 13. A 2500-meter triangular course for a sailing race is marked off by buoys. The second leg is 50 meters longer than the first, and the third leg is 150 meters longer than the second. How long is the first leg? **750 m**

14. Kay has 6 more dimes than quarters and 3 fewer nickels than quarters. If she has 18 coins in all, what is their value? **$2.45**

15. During three summer months Ann earned $625. In August she earned twice as much as in July, and in September she earned $25 less than in August. How much did she make in each of the three months? *(below)*

16. Miguel weighs twice as much as Sally and 10 kilograms more than Bob. If their com-

15. $130 in July, $260 in August, $235 in September
16. Sally: 40 kg; Miguel: 80 kg; Bob: 70 kg

12. The edges of a long rectangular sheet 30 centimeters wide are bent up at right angles to form a trough whose width is 6 centimeters less than twice its height. What is the height of the trough? **9 cm**

$2h - 6$

bined weight is 190 kilograms, find the weight of each. *(below)*

17. The Katzes have 250 meters of fencing with which to enclose a rectangular plot and divide it into two parts with a fence parallel to the shorter sides. What should the dimensions of the plot be if it is to be 15 meters longer than it is wide? **44 m wide; 59 m long**

18. After the game was tied, the A's made 3 runs and the B's doubled their score. If the sum of the final scores was 15, who won? **B's**

Biographical Note
Benjamin Banneker

Benjamin Banneker* (1731–1806) was born and educated in Maryland. He became interested in science and mathematics, later specializing in astronomy. In 1789 he predicted a solar eclipse with a high degree of accuracy, and in 1791 he published his first almanac.

   He was appointed to serve on the commission to define the boundary of the District of Columbia and to lay out its streets. After that, he returned to his home in Maryland and resumed publication of his almanacs.

* Pronounced *Ban-eck-er.*

4-3 Equations Having the Variable in Both Members

OBJECTIVE To learn how to solve equations having the variable in both members.

Because variables represent numbers, you may transform an equation by adding (or subtracting) a variable expression to each member.

Example 1   Solve $5x - 3 = 2x + 9$

Solution

$$5x - 3 = 2x + 9$$
$$5x - 3 + 3 = 2x + 9 + 3$$
$$5x = 2x + 12$$
$$5x - 2x = 2x + 12 - 2x$$

$$3x = 12$$
$$\frac{3x}{3} = \frac{12}{3}$$
$$x = 4$$

Check: If $x = 4$, then $5x - 3 = 5 \cdot 4 - 3 = 20 - 3 = 17$
and $2x + 9 = 2 \cdot 4 + 9 = 8 + 9 = 17$ ✓
∴ the solution is 4.   *Answer*

It is possible that an equation may have *no* roots, or that it may be satisfied by *every* real number. Study the next two examples.

Example 2   Solve $3(2 - z) + 5z = 2(z + 4)$

Solution $3(2 - z) + 5z = 2(z + 4)$
$$6 - 3z + 5z = 2z + 8$$
$$6 + 2z = 2z + 8$$
$$2z - 2z = 8 - 6$$
$$0 = 2$$
Since the given equation is equivalent to the false statement $0 = 2$, it has no root.   *Answer*

It is convenient to call the set with no members the **empty set**, or the **null set**. It is denoted by the symbol ∅. Thus, we may say that the solution set of the equation in Example 2 is ∅.

Example 3 Solve $\frac{1}{3}(6t - 9) + 8 = 7 + 2(t - 1)$.

Solution $\frac{1}{3}(6t - 9) + 8 = 7 + 2(t - 1)$
$$2t - 3 + 8 = 7 + 2t - 2$$
$$2t + 5 = 5 + 2t$$
The given equation is equivalent to $2t + 5 = 5 + 2t$, which is satisfied by every real number.
∴ the solution set is the set of real numbers. **Answer**

An equation which is true for every numerical replacement of the variable(s) is called an **identity**. Thus,

$$\frac{1}{3}(6t - 9) + 8 = 7 + 2(t - 1)$$

is an identity.

Oral Exercises

Give the solution set of each equation.

1. $2x = x + 3$ {3}
2. $z + 5 = 2z$ {5}
3. $3t + 1 = 4t$ {1}
4. $2u - 4 = 3u$ {−
5. $x + 3 = 2 + x$ ∅
6. $2y = 3 + 2y$ ∅
7. $2x = x + x$
8. $2x = x$ {0}
9. $2x = x + 2$ {2}
10. $2x + 1 = 2x + 2$ ∅
11. $2(x + 1) = 2x + 2$
12. $2(x + 1) = 2x$ ∅

7. and **11.** set of real numbers

Written Exercises

Solve each equation. If the equation is an identity, or if it has no root, state that fact.

A
1. $7u = 5u + 8$ 4
2. $11t = 30 + 6t$ 6
3. $2x = 60 - x$ 20
4. $z = 49 - 6z$ 7
5. $10h - 35 = 3h$ 5
6. $4y + 37 = 1$ −9
7. $27u + 48 = 21u$ −8
8. $30k - 63 = 23k$ 9
9. $84 - 3x = 4x$ 12
10. $28 + 10r = 3r$ −4
11. $4z = 11z + 35$ −5
12. $6s = 10s + 24$ −6
13. $7x + 33 = 4x$ −11
14. $-6t = t - 14$ 2
15. $-3v = -8v - 15$ −
16. $-5k - 14 = -12k$ 2
17. $3z = -12 + 3z$ no root
18. $7t = 11t + 444$ −111
19. $5u + 3 = 3u - 5$ −4
20. $3r - 2 = r + 6$ 4
21. $7x - 2 = 2x + 13$ 3
22. $6w + 4 = -2 + 6w$ no root
23. $41 - 2n = 2 + n$ 13
24. $2 - k = 6k + 23$ −3

B
25. $3(x + 2) = 2x$ −6
26. $2(u - 3) = u - 1$ 5
27. $5(1 + t) = 2(10 + t)$ 5
28. $6(2 + t) = 4(3 - t)$ 0
29. $3k + 3(1 - k) = k - 6$ 9
30. $2(2 + r) - 3r = r + 8$ −2

31. $4(2y - 1) + 3 = 3y - 1$ 0
32. $3(z - 4) - z = 2(z - 6)$ identity
33. $4s - 2(1 - s) = 2(3s - 2)$ no root
34. $3x + 2(1 - x) = 2 + x$ identity
35. $4(v + 1) = 6 - 2(1 - 2v)$ identity
36. $n + 2(n + 4) = 1 + 3(n + 2)$ no root

C 37. $2[1 - 3(x + 2)] + x = 0$ -2
38. $3(1 + t) = 2[3(t + 2) - (t + 1)]$ -7
39. $2[3(1 + v) - (1 - v)] = 5(v + 2) - 2(2 - v)$ 2
40. $y - [2(1 - 2y) - 3(2 - y)] = 2(y + 2)$ identity

Problems

Solve.

A 1. Find a number which is 18 greater than its opposite.   9

2. Find a number which is 12 less than its opposite. -6

3. Find a number which is 24 greater than twice its opposite.   8

4. Find a number whose product with 3 is the same as its sum with 30.   15

5. Joan had three times as much money as her brother Jim, but when their uncle gave each of them three dollars, Joan had twice as much as Jim. How much did each have originally?   Jim: \$3; Joan: \$9

6. Steve has 10 steel balls of equal weight. If he puts 6 of them in one pan of a beam balance and the rest of them and a 50 gram

6. 25 g   7. quarters

weight in the other pan, the pans balance each other. How much does each ball weigh?

7. Maria and Judy pool their money and find that they have a dollar bill and 18 coins of the same kind. To divide the money equally, Maria takes 11 of the coins and gives Judy what remains. What kind of coins are they?

8. The sum of two numbers is 15, and their difference is 3. Find the numbers.   6 and 9

9. The difference between two numbers is 14 and their sum is 8. Find the numbers.   11, -3

10. Originally, Dave's father weighed three times as much as Dave. After Dave gained 15 kilograms and his father lost the same amount, his father weighed only twice as much. Find their original weights.   Dave: 45 kg
father: 135 kg

B 11. On Monday, Mike and Steve shot baskets, and Mike made three times as many as Steve. On Tuesday, Mike made 7 fewer baskets than he did on Monday, while Steve made 9 more. If they tied on Tuesday, what were their scores on Monday?   Steve: 8; Mike: 24

12. If the Panama Canal, opened in 1914, were 2 kilometers (km) longer, it would be half as long as the Suez Canal, which was opened 45 years earlier. How long is each canal if their combined length is 250 km?   (*below*)

13. A banana contains 3 more milligrams (mg)

12. Panama Canal: 82 km
Suez Canal: 168 km

of calcium than an apple and 40 mg of calcium less than an orange. How much calcium is there in an orange, if it contains the same amount as 5 apples and a banana?   51 mg

14. The three most populous countries of the world are China, India, and the Soviet Union, with a combined population of 1,650 million. Two hundred million more people live in China than in India, and the combined population of India and the Soviet Union is 50 million more than that of China. How many people live in each country?

India: 600 million
China: 800 million
Soviet Union: 250 million

4-4 Age Problems

> **OBJECTIVE** To learn how to solve some problems involving several ages.

Example Jim is five times as old as his dog, Arf. In nine years Jim will be twice as old as Arf. What are their ages now?

Solution

Step 1 The problem asks us to find the ages of Jim and Arf.

Step 2 Let x = Arf's age. Then $5x$ = Jim's age.

Step 3 The chart at the right shows some of the facts of the problem. This arrangement will help in setting up an equation. In nine years:

	Arf	Jim
Age now	x	$5x$
Age in 9 years	$x + 9$	$5x + 9$

Jim's age will be twice Arf's age.

$$5x + 9 \stackrel{?}{=} 2(x + 9)$$

Step 4
$$5x + 9 = 2x + 18$$
$$5x - 2x = 18 - 9$$
$$3x = 9$$
$$x = 3 \quad \text{(Arf's age)}$$
$$5x = 15 \quad \text{(Jim's age)}$$

Step 5 *Check:* Is Jim five times as old as Arf? $15 = 5 \times 3$ ✓
In nine years their ages will be $15 + 9$, or 24, and $3 + 9$, or 12; will Jim be twice as old as Arf? $24 = 2 \times 12$. ✓
∴ Jim's age is 15, and Arf's age is 3. *Answer*

Oral Exercises

Give an expression in answer to each question.

1. If Sol is y years old, how old was he 2 years ago? How old will he be 3 years from now? $y - 2; y + 3$

2. If Luisa is b years old, how old will she be in 4 years? How old was she 3 years ago? $b + 4; b - 3$

3. If Penny was *d* years old 10 years ago, how old is she now? *d* + 10
4. If Peter will be *q* years old 8 years from now, how old is he now? *q* − 8

Problems

Solve.

A 1. Karen is three times as old as she was eight years ago. How old is she now? **12 years old**

2. How old is Fred if next year he will be twice as old as he was seven years ago? **15 years old**

3. Roger is seven years older than his sister. In two years he will be twice as old as she. How old are they now? **Roger: 12; sister: 5**

4. Melissa's cat is five years younger than she

4. Melissa: 8; cat: 3
is. In two years Melissa will be twice as old as her cat. How old are they now?

5. A mother, aged thirty, has a seven-year-old son. In how many years will she be twice as old as he? **16 years**

6. Twelve-year-old Joe's grandfather is sixty-six. How many years ago was his grandfather ten times as old as Joe? **6 years ago**

B 7. Each of Ruby's parents is twenty-four years older than she. The sum of the three ages is sixty-six greater than Ruby's age. How old are they? **33 years old**

8. Juan is six years older than Anna, and the average of their ages is twice Anna's age. How old are they? **Anna: 3; Juan: 9**

★ *Self-Test 1*

Be sure that you understand these terms:

term (p. 101)   coefficient (p. 101)   equivalent expressions (p. 102)
simplifying expressions containing variables (p. 102)   similar terms (p. 102)
empty set (p. 107)   identity (p. 108)

Be sure that you understand this symbol:

Ø (p. 107)

Simplify.

1. $3x + 4x$ 2. $3a - 2b + a + b$ Objective 4-1, p. 101

Solve.

3. $2y + 3(y - 1) = 12$ 4. $5c - 2 - 3c = 16$ Objective 4-2, p. 104

5. The length of a rectangle is 5 centimeters less than twice its width, and the perimeter is 32 centimeters. Find the dimensions of the rectangle.

6. $2x - 4 = x + 2$ 7. $3(1 - t) + 2 = 2(t - 10)$ Objective 4-3, p. 107

8. Tom is twice as old as Ann. How old are they if the difference in their   Objective 4-4, p. 110
   ages is 6 years?

Check your answers with those printed at the back of the book.

Applications
Finding the Selling Price

The difference between the selling price and the cost of a product is called
the margin:

$$S - C = M$$

The selling price is often determined by deciding that the margin should be
a certain percent* of the selling price.

Suppose that the margin is to be 20% of the selling price. Then:

$$S - C = 0.2S$$
$$S - 0.2S = C$$
$$0.8S = C$$
$$S = \frac{C}{0.8}$$
$$S = 1.25C$$

Thus, an article that cost $8 would be sold at 1.25 × $8, or $10. This can
be checked by finding the margin: $10 − $8 = $2. Then $\frac{2}{10} = \frac{20}{100} = 20\%$ of
the selling price, as desired.

Find the missing values:

	Cost	% Margin Is of Selling Price	Selling Price		Amount of Margin		% (Check)	
Sample	$12	25%	$16		$4		$\frac{4}{16} = 25\%$	
1.	$30	25%	?	$40	?	$10	?	10/40 = 25%
2.	$18	25%	?	$24	?	$6	?	6/24 = 25%
3.	$16	20%	?	$20	?	$4	?	4/20 = 20%
4.	$20	20%	?	$25	?	$5	?	5/25 = 20%
5.	$27	10%	?	$30	?	$3	?	3/30 = 10%
6.	$36	10%	?	$40	?	$4	?	4/40 = 10%

* Review work with percents on page 99.

4-5 Problems Involving Integers

> **OBJECTIVE** To learn how to solve some problems involving integers.

You know (page 32) that the set of integers is

$$\{\ldots, -3, -2, -1, 0, 1, 2, 3, \ldots\}.$$

If you count by ones from any given integer, then you obtain **consecutive integers.** For example, 8, 9, 10, 11 are four consecutive integers; so are $-1, 0, 1, 2$. If n is any integer, then $\{n, n + 1, n + 2\}$, $\{n - 2, n - 1, n\}$, and $\{n - 1, n, n + 1\}$ are sets of three consecutive integers.

Example 1 Find four consecutive integers whose sum is 50.

Solution

Step 1 We are to find four consecutive integers whose sum is 50.

Step 2 Let $n =$ the least integer.
  Then the other integers are $n + 1$, $n + 2$, and $n + 3$.

Step 3 $\underbrace{\text{The sum of the integers}}$ is 50.
$$n + (n + 1) + (n + 2) + (n + 3) = 50$$

Step 4
$$4n + 6 = 50$$
$$4n = 44$$
$$n = 11$$
$$n + 1 = 12, n + 2 = 13, n + 3 = 14$$

Step 5 *Check:* 11, 12, 13, and 14 are consecutive integers, and
$$11 + 12 + 13 + 14 = 50 \checkmark$$
∴ the four required integers are 11, 12, 13, and 14. *Answer*

Alternatively, we might have chosen n to be the next to largest:

$$(n - 2) + (n - 1) + n + (n + 1) = 50$$
$$4n - 2 = 50$$
$$4n = 52$$
$$n = 13$$

The four integers would then be:

$$n - 2 = 11, n - 1 = 12, n = 13, \quad \text{and} \quad n + 1 = 14.$$

You call 24 a *multiple* of 3 because $24 = 3 \times 8$. In general:

> The product of any real number and an *integer* is called a **multiple** of the real number.

The multiples of 2 are the **even integers:**

$$\ldots -6, -4, -2, 0, 2, 4, 6, \ldots$$

If you count by two's from any even integer, you obtain **consecutive even integers.** For example, 8, 10, and 12 are three consecutive even integers, and so are n, $n + 2$, and $n + 4$ if n is any even integer.

The odd integers are those which are not even:

$$\ldots -5, -3, -1, 1, 3, 5, \ldots$$

Counting by two's from an odd integer yields **consecutive odd integers.** Do you see that if n is *odd,* then n, $n + 2$, and $n + 4$ are three consecutive odd integers?

Oral Exercises

1. If $n = 2$, what are $n + 1$, $n + 2$, and $n + 3$?   3, 4, 5
2. If $k = -1$, what are $k + 1$, $k + 2$, and $k + 3$?   0, 1, 2
3. If $m = 6$, what are $m - 1$, $m - 2$, and $m - 3$?   5, 4, 3
4. If $r = 1$, what are $r - 1$, $r - 2$, and $r - 3$?   0, −1, −2
5. If m is odd, is $m - 1$ odd or even? What is $m + 2$? $m + 1$? $m + 4$?   even; odd; even; odd
6. If k is even, is $k + 1$ odd or even? What is $k + 2$? $k - 1$? $k + 4$? $k + 5$?   odd; even; odd; even; odd
7. If m is odd and n is even, is $m + n$ odd or even?   odd
8. If m and n are even is $m + n$ odd or even?   even
9. If m and n are odd, is $m + n$ odd or even?   even
10. If n is an integer, is $2n$ odd or even? Is $2n + 1$ odd or even?   even; odd
11. If n is an integer, $2n$ is even. What is the next greater even integer? the next greater odd integer? $2n + 2$; $2n + 1$
12. If k is an integer, $2k + 1$ is odd. What is the next greater odd integer? the preceding even integer? $2k + 3$; $2k$

13. If *r* is a multiple of 3, what are the next two multiples of 3? the preceding multiple of 3?   *r* + 3, *r* + 6; *r* − 3

14. If *m* is a multiple of 10, what are the next two multiples of 10? the preceding multiple of 10?   *m* + 10, *m* + 20; *m* − 10

Problems

Solve.

A   1. Find two consecutive integers whose sum is 33.   16, 17

2. Find three consecutive integers whose sum is −9.   −4, −3, −2

3. Find three consecutive even integers whose sum is 60.   18, 20, 22

4. Find four consecutive even integers whose sum is 116.   26, 28, 30, 32

5. Find four consecutive odd integers whose sum is 0.   −3, −1, 1, 3

6. Find two consecutive even integers whose sum is 46.   22, 24

7. The sum of the least and greatest of three consecutive integers is 50. What is the middle integer?   25

8. The sum of the least and greatest of three consecutive odd integers is 110. What are the integers?   53, 55, 57

9. The larger of two consecutive integers is 10 greater than twice the smaller. Find the integers.   −9, −8

10. The larger of two consecutive odd integers is 7 greater than twice the smaller. Find the integers.   −5, −3

B 11. Find three consecutive odd integers such that the sum of the largest and twice the smallest is 25.   7, 9, 11

12. Find four consecutive integers such that the sum of the two largest subtracted from twice the sum of the two smallest is 15.   9, 10, 11, 12

Supply one of the words "always" or "never" to make the sentence true and give your reasons. You may find it helpful to express an even integer as 2*n* and an odd integer as 2*n* + 1.

Sample   The sum of two consecutive even integers is __?__ a multiple of 4.

Solution
   Let the consecutive even integers be 2*n* and 2*n* + 2. Their sum is 4*n* + 2. Since 4*n* is a multiple of 4, 4*n* + 2 is not.
   ∴ the blank should be filled with "never."   *Answer*

13. Twice an even integer is __?__ a multiple of 4.   always

14. Twice an odd integer is __?__ a multiple of 4.   never

15. The sum of three consecutive integers is __?__ a multiple of 3.   always

16. The sum of two consecutive odd integers is __?__ a multiple of 4.   always

17. The sum of three consecutive odd integers is __?__ a multiple of 6.   never

18. The sum of three consecutive even integers is __?__ a multiple of 6.   always

4-6 Adding and Subtracting Polynomials

> **OBJECTIVE** To learn how to add and subtract polynomials.

Terms like 3, x, $2y^3$, and $-4az$ are called *monomials* (mo-*no*-me-als).

> A **monomial** is a term which is either a numeral (3), a variable (x) or a product of a numeral and one or more variables ($2y^3$ or $-4az$).

A numeral is also called a **constant**. In an expression like $3x^2 + x + 4$, 4 is called the **constant term** or the **constant monomial**.

The **degree of a monomial in a variable** is the number of times that variable occurs as a factor in the monomial. For example,

$$7x^2y^6z \text{ is of degree } \begin{cases} 2 \text{ in } x; \\ 6 \text{ in } y; \\ 1 \text{ in } z. \end{cases}$$

The **degree of a monomial** is the sum of the degrees in each of its variables. Thus, the degree of $7x^2y^6z$ is $2 + 6 + 1$, or 9. A nonzero constant monomial has degree zero. The monomial 0 has no degree.

> A sum of monomials is called a **polynomial** (pol'-ee-*no*-me-al).

A polynomial such as

$$r^3 + (-3r^2) + (-r) + 4$$

is usually written as

$$r^3 - 3r^2 - r + 4.$$

A monomial may be thought of as a polynomial of *one* term. (*Mono-* means *one; poly-* means *many*.)

A polynomial of *two* terms, such as $x^3 - y^3$, is called a **binomial**. (*Bi-* means *two*.)

A polynomial of *three* terms, such as $ax^2 + bx + c$, is called a **trinomial**. (*Tri-* means three.)

A polynomial having no two terms similar is simplified or in simple form. The **degree of a polynomial** is the greatest of the degrees of its terms after it has been simplified. Since

$$2x^3 + 4x^2 - 2x^3 - 8x$$

can be simplified to

$$4x^2 - 8x,$$

its degree is **2,** *not* 3.

To *add* two polynomials, such as

$$3x^2y + y^2 + 5 \text{ and } x^2y - 2,$$

you write the sum and simplify by adding similar terms:

$$(3x^2y + y^2 + 5) + (x^2y - 2) = (3 + 1)x^2y + y^2 + (5 - 2)$$
$$= 4x^2y + y^2 + 3.$$

You may also write the addition vertically, as shown below. To the right is a partial check obtained by using the value 2 for x and 3 for y:

$$\begin{array}{l} 3x^2y + y^2 + 5 \longrightarrow 3 \cdot 2^2 \cdot 3 + 3^2 + 5 = 50 \\ \underline{x^2y - 2} \longrightarrow \underline{1 \cdot 2^2 \cdot 3 - 2 = 10} \\ 4x^2y + y^2 + 3 \qquad \text{Is } 4 \cdot 2^2 \cdot 3 + 3^2 + 3 = 60? \quad \text{Yes} \end{array}$$

In general:

> To add two or more polynomials, add the similar terms.

To *subtract* one polynomial from another, you write the difference and simplify. For example:

$$(10az^2 - 3z + 2a) - (7az^2 + z - 5a)$$
$$= 10az^2 - 3z + 2a - 7az^2 - z + 5a$$

$$= 3az^2 - 4z + 7a$$

Check by addition:

$$\begin{array}{l} 10az^2 - 3z + 2a \\ 7az^2 + z - 5a \\ \hline 3az^2 - 4z + 7a \\ 7az^2 + z - 5a \\ 3az^2 - 4z + 7a \\ \hline 10az^2 - 3z + 2a \end{array}$$

In general:

> To subtract one polynomial from another, add the opposite (the negative) of each term you are subtracting.

Oral Exercises

State the degree of the monomial and the degree in each variable.

1. $3x^2y^3$ 2. $5a^4b^2$ 3. $-2pq^3$ 4. $-7c^5y$ 5. $-2r^2v^3$ 6. $7s^7w^5$

7. xyz^3 8. $-r^2st^2$ 9. $2^3x^4y^7$ 10. $3^2a^3b^5$ 11. $(-1)^5c^4d^3$ 12. $(-1)^4x^3y^2$

Give the degree and the number of terms in each polynomial. If it is a binomial or trinomial, so state.

13. $3 + 2x - x^2$ 2; trinomial 14. $x^2 + y^2$ 2; binomial   15. $x^2y^2 - z^3$ 4; binomial

16. $t^3 - 3t^2 + 4t$ 3; trinomial 17. $uv^3 + u^3v + u^2v + uv^2$ 4; 4 terms   18. $r^4 + 3s^4 + 2rs + r^3s^3$
6; 4 terms

Simplify each expression for a sum.

19. $2x + 4$
$\underline{3x + 1}$ $5x + 5$

20. $x - 2$
$\underline{2x + 3}$ $3x + 1$

21. $x^2 - 2$
$\underline{x^2 + 6}$ $2x^2 + 4$

22. $t^2 + 1$
$\underline{2t^2 - 4}$ $3t^2 - 3$

23. $u + 2v + 1$
$\underline{2u + v - 1}$ $3u + 3v$

24. $x + y - z$
$\underline{x - y + 2z}$ $2x + z$

25. $t^2 - 2t + 3$
$\underline{2t^2 - t + 2}$ $3t^2 - 3t + 5$

26. $x^2 - 2xy + y^2$
$\underline{x^2 + xy - y^2}$ $2x^2 - xy$

27–34. In Exercises 19–26, subtract the lower polynomial from the upper one.

27. $-x + 3$ 28. $-x - 5$ 29. -8 30. $-t^2 + 5$
31. $-u + v + 2$ 32. $2y - 3z$ 33. $-t^2 - t + 1$ 34. $-3xy + 2y^2$

Written Exercises

Add. Check by evaluation, using 2 for x, 3 for y, 4 for a, and 5 for b.   (below)

A 1. $4x + 2$
$\underline{x - 1}$

2. $2a + 5$
$\underline{a + 2}$

3. $3a + 2b$
$\underline{a - b}$

4. $2x + y$
$\underline{x - y}$

5. $5a - 2b + 4$
$\underline{2a + b + 2}$

6. $4x + 5y + 6$
$\underline{3x - y}$

7. $x^2 - 2x + 3$
$\underline{x^2 + 5x}$

8. $3a^2 + 4$
$\underline{2a^2 + 3a - 1}$

9. $x^2y - a^2$
$\underline{-x^2y + 2a^2}$

10. $x^2 + y^2 - ab$
$\underline{x^2 - y^2 + ab}$

11. $a^2 - 2ab + b^2$
$\underline{a^2 + 2ab + b^2}$

12. $2x^2 + ax + b^2$
$\underline{3x^2 - 2ax - b^2}$

13–24. In each of 1–12, subtract the lower polynomial from the upper one, and check by addition.   13. $3x + 3$ 14. $a + 3$ 15. $2a + 3b$ 16. $x + 2y$
17. $3a - 3b + 2$ 18. $x + 6y + 6$ 19. $-7x + 3$ 20. $a^2 - 3a + 5$
21. $2x^2y - 3a^2$ 22. $2y^2 - 2ab$ 23. $-4ab$ 24. $-x^2 + 3ax + 2b^2$

Solve.

25. $3x - (2x + 4) = 2$ 6

26. $4t - (t - 3) = 3$ 0

27. $(2u - 3) - (u + 3) = 0$ 6

28. $(r - 2) - (3 - r) = 1$ 3

29. $(4x - 1) - (2x + 2) = x + 5$ 8

30. $(2t - 3) - (3 - t) = t - 2$ 2

B 31. $(x^2 - 2x + 1) - (x^2 - 4x + 3) = 4$ 3
32. $(p^2 + p + 1) - (3 - 3p + p^2) = 10$ 3
33. $(z^2 - 4) - (4 - z^2) = 2z^2 + z - 1$ -7
34. $(x - x^2) - (2x^2 + x - 1) = 5 + 2x - 3x^2$ -2
35. $2x - [6 - (x + 3)] = 12$ 5
36. $v - [(v - 2) - (3 - v)] = 3$ 2

★ *Self-Test 2*

Be sure that you understand these terms:

consecutive integers (p. 113)
consecutive even integers (p. 114)

multiple (p. 114)
consecutive odd integers (p. 114)

monomial (p. 116)   constant (p. 116)
polynomial (p. 116)   binomial (p. 116)
simple form (p. 117)   degree of a polynomial (p. 117)

degree of a monomial (p. 116)
trinomial (p. 116)

1. The larger of two consecutive odd integers is 8 less than 3 times the   Objective 4-5, p. 113
smaller. Find the integers.

Give the degree in x and then the degree.

2. $7x^3y^2z$ 3. 2^3xy^2 4. $x^2y^3 - 4x^3y$ Objective 4-6, p. 116
5. Put $3x^3 + 4y^2 - x^3 - 2y^2 - 2x^3 + 1$ into simple form and state its degree.

6. Add: $u - 2y + 3$ 7. Subtract: $2x + y - a$
         $3u + 2y - 1$ $x - 2y - 2a$

Simplify.

8. $(2z^2 - z + 4) + (z^2 + 2z - 1)$
9. $(2s^2 - 2st + t^2) - (s^2 + st - t^2)$

Check your answers with those printed at the back of the book.

Puzzle Time ∘°◯◯◯ ◯◯ ∘∘∘° ◯ ◯ ∘◯◯∘°

David is three times as old as Susan was when David was as old as Susan is now. Susan is now 16. How old is David now?   **24 years old**
Hint: The difference between their ages is always the same.

Multiplication

4-7 Multiplying Monomials

> **OBJECTIVE** To learn how to multiply monomials.

Recall that c^4 (read "c to the fourth power", or "c fourth") stands for $c \cdot c \cdot c \cdot c$, and that c^2 stands for $c \cdot c$. Therefore:

$$c^4 \cdot c^2 = \underbrace{(c \cdot c \cdot c \cdot c)}_{4 \text{ factors}} \cdot \underbrace{(c \cdot c)}_{2 \text{ factors}} = c^6 = c^{4+2}$$

(overbrace: 6 factors)

Similarly,

$$b^3 \cdot b^5 = \underbrace{(b \cdot b \cdot b)}_{3 \text{ factors}} \cdot \underbrace{(b \cdot b \cdot b \cdot b \cdot b)}_{5 \text{ factors}} = b^8 = b^{3+5}$$

(overbrace: 8 factors)

and

$$b^m \cdot b^n = \underbrace{(b \cdot b \cdot \cdots \cdot b)}_{m \text{ factors}} \cdot \underbrace{(b \cdot b \cdot \cdots \cdot b)}_{n \text{ factors}} = b^{m+n}$$

(overbrace: $m + n$ factors)

Thus, when you multiply two powers *having the same base,* you obtain a power having that base and whose exponent is the *sum* of the exponents of the factors.

> **Rule of Exponents for a Product of Powers**
>
> For all positive integers m and n:
>
> $$b^m \cdot b^n = b^{m+n}$$

CAUTION! You cannot use this rule of exponents unless the bases of the powers are the *same.*

> **To multiply monomials,** you use the rule for a product of powers together with the associative and commutative axioms of multiplication to find the numerical factor and the variable factors of the product.

For example:

$$(3u^3v^3) \cdot (-5u^4v) = [3 \cdot (-5)](u^3 \cdot u^4)(v^3 \cdot v)$$
$$= -15u^{3+4}v^{3+1}$$
$$= -15u^7v^4$$

Do you see that the degree of the product (11) is the sum of the degrees of the factors (6 + 5)? This may be used as a partial check.

Oral Exercises

Simplify each expression.

1. $a \cdot a \cdot a$ a^3
2. $z \cdot z \cdot z \cdot z$ z^4
3. $c^2 \cdot c$ c^3
4. $b^2 \cdot b^2$ b^4

5. $r^3 \cdot r^3$ r^6
6. $(-t^2)(-t^2)$ t^4
7. $(-x^3)(-x^3)$ x^6
8. $(2x)(3x^2)$ $6x^3$

9. $(3ab)(5a^2b)$ $15a^3b^2$
10. $r^2(3rs^3)$ $3r^3s^3$
11. $(-2pq)(-p^2q)$ $2p^3q^2$
12. $(-2xz)(4x^2z)$ $-8x^3z^2$

13. $x(xy)(x^2z)$ x^4yz
14. $(2r)(3st)(rst)$ $6r^2s^2t^2$
15. $2x^3(-3xy^2)(-x^3y^4)$ $6x^7y^6$
16. $wz^2(-w^3yz^2)(yz^4)$

17. $x \cdot x^n$ x^{n+1}
18. $y^n \cdot y^n$ y^{2n}
19. $z^2 \cdot z^{n-2}$ z^n
20. $t^{2n} \cdot t^n$ $-w^4y^2z^8$ t^{3n}

Written Exercises

3. $-4h^4k^3$
6. $12c^3d^3$
9. $-6p^5q^5$
12. $-2p^3q^3$
15. $k^3l^3m^3$

Simplify each expression.

A
1. $(4ab^2)(2a^2b)$ $8a^3b^3$
2. $(xy)(3y^2)$ $3xy^3$
3. $(-2hk^2)(2h^3k)$

4. $(4pq)(-p^2q^3)$ $-4p^3q^4$
5. $m(3mn)(2n)$ $6m^2n^2$
6. $(2c)(3c^2d)(2d^2)$

7. $2x(-xy)(-y^2)$ $2x^2y^3$
8. $-r^2(-2rs)(r^2s)$ $2r^5s^2$
9. $(3pq)(-p)(2p^3q^4)$

10. $x^2(-2xz)(4z^5)$ $-8x^3z^6$
11. $(-a)(-ab)(-b)$ $-a^2b^2$
12. $(-p^2)(-2pq)(-q^2)$

13. $(u^2vw^2)(uv^2w)$ $u^3v^3w^3$
14. $(ab^2c^3)(a^3b^2c)$ $a^4b^4c^4$
15. $\left(\dfrac{1}{2}klm\right)(2k^2l^2m^2)$

16. $(3pq^2r^3)\left(\dfrac{1}{3}q^2r\right)$ pq^4r^4
17. $(-x)(-2xy)(-3xyz)$ $-6x^3y^2z$
18. $(5r^3)(-3r^2s)(-rs^2t)$ $15r^6s^3t$

19. $x^n \cdot x$ x^{n+1}
20. $z^n \cdot z^n$ z^{2n}
21. $a^r \cdot a^r \cdot a^r$ a^{3r}

22. $c^k \cdot c^{2k} \cdot c^{3k}$ c^{6k}
23. $(-b^{n-2})(-b^2)$ b^n
24. $(-r^{k-2})(r^{k+2})$ $-r^{2k}$

Sample $(ab^2)(3a^2)(2abc) - (2a^2b^2)(-a^2bc) = 6a^4b^3c - (-2a^4b^3c)$
$$= 8a^4b^3c \text{ Answer}$$

B
25. $(2a)(3a^3) + (2a^2)(a^2)$ $8a^4$
26. $(c^2)(4c^2) + (-c)(2c^3)$ $2c^4$

27. $(3x)(-x^2)(-x) + (2x^2)(4x^2)$ $11x^4$
28. $(r^2)(-2r)(-6r^2) + (5r^2)(-2r^3)$ $2r^5$

29. $(a^2b)(2a^2b^3) - (a^2b^2)(-3a^2b^2)$ $5a^4b^4$
30. $(s^2t)(4st^2)(s^2t^2) - (-s^2t^2)(s^3t^3)$ $5s^5t^5$

31. $(2xy^2z)(5x^2y^2z^2) + y(-xyz)(-6x^2y^2z^2)$ $16x^3y^4z^3$
32. $(a^2bc)(ab^2c)(abc^2) - (2abc)(-a^3b^3c^3)$ $3a^4b^4c^4$

4-8 Powers of Monomials

> **OBJECTIVE** To learn how to find powers of monomials.

The expressions $2c^3$ and $(2c)^3$ are not equal (unless c has the value 0). You have:

$$2c^3 = 2 \cdot c \cdot c \cdot c \quad \text{but} \quad (2c)^3 = (2c) \cdot (2c) \cdot (2c)$$
$$= (2 \cdot 2 \cdot 2) \cdot (c \cdot c \cdot c)$$
$$= 2^3 c^3$$
$$= 8c^3$$

In general, if m is a positive integer:

$$(ab) \text{ is a factor } m \text{ times} \qquad m \text{ factors} \qquad m \text{ factors}$$
$$(ab)^m = \overbrace{(ab)(ab) \cdots (ab)} = \overbrace{(a \cdot a \cdot \cdots \cdot a)} \cdot \overbrace{(b \cdot b \cdot \cdots \cdot b)} = a^m b^m$$

This result may be stated as follows:

> **Rule of Exponents for a Power of a Product**
>
> For every positive integer m:
> $$(ab)^m = a^m b^m$$

For example:

$$(-2x)^4 = (-2)^4 x^4 = 16x^4$$

and

$$(7uv)^2 = 7^2 u^2 v^2 = 49u^2 v^2.$$

The base of a power may itself be a power:

$$(c^2)^3 = c^2 \cdot c^2 \cdot c^2 = c^{2+2+2}$$
$$= c^6 = c^{2 \cdot 3}$$

In general:

$$b^m \text{ is a factor } n \text{ times} \qquad n \text{ terms}$$
$$(b^m)^n = \overbrace{(b^m)(b^m) \cdots (b^m)} = \overbrace{b^{m+m+\cdots+m}} = b^{m \cdot n}$$

This leads to another rule of exponents:

> **Rule of Exponents for a Power of a Power**
> For all positive integers m and n:
> $$(b^m)^n = b^{mn}$$

You use both of these rules in this example:

$$(-5r^4s^6)^3 = (-5)^3(r^4)^3(s^6)^3 = -125r^{12}s^{18}$$

Oral Exercises

Simplify.

1. $(3x)^2$ $9x^2$
2. $(2z)^3$ $8z^3$
3. $(-2a)^3$ $-8a^3$
4. $(-4r)^2$ $16r^2$
5. $(t^2)^3$ t^6
6. $(s^3)^2$ s^6
7. $(r^3)^3$ r^9
8. $(m^4)^4$ m^{16}
9. $(ax)^4$ a^4x^4
10. $(cz^2)^2$ c^2z^4
11. $(-b^2c^3)^2$ b^4c^6
12. $(-u^3v^3)^2$ u^6v^6
13. $(-x^2)^2$ x^4
14. $-(x^2)^2$ $-x^4$
15. $a(ab)^2$ a^3b^2
16. $h(h^2k)^2$ h^5k^2
17. $(-a^2)^3$ $-a^6$
18. $-(a^2)^3$ $-a^6$
19. $-(-c^2)^3$ c^6
20. $-(-c^2)^4$ $-c^8$
21. $(b^2)^n$ b^{2n}
22. $(b^n)^2$ b^{2n}
23. $(ab^2)^m$ a^mb^{2m}
24. $(a^mb^n)^2$ $a^{2m}b^{2n}$

Written Exercises

9. $-24s^4t^3$ 10. $-3m^7n^2$ 11. $32w^7$ 12. $-4k^7$
13. $-4x^7y^8$ 14. $-s^7t^{11}$ 15. a^9b^7 16. $8u^6v^{10}$
17. $2x^6y^4z^4$ 18. $4u^8v^3w$ 19. $27c^7d^2$ 20. $-25p^{10}q^3$

Simplify.

A

1. $(5c)^2$ $25c^2$
2. $(2c)^5$ $32c^5$
3. $(-2x^2)^3$ $-8x^6$
4. $(-3r^3)^2$ $9r^6$
5. $a(2a^2)^3$ $8a^7$
6. $3t(2t)^2$ $12t^3$
7. $a^2(ab^2)^2$ a^4b^4
8. $r^3(r^2s)^3$ r^9s^3
9. $3s(-2st)^3$
10. $(-3m)(-m^3n)^2$
11. $(2w)^3(2w^2)^2$
12. $(-k)^3(-2k^2)^2$
13. $(-xy^2)^3(-2x^2y)^2$
14. $(s^2t)^2(-st^3)^3$
15. $(ab)^2(a^2b)^3(ab^2)$
16. $(-uv)^2(2v^2)^3(u^2v)^2$
17. $2x^2(xy^2)^2(xz^2)^2$
18. $(2u)^2(u^2v)^3(w)$
19. $(3c)^3(-1)^4(c^2d)^2$
20. $(-1)^5(5p^2)^2(p^2q)^3$

B

21. $a^2(ab)^{n-2}b^2$ a^nb^n
22. $(x^2y)^n(xy^2)^n$ $x^{3n}y^{3n}$
23. $x^{n+1}y^2(xy^2)^{n-1}$ $x^{2n}y^{2n}$
24. $(a^{n-1}b)^2(ab^{n-1})^2$ $a^{2n}b^{2n}$

Sample $3t(s^2t)^3 - (-s^3t^2)^2 = 3t \cdot s^6t^3 - s^6t^4$
$$= 3s^6t^4 - s^6t^4 = 2s^6t^4 \quad \textit{Answer}$$

25. $a^2(ab^3)^2 + b^2(a^2b^2)^2$ $2a^4b^6$
26. $u^3(uv^2)^2 + u(-uv)^4$ $2u^5v^4$
27. $x(3xy^2)^2 + y(-xy)^3$ $8x^3y^4$
28. $(2u)^3(uv)^2 + (2uv)^2(-u^3)$ $4u^5v^2$
29. $(-h^2k)^2(2h^2k)^3 + (-h^2k)^5$ $7h^{10}k^5$
30. $(r^2s)^3(rs^2)^2 - r(-rs)^7$ $2r^8s^7$

4-9 Multiplying a Polynomial by a Monomial

> **OBJECTIVE** To learn how to multiply a polynomial by a monomial.

You can multiply any polynomial by a monomial by using the distributive axiom and the rules of exponents. For example:

$$2c(3c^2 + d) = 2c(3c^2) + 2c(d)$$
$$= 6c^3 + 2cd.$$

If there are several terms in the polynomial, a vertical arrangement may be helpful:

$$3x^2y(x^2 - 2xy + 3y^2) = 3x^4y - 6x^3y^2 + 9x^2y^3 \implies \begin{cases} x^2 - 2xy + 3y^2 \\ 3x^2y \\ \hline 3x^4y - 6x^3y^2 + 9x^2y^3 \end{cases}$$

In general:

> To multiply a polynomial by a monomial, multiply each term of the polynomial by the monomial and write the sum of the products.

Oral Exercises

Multiply.

1. $3(x - 4)$ $3x - 12$
2. $2(2a - 1)$ $4a - 2$
3. $2(4 - c)$ $8 - 2c$
4. $-2(k - 1)$ $-2k +$
5. $x(x + 2)$ $x^2 + 2x$
6. $r(2r + 3)$ $2r^2 + 3r$
7. $t(2t - 3)$ $2t^2 - 3t$
8. $2c(c - 2)$ $2c^2 -$
9. $-a(2 - a)$ $-2a + a^2$
10. $-z(1 - 2z)$ $-z + 2z^2$
11. $x^2(x - 1)$ $x^3 - x^2$
12. $y^3(2y + 1)$ $2y^4 +$

13. $a - b$
    $\underline{a^2}$
14. $a^2 - b^2$
    $\underline{a}$
15. $x^2 - 2x + 1$
    $\underline{-x}$
16. $x^2 + x - 2$
    $\underline{2x}$

17. $c^2 + 3c - 2$
    $\underline{c}$
    $c^3 + 3c^2 - 2c$
18. $t^2 - 4t + 1$
    $\underline{3t}$
    $3t^3 - 12t^2 + 3t$
19. $y^2 + 2y + 3$
    $\underline{-2y}$
    $-2y^3 - 4y^2 - 6y$
20. $z^2 - z + 4$
    $\underline{-3z}$
    $-3z^3 + 3z^2 - 12z$

13. $a^3 - a^2b$
14. $a^3 - ab^2$
15. $-x^3 + 2x^2 - x$
16. $2x^3 + 2x^2 - 4x$

Written Exercises

7. $c^4d^4 + 2c^3d^3 + c^2d^2$
9. $-2a^3b + 6a^2b^2 + 4ab^3$
11. $-w^2z^3 + 2wz^3 - z^3$

8. $4xy^2 - 2x^2y^2 - 2x^3y^3$
10. $-r^4 + 4r^3s - 4r^2s^2$
12. $-p^3q - 4p^2q^2 - 4pq^3$

Multiply.

A **1.** $2(x^2 - xy + 3y^2)$ $2x^2 - 2xy + 6y^2$

2. $3(2r^2 - rs + s^2)$ $6r^2 - 3rs + 3s^2$

3. $-3(2 - x - x^2)$ $-6 + 3x + 3x^2$

4. $-1(3 + y - y^2)$ $-3 - y + y^2$

5. $2a(a^2 - b^2)$ $2a^3 - 2ab^2$

6. $3t^2(t^2 + 2t - 1)$ $3t^4 + 6t^3 - 3t^2$

7. $c^2d(c^2d^3 + 2cd^2 + d)$

8. $2xy^2(2 - x - x^2y)$

9. $(a^2 - 3ab - 2b^2)(-2ab)$

10. $(r^2 - 4rs + 4s^2)(-r^2)$

11. $(w^2z - 2wz + z)(-z^2)$

12. $(p^2 + 4pq + 4q^2)(-pq)$

13. $3x^2y(y - 2xy^2 + 3x^2y^3 - 4x^3y^4)$

14. $-2r^2s^3(r^4s^3 - r^3s^2 + 3r^2s - 3r)$

15. $-6k^2m^2(2k - 3m + 4km - k^2m^2)$

16. $5uv^3(u^3 - 2u^2v - 3uv^2 + 4u^2)$

13. $3x^2y^2 - 6x^3y^3 + 9x^4y^4 - 12x^5y^5$
15. $-12k^3m^2 + 18k^2m^3 - 24k^3m^3 + 6k^4m^4$

14. $-2r^6s^6 + 2r^5s^5 - 6r^4s^4 + 6r^3s^3$
16. $5u^4v^3 - 10u^3v^4 - 15u^2v^5 + 20u^3v^3$

Solve.

17. $2(x - 2) + 1 = 7$ 5

18. $3(y - 1) + 2 = 8$ 3

19. $3(t - 2) + 2t = 9$ 3

20. $5s + 3(2 - s) = 10$ 2

21. $2z + 3(2z + 3) = 25$ 2

22. $3(5 - 2x) + x = 5$ 2

23. $6x - 5(2x - 3) = 3$ 3

24. $15t + 6(4 - 3t) = 0$ 8

25. $3(x - 1) = x + 11$ 7

26. $y + 1 = 2(3y - 3) - 8$ 3

27. $2n - 3 = 3(n + 5)$ -18

28. $2(2t - 3) = 9 - t$ 3

Write a polynomial which represents the number described. Be sure to tell what each variable represents. Answers may vary.

Sample The area of a rectangular field which is enclosed by 60 meters of fencing.

Solution Let w = width, in meters,
and l = length, in meters.
Then $2w + 2l = 60$
$w + l = 30$
$l = 30 - w$
Area = $w(30 - w) = 30w - w^2$. *Answer*
Or:
$w = 30 - l$
Area = $l(30 - l) = 30l - l^2$. *Answer*

29. The area of a rectangle whose length is twice its width. $2w^2$ (w = width)

30. The area of a rectangle which is 10 cm longer than it is wide. $w^2 + 10w$ (w = width)

31. The area of a triangle in which the altitude is 3 meters less than the length of the base. $\frac{1}{2}b^2 - \frac{3}{2}b$ (b = length of base)

32. The area of a triangle in which the altitude is 3 times the length of the base. $\frac{3}{2}b^2$ (b = length of base)

B 33. The total amount of money you would earn in a year if you started at a certain rate per month and got a raise of $20 per month at the end of every three months. $12r + 360$ (r = rate/mo. the first 3 mos.)

34. The total amount of money you would earn in a year if you started at a certain rate per month and this rate was doubled at the end of every three months. $45r$ (r = rate/mo. the first 3 mos.)

35. Work the problem of the Sample if a river along one length of the field makes fencing on that side unnecessary. $60w - 2w^2$ (w = width)

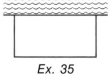

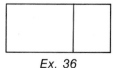

Ex. 35

36. Work the problem of the Sample if the 60 meters of fencing also provides for a dividing fence parallel to the shorter sides. $30w - \frac{3}{2}w^2$ (w = width)

Ex. 36

Solve.

37. $3(s + 2) - 2(s - 2) = 0$ $\quad$ -10

38. $2(y + 1) + 3(y - 1) = 9$ $\quad$ 2

39. $2(2x - 1) + 5x = 3(x - 2) + 10$ $\quad$ 1

40. $-4r + 3(1 - 2r) = 3(5 - 2r)$ $\quad$ -3

41. $2[4t - (t - 2)] - 3t = 2(t - 5)$ $\quad$ -14

42. $2x + 3[2(2x - 1) + 3(1 - x)] = 2(2x + 5)$ $\quad$ 7

43. $t(t - 2) + 2(2t - 1) = t^2 + 4$ $\quad$ 3

44. $z(1 - z) + z(z + 1) = 6 - z$ $\quad$ 2

Career Note
Environmental Health
Technician

Environmental health technicians may work on air and water pollution control, noise control, or the enforcement of sanitation laws. They may be employed in health laboratories, food processing companies, water treatment plants, or sewage disposal plants. Their work includes chemical and bacteriological analyses of food or water samples. There are positions for environmental health technicians in local, state, and federal government agencies. These technicians inspect restaurants and hotels to see that sanitation regulations are observed.

The usual educational requirement is an associate degree or two years of college with courses in the natural sciences and mathematics. Some programs also provide a year of technical training. For government positions in the environmental health field it is necessary to pass a civil service examination.

Extra for Experts ExtraExtraExtraExtraExtraExt

A Shortcut for Finding Averages

A scientist wants to find the average of several measurements. This can be done directly as shown at the left below or by using the shortcut shown at the right.

Shortcut

1.233 = 1.235 − 0.002
1.244 = 1.235 + 0.009
1.238 = 1.235 + 0.003 → + 0.012
1.235 = 1.235 + 0 → − 0.005
1.232 = 1.235 − 0.003 → + 0.007

$$\frac{0.007}{5} = 0.0014 \doteq 0.001$$

5)6.182
1.2364
≐ 1.236

Average ≐ 1.235 + 0.001 = 1.236.

Shortcut method:

1. Select a value between the largest and smallest values.
2. Find the *deviations* from this value, and find the average of the deviations.
3. Find the sum of the selected number and the average of the deviations.

Why does this shortcut work?

To average five values, select a value and denote it by S.

$$\text{Average} = \frac{(S + a) + (S + b) + (S + c) + (S + d) + (S + e)}{5}$$

$$= \frac{5S}{5} + \frac{a + b + c + d + e}{5}$$

$$= S + \frac{a + b + c + d + e}{5}$$

Clearly this method will work for any number of values.

Use deviations to find the average of each set of values. Round the average to the same number of places as in the given values.

1. 208, 210, 194, 204, 186   200

2. 2.8, 3.6, 2.9, 2.8, 3.2   3.1

3. 2, 3, 1, 5, 7, 8, 5, 4, 1, 7   4

4. 9, 8, 7, 2, 3, 4, 8, 4, 3, 5   5

5. −1, 0, 3, 2, −2, 4, 5, −1, 4, 2   2

6. −7, −6, −8, −5, −4, −5, −8, −9, −8, −5   −6.5

4-10 Multiplying Polynomials

> **OBJECTIVE** To learn how to multiply polynomials.

To express the product $(a + b)(c + d)$ as a polynomial, first treat $(c + d)$ as a number to be multiplied by $(a + b)$ and apply the distributive axiom:

$$a(c + d) + b(c + d)$$

Then apply the distributive axiom to each product:

$$ac + ad + bc + bd$$

Sometimes the resulting polynomial can be simplified:

$$
\begin{aligned}
(2x + 5)(3x + 2) &= 2x(3x + 2) + 5(3x + 2) \\
&= 2x \cdot 3x + 2x \cdot 2 + 5 \cdot 3x + 5 \cdot 2 \\
&= 6x^2 + 4x + 15x + 10 \\
&= 6x^2 + 19x + 10
\end{aligned}
$$

It is often convenient to set up the multiplication of polynomials in vertical form, and to work from left to right, as shown:

$$
\begin{array}{r}
3x + 2 \\
2x + 5 \\
\hline
6x^2 + 4x \\
15x + 10 \\
\hline
6x^2 + 19x + 10
\end{array}
$$

This is $2x(3x + 2)$ ———→ $6x^2 + 4x$
This is $5(3x + 2)$ ———→ $15x + 10$
This is $(2x + 5)(3x + 2)$ ———→ $6x^2 + 19x + 10$

In general:

> To multiply one polynomial by another, multiply each term of one polynomial by each term of the other, and write the sum of the products.

It is sometimes helpful to arrange the terms of a polynomial in order of either decreasing degree or increasing degree.

In order of decreasing degree in x: $x^4 - 3x^2 + 2x + 5$

In order of increasing degree in n: $2 + 2n - n^2$

In order of decreasing degree in t: $st^3 + 2s^3t^2 - 3t + s^2$

Example Express as a polynomial in simple form:

$$(a + b)(a^2 + 2b^2 - ab)$$

Solution Arrange in vertical form with both polynomials in order of decreasing degree in the same variable.

$$
\begin{array}{l}
a^2 - ab + 2b^2 \\
\underline{a + b} \\
a^3 - a^2b + 2ab^2 \\
 a^2b - ab^2 + 2b^3 \\
\hline
a^3 + 0 + ab^2 + 2b^3 \\
a^3 + ab^2 + 2b^3 \quad \textit{Answer}
\end{array}
$$

Oral Exercises

Arrange in order of decreasing degree in the indicated variable.

1. $2z - 1 + z^2$; $z \quad z^2 + 2z - 1$

2. $t^3 + 4t^4 - t^2$; $t \quad 4t^4 + t^3 - t^2$

3. $2rs + r^2 - s^2$; $r \quad r^2 + 2rs - s^2$

4. $2c^2d + c^3 - d^3$; $c \quad c^3 + 2c^2d - d^3$

Arrange in order of increasing degree in the indicated variable.

5. $4 + 3x^2y + xy^2 + y^3$; $y \quad 4 + 3x^2y + xy^2 + y^3$

6. $4 + 3x^2y + xy^3 + y^3$; $x \quad 4 + y^3 + xy^3 + 3x^2y$

7. $c^3d^2 - c^2d + cd$; $c \quad cd - c^2d + c^3d^2$

8. $r^3s^3 - 3r^2s^2 + rs$; $r \quad rs - 3r^2s^2 + r^3s^3$

State the symbol which should replace the question mark.

9. $(x + 2)(x + 1) = x(x + 1) + \underline{?}(x + 1)$ 2

10. $(y + 3)(y + 2) = y(y + 2) + \underline{?}(y + 2)$ 3

11. $(a + 1)(a + 2) = a(a + 2) + 1(a + 2) = a^2 + 2a + \underline{?} + 2$ a

12. $(r + 2)(r + 3) = r(r + 3) + 2(r + 3) = r^2 + \underline{?}r + 2r + 6$ 3

13. $(t + 2)(t + 4) = t^2 + 4t + 2t + \underline{?}$ 8

14. $(z + 5)(z + 3) = z^2 + 3z + 5z + \underline{?}$ 15

15. $(x + 2)(x - 3) = x^2 - 3x + 2x + \underline{?}$ -6

16. $(u - 2)(u + 5) = u^2 + 5u - 2u + \underline{?}$ -10

17. $(v - 2)(v - 5) = v^2 - 5v - 2v + \underline{?}$ 10

18. $(a - 3)(a - 3) = a^2 - 3a - 3a + \underline{?}$ 9

1. $c^2 + 3c + 2$ 2. $x^2 + 7x + 12$ 3. $t^2 + t - 2$
4. $h^2 + 2h - 8$ 5. $a^2 - 4$ 6. $a^2 + 4a + 4$
7. $z^2 - 6z + 9$ 8. $z^2 - 9$ 9. $2x^2 + 5x + 2$

Written Exercises

10. $2y^2 + 5y + 2$ 11. $3r^2 + 10r - 8$ 12. $3t^2 - 7t - 6$

Multiply.

A 1. $(c + 2)(c + 1)$ 2. $(x + 3)(x + 4)$ 3. $(t - 1)(t + 2)$ 4. $(h + 4)(h - 2)$

5. $(a + 2)(a - 2)$ 6. $(a + 2)(a + 2)$ 7. $(z - 3)(z - 3)$ 8. $(z - 3)(z + 3)$

9. $(2x + 1)(x + 2)$ 10. $(y + 2)(2y + 1)$ 11. $(r + 4)(3r - 2)$ 12. $(3t + 2)(t - 3)$

13. $(z - 2)(2z - 1)$ 14. $(5n - 1)(n - 2)$ 15. $(2u + 1)(3u + 2)$ 16. $(4v + 3)(2v + 3)$

17. $(3x - 1)(3x + 1)$ 18. $(5k - 2)(2k + 5)$ 19. $(2a - 3)(3a - 4)$ 20. $(3c - 2)(3c - 2)$

21. $(a + b)(a + 2b)$ 22. $(2c + d)(c + 2d)$ 23. $(2c - 5d)(2c - 5d)$ 24. $(2r + 3s)(2r - 3s)$

13. $2z^2 - 5z + 2$ 14. $5n^2 - 11n + 2$ 15. $6u^2 + 7u + 2$ 16. $8v^2 + 18v + 9$
17. $9x^2 - 1$ 18. $10k^2 + 21k - 10$ 19. $6a^2 - 17a + 12$ 20. $9c^2 - 12c + 4$
21. $a^2 + 3ab + 2b^2$ 22. $2c^2 + 5cd + 2d^2$ 23. $4c^2 - 20cd + 25d^2$ 24. $4r^2 - 9s^2$

B 25. $(a^2 + 1)(a^2 - 1)$ 26. $(s^2 - 4)(s^2 - 4)$ 27. $(u^2 - 2v^2)(u^2 - 2v^2)$

28. $(3a^2 - 2b^2)(3a^2 + 2b^2)$ 29. $(a + 1)(a^2 + 2a - 3)$ 30. $(x + 1)(x^2 - 3x + 2)$

31. $(r + 3)(r^2 - 2r - 1)$ 32. $(s - 2)(s^2 - s + 3)$ 33. $(2x - 1)(x^2 + x + 3)$

34. $(h + k)(h^2 - 2hk + 3k^2)$ 35. $(s + 2t)(s^2 + t^2 - st)$ 36. $(a - 2b)(b^2 - ab + 2a^2)$

37. $(x + 2)(2x - 1) + (x - 1)(x + 3)$ 38. $(2c - 3)(c - 1) + c(2c + 1)$

39. $(x^2 + 2x + 3)(x^2 - x - 2)$ 40. $(y^2 - y + 3)(y^2 + 2y + 2)$

41. $(a - b)(a^2 + ab + b^2)$ 42. $(a + b)(a^2 - ab + b^2)$

43. $(s - t)(s^3 + s^2t + st^2 + t^3)$ 44. $(s + t)(s^3 - s^2t + st^2 - t^3)$

45. $(x + y)(x^3 + 2x^2y - xy^2 - y^3)$ 46. $(c - d)(3c^3 - c^2d - 2cd^2 + d^3)$

Answers to Exs. 25–46 on page A1 at the back of the book.

Just for Fun

Find the values to put into each __?__ for different values of x. Put the sums of the diagonals into the ovals. Try $x = 1$, $x = -1$, and $x = 2$.

Answer given for $x = 1$; others on page A1 at the back of the book.

			(?) 15
$2x^2 + x + 4 =$ __?__ 7	$-x^2 - 2x + 3 =$ __?__ 0	$-x^2 + x + 8 =$ __?__ 8	__?__ 15
$-x^2 - 2x + 9 =$ __?__ 6	$-x^2 + x + 5 =$ __?__ 5	$2x^2 + x + 1 =$ __?__ 4	__?__ 15
$-x^2 + x + 2 =$ __?__ 2	$2x^2 + x + 7 =$ __?__ 10	$-x^2 - 2x + 6 =$ __?__ 3	__?__ 15
__?__ 15	__?__ 15	__?__ 15	(?) 15

4-11 Some Applications Involving Areas

OBJECTIVE To learn how to solve some problems involving areas.

You can now use your skills in multiplying polynomials to solve some problems involving areas. Diagrams are especially helpful in analyzing such problems.

Example A rectangular pond used in raising catfish for food is 10 meters longer than it is wide. A walkway 2 meters wide surrounds the pond. Find the dimensions of the pond if the area of the walkway is 216 square meters.

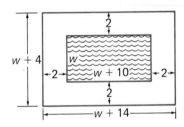

Solution

Step 1 The problem asks for the dimensions (length and width) of the pond.

Step 2 Let w = width of pond in meters.
Then $w + 10$ = length of pond in meters.

Step 3

Area of pond and walkway	minus	Area of pond	equals	Area of walkway
$(w + 4)(w + 14)$	$-$	$w(w + 10)$	$=$	216

Step 4 $(w^2 + 18w + 56) - (w^2 + 10w) = 216$
$$8w + 56 = 216$$
$$8w = 160$$
$$w = 20$$
$$w + 10 = 30$$

Step 5 *Check* (1) Is the length 10 meters greater than the width?
$30 - 20 = 10$. Yes.
(2) Is the area of the walkway 216 square meters?
Area of pond and walkway − area of pond
$= \quad 24 \times 34 \quad - \quad 20 \times 30$
$= \quad 816 \quad - \quad 600 \ = 216$ Yes

∴ dimensions of pond: 20 meters by 30 meters. *Answer*

Problems

Solve each problem. If no diagram is given, make a sketch.

A 1. The screen of a Model 610 television set is a rectangle, 10 centimeters (cm) wider than it is high. Model 702 has a screen which is 2 cm wider and 3 cm higher and has 240 square centimeters more area. Find the dimensions of the Model 610 screen. **40.8 cm by 50.8 cm**

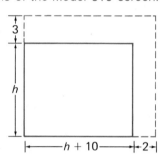

2. A tunnel is to have a rectangular cross section twice as wide as it is high. Its walls are of reinforced concrete 1 meter thick and its roof is of concrete 2 meters thick. The cross-sectional area of the concrete is 62 square meters. What are the width and height of the rectangular hole needed to accommodate the tunnel and its walls and roof? **11⅔ m by 21⅓ m**

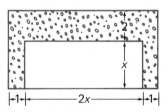

3. A rectangular swimming pool is 7 meters longer than it is wide. It is surrounded by a concrete walk 1.5 meters wide, the area of which is 120 square meters. Find the dimensions of the pool. **15 m by 22 m**

4. The playing area of a basketball arena is a rectangle 10 meters longer than it is wide. It is surrounded by 20 rows of seats with each row occupying 1.5 meters from front to back.

5. Ace: 3 m
Goliath: 4 m

Find the area of the building if the area devoted to seats is 7200 square meters. **8075 m**

5. An Ace paving machine can pave a strip five times as long as it is wide in one hour. A Goliath machine paves a strip one meter wider than the Ace. In one hour the Goliath travels 3 meters farther than the Ace and paves an area 27 square meters greater. Find the width of the strip each machine paves. *(above)*

6. When a ditch 2 meters wide and 1 meter deep was dug around a square building (and adjacent to it) the volume of earth removed was 192 cubic meters. Find the dimensions of the building. **22 m by 22 m**

7. The figure shows a cross section of a semicircular tunnel. The concrete is 1 meter thick and the cross-sectional area of the concrete is 17⅖ square meters. Find the radius of the tunnel. Use 22/7 for π. **5 m**

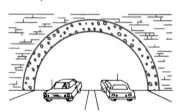

8. The figure shows a running track. The infield consists of a rectangle twice as long as it is wide and two semicircles. The track itself is 7 meters wide and has area 1354 square meters. Find the inner radius of the semicircular end of the track. Use 22/7 for π. **12 m**

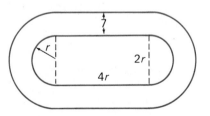

9. A rectangular picture is three times as wide as it is tall. When it is in a frame 10 centimeters wide, the total area is 3600 square centimeters more than that of the picture itself. Find the dimensions of the picture itself.   **40 cm by 120 cm**

10. A square corner lot lost 94 square meters of area when the two adjacent streets were widened, one by 2 meters and the other by 3 meters. Find the original dimensions of the lot.   **20 m by 20 m**

★ Self-Test 3

Simplify.

1. $z \cdot z \cdot z \cdot z$

2. $(-3x^5)(-2x)$

3. $(2a^2b^2)^3$

4. $k^2(3c^2d)^3$

5. $2a(x^2 + a^2)$

6. $y(y + 5)$

7. $(3u^2 - 1)(3u^2 + 1)$

8. $(t - 1)(t^2 + t + 1)$

Objective 4-7, p. 120
Objective 4-8, p. 122
Objective 4-9, p. 124
Objective 4-10, p. 128

9. A rectangular picture is 2 decimeters taller than it is wide. It is surrounded by a frame 1 decimeter wide, whose area is 20 square decimeters. Find the dimensions of the picture.

Objective 4-11, p. 131

Check your answers with those printed at the back of the book.

Chapter Summary

1. Polynomials are added and subtracted by applying the distributive axiom as needed.

2. Rules of exponents:
   $$b^m \cdot b^n = b^{m+n} \qquad (ab)^m = a^m b^m \qquad (b^m)^n = b^{mn}$$

3. Monomials and polynomials are multiplied by applying the distributive axiom and using the preceding rules of exponents.

Just for Fun

Find all sets of three consecutive multiples of 5 whose sum is between 78 and 123.   **25, 30, 35; 30, 35, 40; 35, 40, 45**

Chapter Test

Simplify.

4-1 1. $x^4 - x^2 + 1 + x^2 - x^4 + x^6$ $x^6 + 1$ 2. $a^3x + x^3a - a^2x^2 + ax^3$ $a^3x - a^2x^2 + 2ax^3$

Solve.

4-2 3. $4x - 3 - x = 12$ 5 4. $2(b + 1) - (b - 2) = 0$ -4

4-3 5. $2a + 4 = 3a - 7$ 11 6. $2(n + 1) + 3(2n - 1) = 15$ 2

4-4 7. Dave's father is three times as old as Dave. In 10 years, he will be only twice as old as Dave. How old are they now? Dave: 10; father: 30

4-5 8. Find three consecutive odd integers whose sum is 57. $17, 19, 21$

For each pair of polynomials:
a. Add.   b. Subtract the second from the first.

4-6 9. $3x^2 - 2x + 5$, $2x^2 - 2x - 3$ **a.** $5x^2 - 4x + 2$ **b.** $x^2 + 8$

10. $ay^3 - a^2y + 3a^4$, $a^3y + ay^3$ **a.** $2ay^3 - ay^2 + a^3y + 3a^4$
   b. $-a^2y + 3a^4 - a^3y$

Simplify.

4-7 11. $(3u^2v)(2uv^2)$ $6u^3v^3$ 12. $a(-az^3)(5a^2z)$ $-5a^4z^4$

4-8 13. $x^2(2x^2y)^3$ $8x^8y^3$ 14. $s(2st^2)^2 + 4t(-st)^3$ 0

4-9 15. $-x(x - 2y)$ $-x^2 + 2xy$ 16. $3uv(u^2 - 2uv + v^2)$ $3u^3v - 6u^2v^2 + 3uv^3$

4-10 17. $(x + 3)(x - 2)$ $x^2 + x - 6$ 18. $(3a + b)(a - 3b)$ $3a^2 - 8ab - 3b^2$

4-11 19. A rectangular sheet of paper was originally 6 centimeters longer than it was wide. When a 1-centimeter-wide strip was trimmed from each of its four edges, its area decreased by 68 square centimeters. Find its original dimensions. 15 cm by 21 cm

Consumer Note $$
A Computation Shortcut

Suppose that you are buying 6 articles costing $4.99 each. Can you find the total cost mentally? Use the distributive property for multiplication with respect to subtraction:

$$6(4.99) = 6(5 - 0.01)$$
$$= 30 - 0.06 = 29.94$$

Find:

1. $5(2.95)$ 2. $4(3.98)$ 3. $7(1.99)$ 4. $10(5.95)$ 5. $3(7.98)$ 6. $8(3.99)$
   14.75   15.92   13.93   59.5   23.94   31.92

Programmed Chapter Review

4-1　　1. Terms that are exactly alike or differ only in their numerical
　　　　　coefficients are called __?__ .　　　　　　　　　　　　similar

　　　　2. In changing $2a + 3a$ to $5a$, you use the __?__ axiom.　　distributive

　　　　3. $2x + 7y - y + x =$ __?__　　　　　　　　　　　　　$3x + 6y$

4-2　　4. If $2n + 1 - n = 5$, then $n =$ __?__ .　　　　　　　　　4

　　　　5. If $2(p - 2) + 3(p + 4) = 23$, then $p =$ __?__ .　　　　3

4-3　　6. If $5x + 2 = 3x - 4$, then $x =$ __?__ .　　　　　　　　　-3

　　　　7. "$3x + 2x = 5x$" is a special kind of equation, called an __?__ .　identity

　　　　8. The solution set of the equation "$3n + 1 = 3n - 4$" is __?__ .　∅

4-4　　9. If Audrey is y years old now, in 3 years she will be __?__ years　$y + 3$
　　　　　old.

　　　10. Carl is 4 years older than Gertrude. In 7 years, Carl will be __?__　4
　　　　　years older than Gertrude.

4-5　　11. If the second of three consecutive multiples of 6 is n, then the
　　　　　other two are __?__ and __?__ .　　　　　　　　　　　$n - 6, n + 6$

　　　12. Three consecutive integers whose sum is -24 are __?__ , __?__ ,　$-9, -8$
　　　　　and __?__ .　　　　　　　　　　　　　　　　　　　　-7

4-6　　13. A term which is either a numeral, a variable, or a product of
　　　　　a numeral and one or more variables is called a __?__ .　　monomial

　　　14. The degree of $-8x^2y^3z$ is __?__ .　　　　　　　　　　6

　　　15. A sum of monomials is called a __?__ .　　　　　　　　polynomial

　　　16. To add two polynomials, add the __?__ terms.　　　　　similar

　　　17. $(2x^2 + 6x - 7) + (x^2 - 4x - 2) =$ __?__　　　　　　$3x^2 + 2x - 9$

　　　18. To subtract one polynomial from another, add the __?__ of each　opposite (or
　　　　　term you are subtracting.　　　　　　　　　　　　　　negative)

　　　19. $(u^3 - 2u^2 + 7) - (u^2 + u + 7) =$ __?__　　　　　　$u^3 - 3u^2 - u$

　　　20. If $(3x - 4) - (x - 2) = x + 1$, then $x =$ __?__ .　　　　3

136 *Chapter 4*

4-7 **21.** The exponent of the product of two powers having the same
  base is the __?__ of the exponents.

  22. The rule of exponents for a product of powers __?__ be used
  to simplify x^3y^5.

  23. $3^{57} \cdot 3^{43} = $ __?__

  24. $(2x^3)(3x^2) = $ __?__

  25. $2u(-3u^2v)(4u^3v^2) = $ __?__

4-8 **26.** For all positive integers m and n, $(ab)^m = $ __?__ and
  $(a^m)^n = $ __?__ .

  27. $(-3ab)^2 = $ __?__

  28. $x^3(x^2y)^3 = $ __?__

4-9 **29.** To multiply a polynomial by a monomial, you use the __?__
  axiom.

  30. $2x(x - 3) = $ __?__

  31. If $x(2x + 4) + 2x(3 - x) = 100$, then $x = $ __?__ .

4-10 **32.** $(a + b)(x + 1) = a(\underline{\ ?\ }) + b(\underline{\ ?\ })$

  33. $(t - 7)(t + 8) = t^2 + t + $ __?__

  34. $(x - 2)(x + 1) = $ __?__

4-11 **35.** A rectangular swimming pool is twice as long as it is wide. It
  is surrounded by a concrete deck 2 meters wide. If the area
  of the deck is 256 square meters, the dimensions of the pool
  are __?__ m by __?__ m.

sum
cannot
3^{100}
$6x^5$
$-24u^6v^3$
a^mb^m
a^{mn}
$9a^2b^2$
x^9y^3
distributive
$2x^2 - 6x$
10
$x + 1, x + 1$
-56
$x^2 - x - 2$
20, 40

Maintaining Skills

Remember how?

$$\frac{12}{24} = \frac{1 \cdot 12}{2 \cdot 12} = \frac{1}{2}$$

$$\frac{6}{15} = \frac{2 \cdot 3}{5 \cdot 3} = \frac{2}{5}$$

Now practice:

1. $\frac{4}{8}$ $\frac{1}{2}$ 2. $\frac{15}{20}$ $\frac{3}{4}$ 3. $\frac{11}{33}$ $\frac{1}{3}$ 4. $\frac{18}{24}$ $\frac{3}{4}$

5. $\frac{10}{14}$ $\frac{5}{7}$ 6. $\frac{32}{48}$ $\frac{2}{3}$ 7. $\frac{8}{18}$ $\frac{4}{9}$ 8. $\frac{27}{36}$ $\frac{3}{4}$

Remember how?

$$\frac{3}{8} - \frac{2}{8} = \frac{3-2}{8} = \frac{1}{8}$$

$$\frac{5}{12} + \frac{3}{12} = \frac{5+3}{12} = \frac{8}{12} = \frac{2 \cdot 4}{3 \cdot 4} = \frac{2}{3}$$

Now practice:

9. $\frac{5}{11} + \frac{2}{11}$ $\frac{7}{11}$ 10. $\frac{12}{7} - \frac{8}{7}$ $\frac{4}{7}$ 11. $\frac{7}{15} + \frac{3}{15}$ $\frac{2}{3}$

12. $\frac{8}{9} - \frac{2}{9}$ $\frac{2}{3}$ 13. $\frac{5}{16} + \frac{7}{16}$ $\frac{3}{4}$ 14. $\frac{11}{24} - \frac{3}{24}$ $\frac{1}{3}$

Remember how?

$$\frac{5}{6} + \frac{2}{3} = \frac{5}{6} + \frac{2 \cdot 2}{3 \cdot 2} = \frac{5}{6} + \frac{4}{6}$$

$$= \frac{9}{6} = \frac{3 \cdot 3}{2 \cdot 3} = \frac{3}{2}$$

Now practice:

15. $\frac{3}{5} + \frac{3}{10}$ $\frac{9}{10}$ 16. $\frac{2}{7} + \frac{5}{14}$ $\frac{9}{14}$ 17. $\frac{11}{15} - \frac{3}{5}$ $\frac{2}{15}$

18. $\frac{17}{18} - \frac{1}{6}$ $\frac{7}{9}$ 19. $\frac{13}{20} + \frac{3}{5}$ $\frac{5}{4}$ 20. $\frac{5}{8} - \frac{1}{4}$ $\frac{3}{8}$

Remember how?

$$\frac{2}{3} \times \frac{4}{5} = \frac{2 \times 4}{3 \times 5} = \frac{8}{15}$$

$$\overset{1}{\cancel{3}} \times \frac{5}{\underset{2}{\cancel{6}}} = \frac{5 \times 1}{7 \times 2} = \frac{5}{14}$$

Now practice:

21. $\frac{3}{5} \times \frac{2}{7}$ $\frac{6}{35}$ 22. $\frac{8}{3} \times \frac{1}{5}$ $\frac{8}{15}$ 23. $\frac{5}{8} \times \frac{2}{3}$ $\frac{5}{12}$

24. $\frac{3}{7} \times \frac{5}{6}$ $\frac{5}{14}$ 25. $\frac{11}{12} \times \frac{4}{5}$ $\frac{11}{15}$ 26. $\frac{6}{5} \times \frac{5}{3}$ 2

Remember how?

$$\frac{4}{5} \div \frac{8}{15} = \frac{\overset{1}{\cancel{4}}}{\cancel{5}} \times \frac{\overset{3}{\cancel{15}}}{\underset{2}{\cancel{8}}} = \frac{3}{2}$$

Now practice:

27. $\frac{3}{5} \div \frac{2}{7}$ $\frac{21}{10}$ 28. $\frac{11}{12} \div \frac{5}{6}$ $\frac{11}{10}$ 29. $\frac{3}{4} \div \frac{5}{2}$ $\frac{3}{10}$

30. $\frac{2}{3} \div \frac{7}{6}$ $\frac{4}{7}$ 31. $5 \div \frac{5}{6}$ 6 32. $12 \div \frac{3}{4}$ 16

Factoring

Physical Science This lacy pattern is formed by the crystallization of a material called Stilben. It is one of the basic components of whitewash.

5

Quotients and Factoring

5-1 Factoring Integers

OBJECTIVE To learn how to factor integers in specified ways.

You *factor* 24 into a product of integers when you write

$$24 = 2 \cdot 12 \quad \text{or} \quad 24 = 3 \cdot 8.$$

The numbers 2 and 12, and 3 and 8 are *factors* (recall page 7) of 24. Of course, $24 = \frac{1}{2} \cdot 48$, so that $\frac{1}{2}$ and 48 might be called factors of 24. We usually allow only certain kinds of factors of a given number, and so we specify the set from which the factors may be selected. We then say that the given number is **factored over the specified set**, called the **factor set**. In our work *integers will be factored over the set of integers* unless the contrary is stated. Such factors are called **integral factors**.

Factors can be found by division. If the remainder is zero, the divisor is a factor:

$$\frac{105}{7} = 15 \quad \text{and so} \quad 105 = 7 \cdot 15;$$

$$\frac{105}{-7} = -15 \quad \text{and so} \quad 105 = (-7)(-15).$$

$$\frac{107}{7} = 15 \text{ R2 and so 7 is not a factor of 107.}$$

139

The basic set of numbers used in factoring is the set of *prime numbers,* or *primes:*

> A **prime number,** or **prime,** is an integer, greater than one, which has no positive integral factor other than itself and one.

The first prime numbers are

$$2, 3, 5, 7, 11, 13, 17, 19, 23, 29, \ldots .$$

By dividing by primes, you can find that

$$\frac{105}{3} = 35, \frac{35}{5} = 7, \quad \text{and so} \quad 105 = 3 \cdot 5 \cdot 7.$$

Similarly, you can find that

$$24 = 2 \cdot 2 \cdot 2 \cdot 3 = 2^3 \cdot 3.$$

A systematic way of finding the prime factors of larger positive integers is illustrated at the right. You try the primes, in order, as factors, using each as many times as possible before going on to the next. The result in this case is

$$504 = 2^3 \cdot 3^2 \cdot 7.$$

$$504 = 2 \cdot 252$$
$$= 2 \cdot 2 \cdot 126$$
$$= 2 \cdot 2 \cdot 2 \cdot 63$$
$$= 2 \cdot 2 \cdot 2 \cdot 3 \cdot 21$$
$$= 2 \cdot 2 \cdot 2 \cdot 3 \cdot 3 \cdot 7$$
$$= 2^3 \cdot 3^2 \cdot 7$$

> The expression of a positive integer as a product of prime factors is called the **prime factorization** of the integer.

It can be proved by advanced methods that the prime factorization of an integer is *unique* (one and only one) except for the order in which the factors may be written. (If 1 were considered as a prime factor, the factorization would not be unique, because any number of factors 1 could be written.)

Sometimes you will need to find all possible *pairs of integral factors of an integer.* For example:

$$24 = (1)(24) = (2)(12) = (3)(8) = (4)(6)$$
$$= (-1)(-24) = (-2)(-12) = (-3)(-8) = (-4)(-6)$$

Also: $-24 = (-1)(24) = (-2)(12) = (-3)(8) = (-4)(6)$
$\qquad = (1)(-24) = (2)(-12) = (3)(-8) = (4)(-6)$

You can find the positive integral factors
of a positive integer by dividing it by the
positive integers in succession. Thus:

$$36 = (1)(36) = (2)(18) = (3)(12)$$
$$= (4)(9) = (6)(6)$$

$$36 = 1 \cdot 36$$
$$= 2 \cdot 18$$
$$= 3 \cdot 12$$
$$= 4 \cdot 9$$
$$= 6 \cdot 6$$

Do you see that there is no integral factor between half the number
and the number itself?

Oral Exercises

Find a second factor by dividing by the given factor.

Sample 18; 2   *Solution* $\frac{18}{2} = 9$, another factor of 18 *Answer*

1. 27; 3 9   2. -24; 8 -3 3. 12; -6 -2 4. 35; -7 -5 5. -30; 5 -6 6. 32; 8 4
7. -20; 5 -4 8. 48; 6 8   9. -54; 9 -6 10. -63; -3 21 11. 56; -8 -7 12. -60; -4 15

Give the prime factorization of each integer.
13. 10 $2 \cdot 5$ 14. 6 $2 \cdot 3$ 15. 15 $3 \cdot 5$ 16. 21 $3 \cdot 7$ 17. 8 2^3 18. 9 3^2
19. 18 $2 \cdot 3^2$ 20. 28 $2^2 \cdot 7$ 21. 20 $2^2 \cdot 5$ 22. 30 $2 \cdot 3 \cdot 5$ 23. 40 $2^3 \cdot 5$ 24. 50 $2 \cdot 5^2$

Written Exercises

Find the prime factorization of each integer.

A 1. 51 $3 \cdot 17$ 2. 52 $2^2 \cdot 13$ 3. 144 $2^4 \cdot 3^2$ 4. 300 $2^2 \cdot 3 \cdot 5^2$ 5. 160 $2^5 \cdot 5$ 6. 280 $2^3 \cdot 5 \cdot 7$
7. 600   8. 252   9. 248 $2^3 \cdot 31$ 10. 408 $2^3 \cdot 3 \cdot 17$ 11. 455 $5 \cdot 7 \cdot 13$ 12. 576 $2^6 \cdot 3^2$
$\quad 2^3 \cdot 3 \cdot 5^2$ $\quad 2^2 \cdot 3^2 \cdot 7$

Find all the positive integral factors of each integer. (*below*)

13. 21   14. 35   15. 70   16. 42   17. 72   18. 96
19. 48   20. 250   21. 88   22. 56   23. 45   24. 84

25–36. Write all the pairs of positive and negative factors of the integers in
Exercises 13–24. Answers on page A1 at the back of the book.

37–48. Write all the pairs of positive and negative factors of the negatives
of the integers in Exercises 13–24. Answers on page A1 at the back of the book.

13. 1, 3, 7, 21   **14.** 1, 5, 7, 35   **15.** 1, 2, 5, 7, 10, 14, 35, 70   **16.** 1, 2, 3, 6, 7, 14, 21, 42
17. 1, 2, 3, 4, 6, 8, 9, 12, 18, 24, 36, 72   **18.** 1, 2, 3, 4, 6, 8, 12, 16, 24, 32, 48, 96
19. 1, 2, 3, 4, 6, 8, 12, 16, 24, 48   **20.** 1, 2, 5, 10, 25, 50, 125, 250   **21.** 1, 2, 4, 8, 11, 22, 44, 88
22. 1, 2, 4, 7, 8, 14, 28, 56   **23.** 1, 3, 5, 9, 15, 45   **24.** 1, 2, 3, 4, 6, 7, 12, 14, 21, 28, 42, 84

> The greatest integer which is a factor of each of two or more integers is called the **greatest common factor** of the integers.

Find the greatest common factor of each pair of integers.

Sample 504; 945

Solution Find the prime factorizations:

$$504 = 2^3 \cdot 3^2 \cdot 7; \qquad 945 = 3^3 \cdot 5 \cdot 7$$

The greatest common factor of 504 and 945 is $3^2 \cdot 7$, or 63. *Answer*

49. 39, 26 13	50. 30, 42 6	51. 420, 378 42	52. 1000, 520
53. 980, 1344 28	54. 1545, 1960 5	55. 588, 840 84	56. 1008, 525

Extra for Experts Extra Extra Extra Extra Extra Ext
Divisibility of Integers

You probably know these tests for divisibility of integers:

> If the last digit is 0, 2, 4, 6, 8, the number is divisible by 2.
> If the last digit is 0, 5,   the number is divisible by 5.
> If the last digit is 0,   the number is divisible by 10.

To discover other tests, we shall use general expressions for numbers written in base 10:

A 2-digit number:

$$37 = 3(10) + 7 \longrightarrow a_1(10) + a_0 \qquad \left[\begin{array}{l} a_1 \text{ is read ``a sub 1."} \\ _1 \text{ is called a } subscript. \end{array}\right]$$

A 3-digit number:

$$245 = 2(10)^2 + 4(10) + 5 \longrightarrow a_2(10)^2 + a_1(10) + a_0$$

A 4-digit number:

$$6189 = 6(10)^3 + 1(10)^2 + 8(10) + 9 \longrightarrow a_3(10)^3 + a_2(10)^2 + a_1(10) + a_0$$

The next few tests are developed with 4-digit numbers, but the methods can be extended to any number of digits.

Tests involving the sum of the digits ($a_3 + a_2 + a_1 + a_0$):

$$a_3(1000) + a_2(100) + a_1(10) + a_0$$
$$= a_3(999 + 1) + a_2(99 + 1) + a_1(9 + 1) + a_0$$
$$= \underbrace{[a_3(999) + a_2(99) + a_1(9)]}_{\text{Divisible by 9}} + (a_3 + a_2 + a_1 + a_0)$$

> If $a_3 + a_2 + a_1 + a_0$ is divisible by 3, the number is divisible by 3.
> If $a_3 + a_2 + a_1 + a_0$ is divisible by 9, the number is divisible by 9.

For example, 2637 is divisible by 9 because $2 + 6 + 3 + 7 = 18 = 2 \cdot 9$.
75 is divisible by 3 because $7 + 5 = 12 = 3 \cdot 4$.

Tests involving the last 2 digits:

$$\underbrace{a_3(1000) + a_2(100)}_{\text{Divisible by 4, 25}} + [a_1(10) + a_0]$$

> If $a_1(10) + a_0$ is divisible by 4, the number is divisible by 4.
> If $a_1(10) + a_0$ is divisible by 25, the number is divisible by 25.

For example, 2676 is divisible by 4; 2675 is divisible by 25.

Other tests:
Notice that $1000 + 1$, $100 - 1$, $10 + 1$, are divisible by 11.
Then: $\underbrace{[a_3(1000 + 1) + a_2(100 - 1) + a_1(10 + 1)]}_{\text{Divisible by 11}} + [a_0 - a_1 + a_2 - a_3]$

> If $a_0 - a_1 + a_2 - a_3$ is divisible by 11, then the number is divisible by 11.

For example, 1617 is divisible by 11 because $7 - 1 + 6 - 1 = 11$.

Verify that 1001 is divisible by 7 and 13.
Now consider a 6-digit number:

$$a_5(100,000) + a_4(10,000) + a_3(1000) + a_2(100) + a_1(10) + a_0$$
$$= \underbrace{[a_5(100,100) + a_4(10,010) + a_3(1001)]}_{\text{Divisible by 7, 13}} + [a_2(100) + a_1(10) + a_0$$
$$- a_5(100) - a_4(10) - a_3]$$

> If $a_2(100) + a_1(10) + a_0 - [a_5(100) + a_4(10) + a_3]$ is divisible by 7, the number is divisible by 7.
> If $a_2(100) + a_1(10) + a_0 - [a_5(100) + a_4(10) + a_3]$ is divisible by 13, the number is divisible by 13.

For example, 542,516 is divisible by 13, because $516 - 542$, or -26, is divisible by 13.

Using $a_3(1000) + a_2(100) + a_1(10) + a_0$, verify the rule for: See *Solution Key* for Exs. 1–4, 8, 9.

1. Divisibility by 2.   2. Divisibility by 5.   3. Divisibility by 10.

4. Verify that 999,999 is divisible by 7 and 13, and extend the rules for 7 and 13 to a 9-digit number.

5. If a number is divisible by 2 and 3, is it necessarily divisible by 6?   Yes

6. If a number is divisible by 2 and 6, is it necessarily divisible by 12?   No (e.g., 18)

7. If a number is divisible by 3 and 4, is it necessarily divisible by 12?   Yes

8. Show that a number is divisible by 4 if $2a_1 + a_0$ is divisible by 4.

9. Show that a number is divisible by 8 if $4a_2 + 2a_1 + a_0$ is divisible by 8.

Computer Activity

If you have access to a computer that will accept BASIC, try this program.
It will test factors for you.

```
10   PRINT "WHAT IS YOUR INTEGER";
20   INPUT N
30   PRINT "WHAT FACTOR DO YOU WISH TO TEST";
40   INPUT F
50   LET Q=N/F
60   IF Q=INT(Q) THEN 90
70   PRINT "NOT A FACTOR; TRY AGAIN."
80   GOTO 30
90   PRINT "CORRECT. ";F;" IS A FACTOR OF ";N;"."
100  END
```

Note. "IF Q=INT(Q)" in line 60 tests whether the divisor is a factor.

5-2 Division and Factoring of Monomials

> **OBJECTIVE** To learn how to divide and factor monomials.

Factoring can be used to simplify division. For example:

$$\frac{768}{48} = \frac{32 \cdot 24}{8 \cdot 6} = \frac{32}{8} \cdot \frac{24}{6} = 4 \cdot 4 = 16$$

In general, if $cd \neq 0$:

$$\frac{xy}{cd} = xy\left(\frac{1}{cd}\right) \qquad \text{Rule for division}$$

$$= xy\left(\frac{1}{c} \cdot \frac{1}{d}\right) \qquad \text{Example 2, page 89}$$

$$= \left(x \cdot \frac{1}{c}\right)\left(y \cdot \frac{1}{d}\right) \qquad \begin{array}{l}\text{Commutative and associative axioms}\\\text{for multiplication}\end{array}$$

$$= \frac{x}{c} \cdot \frac{y}{d} \qquad \text{Rule for division}$$

Thus, we have:

> ### Property of Quotients
> For all real numbers x and y and nonzero real numbers c and d:
> $$\frac{xy}{cd} = \frac{x}{c} \cdot \frac{y}{d}$$

This property is helpful in simplifying quotients of powers. If $a \neq 0$:

$$\frac{a^8}{a^5} = \frac{a^5 \cdot a^3}{a^5} = \frac{a^5}{a^5} \cdot a^3 = 1 \cdot a^3 \qquad \frac{a^5}{a^8} = \frac{a^3}{a^3 \cdot a^5} = \frac{a^3}{a^3} \cdot \frac{1}{a^5} = 1 \cdot \frac{1}{a^5}$$

$$\frac{a^8}{a^5} = a^3 = a^{8-5} \qquad \frac{a^5}{a^8} = \frac{1}{a^3} = \frac{1}{a^{8-5}}$$

In general:

> ### Rules of Exponents for Division
> For $a \neq 0$ and m and n positive integers:
>
> | If $m - n$ is positive: | If $n - m$ is positive: |
> |:---:|:---:|
> | $\dfrac{a^m}{a^n} = a^{m-n}$ | $\dfrac{a^m}{a^n} = \dfrac{1}{a^{n-m}}$ |

When you simplify a quotient of monomials, use these rules together with the property of quotients. Be sure that no base appears more than once, and that there are no "powers of powers."

Example 1 $\dfrac{18x^6y^5}{-3x^3y} = \dfrac{18}{-3} \cdot \dfrac{x^6}{x^3} \cdot \dfrac{y^5}{y}$

$$= -6x^{6-3}y^{5-1} = -6x^3y^4 \quad \textit{Answer}$$

Example 2 $\dfrac{-6a^7b^5}{-24a^2b^8} = \dfrac{-6}{-24} \cdot \dfrac{a^7}{a^2} \cdot \dfrac{b^5}{b^8}$

$$= \dfrac{1}{4} a^{7-2} \cdot \dfrac{1}{b^{8-5}}$$

$$= \dfrac{1}{4} a^5 \cdot \dfrac{1}{b^3} = \dfrac{a^5}{4b^3} \quad \textit{Answer}$$

Or you can use some shortcuts:

$$\dfrac{-6a^7b^5}{-24a^2b^8} = \dfrac{1 \cdot a^{7-2} \cdot 1}{4 \cdot 1 \cdot b^{8-5}} = \dfrac{a^5}{4b^3} \quad \textit{Answer}$$

Example 3 Find the missing factor:

$$30r^5s^3t = (5r^2s^2)(\underline{\quad ? \quad})$$

Solution $\dfrac{30r^5s^3t}{5r^2s^2} = 6r^3st \quad \textit{Answer}$

Oral Exercises

Simplify each expression, assuming that no denominator is equal to 0.

1. $\dfrac{3c}{c}$ 3 2. $\dfrac{2a^2}{a^2}$ 2 3. $\dfrac{u^6}{u^2}$ u^4 4. $\dfrac{r^5}{r^3}$ r^2 5. $\dfrac{s^7}{-s^2}$ $-s^5$ 6. $\dfrac{-t^9}{t^3}$ $-t^6$

7. $\dfrac{6x^3}{2x}$ $3x^2$ 8. $\dfrac{10m^{10}}{5m^5}$ $\dfrac{}{2m^5}$ 9. $\dfrac{ab^3}{ab}$ b^2 10. $\dfrac{x^2y^2}{xy^2}$ x 11. $\dfrac{6a^2b^3}{-2a^2b}$ $\dfrac{}{-3b^2}$ 12. $\dfrac{-4u^3v^5}{-2uv^5}$ $2u^2$

Find the missing factor.

13. $4xy = (2x)(\underline{\quad ? \quad})$ $2y$ 14. $6ab = (\underline{\quad ? \quad})(2b)$ $3a$ 15. $u^2v^3 = (uv^2)(\underline{\quad ? \quad})$ uv

16. $4r^2s = r(\underline{\quad ? \quad})$ $4rs$ 17. $10xyz^2 = (\underline{\quad ? \quad})(5xz)$ $2yz$ 18. $9x^3y^2z = (3xyz)(\underline{\quad ? \quad})$ $3x^2y$

Find the monomial of greatest degree and greatest integral coefficient which is a factor of both monomials.

Sample $12x^2y^3$; $18x^3yz$

Solution The greatest common factor of 12 and 18 is 6. The required monomial is $6x^2y$. *Answer*

19. $6x$; $2xy$ $2x$

20. $2a^2$; $6a$ $2a$

21. $5a^2b$; $10ab^2$ $5ab$

22. $12u^3v^2$; $7uv^3$ uv^2

23. $14s^4t^2$; $21s^3t^3$ $7s^3t^2$

24. $25x^2y^4$; $15x^3y^5$ $5x^2y^4$

Written Exercises

Simplify each expression, assuming that no denominator is equal to 0.

A 1. $\dfrac{m^{10}}{m^5}$ m^5

2. $\dfrac{c^{12}}{c^2}$ c^{10}

3. $\dfrac{2k^5}{k}$ $2k^4$

4. $\dfrac{6s^3}{s^3}$ 6

5. $\dfrac{x^3y^2}{2x^2y^2}$ $\dfrac{x}{2}$

6. $\dfrac{-6r^4s^3}{2r^2s}$ $-3r^2s^2$

7. $\dfrac{-24s^7t^9}{-8s^2t^7}$ $3s^5t^2$

8. $\dfrac{13c^9d^{10}}{-26c^9d}$ $-\dfrac{d^9}{2}$

9. $\dfrac{4ab^3}{2a^2b^2}$ $\dfrac{2b}{a}$

10. $\dfrac{3h^3k^2}{9h^5k}$ $\dfrac{k}{3h^2}$

11. $\dfrac{27u^2v^3}{-18u^4v^5}$ $-\dfrac{3}{2u^2v^2}$

12. $\dfrac{-18x^6y^2}{12x^{10}y^7}$ $-\dfrac{3}{2x^4y^5}$

Find the missing factor in each case.

13. $24a^2b^3 = (8ab)(\underline{\ ?\ })$ $3ab^2$

14. $56s^2t^3 = (4s^2t)(\underline{\ ?\ })$ $14t^2$

15. $-52x^3y^2z = (13xy^2)(\underline{\ ?\ })$ $-4x^2z$

16. $-96h^3kn^3 = (-4hkn)(\underline{\ ?\ })$ $24h^2n^2$

17. $100r^3s^2t = (-4rs)(\underline{\ ?\ })$ $-25r^2st$

18. $144xy^3z^5 = (-9y^2z)(\underline{\ ?\ })$ $-16xyz^4$

19. $105x^{10}y^{20} = (15x^5y^{10})(\underline{\ ?\ })$ $7x^5y^{10}$

20. $225a^{16}b^8 = (15a^8b^4)(\underline{\ ?\ })$ $15a^8b^4$

Find the monomial of greatest degree and greatest integral coefficient which is a factor of all monomials in each set.

21. $24x^3y^2$; $16x^2y^3$ $8x^2y^2$

22. $35u^2v^2$; $45u^3v$ $5u^2v$

23. $48a^3bc$; $72a^4bc^2$ $24a^3bc$

24. $124x^2y^3z^2$; $144x^3y^2z^2$ $4x^2y^2z^2$

25. $15ab^2$; $25a^2b$; $35a^2b^2$ $5ab$

26. $21x^3y^2$; $14x^2y^3$; $35x^4y$ $7x^2y$

For each pair of monomials, find the highest power of the first monomial which is a factor of the second.

Sample $2x^2$; $24ax^5$ *Solution* $(2x^2)^1 = 2x^2$, and $24ax^5 = (2x^2)(12ax^3)$
$(2x^2)^2 = 4x^4$, and $24ax^5 = (4x^4)(6ax)$
$(2x^2)^3 = 8x^6$, but x^6 is not a factor of x^5.
$\therefore$ the highest power is $(2x^2)^2$. *Answer*

27. $2x$; $16x^3y$ $(2x)^3$

28. a^2; $3a^5b$ $(a^2)^2$

29. u^3; $5u^{10}v^5$ $(u^3)^3$

30. $3s$; $27s^2t^3$ $(3s)^2$

31. $2ab$; $24a^4b^2$ $(2ab)^2$

32. ab^2; $5a^3b^5$ $(ab^2)^2$

33. $5x^2y$; $625x^7y^3$ $(5x^2y)^3$

34. $4r^3s$; $64r^4s^4$ $(4r^3s)^1$

Applications
Scientific Notation

Scientists have used positive and negative exponents to develop a convenient notation for dealing with very large and very small numbers. Up to now we have used only positive exponents. To generalize the rules to include negative exponents, we need some new definitions.

Recall that the rules of exponents for division (page 145) state that for $a \neq 0$ and m and n positive:

$$\frac{a^m}{a^n} = a^{m-n} \text{ if } m - n \text{ is positive;} \qquad \frac{a^m}{a^n} = \frac{1}{a^{n-m}} \text{ if } n - m \text{ is positive}$$

If $m = n$, $\frac{a^m}{a^m} = 1$, and so we define

$$a^{m-m} = a^0 = 1.$$

According to the above rules

$$\frac{a^7}{a^2} = a^{7-2} = a^5 \quad \text{and} \quad \frac{a^2}{a^7} = \frac{1}{a^{7-2}} = \frac{1}{a^5},$$

and so we define a^{-5} as follows

$$\frac{a^2}{a^7} = a^{2-7} = a^{-5} = \frac{1}{a^5}.$$

Combining these definitions with the rules on page 145, we have:

> ### General Rules of Exponents for Division
>
> For all integers m and n and $a \neq 0$,
>
> $$\frac{a^m}{a^n} = a^{m-n}; \quad a^0 = 1; \quad a^{m-n} = \frac{1}{a^{n-m}}$$

The expression 0^0 does not name a number.

Now notice that:

$$2{,}000{,}000 \text{ can be written as } 2 \times 10^6;$$
$$0.004 \text{ can be written as } 4 \times 10^{-3}.$$

Scientific (or standard) *notation* is defined as follows:

> ### Scientific Notation
>
> Express the number as the product of a number between 1 and 10 and an integral power of 10.

Study the changes in the exponent of 10:

$$0.00764 = 7.64 \times 0.001 = 7.64 \times 10^{-3}$$
$$0.0764 = 7.64 \times 0.01 = 7.64 \times 10^{-2}$$
$$0.764 = 7.64 \times 0.1 = 7.64 \times 10^{-1}$$
$$7.64 = 7.64 \times 1 = 7.64 \times 10^{0}$$
$$76.4 = 7.64 \times 10 = 7.64 \times 10^{1}$$
$$764. = 7.64 \times 100 = 7.64 \times 10^{2}$$
$$7640. = 7.64 \times 1000 = 7.64 \times 10^{3}$$

The effect of multiplying or dividing by a power of 10 a number written in decimal notation is to shift the position of the decimal point.

Numbers expressed in scientific notation can be multiplied or divided readily.

Example The speed of light is 299,792 kilometers per second. This is approximately 300,000, or 3×10^5, km/s. Since 1 km = 1000, or 10^3, m, the speed of light is approximately $3 \times 10^5 \times 10^3$, or 3×10^8, m/s.

Speed of light $\doteq 3 \times 10^8$ m/s

Astronomers use very large numbers. Distance may be measured in *light-years*. A **light-year** is the distance that light will travel in a year.

1. Verify that the number of seconds in a year is approximately 3.2×10^7. $60 \cdot 60 \cdot 24 \cdot 365 = 31,536,000 \doteq 3.2 \times 10^7$

2. Verify that a light-year is approximately 10^{13} kilometers. *(below)*

3. The **astronomical unit** is the average distance of the Earth from the Sun, that is, about 1.55×10^8 kilometers. About how many astronomical units are there in a light-year? 65,000

4. The maximum distance from the Sun to Pluto is about 50 astronomical units. What part of a light-year is that? $\frac{1}{1300}$

The speed of electromagnetic waves is the same as the speed of light. This formula holds:

Speed = Wavelength $\times$ Frequency

Frequency is often measured in kilohertz [kilocycles (10^3 cycles) per second] or megahertz [megacycles (10^6 cycles) per second].

5. An AM radio station broadcasts on a frequency of 600 kilohertz. What is the wavelength in meters? 500 m

6. An FM radio station broadcasts on a frequency of 100 megahertz. What is the wavelength in meters? 3 m

2. $(3 \times 10^8)(3.2 \times 10^7) = 9.6 \times 10^{15} \doteq 10 \times 10^{15} = 10^{16}$ m $= 10^{13}$ km

Atomic scientists use very small numbers. One example is the unit used to measure the mass of one atom of an element.

7. The mass of a carbon-12 atom is 12 atomic mass units. If an atomic mass unit is 1.660×10^{-24} grams, express the mass of a carbon-12 atom in grams in scientific notation. 1.992×10^{-23} grams

8. The mass of a lead atom is 207 atomic mass units. Express the mass of a lead atom in grams in scientific notation. 3.436×10^{-22} grams

9. A silver atom has a mass of 108 mass units. Express the mass of a silver atom in grams in scientific notation. 1.793×10^{-22} grams

Historical Note
Exponents

As has been the case for most algebraic symbols, many versions were tried before usage became standardized. As early as 1484, Nicolas Chuquet in France used a form of exponent to describe powers of a variable. His notation omitted the variable entirely; that is, he wrote

$$.2.^0, \ .2.^1, \ .2.^2, \ldots \text{ for } 2, 2x, 2x^2 \ldots$$

He also wrote $.2.^{2.m.}$ to mean $2x^{-2}$.
To represent what we would write as

$$x^4 + 3x^2 - 7x,$$

Jobst Burgi (1522–1632), a Swiss clockmaker, used

$$\begin{array}{ccc} \text{iv} & \text{ii} & \text{i} \\ 1 + 3 & - & 7 \end{array}$$

and Simon Stevin (1548–1620), a Flemish engineer, wrote:

$$\begin{array}{ccc} 4 & 2 & 1 \\ 1 + 3 & - & 7 \end{array}$$

Albert Girard (1590–1633), also Flemish, suggested placing the circled numerals to the left of a coefficient to indicate a power of that number and to the right to indicate a power of the variable. René Descartes (1596–1650), a French mathematician, introduced the use of small numerals with variables, and expressed powers as $x, xx, x^3, x^4, \ldots$. Eventually, mathematicians used x^2 for xx.

As you can see from the dates, all this was going on while other Europeans were exploring and settling North America.

5-3 Monomial Factors of Polynomials

OBJECTIVE To learn how to divide a polynomial by a monomial and how to find a monomial factor of a polynomial.

You factor a polynomial by expressing it as a product of polynomials chosen from a specified set. Unless otherwise stated, *the factor set for a polynomial having integral coefficients is the set of all polynomials having integral coefficients*.

You test for factors by division. Suppose that a, b, and c represent monomials, $c \neq 0$. Then:

$$\frac{a + b}{c} = \frac{1}{c}(a + b) \qquad \text{Rule for division}$$

$$= \frac{1}{c} \cdot a + \frac{1}{c} \cdot b \qquad \text{Distributive axiom}$$

$$= \frac{a}{c} + \frac{b}{c} \qquad \text{Rule for division}$$

In general:

To divide a polynomial by a monomial, divide each term of the polynomial by the monomial, and then add the quotients.

Example 1 $\dfrac{27t^4 + 21t^3 - 6t^2}{3t^2}$

Solution $\dfrac{27t^4 + 21t^3 - 6t^2}{3t^2}$

$$= \frac{27t^4}{3t^2} + \frac{21t^3}{3t^2} - \frac{6t^2}{3t^2}$$

$$= 9t^2 + 7t - 2 \quad \textit{Answer}$$

Example 2 $\dfrac{x^2y^2 + x - y}{xy}$

Solution $\dfrac{x^2y^2 + x - y}{xy}$

$$= \frac{x^2y^2}{xy} + \frac{x}{xy} - \frac{y}{xy}$$

$$= xy + \frac{1}{y} - \frac{1}{x} \quad \textit{Answer}$$

Notice that $27t^4 + 21t^3 - 6t^2$ is evenly divisible by $3t^2$, but $x^2y^2 + x - y$ is not evenly divisible by xy. We say that one polynomial is *evenly divisible*, or simply *divisible*, by another polynomial if the quotient is also a polynomial.

Since the division in Example 1 is exact, $3t^2$ is a factor of $27t^4 + 21t^3 - 6t^2$:

$$27t^4 + 21t^3 - 6t^2 = 3t^2(9t^2 + 7t - 2)$$

Since $3t^2$ is a monomial, you say that $3t^2$ is a **monomial factor** of the polynomial $27t^4 + 21t^3 - 6t^2$.

Notice that 3 and t^2 are also monomial factors of $27t^4 + 21t^3 - 6t^2$. You should be sure to continue factoring until you find the *greatest monomial factor*. The **greatest monomial factor** of a polynomial is the monomial factor having the greatest numerical coefficient and the greatest degree. The greatest monomial factor of a polynomial is the *greatest common factor* of the terms of the polynomial.

Notice the factoring in the following examples:

Given Polynomial	*Factors*		*Factored Expression*
$2a + 3b$	1	$2a + 3b$	$1(2a + 3b)$ or $2a + 3b$
$2x^3 + 5x^2$	x^2	$2x + 5$	$x^2(2x + 5)$
$5n + 10n^2$	$5n$	$1 + 2n$	$5n(1 + 2n)$
$3x^3 - 6x^2 + 15x$	$3x$	$x^2 - 2x + 5$	$3x(x^2 - 2x + 5)$
$12r^3s^2 - 18r^2st$	$6r^2s$	$2rs - 3t$	$6r^2s(2rs - 3t)$

Check each factoring exercise by multiplying the factors to be sure that the product is the number or expression that you are factoring.

Oral Exercises

Express each quotient as a sum. Assume that divisors are not zero.

1. $\dfrac{2a + 6}{2}$ $a + 3$

2. $\dfrac{6x - 9}{3}$ $2x - 3$

3. $\dfrac{10u - 15}{5}$ $2u - 3$

4. $\dfrac{24 + 6s}{6}$ $4 + s$

5. $\dfrac{2c^2 - 6}{2}$ $c^2 - 3$

6. $\dfrac{6z^3 - 12}{3}$ $2z^3 - 4$

7. $\dfrac{2a + 6b}{2}$ $a + 3b$

8. $\dfrac{9u - 6v}{3}$ $3u -$

9. $\dfrac{a^2 + 2a}{a}$ $a + 2$

10. $\dfrac{r^2 - rs}{r}$ $r - s$

11. $\dfrac{a - 2}{a}$ $1 - \dfrac{2}{a}$

12. $\dfrac{2c + 4}{2c}$ $1 + \dfrac{2}{c}$

Find the greatest monomial factor of each polynomial.

13. $5a + 10$ 5

14. $2x - 6$ 2

15. $6u - 3v$ 3

16. $8r + 4s$ 4

17. $x^2 + 4xy$ x

18. $2h^2k + 2k$ $2k$

19. $3x^2 + y^2$ 1

20. $x^2y - xy^2$ xy

21. $2a^3 - 6ab^2$ $2a$

22. $5xy + 7z^2$ 1

23. $10x^2 + 15xy$ $5x$

24. $4a^2b - 6ac^2$ 2

Written Exercises

Express each quotient as a sum. Assume that divisors are not zero.

A 1. $\dfrac{6x - 9}{3}$ $2x - 3$

2. $\dfrac{14a + 35}{7}$ $2a + 5$

3. $\dfrac{33 - 22u}{11}$ $3 - 2u$

4. $\dfrac{27 - 18y}{9}$ $3 - 2y$

5. $\dfrac{4a^2 + 6a}{2a}$ $2a + 3$

6. $\dfrac{10a^3 - 5a^2}{5a}$ $2a^2 - a$

7. $\dfrac{4r^3 - 6r^4}{2r^2}$ $2r - 3r^2$

8. $\dfrac{z^5 - z}{z}$ $z^4 - 1$

9. $\dfrac{xy^2 + x^2y}{xy}$ $y + x$

10. $\dfrac{a^2 - 2ab}{a}$ $a - 2b$

11. $\dfrac{a^2 + 2}{a}$ $a + \dfrac{2}{a}$

12. $\dfrac{r + 4}{r}$ $1 + \dfrac{4}{r}$

13. $\dfrac{25u^2 - 15u - 5}{-5}$ $-5u^2 + 3u + 1$

14. $\dfrac{9 - 6t - 3t^2}{-3}$ $-3 + 2t + t^2$

15. $\dfrac{8a^3 - 4a^2 + 2a}{2a}$ $4a^2 - 2a + 1$

16. $\dfrac{12x^2 - 9x^3 + 6x^4}{3x}$ $4x - 3x^2 + 2x^3$

17. $\dfrac{x^3y - 2x^2y^2 + xy^3}{xy}$ $x^2 - 2xy + y^2$

18. $\dfrac{2u^3v + 4u^2v^2 + 6uv^3}{2uv}$ $u^2 + 2uv + 3v^2$

Simplify.

19. $\dfrac{6x - 4}{2} + \dfrac{3x + 6}{3}$ $4x$

20. $\dfrac{5a + 10}{5} + \dfrac{6 - 9a}{3}$ $4 - 2a$

21. $\dfrac{t^2 + 3t}{t} - \dfrac{4t^2 - 6t}{2t}$ $-t + 6$

22. $\dfrac{s^2 + 2s}{s} - \dfrac{2s - 4}{2}$ 4

23. $\dfrac{x^3y + 2x^2y^2}{xy} - \dfrac{2x^3 - 6x^2y}{2x}$ $5xy$

24. $\dfrac{a^3b^2 - 2a^2b^3}{a^2} + \dfrac{a^2b^4 - 4a^5b^2}{ab^2}$ $2ab^2 - 2b^3 - 4a^4$

Find the greatest monomial factor and then write in factored form. Check by multiplying your factors. Exs. 25–36 below.

25. $5u^2 - 10$

26. $21 + 14z$

27. $4a^2 + 9a$

28. $3u - 6u^2$

29. $6r^4 - 2r^2$

30. $8t^3 - 3t^2$

31. $2x^2 - 10xy$

32. $6uv + 9v^2$

33. $12a^3b + 15ab^3$ $3y^2(2y^2 - 3y + 4)$

34. $24r^2s^2 - 30r^3s$ $5t^2(7 - 5t + 3t^2)$

35. $4x^2 - 4x - 6$

36. $6z^2 - 3z + 9$ $ax(a^2x^2 - ax + 2)$

37. $6y^4 - 9y^3 + 12y^2$

38. $35t^2 - 25t^3 + 15t^4$

39. $a^3x^3 - a^2x^2 + 2ax$

40. $42h^2k - 35h^2k^2 + 14h^2k^3$ $7h^2k(6 - 5k + 2k^2)$

41. $18xy^4 - 12xy^3 + 24xy^2$ $6xy^2(3y^2 - 2y + 4)$

42. $9u^3v + 12u^2v^2 + 15uv^3$ $3uv(3u^2 + 4uv + 5v^2)$

Solve each equation.

B 43. $\dfrac{3x^2 - 2x}{x} = 2x + 5$ $x = 7$

44. $\dfrac{6z^2 - 8z}{2z} = z + 7$ $z = 5\dfrac{1}{2}$

45. $\dfrac{y^3 + 6y^2}{y^2} = \dfrac{6y - 4y}{2y}$ $y = -5$

46. $\dfrac{2t^3 - 4t^2 - 6t}{2t} = \dfrac{3t^2 - 12t + 15}{3}$ $t = 4$

25. $5(u^2 - 2)$ 26. $7(3 + 2z)$ 27. $a(4a + 9)$ 28. $3u(1 - 2u)$

29. $2r^2(3r^2 - 1)$ 30. $t^2(8t - 3)$ 31. $2x(x - 5y)$ 32. $3v(2u + 3v)$

33. $3ab(4a^2 + 5b^2)$ 34. $6r^2s(4s - 5r)$ 35. $2(2x^2 - 2x - 3)$ 36. $3(2z^2 - z + 3)$

Problems

Write an expression in factored form for the area A of the shaded region shown.

Sample

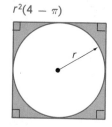

Solution

A = Area of rectangle − area of circle
(two semicircles)

$= 4r \cdot 2r \qquad\qquad - \pi r^2$

$= 8r^2 - \pi r^2$

$= (8 - \pi)r^2$ *Answer*

A 1.

$r^2(4 + \pi)$

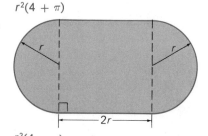

2.

$2r^2(6 - \pi)$

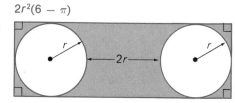

3.

$r^2(4 - \pi)$

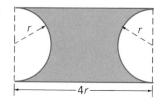

4.

$r^2(\pi - 2)$

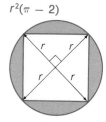

Hint: Think of the square as made up of two triangles.

5.

$r(2s + \pi r)$

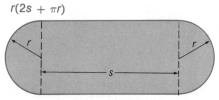

6.

$3r^2(4 - \pi)$

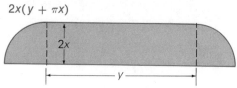

7.

$2x(y + \pi x)$

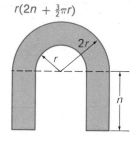

8.

$r(2n + \tfrac{3}{2}\pi r)$

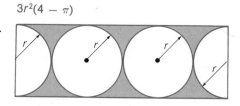

Career Note
Technical Writer

Technical writers prepare materials which explain the work of scientists and engineers to technicians, repair personnel, business managers, and consumers. They may be assigned to write press releases, contract proposals, manuals for the operation and maintenance of equipment, or articles for scientific and engineering periodicals. Technical writers may also prepare tables, charts, and diagrams for their materials.

The obvious and most important requirement for a career in technical writing is good writing skills. The materials a technical writer produces must be clear and easy to understand. The writer must be able to learn specialized vocabulary and use it accurately. The educational requirement is a bachelor's degree, with courses in science or engineering and English or journalism.

 Self-Test 1

Be sure that you understand these terms:

factor set (p. 139)
prime factors (p. 140)
greatest monomial factor (p. 152)

integral factors (p. 139)
prime factorization (p. 140)

prime numbers (p. 140)
monomial factors (p. 152)

1. Find the prime factorization of 60.

Objective 5-1, p. 139

2. Find all pairs of integral factors of 42.

3. Find the greatest common factor of 42 and 60.

4. Simplify $\dfrac{-18a^4b^2}{3a^2b^2}$.

Objective 5-2, p. 145

Find the missing factor.

5. $-72 = -6(\underline{\ ?\ })$

6. $48a^3b^5 = (6ab^2)(\underline{\ ?\ })$

7. Simplify $\dfrac{15t^4 + 12t^3 - 9t^2}{3t^2}$.

Objective 5-3, p. 151

8. Factor $3x^3y^2 - 6x^2y^2 + 6xy^2$.

Check your answers with those printed at the back of the book.

Special Products and Factoring

5-4 Differences of Squares

OBJECTIVE   To learn how to simplify products of the form $(a + b)(a - b)$ and to factor differences of squares.

Study these products of binomials:

$$
\begin{array}{l}
x + 3 \\
\underline{x - 3} \\
x^2 + 3x \\
 \underline{- 3x - 9} \\
x^2 - 9
\end{array}
\qquad
\begin{array}{l}
5s - 2t \\
\underline{5s + 2t} \\
25s^2 - 10st \\
 \underline{10st - 4t^2} \\
25s^2 - 4t^2
\end{array}
\qquad
\begin{array}{l}
a + b \\
\underline{a - b} \\
a^2 + ab \\
 \underline{- ab - b^2} \\
a^2 - b^2
\end{array}
$$

Do you see that the product of the sum and difference of two numbers is the square of the first number minus the square of the second?

$$(a + b)(a - b) = a^2 - b^2$$

This rule is illustrated in Figure 5-1:

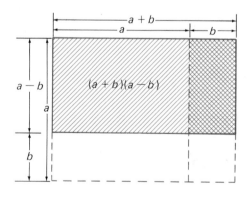
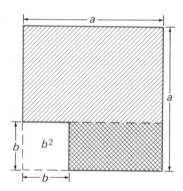

$$(a + b)(a - b) = a^2 - b^2$$

Figure 5-1

By the symmetric property of equality, we can write the statement $(a + b)(a - b) = a^2 - b^2$ as:

$$a^2 - b^2 = (a + b)(a - b)$$

You use this rule to factor a polynomial consisting of the difference of two squares:

Example 1 $x^2 - 9 = (x + 3)(x - 3)$

Example 2 $r^4 - 16s^2 = (r^2 + 4s)(r^2 - 4s)$

Example 3 $4a^2 - b^2 = (2a + b)(2a - b)$

Example 4 $x^2y^2 - z^6 = (xy + z^3)(xy - z^3)$

If, as in $64a^6x^2$, the degree in *each* variable in a monomial is even, and the numerical coefficient is the square of an integer, then the monomial is a square:

$$64a^6x^2 = (8a^3x)^2.$$

You can tell from the table of squares at the back of the book whether or not any integer from 1 to 10,000 is a square. For example, 3361 is not a square, and so it does not appear in the column headed "Square," but $3364 = (58)^2$ does appear.

Example 5 $64a^6x^2 - 3364b^2y^4 = (8a^3x + 58by^2)(8a^3x - 58by^2)$

Oral Exercises

Square each monomial.

Sample 1 $-6z^3$ *Solution* $(-6z^3)^2 = 36z^6$ *Answer*

 1. $5a$ $25a^2$ 2. $3x$ $9x^2$ 3. $2a^3$ $4a^6$ 4. $-3r^2$ $9r^4$ 5. $-5xy^3$ $25x^2y^6$ 6. $8a^3c^2$ $64a^6c^4$

Express each product as a polynomial.

Sample 2 $(3t - 1)(3t + 1)$ *Solution* $9t^2 - 1$ *Answer*

 7. $(x + 5)(x - 5)$ $x^2 - 25$ 8. $(r - 3)(r + 3)$ $r^2 - 9$ 9. $(s - t)(s + t)$ $s^2 - t^2$
10. $(z + a)(z - a)$ $z^2 - a^2$ 11. $(2k + 1)(2k - 1)$ $4k^2 - 1$ 12. $(3s - 1)(3s + 1)$ $9s^2 - 1$

Tell whether or not the given binomial is the difference of two squares.
If it is, give its factors.

Sample 3 $x^3 - 9$ **Sample 4** $a^2 - 6$ **Sample 5** $t^6 - 4$

Solution No   *Solution* No   *Solution* Yes $(t^3 + 2)(t^3 - 2)$

13. $x^2 - 9$ 14. $c^2 - 4$ 15. $z^2 + 4$ 16. $r^2 - s^2$

17. $h^3 - 12$ 18. $x^6 - y^2$ 19. $4a^2 - b^4$ 20. $25s^4 - z^6$

13. Yes; $(x + 3)(x - 3)$ **14.** Yes; $(c + 2)(c - 2)$ **15.** No   **16.** Yes; $(r + s)(r$
17. No   **18.** Yes; $(x^3 + y)(x^3 - y)$ **19.** Yes; $(2a + b^2)(2a - b^2)$ **20.** Yes;
$(5s^2 + z^3)(5s^2 -$

Written Exercises

1. $9z^2 - 25$ **2.** $1 - 49k^2$ **3.** $4x^2 - y^4$
4. $9a^4 - c^2$ **5.** $100a^2b^2 - 9c^4$ **6.** $4u^6 - v^4w^4$

Express each product as a polynomial.

A 1. $(3z - 5)(3z + 5)$ 2. $(1 - 7k)(1 + 7k)$ 3. $(2x + y^2)(2x - y^2)$
    4. $(3a^2 + c)(3a^2 - c)$ 5. $(10ab - 3c^2)(10ab + 3c^2)$ 6. $(2u^3 - v^2w^2)(2u^3 + v^2w^2)$
    7. $x^2(x^2 - 5y)(x^2 + 5y)$ 8. $c^3(a^2 + 3c^2)(a^2 - 3c^2)$ 9. $st(rs + 6t)(rs - 6t)$
   10. $ab(2b^2 - 7a^2)(2b^2 + 7a^2)$ 11. $mn^2(m^2 - n)(m^2 + n)$ 12. $p^2q(4p - q^2)(4p + q^2)$

Multiply **(a)** by using the form $(a + b)(a - b)$; **(b)** by using the distributive axiom.

7. $x^6 - 25x^2y^2$
8. $a^4c^3 - 9c^7$
9. $r^2s^3t - 36st^3$
10. $4ab^5 - 49a^5b$
11. $m^5n^2 - mn^4$
12. $16p^4q - p^2q^5$

Sample 1 67×73

Solution (a) $67 \times 73 = (70 - 3)(70 + 3) = 4900 - 9 = 4891$
        (b) $67 \times 73 = 60 \times 73 + 7 \times 73 = 4380 + 511 = 4891$
        Ordinary multiplication, which uses the distributive axiom, can
        also be used for part (b).

13. 13×7 91   14. 8×12 96   15. 28×32 896   16. 61×59 3599

17. 55×65 3575   18. 105×95 9975   19. 208×192 39,936   20. 493×507
                                                                                        249,951

Factor and check by multiplication. Use the table of squares as needed. *(below)*

21. $z^2 - 16$ 22. $a^2 - 36$ 23. $25r^2 - 1$ 24. $9t^2 - 4$
25. $16u^2 - v^2$ 26. $r^2 - 9s^2$ 27. $s^2 - 121t^2$ 28. $169m^2 - 4u^2$
29. $a^4 - c^6$ 30. $z^8 - 16a^2$ 31. $196s^6 - 625t^2$ 32. $225a^2b^2 - 256$

Sample 2 $8a^3 - 18ax^2 = 2a(4a^2 - 9x^2)$
          $= 2a(2a + 3x)(2a - 3x)$

$x(x + 4)(x - 4)$ $2a(a + 1)(a - 1)$ $2z(5z + 1)(5z - 1)$ $4(1 + 2t^2)(1 - 2t^2)$
33. $x^3 - 16x$ 34. $2a^3 - 2a$ 35. $50z^3 - 2z$ 36. $4 - 16t^4$

37. $xy^3 - x^3y$ 38. $u^5 - 9u^3v^2$ 39. $450a^5 - 8a$ 40. $27x^3 - 363xy^2$
$xy(y + x)(y - x)$ $u^3(u + 3v)(u - 3v)$ $2a(15a^2 + 2)(15a^2 - 2)$ $3x(3x + 11y)(3x - 1$

21. $(z + 4)(z - 4)$ **22.** $(a + 6)(a - 6)$ **23.** $(5r + 1)(5r - 1)$ **24.** $(3t + 2)(3t - 2)$
25. $(4u + v)(4u - v)$ **26.** $(r + 3s)(r - 3s)$ **27.** $(s + 11t)(s - 11t)$ **28.** $(13m + 2u)(13m - 2$
29. $(a^2 + c^3)(a^2 - c^3)$ **30.** $(z^4 + 4a)(z^4 - 4a)$ **31.** $(14s^3 + 25t)(14s^3 - 25t)$ **32.** $(15ab + 16)(15ab -$

In the following, assume that n denotes a positive integer.

Sample 3 $x^{4n} - 4y^2 = (x^{2n} + 2y)(x^{2n} - 2y)$

B 41. $a^{2n} - b^{2n}$ *(below)*   42. $x^{2n} - 16$ 43. $4u^{2n} - 169$ 44. $s^{4n} - t^2$

45. $x^{4n} - 4y^{2n}$ 46. $4u^{4n} - v^{2n}$ 47. $x^{2n+1} - xy^4$ 48. $a^{2n+1}b - ab^{2n+1}$

49. Which digits can occur as the last digit of a square? Hint: Square each of the digits 0, 1, . . . , 9.   **0, 1, 4, 5, 6, and 9**

50. Show that the square of an odd integer is odd. $(2n + 1)^2 = 4n^2 + 4n + 1 = 2(2n^2 + 2n) + 1$

C 51. Show that the difference of the squares of two consecutive integers is the sum of the integers. $(x + 1)^2 - x^2 = x^2 + 2x + 1 - x^2 = 2x + 1 = x + (x + 1)$

52. Show that the difference of the squares of two consecutive even integers is twice the sum of the integers. $(2n + 2)^2 - (2n)^2 = 4n^2 + 8n + 4 - 4n^2 = 8n + 4$
$$= 2[2n + (2n + 2)]$$

41. $(a^n + b^n)(a^n - b^n)$ 42. $(x^n + 4)(x^n - 4)$ 43. $(2u^n + 13)(2u^n - 13)$
44. $(s^{2n} + t)(s^{2n} - t)$ 45. $(x^{2n} + 2y^n)(x^{2n} - 2y^n)$ 46. $(2u^{2n} + v^n)(2u^{2n} - v^n)$
47. $x(x^n + y^2)(x^n - y^2)$ 48. $ab(a^n + b^n)(a^n - b^n)$

Just for Fun

With a bit of practice, you can mystify your friends with an algebraic "magic" trick.

Here's what you do:

                                          Hidden algebra

1. Ask your friend to think of a number: n

2. Tell your friend to multiply it by 3: $3n$

3. Tell your friend to add 10 to the result: $3n + 10$

4. Tell your friend to subtract twice the original number: $3n + 10 - 2n$

5. Ask your friend to tell you the result: $n + 10$

6. You can tell your friend what the original number was by subtracting 10 from the result.

Once you have mastered this trick, you can make up similar tricks with your own formulas.

5-5 Finding and Factoring Squares of Binomials

OBJECTIVE To learn how to square binomials mentally and how to factor trinomial squares.

The usual method of multiplication is used below to find the squares of the binomials $a + b$ and $a - b$.

$$\begin{array}{r} a + b \\ a + b \\ \hline a^2 + ab \\ ab + b^2 \\ \hline a^2 + 2ab + b^2 \end{array} \qquad \begin{array}{r} a - b \\ a - b \\ \hline a^2 - ab \\ - ab + b^2 \\ \hline a^2 - 2ab + b^2 \end{array}$$

In each case the product is a **trinomial square,** whose terms follow this pattern:

$$\left[\begin{array}{l}\text{The square of} \\ \text{the first term}\end{array}\right] \begin{array}{c}\text{plus} \\ \text{or} \\ \text{minus}\end{array} \left[\begin{array}{l}\text{Twice the product} \\ \text{of the two terms}\end{array}\right] \text{plus} \left[\begin{array}{l}\text{The square of} \\ \text{the second term}\end{array}\right]$$

Because they occur so frequently, you should remember these rules:

$$(a + b)^2 = a^2 + 2ab + b^2 \qquad (a - b)^2 = a^2 - 2ab + b^2$$

The first of these rules is illustrated in Figure 5-2:

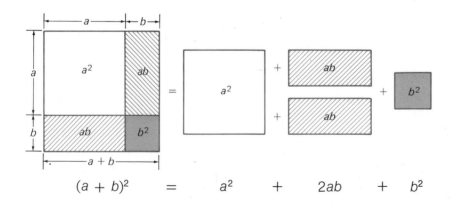

$$(a + b)^2 \quad = \quad a^2 \quad + \quad 2ab \quad + \quad b^2$$

Figure 5-2

With the help of these rules, you can square a binomial without using long multiplication:

Example 1 $(x + 3)^2 = x^2 + 6x + 9$

Example 2 $(u - 1)^2 = u^2 - 2u + 1$

Example 3 $(2s - 5t)^2 = 4s^2 - 20st + 25t^2$

Example 4 $(2x^2 + yz)^2 = 4x^4 + 4x^2yz + y^2z^2$

Example 5 $(-3a + 4c)^2 = (4c - 3a)^2 = 16c^2 - 24ac + 9a^2$

By reversing the rules stated above, you obtain these formulas for factoring:

$$a^2 + 2ab + b^2 = (a + b)^2 \qquad a^2 - 2ab + b^2 = (a - b)^2$$

Before you use one of these equations for factoring, you must be sure that the polynomial to be factored is a trinomial square. Arrange the terms of the trinomial with exponents of some chosen variable in descending order. Then examine the terms to see if they fit the pattern displayed above.

Example 6 Factor $9x^2 - 6xy + y^2$.

Solution

Is the first term a square?	Yes, $9x^2 = (3x)^2$
Is the third term a square?	Yes, $y^2 = (y)^2$
Is the middle term (neglecting the sign) twice the product of 3x and y?	Yes, $6xy = 2(3x)(y)$.

Therefore this trinomial is a square. Since the middle term is preceded by a *minus* sign, the trinomial is the square of a *difference*:

$$9x^2 - 6xy + y^2 = (3x - y)^2 \quad \text{Answer}$$

Oral Exercises

Express each power as a trinomial.

1. $(x - y)^2$ $x^2 - 2xy + y^2$ 2. $(c + 1)^2$ $c^2 + 2c + 1$ 3. $(u + 2)^2$ $u^2 + 4u + 4$ 4. $(s - 2)^2$ $s^2 - 4s + 4$

5. $(r + 5)^2$ $r^2 + 10r + 25$ 6. $(u + v)^2$ $u^2 + 2uv + v^2$ 7. $(t - 10)^2$ $t^2 - 20t + 100$ 8. $(a - 6)^2$ $a^2 - 12a + 36$

Is the trinomial the square of a binomial? If so, which binomial?

9. $a^2 + 2a + 1$ Yes; $a + 1$ 10. $c^2 + c + 1$ No   11. $x^2 - 2x + 4$ No   12. $z^2 - 2z + 1$ Yes; z

13. $x^2 + 4xy + 4y^2$ Yes; $x + 2y$ 14. $a^2 - 10ab + 25b^2$ Yes; $a - 5b$ 15. $h^2 - 4hk + 4k^2$ Yes; $h - 2k$ 16. $a^2 + b^2 + c^2$ N

Written Exercises

1. $x^2 - 16x + 64$ 2. $z^2 + 18z + 81$ 3. $4a^2 + 12ab +$

4. $36s^2 - 12st + t^2$ 5. $c^2d^2 + 14cd + 49$ 6. $x^2y^2 - 12xy -$

Write each power as a trinomial.   7. $4a^4 - 12a^2b + 9b^2$ 8. $9u^6 + 30u^3v + 25v^2$

A   1. $(x - 8)^2$ 2. $(z + 9)^2$ 3. $(2a + 3b)^2$ 4. $(6s - t)^2$

5. $(cd + 7)^2$ 6. $(xy - 6)^2$ 7. $(2a^2 - 3b)^2$ 8. $(3u^3 + 5v)^2$

9. $(-rs + 10t^2)^2$ 10. $(x^2y - 2z^3)^2$ 11. $(-u^2 - 6vw)^2$ 12. $(-abc + 10)^2$

$r^2s^2 - 20rst^2 + 100t^4$ $x^4y^2 - 4x^2yz^3 + 4z^6$ $u^4 + 12u^2vw + 36v^2w^2$ $a^2b^2c^2 - 20abc + 100$

Factor and check by multiplying.

13. $h^2 + 4h + 4$ $(h + 2)^2$ 14. $u^2 - 6u + 9$ $(u - 3)^2$ 15. $a^2 - 8a + 16$ $(a - 4)^2$

16. $x^2 + 10x + 25$ $(x + 5)^2$ 17. $36 - 12u + u^2$ $(6 - u)^2$ 18. $49 + 14t + t^2$ $(7 + t)^2$

19. $4v^2 + 20v + 25$ $(2v + 5)^2$ 20. $9c^2 - 12c + 4$ $(3c - 2)^2$ 21. $a^2 - 6ab + 9b^2$ $(a - 3b)^2$

22. $u^2 - 16uv + 64v^2$ $(u - 8v)^2$ 23. $25t^2 + 10t + 1$ $(5t + 1)^2$ 24. $100h^2 + 20h + 1$ $(10t + 1)^2$

Sample 1 $12x^3 - 12x^2 + 3x = 3x(4x^2 - 4x + 1) = 3x(2x - 1)^2$

B   25. $4a^3 + 8a^2 + 4a$ (below)   26. $5c + 20c^2 + 20c^3$ 27. $16ax^2 - 80ax + 100a$

28. $18uv^2 - 48uv + 32u$ 29. $a^3b + 2a^2b^2 + ab^3$ 30. $100s^2t^2 - 40s^2t + 4s^2$

31. $8c^3d^3 - 24c^2d^2 + 18cd$ 32. $x^4y - 6x^3y^2 + 9x^2y^3$ 33. $9u^3v - 12u^2v^2 + 4uv^3$

34. $4h^4 - 20h^3k + 25h^2k^2$ 35. $49s^6t^2 + 14s^3t^4 + t^6$ 36. $a^4b^6 - 22a^3b^4c + 121a^2b^2c^2$

Sample 2 $x^2 - 4x + 4 - 4y^2 = (x - 2)^2 - 4y^2 = [(x - 2) + 2y][(x - 2) - 2y]$
$$= (x + 2y - 2)(x - 2y - 2)$$

37. $a^2 + 2a + 1 - c^2$ $(a + c + 1)(a - c + 1)$ 38. $u^2 - 6u + 9 - 9v^2$ $(u + 3v - 3)(u - 3v - 3)$ 39. $4s^2 - 4t^2 - 4t - 1$ $(4s - 2t - 1)(4s + 2t + 1)$

40. $x^2 - 1 - 2y - y^2$ $(x + y + 1)(x - y - 1)$ 41. $x^2 - 6xy + 9y^2 - z^2$ $(x - 3y + z)(x - 3y - z)$ 42. $a^2 + 2ab + b^2 - 4c^2$ $(a + b + 2c)(a + b - 2c)$

Find k so that the trinomial will be a square.

43. $x^2 + kx + 4$ 4   44. $4a^2 - 12a + k$ 9   45. $kz^2 - 24z + 9$ 16   46. $ku^2 + 18u + 9$ 9

47. $z^2 - 4z + k$ 4   48. $a^2 + ka + 9$ 6   49. $9x^2 + 2kx + 4$ 6   50. $4u^2 - 20u + k$ 25

25. $4a(a + 1)^2$ 26. $5c(1 + 2c)^2$ 27. $4a(2x - 5)^2$ 28. $2u(3v - 4)^2$

29. $ab(a + b)^2$ 30. $4s^2(5t - 1)^2$ 31. $2cd(2cd - 3)^2$ 32. $x^2y(x - 3y)^2$

33. $uv(3u - 2v)^2$ 34. $h^2(2h - 5k)^2$ 35. $t^2(7s^3 + t^2)^2$ 36. $a^2b^2(ab^2 - 11c)^2$

Express the indicated area *in factored form* in terms of the specified variables.

Sample 3   Area *A* between two circles: *r* and *w*.

Solution   The radius of the larger circle is $r + w$; therefore its area is $\pi(r + w)^2$. The area of the smaller circle is πr^2.

$$\therefore A = \pi(r + w)^2 - \pi r^2 = \pi[(r + w)^2 - r^2]$$
$$= \pi[r^2 + 2rw + w^2 - r^2] = \pi(2rw + w^2)$$
$$= \pi w(2r + w). \quad \textbf{\textit{Answer}}$$

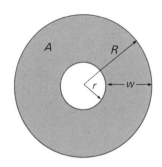

C 51. Area *A* between two circles; *R* and *r* $A = \pi(R + r)(R - r)$

52. Area *A* between two circles; *R* and *w* $A = \pi w(2R - w)$

53. $A = (b + a)(b - a)$
54. $A = 4w(a + w)$
55. $A = 4w(b - w)$

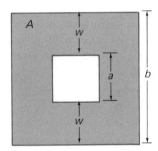

53. Area *A* between two squares; *a* and *b*

54. Area *A* between two squares; *a* and *w*

55. Area *A* between two squares; *b* and *w*

56. $A = r(2s + \pi r)$
57. $A = (R - w)[2s + \pi(R - w)]$
58. $T = (R - r)[2s + \pi(R + r)]$
59. $T = w[2s + \pi(2r + w)]$

56. Area *A* of infield; *r* and *s*

57. Area *A* of infield; *R*, *w*, and *s*

58. Area *T* of track; *R*, *r*, and *s*

59. Area *T* of track; *r*, *w*, and *s*

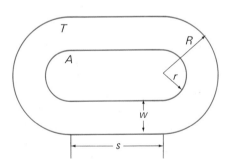

60. Show that *T* is the product of *w* and the distance around the track halfway between the inner and outer edges.   *(below)*

61. If it is decided to make $s = 4r$ and $w = r$, find *T* in terms of *r*. $T = r^2(8 + 3\pi)$

Running track with area *T*
Infield with area *A*

62. Draw a diagram similar to Figure 5-2 to illustrate:

$$(a - b)^2 = a^2 - 2ab + b^2$$

60. The distance around the track halfway between the inner and outer

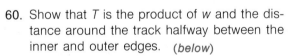

edges is $s + s + 2\pi\left(r + \dfrac{w}{2}\right) = 2s + \pi(2r + w)$. From Exercise 29,

$T = w[2s + \pi(2r + w)]$.

Show that each diagram illustrates the statement below it.

63.

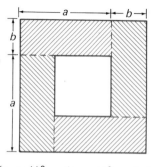

$$(a + b)^2 - (a - b)^2 = 4ab$$

64.

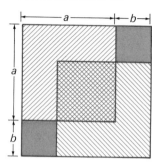

$$(a + b)^2 + (a - b)^2 = 2(a^2 + b^2)$$

65. Find $(a + b + c)^2$ and draw a diagram to illustrate it.

$$(a + b + c)^2 = a^2 + b^2 + c^2 + 2ab + 2bc + 2ac$$

★ *Self-Test 2*

Be sure that you understand this term:

trinomial square (p. 160)

Express each product as a polynomial.

1. $(2x - 3)(2x + 3)$

2. $ax(x^2 + a^2)(x^2 - a^2)$

Objective 5-4, p. 156

Factor.

3. $49z^4 - 81$

4. $ab^4 - a^3b^2$

Express each product as a polynomial.

5. $(x + 6)^2$

6. $(2c - 3)^2$

Objective 5-5, p. 160

7. $yz(y - 3z)^2$

8. $x(x^2 + 2x)^2$

Factor.

9. $n^2 - 4n + 4$

10. $9x^2 - 6x + 1$

11. $a^4 + 2a^2b^3 + b^6$

12. $4x^4y - 12x^3y^2 + 9x^2y^3$

Check your answers with those printed at the back of the book.

5-6 Multiplying Binomials Mentally

> **OBJECTIVE** To learn how to find the product of two binomials.

You will save much time if you learn to find products of the form $(ax + b)(cx + d)$ mentally. Consider, for example, the product $(3x - 4)(5x + 2)$:

Long Multiplication:

$(3x - 4)(5x + 2)$

$$\begin{array}{r} 5x + 2 \\ 3x - 4 \\ \hline 15x^2 + 6x \\ -20x - 8 \\ \hline 15x^2 - 14x - 8 \end{array}$$

$(ax + b)(cx + d)$

$$\begin{array}{r} cx + d \\ ax + b \\ \hline acx^2 + adx \\ bcx + bd \\ \hline acx^2 + (ad + bc)x + bd \end{array}$$

Short Method:

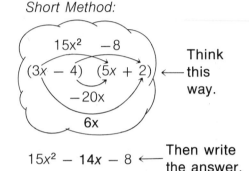

← Think this way.

$15x^2 - 14x - 8$ ← Then write the answer.

To find the terms in the trinomial product of two binomials, $(ax + b)(cx + d)$, mentally:

1. Multiply the first terms of the binomials.

2. Multiply the first term of each binomial by the last term of the other, and add these products.

3. Multiply the last terms of the binomials.

Each term of a trinomial like $15x^2 - 14x - 8$ has a name. A **quadratic term** is a term of degree *two* in the variable. A **linear term** is a term of degree *one* in the variable. As defined earlier a *constant term* is a numerical term with no variable factor. The trinomial itself is called a **quadratic polynomial** because it is of degree two. (Recall Section 4-6.)

quadratic term, $15x^2$
linear term, $-14x$
constant term, -8

$$15x^2 - 14x - 8$$

Oral Exercises

State the quadratic, linear, and constant terms, and read the product of a trinomial.

5. $z^2 + 9z + 14$
6. $k^2 + 8k + 15$
7. $y^2 - 9y + 18$
8. $r^2 - 8r + 7$

Sample $(y - 3)(y + 2)$

Solution   Quadratic term, y^2; linear term $-y$; constant term -6; $y^2 - y - 6$.   *Answer*

$x^2 + 4x + 3$
1. $(x + 3)(x + 1)$

$u^2 + 3u + 2$
2. $(u + 1)(u + 2)$

$t^2 - 5t + 6$
3. $(t - 2)(t - 3)$

$s^2 - 5s + 4$
4. $(s - 1)(s - 4)$

5. $(z + 7)(z + 2)$

6. $(k + 5)(k + 3)$

7. $(y - 6)(y - 3)$

8. $(r - 7)(r - 1)$

9. $(h + 4)(h - 1)$
$h^2 + 3h - 4$

10. $(v + 2)(v - 1)$
$v^2 + v - 2$

11. $(r - 7)(r + 2)$
$r^2 - 5r - 14$

12. $(x - 4)(x + 3)$
$x^2 - x - 12$

Written Exercises

1. $n^2 - 9n + 14$
4. $z^2 + 2z - 24$
7. $2y^2 + 5y + 3$
10. $3s^2 + 13s - 10$

2. $k^2 + 8k + 15$
5. $18 + 3t - t^2$
8. $3t^2 + 10t + 3$
11. $12u^2 - u - 6$

3. $x^2 - 3x - 10$
6. $35 + 2u - u^2$
9. $3r^2 - 10r - 8$
12. $10h^2 + 19h - 1$

Write each product as a trinomial.

A
1. $(n - 7)(n - 2)$
2. $(k + 5)(k + 3)$
3. $(x - 5)(x + 2)$
4. $(z - 4)(z + 6)$

5. $(6 - t)(3 + t)$
6. $(5 + u)(7 - u)$
7. $(2y + 3)(y + 1)$
8. $(3t + 1)(t + 3)$

9. $(3r + 2)(r - 4)$
10. $(s + 5)(3s - 2)$
11. $(4u - 3)(3u + 2)$
12. $(5h - 3)(2h + 5)$

Sample $(3x - 2y)(x - 5y)$

Solution   Think $\longrightarrow$

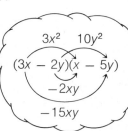

13. $x^2 + 3xy + 2y^2$
15. $4s^2 - 8st + 3t^2$
17. $3h^2 - 7hk - 6k^2$
19. $8z^2 + 2zw - 15w^2$
21. $2a^2b^2 - abyz - y^2z^2$
23. $x^4 - x^2y - 2y^2$

14. $u^2 - 5uv + 6v^2$
16. $6r^2 - 7rs - 3s^2$
18. $7m^2 - 50mn + 7n^2$
20. $15u^2 + 2uv - 8v^2$
22. $2c^2d^2 + 7cdpq + 3p$
24. $2r^4 - 3r^2s - 2s^2$

$3x^2 - 17xy + 10y^2$ *Answer*

13. $(x + y)(x + 2y)$
14. $(u - 2v)(u - 3v)$
15. $(2s - t)(2s - 3t)$

16. $(3r + s)(2r - 3s)$
17. $(3h + 2k)(h - 3k)$
18. $(7m - n)(m - 7n)$

19. $(2z + 3w)(4z - 5w)$
20. $(5u + 4v)(3u - 2v)$
21. $(ab - yz)(2ab + yz)$

22. $(2cd + pq)(cd + 3pq)$
23. $(x^2 - 2y)(x^2 + y)$
24. $(r^2 - 2s)(2r^2 + s)$

Solve each equation and check.

B
25. $(x + 1)(x + 5) = (x + 2)(x + 3)$ 1
26. $(x - 3)(x - 1) = (x - 1)(x - 5)$ 1

27. $(4x - 3)(x + 2) = (2x - 1)(2x + 1)$ 1
28. $(2x - 3)(2x - 1) = (x - 2)(4x + 3)$ 3

29. $2(x + 1)(2x + 5) = (x + 3)(4x + 3)$ 1
30. $(x + 1)^2 + (x - 1)^2 = (2x - 1)(x + 1)$ 3

31. $(2x + 1)^2 - (2x - 1)^2 = (x + 6)^2 - x^2$ −9
32. $(3x - 2)^2 - (2x - 3)^2 = (5x - 3)(x - 1)$ 1

5-7 Factoring Pattern for $x^2 + bx + c$, c Positive

> **OBJECTIVE** To learn how to factor quadratic trinomials when the coefficient of the quadratic term is 1 and the constant term is positive.

If $x^2 + bx + c$ (c positive) can be factored, then the factorization has the pattern:

$$(x + r)(x + s) = x^2 + (r + s)x + rs$$

rs is positive, and so r and s are $\begin{cases} \textit{both positive} \\ \textit{or both negative.} \end{cases}$

If $r + s$ is positive, then r and s are both positive.
If $r + s$ is negative, then r and s are both negative.

Example 1 Factor $x^2 + 7x + 10$.

Solution
   Compare: $x^2 + (r + s)x + rs$
           $x^2 + \quad 7 \quad x + 10$

Here 7 is positive, and so the factors of 10 must *both* be *positive:*

$$10 = (1)(10) = (2)(5)$$

Try: $rs = 1 \cdot 10$ $rs = 2 \cdot 5$
                $r \quad s$ $r \quad s$

   $r + s = 1 + 10 = 11$ $r + s = 2 + 5 = 7 \checkmark$

$\therefore x^2 + 7x + 10 = (x + 2)(x + 5)$. *Answer*

You can check this by multiplying the factors.

Of course, if at any time you see the right pair of factors, there is no need to write the remaining possibilities.

Example 2 Factor $z^2 - 8z + 12$.

Solution
$$z^2 - 8z + 12 = (z \quad)(z \quad) \left\{ \begin{array}{l} \text{Since } r + s \text{ is negative,} \\ \text{both } r \text{ and } s \text{ are negative.} \end{array} \right.$$
$$= (z - \quad)(z - \quad)$$
$$= (z - 2)(z - 6) \quad \textit{Answer}$$

Check $(z - 2)(z - 6) = z^2 - 8z + 12.$ ✓

Not every quadratic trinomial can be written as a product of binomials having integral coefficients. To try to factor

$$y^2 + 10y + 14,$$

you would have to find integers r and s such that

$$rs = 14 \quad \text{and} \quad r + s = 10$$

The two ways of writing 14 as a product of positive integers are:

$$14 = \underset{\overset{\updownarrow}{r}}{1} \cdot \underset{\overset{\updownarrow}{s}}{14} \qquad\qquad\qquad 14 = \underset{\overset{\updownarrow}{r}}{2} \cdot \underset{\overset{\updownarrow}{s}}{7}$$

$$r + s = 1 + 14 = 15 \neq 10 \qquad r + s = 2 + 7 = 9 \neq 10$$

In each case $r + s \neq 10$; therefore, $y^2 + 10y + 14$ cannot be factored over the set of polynomials with integral coefficients and is said to be *irreducible over this set of polynomials*. A polynomial which is not the product of polynomials of lower positive degree belonging to a specified set is **irreducible** over that set of polynomials.

An irreducible polynomial whose greatest monomial factor is 1 is called a **prime polynomial**. Thus, $3x + 5$ is a prime polynomial. Because $6x + 10 = 2(3x + 5)$, the polynomial $6x + 10$ is irreducible but not prime.

Oral Exercises

For each trinomial, tell which two factors of the constant term have a sum equal to the coefficient of the linear term.

1. $x^2 + 4x + 3$ 1, 3
2. $y^2 + 3y + 2$ 1, 2
3. $t^2 + 6t + 8$ 2, 4
4. $u^2 + 16u + 15$ 1,
5. $t^2 + 9t + 8$ 1, 8
6. $u^2 + 8u + 15$ 3, 5
7. $z^2 - 4z + 3$ -1, -3
8. $h^2 - 3h + 2$ -1, -
9. $x^2 - 5x + 6$ -2, -3
10. $v^2 - 9v + 14$ -2, -7
11. $n^2 - 13n + 22$ -2, -11
12. $x^2 + 7x + 12$ 3, 4

Written Exercises

Answers on pages A1 and A2 at the back of the book.

Factor each trinomial and check by multiplying.

A 1. $z^2 + 7z + 6$ 2. $w^2 + 11w + 10$ 3. $c^2 + 6c + 5$ 4. $t^2 - 6t + 5$

5. $r^2 - 8r + 7$ 6. $m^2 + 10m + 9$ 7. $x^2 + 7x + 12$ 8. $y^2 + 5y + 6$

9. $k^2 - 9k + 20$ 10. $u^2 - 14u + 24$ 11. $21 + 10s + s^2$ 12. $16 + 10v + v^2$

Sample 1 $h^2 - 8hk + 15k^2$.

Solution $h^2 - 8hk + 15k^2 = (h \quad)(h \quad)$
$= (h - \quad)(h - \quad)$
$= (h - 3k)(h - 5k)$ *Answer*

13. $x^2 + 5xy + 4y^2$ 14. $u^2 + 10uv + 9v^2$ 15. $r^2 - 20rs + 19s^2$ 16. $a^2 - 16ab + 15b^2$

17. $m^2 - 15mn + 26n^2$ 18. $s^2 - 10st + 21t^2$ 19. $x^2 + 13ax + 40a^2$ 20. $x^2 + 14xz + 48z^2$

21. $z^2 + 25zw + 100w^2$ 22. $y^2 - 13yz + 42z^2$ 23. $b^2 - 17bc + 52c^2$ 24. $x^2 + 15xy + 50y^2$

Find all integral values of k for which the trinomial can be factored over
the set of polynomials with integral coefficients.

Sample 2 $y^2 + ky + 14$

Solution 14 can be expressed as a product of two integers as follows:
$1 \cdot 14$, $2 \cdot 7$, $(-1)(-14)$, $(-2)(-7)$.
The corresponding values of k are 15, 9, -15, -9. *Answer*

B 25. $z^2 + kz + 6$ 26. $t^2 + kt + 20$ 27. $x^2 + kx + 12$ 28. $y^2 + ky + 18$
7, 5, -7, -5 21, 12, 9, -21, -12, -9 13, 8, 7, -13, -8, -7 19, 11, 9, -19, -11, -9

Find positive integral values of k for which the trinomial can be factored
over the set of polynomials with integral coefficients.

Sample 3 $x^2 + 6x + k$

Solution 6 can be expressed as a sum of positive integers as follows: $1 + 5$,
$2 + 4$, $3 + 3$. The corresponding values of k are 5, 8, 9. *Answer*

29. $y^2 + 4y + k$ 3, 4   30. $u^2 + 5u + k$ 4, 6   31. $x^2 + 7x + k$ 32. $z^2 + 8z + k$
6, 10, 12   7, 12, 15, 16

Factor each expression. Check by multiplying.

C 33. $(u + v)^2 - 5(u + v) + 6$ $(u + v - 2)(u + v - 3)$ 34. $(x + y)^2 + 7(x + y) + 6$ $(x + y + 6)(x + y + 1)$

35. $(x + 3)^2 - 6(x + 3) + 5$ $(x - 2)(x + 2)$ 36. $(a - 2)^2 + 6(a - 2) + 8$ $a(a + 2)$

Show that each polynomial is prime over the set of polynomials with
integral coefficients.

37. $x^2 + 3x + 1$ 38. $x^2 - x + 3$ 39. $x^2 + 4x + 6$ 40. $x^2 + 9x + 12$

37. $1 = 1 \cdot 1 = (-1)(-1)$, but $1 + 1 \neq 3$, $(-1) + (-1) \neq 3$.
38. $3 = 1 \cdot 3 = (-1)(-3)$, but $1 + 3 \neq -1$, $(-1) + (-3) \neq -1$.
39. $6 = 1 \cdot 6 = 2 \cdot 3 = (-1)(-6) = (-2)(-3)$, but $1 + 6 \neq 4$, $2 + 3 \neq 4$, $(-1) + (-6) \neq 4$, $(-2) + (-3) \neq 4$.
40. $12 = 1 \cdot 12 = 2 \cdot 6 = 3 \cdot 4 = (-1)(-12) = (-2)(-6) = (-3)(-4)$, but $1 + 12 \neq 9$, etc.

5-8 Factoring Pattern for $x^2 + bx + c$, c Negative

> **OBJECTIVE** To learn how to factor quadratic trinomials when the coefficient of the quadratic term is 1 and the constant term is negative.

If $x^2 + bx + c$ (c negative) can be factored, then the factorization has the pattern:

$$(x + r)(x + s) = x^2 + (r + s)x + rs$$

rs is negative, and so one of the factors, say r, is *positive* and the other, s, is *negative*.

Example Factor $y^2 + 2y - 15$.

Solution
Compare: $y^2 + (r + s)y + rs$
$y^2 + 2 \quad y + (-15)$

Here 2 is positive, and so we must find a positive and a negative factor of -15 with a *positive* sum:

$$-15 = (15)(-1) = (5)(-3)$$

Try: $\quad rs = 15 \cdot (-1) \qquad\qquad rs = 5 \cdot (-3)$

$r + s = 15 + (-1) = 14 \qquad r + s = 5 + (-3) = 2 \; ✔$

$\therefore y^2 + 2y - 15 = (y + 5)(y - 3)$. *Answer*

On the other hand, to factor $y^2 - 2y - 15$ you would look for two integers of opposite sign but with a *negative* sum. The factorization is

$$y^2 - 2y - 15 = (y - 5)(y + 3).$$

Do you see that $y^2 + 2y - 1$ is irreducible over the set of polynomials with integral coefficients?

Oral Exercises

For each trinomial, tell which two factors of the constant term have a sum equal to the coefficient of the linear term.

Sample $x^2 - x - 20$ *Solution* -5 and 4

1. $z^2 + 2z - 3$ $3, -1$
2. $c^2 + 4c - 5$ $5, -1$
3. $u^2 + 9u - 10$ $10, -1$
4. $t^2 + 6t - 7$ $7, -1$
5. $r^2 - 5r - 6$ $-6, 1$
6. $s^2 - s - 6$ $-3, 2$
7. $n^2 + n - 6$ $3, -2$
8. $x^2 - 8x - 9$ $-9, 1$
9. $k^2 + 2k - 8$ $4, -2$
10. $y^2 + 2y - 8$ $4, -2$
11. $t^2 - 2t - 8$ $-4, 2$
12. $h^2 - h - 6$ $-3, 2$

Written Exercises

Factor each trinomial and check by multiplying.   Answers on page A2 at the back of the book.

A
1. $x^2 + 2x - 8$
2. $y^2 + 3y - 4$
3. $h^2 + 8h - 9$
4. $z^2 + 3z - 10$
5. $u^2 - 10u - 11$
6. $s^2 - 9s - 10$
7. $r^2 + r - 20$
8. $t^2 + t - 6$
9. $k^2 - k - 20$
10. $m^2 - m - 6$
11. $t^2 - 8t - 20$
12. $r^2 + 6r - 16$
13. $z^2 + z - 30$
14. $k^2 + 3k - 18$
15. $y^2 - 7y - 30$
16. $x^2 - 5x - 50$
17. $c^2 - 2c - 24$
18. $a^2 - 5a - 24$
19. $x^2 + 7xy - 8y^2$
20. $m^2 + 5mn - 6n^2$
21. $u^2 - 2uv - 24v^2$
22. $h^2 - 5hk - 24k^2$
23. $a^2 + 4ab - 45b^2$
24. $r^2 + 12rs - 45s^2$

Find all integral values of k for which the given trinomial can be factored over the set of polynomials with integral coefficients.

B
25. $x^2 + kx - 8$
$7, 2, -7, -2$
26. $y^2 + ky - 10$
$9, 3, -3, -9$
27. $z^2 + kz - 20$
$19, 8, 1, -19, -8, -1$
28. $t^2 + kt - 30$
$29, 13, 7, 1, -29, -13, -7, -1$

Find two negative integers k for which the given trinomial can be factored over the set of polynomials with integral coefficients.   Answers may vary.

Sample $x^2 + 2x + k$

Solution We seek negative values of k having one positive factor and one negative factor such that the sum of the factors is 2. Thus:
$$2 = 3 + (-1); \quad k = 3(-1) = -3$$
$$2 = 4 + (-2); \quad k = 4(-2) = -8$$
$\therefore$ two possible values for k are -3 and -8. *Answer*

29. $x^2 + x + k$ $-2, -6$
30. $y^2 - 2y + k$ $-3, -8$
31. $t^2 - 3t + k$ $-4, -10$
32. $v^2 + 4v + k$
$-5, -12$

Factor each expression. Check by multiplying.
C
33. $(u + v)^2 - (u + v) - 6$ $(u + v - 3)(u + v + 2)$
34. $(x + y)^2 - 5(x + y) - 6$ $(x + y - 6)(x + y + 1)$
35. $(t + 1)^2 - 2(t + 1) - 48$ $(t - 7)(t + 7)$
36. $(z - 2)^2 + 4(z - 2) - 60$ $(z + 8)(z - 8)$

5-9 Factoring Pattern for $ax^2 + bx + c$, a Positive

> **OBJECTIVE** To learn how to factor quadratic trinomials when the coefficient of the quadratic term is a positive integer, not 1.

If $ax^2 + bx + c$ (*a* positive) can be factored, then the factorization has the pattern:

$$(mx + r)(nx + s) = mnx^2 + (ms + nr)x + rs$$

Here it is necessary to consider factors m and n as well as factors r and s.

Example 1 Factor $7x^2 - 19x - 6$.

Solution

First clue: The constant term is negative and the linear term has a negative coefficient. Therefore one of the factors, r and s, is positive and the other is negative.

Second clue: The product of the linear terms of the binomial factors is $7x^2$, and the product of their constant terms is -6.

The possible pair of factors of $7x^2$ are:	The possible pairs of factors of -6 are:
x and $7x$ $\longleftrightarrow$	$\begin{cases} 1 \text{ and } -6, 6 \text{ and } -1 \\ 2 \text{ and } -3, 3 \text{ and } -2 \end{cases}$

∴ the possibilities are:

	Possible factors	Corresponding linear term
$m = 1$	$(x - 6)(7x + 1)$	$x - 42x = -41x$
$n = 7$	$(x - 1)(7x + 6)$	$6x - 7x = -x$
	$(x - 3)(7x + 2)$	$2x - 21x = -19x$ ⇐
	$(x - 2)(7x + 3)$	$3x - 14x = -11x$

Third clue: The linear term of the trinomial is $-19x$. Only the third possibility satisfies all three clues.

∴ $7x^2 - 19x - 6 = (x - 3)(7x + 2)$. *Answer*

Example 2 Factor $15x^2 - 26x + 8$.

Solution

First clue: The constant term is positive and the linear term has a negative coefficient. Therefore, r and s are both negative.

Second clue: The product of the linear terms of the binomial factors is $15x^2$, and the product of their constant terms is 8.

The possible pairs of factors of $15x^2$ are:

The possible pairs of factors of 8 are:

$$\left.\begin{array}{l} x \text{ and } 15x \\ 3x \text{ and } 5x \end{array}\right\} \longleftrightarrow \left\{\begin{array}{l} -1 \text{ and } -8 \\ -2 \text{ and } -4 \end{array}\right.$$

$\therefore$ the possibilities are:

Possible factors	Corresponding linear term
$m = 1$ $\left\{\begin{array}{l}(x - 1)(15x - 8) \\ (x - 8)(15x - 1) \\ (x - 2)(15x - 4) \\ (x - 4)(15x - 2)\end{array}\right.$	$-8x - 15x = -23x$
	$-x - 120x = -121x$
$n = 15$	$-4x - 30x = -34x$
	$-2x - 60x = -62x$
$m = 3$ $\left\{\begin{array}{l}(3x - 1)(5x - 8) \\ (3x - 8)(5x - 1) \\ (3x - 2)(5x - 4) \\ (3x - 4)(5x - 2)\end{array}\right.$	$-24x - 5x = -29x$
	$-3x - 40x = -43x$
$n = 5$	$-12x - 10x = -22x$
	$-6x - 20x = -26x$ $\Longleftarrow$

Third clue: The linear term of the trinomial is $-26x$.

Only the last possibility satisfies all three clues.

$\therefore 15x^2 - 26x + 8 = (3x - 4)(5x - 2)$. *Answer*

As you gain experience, you will find that often you will not need to write down all the possibilities before discovering the factors.

Example 3 Factor $3x^2 - x - 10$.

Solution $\quad 3x^2 - x - 10 = (x \quad)(3x \quad)$
$$= (x - \quad)(3x + \quad)$$
$$= (x - 2)(3x + 5) \quad \textit{Answer}$$

At the second step in the Solution of Example 3, we might well have written $(x + \quad)(3x - \quad)$. We would then have found by trial that no combination of factors of 10 produced the linear term $-x$.

Written Exercises

1. $(3x + 1)(x + 1)$ 2. $(2u + 3)(u + 1)$ 3. $(2k + 1)(k + 3$
4. $(5t + 1)(t + 2)$ 5. $(5z + 2)(z + 1)$ 6. $(5s + 1)(s + 1$
7. $(3y - 1)(y - 2)$ 8. $(2n - 1)(n - 5)$ 9. $(2x + 3)(x + 2$
10. $(3z + 2)(z + 3)$ 11. $(3z - 2)(z + 1)$ 12. $(3y + 5)(y - 1$
13. $(2t + 3)(t - 2)$ 14. $(2x - 5)(2x + 1)$ 15. $(5h - 7)(h + 1$
16. $(4s - 3)(2s - 1)$ 17. $(5h - 7k)(h + k)$ 18. $(4s - 3t)(2s -$

Factor and check by multiplying.

A 1. $3x^2 + 4x + 1$ 2. $2u^2 + 5u + 3$ 3. $2k^2 + 7k + 3$ 4. $5t^2 + 11t + 2$

 5. $5z^2 + 7z + 2$ 6. $5s^2 + 6s + 1$ 7. $3y^2 - 7y + 2$ 8. $2n^2 - 11n + 5$

 9. $2x^2 + 7x + 6$ 10. $3z^2 + 11z + 6$ 11. $3z^2 + z - 2$ 12. $3y^2 + 2y - 5$

 13. $2t^2 - t - 6$ 14. $4x^2 - 8x - 5$ 15. $5h^2 - 2h - 7$ 16. $8s^2 - 10s + 3$

 17. $5h^2 - 2hk - 7k^2$ 18. $8s^2 - 10st + 3t^2$ 19. $6u^2 - uv - 2v^2$ 20. $2m^2 + mn - 10n^2$

 21. $3x^2 - 13xy + 14y^2$ 22. $2c^2 - 7cd - 4d^2$ 23. $5r^2 + 6rs - 8s^2$ 24. $10p^2 - 37pq + 7q^2$

B 25. $6x^2 + 19x + 15$ 26. $6y^2 + y - 15$ 27. $8t^2 - 6t - 9$

 28. $10r^2 - 31r - 14$ 29. $36c^2 - 5c - 24$ 30. $20h^2 + 27h - 8$

 31. $12a^2 + ab - 6b^2$ 32. $12x^2 + 19xy - 18y^2$ 33. $18a^2 - 19a - 12$

 34. $27c^2 + 42cd + 8d^2$ 35. $6y^2 - 47yz - 63z^2$ 36. $28r^2 + 5rs - 12s^2$
 $(7u + 7v + 2)(2u + 2v + 3)$ $(4x + 4y - 11)(x + y + 2)$

C 37. $14(u + v)^2 + 25(u + v) + 6$ 38. $4(x + y)^2 - 3(x + y) - 22$

 39. $10(r + s)^2 - 11t(r + s) + 3t^2$ 40. $6(p + q)^2 + 13r(p + q) - 15r^2$
 $(5r + 5s - 3t)(2r + 2s - t)$ $(6p + 6q - 5r)(p + q + 3r)$

19. $(3u - 2v)(2u + v)$ 20. $(2m + 5n)(m - 2n)$ 21. $(3x - 7y)(x - 2y)$ 22. $(2c + d)(c - 4d)$
23. $(5r - 4s)(r + 2s)$ 24. $(5p - q)(2p - 7q)$ 25. $(3x + 5)(2x + 3)$ 26. $(3y + 5)(2y - 3)$
27. $(4t + 3)(2t - 3)$ 28. $(5r + 2)(2r - 7)$ 29. $(9c - 8)(4c + 3)$ 30. $(5h + 8)(4h - 1)$
31. $(4a + 3b)(3a - 2b)$ 32. $(4x + 9y)(3x - 2y)$ 33. $(9a + 4)(2a - 3)$ 34. $(9c + 2d)(3c + 4d)$
35. $(6y + 7z)(y - 9z)$ 36. $(7r - 4s)(4r + 3s)$

★ Self-Test 3

Be sure that you understand these terms:

quadratic term (p. 165)   linear term (p. 165)   quadratic polynomial (p. 165)
irreducible polynomial (p. 168)   prime polynomial (p. 168)

Express each product as a polynomial.

1. $(x - 2)(x + 3)$ 2. $(2u + 1)(u + 2)$ Objective 5-6, p. 165

Factor.

3. $x^2 - 11x + 30$ 4. $48 + 14t + t^2$ Objective 5-7, p. 167

5. $c^2 + 4c - 45$ 6. $d^2 - 9d - 36$ Objective 5-8, p. 170

7. $6y^2 + 5y - 1$ 8. $8x^2 - 18xy + 9y^2$ Objective 5-9, p. 172

Check your answers with those printed at the back of the book.

General Factoring

5-10 Factoring by Grouping

> **OBJECTIVE** To learn how to discover factors by grouping terms of a polynomial.

By studying products of binomials, you can discover how to factor some polynomials.

Multiplying	Factoring

Multiplying

$a + b$
$c + d$
_____
$ac + bc$
$\quad\quad + ad + bd$
_____
$ac + bc + ad + bd$

Factoring

Regroup the terms and use the distributive axiom:

$$ac + bc + ad + bd$$
$$= (a + b)c + (a + b)d$$
$$= (a + b)(c + d)$$

In the last step, $(a + b)$ is treated as a single unit when applying the distributive axiom.

Example Factor $6ax - 2b - 3a + 4bx$.

Solution

$$6ax - 2b - 3a + 4bx = (6ax - 3a) + (4bx - 2b)$$
$$= 3a(2x - 1) + 2b(2x - 1)$$
$$= (3a + 2b)(2x - 1) \quad \textit{Answer}$$

There may be more than one convenient way to group terms:

$$6ax - 2b - 3a + 4bx = (6ax + 4bx) + (-3a - 2b)$$
$$= 2x(3a + 2b) + (-1)(3a + 2b)$$
$$= (2x - 1)(3a + 2b) \quad \textit{Answer}$$

Oral Exercises

Factor.

$(x + 2)(a - b)$
1. $x(a - b) + 2(a - b)$

$(a - b)(x - 1)$
2. $a(x - 1) - b(x - 1)$

$(c - 1)(w + 1)$
3. $c(w + 1) - (w + 1)$

4. $2(r - 2) + s(r - 2)$
$(2 + s)(r - 2)$

5. $w(z + 2) + y(z + 2)$
$(w + y)(z + 2)$

6. $a(b - 3) - d(b - 3)$
$(a - d)(b - 3)$

Written Exercises

Write each expression in factored form and check by multiplying.

A
1. $a(a + 3) + (a + 3)$
2. $r(r - 2) + 5(r - 2)$
3. $x^2(2x - 1) + 4(2x - 1)$

4. $t^2(3t + 2) + (3t + 2)$
5. $(t^2 + 1) + (t^2 + 1)t$
6. $(u^2 + 4)u^2 + 4(u^2 + 4)$

7. $a(a - 2b) + b(a - 2b)$
8. $x(x + y) + 2y(x + y)$
9. $r^2(r^2 + s^2) - 2s^2(r^2 + s^2)$

10. $s(s^3 + 4) - (s^3 + 4)$
11. $x(x + 2y) - (x + 2y)$
12. $h(h^2 + k) - k^2(h^2 + k)$

Sample $2x^2 - 3y - 6x + xy$ *Solution* $2x^2 - 3y - 6x + xy = (2x^2 + xy) + (-6x - 3y)$
$= x(2x + y) + (-3)(2x + y)$
$= (x - 3)(2x + y)$ *Answer*

Answers at foot of page.

13. $x^2 + 2x + xy + 2y$
14. $a^2 - 3a + ab - 3b$
15. $t^2 - 2t + 3t - 6$

16. $h^2 + 4h - 2h - 8$
17. $4u^2 + v + 2uv + 2u$
18. $3x^2 - 2z - 6x + xz$

19. $t^3 - t^2 + t - 1$
20. $u^3 + u^2v + uv^2 + v^3$
21. $r^3 - rs^2 + sr^2 - s^3$

22. $yz^2 - y^3 + z^3 - y^2z$
23. $d^3 - d^2 - cd + c$
24. $4w + 8w^3 + 1 + 2w^2$

1. $(a + 1)(a + 3)$
2. $(r + 5)(r - 2)$
3. $(x^2 + 4)(2x - 1)$
4. $(t^2 + 1)(3t + 2)$
5. $(t^2 + 1)(1 + t)$
6. $(u^2 + 4)^2$
7. $(a + b)(a - 2b)$
8. $(x + 2y)(x + y)$
9. $(r^2 - 2s^2)(r^2 + s^2)$
10. $(s - 1)(s^3 + 4)$
11. $(x - 1)(x + 2y)$
12. $(h - k^2)(h^2 + k)$

Computer Activity

If you have access to a computer that will accept BASIC, type in the following program. It contains a loop within a loop and will find odd prime numbers from 3 to 17 by testing odd numbers for odd factors greater than 1. It prints values of N, F, and Q at each stage.

```
10  FOR N=3 TO 17 STEP 2
15  PRINT                              50  NEXT F
20  FOR F=3 TO N/2 STEP 2              60  PRINT N;
30  LET Q=N/F                          65  PRINT " IS PRIME."
35  PRINT "N =";N;" F =";F;" Q =";Q;" ";   70  NEXT N
40  IF Q=INT(Q) THEN 70                80  END
```

After you understand what this program does, delete lines 15, 35, and 65, and change line 10 to FOR N=3 TO 99 STEP 2 to print out the odd primes less than 100.

13. $(x + 2)(x + y)$
14. $(a + b)(a - 3)$
15. $(t + 3)(t - 2)$
16. $(h - 2)(h + 4)$
17. $(2u + v)(2u + 1)$
18. $(3x + z)(x - 2)$
19. $(t^2 + 1)(t - 1)$
20. $(u^2 + v^2)(u + v)$
21. $(r - s)(r + s)^2$
22. $(z - y)(z + y)^2$
23. $(d^2 - c)(d - 1)$
24. $(2w^2 + 1)(4w + 1)$

5-11 Using Several Methods of Factoring

> **OBJECTIVE** To learn how to apply all the methods of factoring that you have studied.

Here is a checklist to use when factoring polynomials:

1 Is there a monomial factor?

Find the greatest monomial factor and then consider the other factor:

$$6x^2 + 24x = 6x(x + 4)$$

The factorization is *complete* since $x + 4$ is *prime* (page 168).

2 Is some factor the difference of two squares?

If so, factor it using the method of Section 5-4:

$$2ab^2 - 8a^3 = 2a(b^2 - 4a^2)$$
$$= 2a(b + 2a)(b - 2a)$$

3 Is some factor a trinomial square?

If so, factor it using the method of Section 5-5:

$$-z^2 + 6z - 9 = -1(z^2 - 6z + 9)$$
$$= -(z - 3)^2$$

4 Is some factor a trinomial which is not a square?

Try to factor it using the methods of Sections 5-7, 5-8, and 5-9.

$$at^3 - at^2 - 2at = at(t^2 - t - 2)$$
$$= at(t + 1)(t - 2)$$
$$r^2s^2 + 2rs^2 - s^2 = s^2(r^2 + 2r - 1)$$

5 Is it possible to find a polynomial factor by grouping terms?

If so, apply the methods mentioned above to each of the resulting factors.

$$a^2b^2 - 4c^2 - 4b^2 + a^2c^2 = a^2b^2 - 4b^2 + a^2c^2 - 4c^2$$
$$= (a^2 - 4)b^2 + (a^2 - 4)c^2$$
$$= (a^2 - 4)(b^2 + c^2)$$
$$= (a + 2)(a - 2)(b^2 + c^2)$$

Always factor a polynomial **completely**, that is, express it as a product of a monomial and prime polynomials.

CAUTION 1. Do not forget to write *all* the factors, including the monomial factor, if any.

CAUTION 2. Do not assume that a polynomial is prime until you have tried all the ways you know to factor it.

Check by multiplying the factors.

Oral Exercises

In Written Exercises 1–22 state the greatest monomial factor.

1. 3   2. 2   3. 1   4
5. 2   6. 5   7. v 8
9. $2x$ 10. $2z$ 11. ax 12
13. k^2 14. $-a$ 15. $2y$ 16
          or $-2y$
17. 1   18. 1   19. 1   20
21. $5t$ 22. x

Written Exercises

Factor completely and check by multiplying.   Answers on page A2 at the back of the book.

A
1. $3t^2 - 3$
2. $2x^2 - 8$
3. $4 + 4r + r^2$
4. $3s^2 + 12$
5. $2y^2 - 4y + 2$
6. $5t^2 + 15t + 10$
7. $u^2v + uv + v$
8. $x^3 - x^2 - 2x$
9. $2x - 2xy^2$
10. $18z + 12z^2 + 2z^3$
11. $ax^3 + 3ax^2 + 4ax$
12. $-4c + 8c^2 - 4c^3$
13. $5k^4 + 8k^3 - 4k^2$
14. $-ab^2 - 4a$
15. $-12y - 2xy + 2x^2y$
16. $4s^2 - 5 - 8s$
17. $11 + 111t + 10t^2$
18. $1 - 13x + 36x^2$
19. $64a^2 - 49b^4$
20. $81u^4 - 169v^2$
21. $5t^3 - 10t^2 - 15t$
22. $100x^3 - 99x^2 - x$
23. $a^2 + 5ab + 4b^2$
24. $6x^2 - xy - y^2$

B
25. $2c^2 - 4cd + 2d^2$
26. $4mn^2 - 4m^2n^2 + m^3n^2$
27. $x^4 - y^2$
28. $x^4 - x^2y^2$
29. $u^2v^2 - 4u^4v^4$
30. $a^3b - 4ab^3$
31. $2hk^3 - 8h^3k$
32. $7r^2s^4 - 63r^4s^2$
33. $12y + 10y^2 - 8y^3$
34. $10t^3 - 15t^2 - 25t$
35. $2ax^3 + 3a^2x^2 + 4a^3x$
36. $4u^2v^2 - 2u^3v - 6$

Sample $2y^4 - 9y^2 + 4$

Solution $2y^4 - 9y^2 + 4 = (y^2 - 4)(2y^2 - 1) = (y + 2)(y - 2)(2y^2 - 1)$ *Answer*

37. $x^4 - 3x^2 - 4$
38. $v^4 - 5v^2 + 4$
39. $z^4 - 1$
40. $y^4 - 16$
41. $x^2y^4 - x^6$
42. $a^4 - 2a^2b^2 + b^4$
43. $r^4 - 13r^2s^2 + 36s^4$
44. $9 + 5z^2 - 4z^4$
45. $x^6 - 8x^4 + 16x^2$
46. $4t^4 - 17t^2 + 4$
47. $x^4y^2 - 10x^3y + 25x^2$
48. $3a^4 - 48$

49. $s^2(s - 1) + 11s(s - 1) + 10(s - 1)$
50. $y^2(y + 1) + 5y(y + 1) + 6(y + 1)$
51. $2h^2(h + 3) + 5h(h + 3) - 3(h + 3)$
52. $4z^2(2z - 1) - 4z(2z - 1) + (2z - 1)$

C
53. $x^2(x^2 - 4) + 4x(x^2 - 4) + 4(x^2 - 4)$
54. $1 - t^2 - 3t(1 - t^2) + 2t^2(1 - t^2)$

55. $t^3 + t^2 - t - 1$
56. $x^3 - x^2 - 4x + 4$
57. $u^2 - 2u + 1 - v^2$
58. $4s^2 - 4 + 4t - t^2$
59. $x^2 + y^2 - z^2 - 2xy$
60. $x^2y^2 - z^2 - y^2 + x^2z^2$

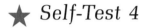 *Self-Test 4*

Factor.

1. $t(t^2 + 4) - 4(t^2 + 4)$ 2. $xz + 2yz + wx + 2wy$ Objective 5-10, p. 175
3. $5z^3 - 13z^2 - 6z$ 4. $2a^2x^3 - 6a^3x^2 - 8a^4x$ Objective 5-11, p. 177

Check your answers with those printed at the back of the book.

Metric System
Meanings of Prefixes

A common metric unit of weight is the **kilogram**.

1 kilogram (kg) = 1000 grams (g)

A kilogram is a little over 2 pounds.
   Special prefixes indicate the powers of ten that relate
each unit to the basic unit.

Prefix	Symbol	Factor
tera	T	10^{12} = 1,000,000,000,000
giga	G	10^{9} = 1,000,000,000
mega	M	10^{6} = 1,000,000
kilo	k	10^{3} = 1,000
hecto	h	10^{2} = 100
deka	da	10 = 10
deci	d	10^{-1} = 0.1
centi	c	10^{-2} = 0.01
milli	m	10^{-3} = 0.001
micro	μ	10^{-6} = 0.000001
nano	n	10^{-9} = 0.000000001
pico	p	10^{-12} = 0.000000000001
femto	f	10^{-15} = 0.000000000000001
atto	a	10^{-18} = 0.000000000000000001

For example: 1 centimeter = 10^{-2} meter = $\frac{1}{100}$ meter

1 kilogram = 10^{3} grams = 1000 grams

1 microsecond (μs) = 10^{-6} second = 0.000001 second

Applications of Factoring

5-12 Solving Equations in Factored Form

> **OBJECTIVE** To learn how to solve equations when one member is in factored form and the other member is 0.

The multiplicative property of 0 (page 92) guarantees that for any two real numbers a and b:

> If $a = 0$ or $b = 0$, then $ab = 0$.

The **converse** of this theorem is obtained by interchanging the "if" and "then" portions:

> If $ab = 0$, then $a = 0$ or $b = 0$.

Although the converse of a theorem is not necessarily true, *this one is* as can be proved in Exercise 19 on page 182. The theorem can be restated as

$$ab = 0 \text{ if } a = 0 \text{ or } b = 0,$$

and the converse can be restated as

$$ab = 0 \text{ only if } a = 0 \text{ or } b = 0.$$

Therefore, the theorem and its converse can be combined as:

> The Zero-Product Property
>
> For all real numbers a and b,
>
> $ab = 0$ if and only if $a = 0$ or $b = 0$.

You can use this property to solve equations in which one member is 0 and the other member is in factored form. For example, the solutions of the equation

$$(x + 3)(x - 2) = 0$$

are those numbers for which one or the other factor in the left-hand member is 0. These numbers are, by inspection, -3 and 2. Or you could have written the equivalent compound sentence

$$x + 3 = 0 \quad \text{or} \quad x - 2 = 0$$

and solved each equation for x. In either case the solution set is $\{-3, 2\}$.

The zero-product property can easily be extended to *any number* of factors: *A product of numbers is zero if and only if at least one of the factors is zero.*

Oral Exercises

Find all values of the variable for which the open sentence becomes a true statement, and justify your answer.

Sample $z(z - 3) = 0$

Solution   0 and 3; because
  for $z = 0$, the sentence becomes $0(-3) = 0$, which is true, and
  for $z = 3$, the sentence becomes $3(0) = 0$, which is true.   *Answer*

1. $x(x - 5) = 0$ 0, 5
2. $2(y - 1) = 0$ 1
3. $3(t - 2) = 0$ 2
4. $2u(u - 3) = 0$ 0, 3
5. $(z - 1)(z - 4) = 0$ 1, 4
6. $(s - 3)(s + 2) = 0$ 3, -2
7. $(r + 2)(r - 4) = 0$ $-2, 4$
8. $3(z - 1)(z - 2) = 0$ 1, 2
9. $(x - 1)(x - x) = 0$ all
10. $(1 + v)(1 - v) = 0$ $-1, 1$
11. $2(2 + t)(4 + t) = 0$ $-2, -4$
12. $0(s - 1)(s - 2) = 0$ all

Written Exercises

Solve.

A
1. $y(y - 2) = 0$ $\{0, 2\}$
2. $2x(x - 2) = 0$ $\{0, 2\}$
3. $3(u - 3)(u - 5) = 0$ $\{3, 5\}$
4. $(t - 5)(t - 10) = 0$ $\{5, 10\}$
5. $(x + 2)(x - 5) = 0$ $\{-2, 5\}$
6. $(r + 4)(r + 1) = 0$ $\{-4, -1\}$
7. $(t + 7)(t - 1) = 0$ $\{-7, 1\}$
8. $(s - 5)(s + 5) = 0$ $\{5, -5\}$
9. $(r + 1)(r + 3)(r - 5) = 0$
10. $(u + 2)(u - u)(u - 2) = 0$
    $\{$all numbers$\}$
11. $s(s - 2)(s - 4) = 0$
    $\{0, 2, 4\}$
12. $x(x - 2)(x + 2) = 0$
    $\{0, 2, -2\}$
9. $\{-1, -3, 5\}$

13. $\{-3, \frac{1}{3}\}$ 14. $\{\frac{2}{3}, -\frac{1}{2}\}$ 15. $\{5, -\frac{1}{5}\}$

Solve.

16. $\{-\frac{5}{2}, \frac{2}{5}\}$ 17. $\{\frac{7}{2}, -\frac{9}{2}\}$ 18. $\{-\frac{2}{3}, -1\}$

Sample $(2y - 1)(y - 2) = 0$ *Solution* $2y - 1 = 0$ or $y - 2 = 0$

$$2y = 1 \qquad\qquad y = 2$$
$$y = \tfrac{1}{2} \qquad\qquad \{\tfrac{1}{2}, 2\} \quad Answer$$

13. $(x + 3)(3x - 1) = 0$ 14. $2(3v - 2)(2v + 1) = 0$ 15. $(10 - 2u)(5u + 1) = 0$

16. $(2z + 5)(5z - 2) = 0$ 17. $6(2y - 7)(2y + 9) = 0$ 18. $2(3s + 2)(s + 1) = 0$

B 19. Give the missing reasons in the proof: If $ab = 0$, then $a = 0$ or $b = 0$.

Case 1. If $a = 0$, then there is nothing to prove.
Case 2. If $a \neq 0$: $ab = 0$ Given

$$\frac{1}{a}(ab) = \frac{1}{a}(0) \qquad\qquad \underline{\ ?\ } \quad \text{Mult. prop. of equality}$$

$$\frac{1}{a}(ab) = 0 \qquad\qquad \underline{\ ?\ } \quad \text{Mult. prop. of zero}$$

$$\left(\frac{1}{a} \cdot a\right)b = 0 \qquad\qquad \underline{\ ?\ } \quad \text{Assoc. axiom of mult.}$$

$$(1)b = 0 \qquad\qquad \underline{\ ?\ } \quad \text{Axiom of inverses for mult.}$$

$$b = 0 \qquad\qquad \underline{\ ?\ } \quad \text{Identity axiom for mult.}$$

Computer Activity

If you have access to a computer that will accept BASIC, you can use the following program to practice calculating with integers:

```
10   PRINT "PRACTICE IN ADDITION, SUBTRACTION, AND MULTIPLICATON"
20   PRINT
30   PRINT
40   FOR I=1 TO 10
50   LET N=INT(3*RND(1)+1)          150   LET C=INT(19*RND(1)-9)
60   LET A=INT(101*RND(1)-50)       160   PRINT A+B;" X (";C;") = ?"
70   LET B=INT(101*RND(1)-50)       170   LET S=(A+B)*C
80   GOTO N OF 90, 120, 150         180   PRINT
90   PRINT A;" + (";B;") = ?"       190   PRINT
100   LET S=A+B                     200   PRINT TAB(50);S
110   GOTO 180                      210   PRINT
120   PRINT A;" - (";B;") = ?"      220   PRINT
130   LET S=A-B                     230   NEXT I
140   GOTO 180                      240   END
```

This program will give you a chance to speed up your computation. Line 200 contains a TAB statement that delays the printing of the answer. Try to find the answer before it is printed.

5-13 Solving Polynomial Equations by Factoring

> **OBJECTIVE** To learn how to solve some polynomial equations by factoring.

You can use the results of previous sections to solve many polynomial equations, that is, equations in which both members are polynomials.

The first step is to transform the given equation into standard form where one member is 0, and the other is a simplified polynomial arranged in descending powers of the variable.

Example 1 Solve $x^2 - 36 = 5x$.

Solution

$$x^2 - 36 = 5x$$

1. Transform into standard form: $\qquad x^2 - 5x - 36 = 0$
2. Factor the left-hand member: $\qquad (x - 9)(x + 4) = 0$
3. Obtain the solutions by inspection (9 and -4),

or

3a. Equate each factor to 0, and solve the resulting equations.

$$x - 9 = 0 \qquad\qquad x + 4 = 0$$
$$x = 9 \qquad\qquad x = -4$$

4. Check in original equation: $x^2 - 36 = 5x$

$$9^2 - 36 = 81 - 36 = 45 \checkmark \qquad\qquad (-4)^2 - 36 = 16 - 36 = -20 \checkmark$$
$$5 \cdot 9 = 45 \checkmark \qquad\qquad\qquad 5(-4) = -20 \checkmark$$

$\therefore$ the solution set is $\{9, -4\}$.   *Answer*

The degree of a polynomial equation is the degree of the polynomial when the equation is written in standard form.

The equation of Example 1 is of degree two and is called a quadratic equation.

An equation of degree one, like $3y - 2 = y + 3$, or $2y - 5 = 0$, is called a linear equation.

An equation, like $z^3 = 4z^2 + 5z$, or $z^3 - 4z^2 - 5z = 0$, whose degree is three is a cubic equation.

Example 2 Solve $z^3 = 4z^2 + 5z$.

Solution

$$z^3 = 4z^2 + 5z$$

1. Transform into standard form: $z^3 - 4z^2 - 5z = 0$
2. Factor the left-hand member: $z(z^2 - 4z - 5) = 0$
   $$z(z + 1)(z - 5) = 0$$

3. Obtain the solutions by inspection
   $(0, -1,$ and $5)$,

   or

3a. Equate each factor to 0, and $z = 0$ $z + 1 = 0$ $z - 5 = 0$
    solve the resulting equations. $z = -1$ $z = 5$
4. Check in original equation: $z^3 = 4z^2 + 5z$

$$\begin{array}{ccc} 0^3 = 0 \checkmark & (-1)^3 = -1 \checkmark & 5^3 = 125 \checkmark \\ 4 \cdot 0^2 + 5 \cdot 0 = 0 & 4(-1)^2 + 5(-1) = -1 & 4 \cdot 5^2 + 5 \cdot 5 = 125 \end{array}$$

$\therefore$ the solution set is $\{0, -1, 5\}$. *Answer*

CAUTION: Never transform an equation by dividing by an expression containing a variable. Notice that in Example 2, the solution 0 would have been lost if we had divided by z.

Division by a nonzero constant is permissible, of course.

After the factorization step, two or more factors may be identical. Such factors yield a *double* or *multiple* root.

Example 3 Solve $2x^3 - 4x^2 - 8x + 16 = 0$.

Solution   The equation is in standard
   form: $2x^3 - 4x^2 - 8x + 16 = 0$
1. Divide each member by 2: $x^3 - 2x^2 - 4x + 8 = 0$
2. Factor the left-hand member: $x^2(x - 2) - 4(x - 2) = 0$
                                     $(x^2 - 4)(x - 2) = 0$
                                     $(x + 2)(x - 2)(x - 2) = 0$

3. Obtain solution by inspection
   $(-2$ and $2)$

   or

3a. Equate each factor to 0 and solve $x + 2 = 0$ $x - 2 = 0$
    the resulting equations $x = -2$ $x = 2$
4. The check is left to you. $2(-2)^3 - 4(-2)^2 - 8(-2) + 16 = 0; 2 \cdot 2^3 - 4 \cdot 2^2 - 8 \cdot 2 + 16 = 0$
$\therefore$ the solution set is $\{-2, 2\}$, and 2 is a double root. *Answer*

Not all polynomial equations can be solved by the methods of this section, of course, because the necessary factorization may not be possible.

Written Exercises

Solve. Answers to Exs. 1–36 on page A2 at the back of the book.

A 1. $z^2 - 4z + 3 = 0$ 2. $x^2 - 5x + 4 = 0$ 3. $t^2 - t - 6 = 0$ 4. $s^2 + 2s - 8 = 0$

5. $x^2 - 49 = 0$ 6. $u^2 - 25 = 0$ 7. $r^2 - 9r = 0$ 8. $n^2 - 16n = 0$

9. $v^3 - 4v = 0$ 10. $y^3 - y = 0$ 11. $x^2 + 9 = 10x$ 12. $z^2 - z = 30$

13. $t^2 = 24 - 5t$ 14. $x^2 = 4x - 4$ 15. $2z^2 - z - 1 = 0$ 16. $3s^2 + 2s - 1 = 0$

17. $2r^2 - 5r + 2 = 0$ 18. $3x^2 - 8x + 4 = 0$ 19. $5t^2 - 19t = 4$ 20. $4u^2 = 8u + 5$

21. $y^4 - 4y^2 = 0$ 22. $x^4 - 16x^2 = 0$ 23. $t^4 - 1 = 0$ 24. $x^4 - 16 = 0$

B 25. $x^3 - 6x^2 + 8x = 0$ 26. $z^3 - 12z^2 + 32z = 0$ 27. $y^3 - 6y^2 + 9y = 0$

28. $t^3 + 10t^2 + 25t = 0$ 29. $v^3 = 10v - 3v^2$ 30. $s^2 = 56s - s^3$

31. $z^4 - 10z^2 + 9 = 0$ 32. $r^4 - 13r^2 + 36 = 0$ 33. $s^4 - 8s^2 + 16 = 0$

34. $y^4 - 2y^2 + 1 = 0$ 35. $t^3 - t^2 - t + 1 = 0$ 36. $s^3 + s^2 - 4s - 4 = 0$

C 37. $4x^3 + 4x^2 - x - 1 = 0$ $\left\{-1, -\frac{1}{2}, \frac{1}{2}\right\}$ 38. $9z^3 - 18z^2 - z + 2 = 0$ $\left\{2, -\frac{1}{3}, \frac{1}{3}\right\}$ 39. $z^5 = z^3$ $\{0, -1, 1\}$

40. $4y^3 = y^5$ $\{0, -2, 2\}$ 41. $(r - 2)(r + 3) = 6$ $\{-4, 3\}$ 42. $(x - 2)(x - 5) = 4$ $\{1, 6\}$

43. $(y - 3)(y - 5) = 2(y - 3)$ $\{3, 7\}$ 44. $(t - 2)^2 = 2(t - 2)$ $\{2, 4\}$

45. $3(r - 3)^2 = (r - 3)$ $\left\{3, \frac{10}{3}\right\}$ 46. $4(s - 1)^2 = 8(s - 1)$ $\{1, 3\}$

47. $(2m - 3)(m - 5)^2 = 9(m - 5)$ $\left\{\frac{1}{2}, 5, 6\right\}$ 48. $(3p - 2)^2 - 2(3p - 2) + 1 = 0$ $\{1\}$

Find an equation having the given solution set.

Sample $\{-2, 5\}$ *Solution* Let the variable be x.

$$x = -2 \quad \text{or} \quad x = 5$$
$$x + 2 = 0 \quad \text{or} \quad x - 5 = 0$$
$$(x + 2)(x - 5) = 0$$
$$x^2 - 3x - 10 = 0 \quad \textit{Answer}$$

49. $\{1, 3\}$ 50. $\{-4, -2\}$ 51. $\{-3, 0, 1\}$ 52. $\{-2, 0, 2\}$ 53. $\{1, 2, 3\}$ 54. $\{-2, -1, 1, 2\}$

49. $x^2 - 4x + 3 = 0$ **50.** $x^2 + 6x + 8 = 0$ **51.** $x^3 + 2x^2 - 3x = 0$

52. $x^3 - 4x = 0$ **53.** $x^3 - 6x^2 + 11x - 6 = 0$ **54.** $x^4 - 5x^2 + 4 = 0$

Puzzle Time

What's wrong?

$$r = t$$
$$r^2 = rt$$
$$r^2 - t^2 = rt - t^2$$
$$(r + t)(r - t) = t(r - t)$$
$$r + t = t$$

If $r = t = 1$, then $2 = 1$.

We can divide by $r - t$ only if $r - t \neq 0$, or $r \neq t$.

5-14 Using Factoring in Solving Problems

> **OBJECTIVE** To learn how to apply the method of solving equations by factoring to solving problems.

Many times you can solve a practical problem by setting up a polynomial equation and then using factoring to find its solutions. As illustrated by the first example, some of the solutions of the equation may not satisfy the conditions of the original problem; these must be rejected.

Example 1 In designing a book, a printer wishes to have a 180-square-centimeter rectangle of printing on each page surrounded by margins of equal width. How wide should the margins be if the page is 16 centimeters by 24 centimeters?

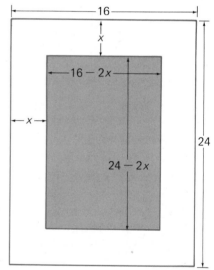

Solution

Step 1 The problem asks for the width of the margin. With all lengths in cm:

Step 2 Let x = width of margins.
Then $16 - 2x$ = width of printing,
and $24 - 2x$ = height of printing.

Step 3 $(16 - 2x)(24 - 2x) = 180$

Step 4 $2(8 - x) \cdot 2(12 - x) = 180$
$(8 - x)(12 - x) = 45$
$96 - 20x + x^2 = 45$
$x^2 - 20x + 51 = 0$
$(x - 3)(x - 17) = 0$

$x - 3 = 0 \quad | \quad x - 17 = 0$
$\quad x = 3 \quad | \quad \quad x = 17$

(Rejected, since page is only 16 cm wide.)

Step 5 *Check:* If the margins are 3 cm wide, the dimensions of the printed rectangle are $16 - 6$, or 10, and $24 - 6$, or 18. Its area will therefore be 10×18, or 180, square centimeters. ✓

∴ the width of the margins is 3 cm. *Answer*

In working a problem, you reason that *if* a number satisfies the conditions of the problem, *then* it satisfies the equation found at Step 2. A solution of the equation, on the other hand, may *not* satisfy all the conditions of the problem. The solution set of the equation gives *possible solutions* of the problem. By checking these possibilities in the statement of the problem you find the *actual solutions*.

In the next example, both solutions of the equation satisfy the conditions of the problem.
We shall use the formula

$$h = rt - 4.9t^2$$

which gives a good approximation to the height h in meters that an object will reach in t seconds, when it is projected upward with an initial speed of r meters per second.

Example 2 A ball is thrown vertically upward with an initial velocity of 34.3 meters per second. When is it directly opposite the top of a tower 49 meters high?

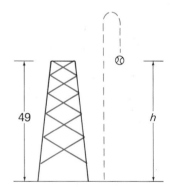

Solution

Step 1 The problem asks for the time when the ball is opposite the top of the tower.

Step 2 Let t = number of seconds after being thrown that the ball is opposite the top of the tower,
and h = height of ball then
    = 49 (meters),
and r = initial velocity
    = 34.3 (meters per second).

Step 3 $h = rt - 4.9t^2$
    $49 = 34.3t - 4.9t^2$
    $\dfrac{49}{4.9} = \dfrac{34.3t}{4.9} - \dfrac{4.9t^2}{4.9}$

Step 4 $10 = 7t - t^2$
    $t^2 - 7t + 10 = 0$
    $(t - 2)(t - 5) = 0$

———— Complete the solution and check both values.

∴ the ball is opposite the top of the tower both 2 and 5 seconds after being thrown. *Answer*

→ $t = 2$ or $t = 5$
    Check: $h = 34.3(2) - 4.9(2)^2 = 49$
        $h = 34.3(5) - 4.9(5)^2 = 49$

Problems

Solve.

A

1. Find two consecutive positive integers whose product is 72.   **8 and 9**

2. Find two consecutive negative integers whose product is 156.   **−13 and −12**

3. The sum of the squares of two consecutive negative odd integers is 202. Find the integers.   **−11 and −9**

4. The sum of the squares of two consecutive positive even integers is 340. Find the integers.   **12 and 14**

5. Find the dimensions of a rectangle having area 10 square centimeters and whose width is 3 cm less than its length.   **2 cm by 5 cm**

6. The length of a rectangle is 5 meters greater than twice its width, and its area is 33 square meters. Find its dimensions.   **3 m by 11 m**

7. The perimeter of a rectangular wildlife preserve is 8 kilometers, and its area is 3 square kilometers. Find its dimensions.   **1 km by 3 km**

8. The sum of the squares of three consecutive positive integers is equal to the sum of the squares of the next two integers. What are the five integers?   **10, 11, 12, 13, 14**

9. When the dimensions of a 2×5 cm rectangle were increased by equal amounts, its area increased by 18 square centimeters. Find the dimensions of the new rectangle.   **4 cm by 7 cm**

10. A corner lot had dimensions 20 by 40 meters before it lost two strips of equal width when the adjacent streets were widened. Find the new dimensions of the lot if its area is now 525 square meters.   **15 m by 35 m**

In Problems 11–15, use the formula stated on page 187. Notice that all numbers appearing are integral multiples of 4.9.

11. A ball is thrown upward with an initial velocity of 24.5 m per second. When is it 29.4 m high? (Two answers)   **after 2 sec and 3 sec**

12. A rifle bullet is fired upward with an initial velocity of 2940 m per second. After how many minutes does it hit the ground?   **10 min**

B

13. A cannon ball is fired upward with an initial velocity of 245 m per second. A man in a balloon 1960 m high sees the ball pass him on the way up. How long will it be before it passes him again on the way down?   **30 sec**

14. A ball is thrown upward from the top of a 98-meter tower with an initial velocity of 39.2 m/s. When does it hit the ground? (Hint: If h is the height of the ball above the top of the tower, then $h = -98$ when the ball hits the ground.)   **10 sec**

15. A ball is thrown upward with an initial velocity of 29.4 m/s. (a) when is the ball 44.1 m high? (b) Explain why 44.1 m is the greatest height attained by the ball.

   (a) after 3 sec
   (b) Since the ball reaches a height of 44.1 m once, this height is the greatest attained.

16. A rug placed in a 10 by 12 m room covers two thirds of the floor area and leaves a uniform strip of bare floor around the edges. What are the dimensions of the rug?   **8 m by 10**

17. A 6 by 9 m rug covers half of the floor area of a room and leaves a uniform strip of bare floor around the edges. What are the dimensions of the room?   **9 m by 12 m**

18. The page of a book is twice as high as it is wide, and there are margins 2 cm wide at the top and sides and 3 cm wide at the bottom. Find the dimensions of the page if the area of the printed part of the page is 152 cm². **12 cm by 24 cm**

19. A long sheet of metal, 30 centimeters wide, is to be made into an open-topped trough having rectangular cross section by bending up equal amounts along the two sides. How much should be bent up if the cross-sectional area is to be 52 square centimeters? (Two answers) **2 cm or 13 cm**

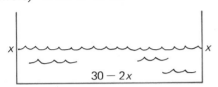

$30 - 2x$

20. A rectangular plot of 28 square meters is to be enclosed by using one part of an existing fence as one side and 15 meters of fencing for the other three sides. Find the dimensions of the plot. (Two answers)
$3\frac{1}{2}$ m by 8 m or 4 m by 7 m

5 m by 40 m or 20 m by 10 m

21. One hundred meters of fencing are to be used to enclose a rectangular field of 200 square meters and divide it into 3 pens, as shown in the diagram. Find the dimensions of the field. (Two answers) (Hint: $2y + 4x = 100$; find y in terms of x.) *(above)*

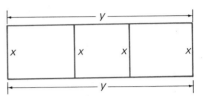

22. A dealer can sell n cars a month if he sets the price per car at $\$(2500 - 25n)$. He started May with 50 cars on hand. How many did he have left at the end of May if his total income from sales was $52,500? **20 cars**

C 23. Six times the volume of a cube is equal to the sum of its surface area and the total length of its edges. Find its dimensions. $2 \times 2 \times 2$

24. A grower has 50 tons of melons in a field and can sell them now at $40 a ton. For each week she waits, the crop will increase by 10 tons, while the price per ton drops by $4. When should she sell the crop to obtain $2160 for it? (Two answers) **1 week or 4 weeks**

25. A room contained 3600 mosquitoes when it was sprayed with an insect killer. At the end of one hour a certain fraction of the mosquitoes had died, and at the end of the second hour, the same fraction of the first hour's survivors had died, leaving only 400. What fraction died each hour? $\frac{2}{3}$

26. A bus holding 30 persons is to be rented for an excursion at the rate of $45 per person if 15 or fewer persons go. If more than 15 go, everyone's fare is reduced by $1 for each person over the basic 15. How many can go for a total of $800? **20 people**

Puzzle Time ₒₒ○◯◯○◯◯ₒₒₒₒ◯○◯ ₒ◯◯◯◌◌

What's wrong?

$$x^2 - 3x - 4 = 0$$
$$x^2 - 3x = 4$$
$$x(x - 3) = 2 \cdot 2$$
$$x = 2 \quad \text{or} \quad x - 3 = 2$$
$$x = 5$$

Show that neither "solution" will check. Find the correct solutions.

The zero-product property does not apply to nonzero products.

If $ab = n$, we can conclude that $a = n$ or $b = n$ only if $n = 0$; in this case (Step 3), $n = 4$. $2^2 - 3 \cdot 2 - 4 = -6 \neq 0$ and $5^2 - 3 \cdot 5 - 4 = 6 \neq 0$. $x^2 - 3x - 4 = (x - 4)(x + 1) = 0$, so $x = 4$ or $x = -1$.

★ *Self-Test 5*

Be sure that you understand these terms:

converse (p. 180)   polynomial equation (p. 183)
standard form of a polynomial equation (p. 183)   degree of a polynomial equation (p. 183)
quadratic equation (p. 183)   linear equation (p. 183)
cubic equation (p. 183)

Solve.

1. $(x - 2)(x - 7) = 0$ 2. $z^2(z + 1)(z - 1) = 0$ Objective 5-12, p. 180

3. $t^2 - 3t + 2 = 0$ 4. $u^2 - 2u = 8$ Objective 5-13, p. 183
5. $2y^2 + 5y - 3 = 0$ 6. $x^3 - 4x^2 + 4x = 0$

7. The sum of the squares of two consecutive positive odd integers is 130. Objective 5-14, p. 186
   Find the integers.
8. When the dimensions of a 3 × 5 meter rectangle were increased by equal
   amounts, the area increased by 48 square meters. Find the new dimensions.

Check your answers with those printed at the back of the book.

Chapter Summary

1. You use division to find prime factors and pairs of integral factors
   of integers.
2. You find a monomial factor of a polynomial by division.
3. After finding formulas for some special products of binomials you
   can apply them in reverse to factor certain polynomials.
4. Some polynomial equations can be solved by factoring.

Chapter Test

5-1   1. Find the prime factorization of 520. $2^3 \cdot 5 \cdot 13$

2. Find the greatest common factor of 520 and 78.   26

5-2   3. Simplify $\dfrac{-6a^3x^2}{2ax^4} \cdot -\dfrac{3a^2}{x^2}$

4. Find the missing factor in $24a^3x^3y^2 = (3a^2xy^2)(\underline{\ ?\ })$. $8ax^2$

5-3   5. Simplify $\dfrac{x^2y^3 - x^3y^2}{xy}$. $xy^2 - x^2y$

6. Factor $3x^3 + 12x$. $3x(x^2 + 4)$

5-4   7. Express $(2x - a)(2x + a)$ as a polynomial. $4x^2 - a^2$

8. Factor $16 - 25z^4$. $(4 + 5z^2)(4 - 5z^2)$

Express each product as a polynomial.

5-5   9. $(3t - 2)^2$ $9t^2 - 12t + 4$ 10. $(x^4 + 3y^2)^2$ $x^8 + 6x^4y^2 + 9y^4$

Factor.

11. $4r^2 + 20r + 25$ $(2r + 5)^2$ 12. $100u^2 - 20uv + v^2$ $(10u - v)^2$

Express each product as a polynomial.

5-6   13. $(2x - 1)(3x + 2)$ $6x^2 + x - 2$ 14. $(a - 2b)(a - 3b)$ $a^2 - 5ab + 6b^2$

Factor.

5-7   15. $s^2 + 7s + 12$ $(s + 3)(s + 4)$ 16. $x^2 - 11xy + 10y^2$ $(x - 10y)(x - y)$

5-8   17. $k^2 + 5k - 6$ $(k + 6)(k - 1)$ 18. $a^2 - 4ab - 12b^2$ $(a - 6b)(a + 2b)$

5-9   19. $3t^2 - 2t - 1$ $(3t + 1)(t - 1)$ 20. $6x^2 + x - 2$ $(3x + 2)(2x - 1)$

5-10   21. $a^2(a + b) + b^2(a + b)$ 22. $2ax + 6bx - ay - 3by$ $(a + 3b)(2x - y)$
$(a + b)(a^2 + b^2)$

5-11   23. $x^5 - 4xy^2$ 24. $u^3 - 2u^2 + u - 2$ $(u - 2)(u^2 + 1)$
$x(x^2 + 2y)(x^2 - 2y)$

Solve.

5-12   25. $(t - 7)(t + 2) = 0$ $\{7, -2\}$ 26. $(x - 1)(x + 2)(x - 3) = 0$ $\{1, -2, 3\}$

5-13   27. $z^3 - 25z = 0$ $\{0, -5, 5\}$ 28. $x^2 - 11x = 12$ $\{12, -1\}$

5-14   29. A rectangle has perimeter 14 centimeters and area 10 square
centimeters. Find its dimensions.   2 cm by 5 cm

Programmed Chapter Review ▓▓▓▓▓▓▓

5-1   1. An integer, greater than one, which has no integral factor other than itself and one is called a __?__ number.

| | prime |

2. The prime factorization of 126 is __?__.

$2 \cdot 3^2 \cdot 7$

3. The greatest common factor of 126 and 105 is __?__.

21

4. The possible pairs of integral factors of 12 are __?__.

(1, 12), (2, 6), (3, 4), (−1, −12), (−2, −6), (−3, −4)

5-2   5. If neither q nor s is zero, then $\dfrac{pr}{qs} = \dfrac{p}{q} \cdot \dfrac{\underline{\;?\;}}{s}$

r

6. If $b \neq 0$ and $m - n$ is positive, then $\dfrac{b^m}{b^n} = \underline{\;?\;}$.

b^{m-n}

7. $\dfrac{12x^2y^3}{4xy} = \underline{\;?\;}$

$3xy^2$

8. $\dfrac{18a^7b^3}{-12a^2b^5} = \underline{\;?\;}$

$-\dfrac{3a^5}{2b^2}$

9. $-63u^2v^3w = (-7uv^2)(\underline{\;?\;})$

$9uvw$

5-3   10. $\dfrac{25x + 15y}{5} = \underline{\;?\;} + \underline{\;?\;}$

$5x,\ 3y$

11. $\dfrac{9a^2 - 15a}{-3a} = \underline{\;?\;}$

$-3a + 5$

12. $\dfrac{u^3v - uv^3}{u^2v^2} = \underline{\;?\;}$

$\dfrac{u}{v} - \dfrac{v}{u}$

13. The factor set for a polynomial having integral coefficients is the set of all polynomials having __?__ coefficients.

integral

14. $6a^3bc + 3a^2b^2c + 12a^2bc^2 = 3a^2bc\,(\underline{\;?\;})$

$2a + b + 4c$

15. The greatest monomial factor of $24x^2yz^2 + 42xy^2z$ is __?__.

$6xyz$

5-4   16. The product of the sum and the difference of two numbers is the __?__ of their __?__.

difference, squares

17. In polynomial form, $(4a - b^3)(4a + b^3) = \underline{\;?\;}$.

$16a^2 - b^6$

18. In factored form, $49x^2 - y^2z^4 = \underline{\;?\;}$.

$(7x + yz^2)(7x - yz^2)$

5-5 19. To make $y^2 + 10y + k$ a trinomial square, k must equal __?__ .

25

20. The trinomial __?__ is equal to $(2x - 3y)^2$.

$4x^2 - 12xy + 9y^2$

21. In factored form, $t^2 + 14t + 49 =$ __?__ .

$(t + 7)^2$

22. In factored form, $4x^4 - 4x^2y + y^2 =$ __?__ .

$(2x^2 - y)^2$

5-6 23. In $3x^2 - 7x - 5$, the quadratic term is __?__ ,
the linear term is __?__ ,
and the constant term is __?__ .

$3x^2$
$-7x$
-5

24. In polynomial form, $(x + 3)(x - 5) =$ __?__ .

$x^2 - 2x - 15$

25. In polynomial form, $(2s - 3t)(5s + 7t) =$ __?__ .

$10s^2 - st - 21t^2$

5-7 26. To factor $x^2 - 9x + 18$ into the form $(x + r)(x + s)$, you must find integers r and s whose product is __?__ and whose sum is __?__ .

18
-9

27. In factored form, $x^2 - 9x + 18 =$ __?__ .

$(x - 3)(x - 6)$

28. In factored form, $a^2 + 7ab + 6b^2 =$ __?__ .

$(a + b)(a + 6b)$

29. Because $x^2 + x + 4$ cannot be factored, it is called a __?__ polynomial.

prime
(also irreducible)

5-8 30. To factor $t^2 + 4t - 12$ into the form $(x + r)(x + s)$, you must find integers r and s whose product is __?__ and whose sum is __?__ .

-12
4

31. In factored form, $t^2 + 4t - 12 =$ __?__

$(t - 2)(t + 6)$

32. $x^2 + kx - 6$ can be factored if k has one of the values __?__ .

$-5, -1, 1, 5$

5-9 33. In factored form, $2u^2 - u - 1 =$ __?__ .

$(2u + 1)(u - 1)$

34. In factored form, $3t^2 + 10t - 8 =$ __?__ .

$(3t - 2)(t + 4)$

5-10 35. In factored form, $2a(a + b) - b(a + b) =$ __?__ .

$(2a - b)(a + b)$

36. In factored form, $6mr - 8nr + 3ms - 4ns =$ __?__ .

$(3m - 4n)(2r + s)$

5-11 37. To factor a polynomial completely, you must express it as a product of a monomial and __?__ polynomials.

prime

38. In factored form, $6t^3 - 4t^2 - 2t =$ __?__ .

$2t(3t + 1)(t - 1)$

39. In factored form, $z^4 - 1 =$ __?__ .

$(z + 1)(z - 1)(z^2 + 1)$

5-12 **40.** The product ab is zero if and only if $a =$ __?__ or $b =$ __?__ . | 0, 0

41. If $(x - 1)(x - 4) = 0$, then $x =$ __?__ or $x =$ __?__ . | 1, 4

42. If $2t(t + 3) = 0$, then $t =$ __?__ or $t =$ __?__ | 0, −3

5-13 **43.** If $x^2 - 3x = 0$, then $x =$ __?__ or $x =$ __?__ . | 0, 3

44. If $k^2 - 14k + 24 = 0$, then $k =$ __?__ or $k =$ __?__ . | 2, 12

45. If $t^2 - 6 = 5t$, then $t =$ __?__ , or $t =$ __?__ | −1, 6

5-14 **46.** When the square of the positive integer __?__ is decreased by 6, the result is 5 times the integer. | 6

47. The dimensions of a city lot which is 15 meters longer than it is wide, and whose area is 700 square meters, are __?__ m and __?__ m. | 20, 35

Biographical Note
Maria Goeppert Mayer

Maria Goeppert Mayer (1906–1972) shared the 1963 Nobel Prize for Physics, awarded for her theories of nuclear shell structure. She received her doctorate at the University of Göttingen in Germany, where she studied physics, chemistry, and mathematics. She accompanied her husband, Joseph E. Mayer, to the United States in 1930, did work in physics as a volunteer at Johns Hopkins University, and then became a lecturer at Columbia University in 1939.

She began work with Enrico Fermi at the University of Chicago in 1945. It was there that she did her work on the theory of nuclear shell structure, one of the most important developments in nuclear physics since World War II. In addition to her work in nuclear physics, Dr. Mayer also made contributions to statistical mechanics and quantum mechanics.

Maintaining Skills

Remember how?

$$2\frac{1}{3} = 2 + \frac{1}{3} = \frac{6}{3} + \frac{1}{3} = \frac{7}{3}$$

$$8\frac{2}{5} = 8 + \frac{2}{5} = \frac{40}{5} + \frac{2}{5} = \frac{42}{5}$$

Now practice:

1. $5\frac{2}{3}$ $\frac{17}{3}$
2. $6\frac{1}{8}$ $\frac{49}{8}$
3. $4\frac{3}{5}$ $\frac{23}{5}$
4. $7\frac{3}{8}$ $\frac{59}{8}$

5. $2\frac{11}{23}$ $\frac{57}{23}$
6. $1\frac{21}{28}$ $\frac{49}{28}$
7. $42\frac{1}{3}$ $\frac{127}{3}$
8. $67\frac{2}{5}$ $\frac{337}{5}$

Remember how?

$$\frac{42}{5} = 8\frac{2}{5}$$

$$
\begin{array}{r}
8 \\
5\overline{)42} \\
40 \\
\hline
2
\end{array}
$$

Now practice:

9. $\frac{17}{10}$ $1\frac{7}{10}$
10. $\frac{24}{5}$ $4\frac{4}{5}$
11. $\frac{61}{11}$ $5\frac{6}{11}$
12. $\frac{33}{2}$ $16\frac{1}{2}$

13. $\frac{48}{17}$ $2\frac{14}{17}$
14. $\frac{52}{6}$ $8\frac{2}{3}$
15. $\frac{38}{3}$ $12\frac{2}{3}$
16. $\frac{105}{12}$ $8\frac{3}{4}$

Remember how?

$$3\frac{1}{4} + 6\frac{2}{5} = \frac{13}{4} + \frac{32}{5}$$

$$= \frac{13 \cdot 5}{4 \cdot 5} + \frac{32 \cdot 4}{5 \cdot 4}$$

$$= \frac{65}{20} + \frac{128}{20} = \frac{193}{20} = 9\frac{13}{20}$$

Now practice:

17. $1\frac{1}{3} + 2\frac{3}{4}$ $4\frac{1}{12}$
18. $4\frac{1}{2} + 7\frac{3}{8}$ $11\frac{7}{8}$

19. $12\frac{2}{5} - 11\frac{1}{3}$ $1\frac{1}{15}$
20. $7\frac{1}{4} - 5\frac{2}{3}$ $1\frac{7}{12}$

21. $12\frac{5}{6} + 7\frac{1}{3}$ $20\frac{1}{6}$
22. $18\frac{5}{6} - 1\frac{1}{2}$ $17\frac{1}{3}$

Remember how?

$$3\frac{1}{3} \times 4\frac{1}{5} = \frac{\overset{2}{\cancel{10}}}{\cancel{3}} \times \frac{\overset{7}{\cancel{21}}}{\cancel{5}} = 14$$

Now practice:

23. $2\frac{1}{3} \times 4\frac{1}{2}$ $10\frac{1}{2}$
24. $3\frac{1}{5} \times 5\frac{3}{10}$ $16\frac{24}{25}$
25. $8\frac{3}{4} \times \frac{2}{5}$ $3\frac{1}{2}$

26. $5\frac{1}{2} \times \frac{11}{12}$ $5\frac{1}{24}$
27. $3\frac{6}{7} \times 2\frac{1}{3}$ 9
28. $1\frac{1}{8} \times 3\frac{11}{15}$ $4\frac{1}{5}$

Remember how?

$$2\frac{3}{4} \div 5\frac{1}{2} = \frac{11}{4} \div \frac{11}{2}$$

$$= \frac{\overset{1}{\cancel{11}}}{\underset{2}{\cancel{4}}} \times \frac{\overset{1}{\cancel{2}}}{\underset{1}{\cancel{11}}} = \frac{1}{2}$$

Now practice:

29. $3\frac{1}{2} \div 1\frac{3}{4}$ 2
30. $3\frac{1}{4} \div 2\frac{5}{8}$ $1\frac{5}{21}$
31. $2\frac{1}{2} \div 3\frac{2}{3}$ $\frac{15}{22}$

32. $1\frac{3}{8} \div 5\frac{1}{2}$ $\frac{1}{4}$
33. $1\frac{2}{7} \div 4\frac{1}{3}$ $\frac{27}{91}$
34. $5\frac{3}{4} \div 3\frac{3}{4}$ $1\frac{8}{15}$

Working with Fractions

Physical Science These circuits are part of a device which helps prevent the loss of data from computer memories. The device can duplicate the programs stored in the main memory of a computer.

6

Fractions and Ratios

6-1 Factoring and Fractions

OBJECTIVE To learn how to use factoring to reduce fractions to lowest terms.

Applying the property of quotients (page 145) to the fraction $\frac{21}{15}$,

$$\text{we have } \frac{21}{15} = \frac{7 \cdot 3}{5 \cdot 3} = \frac{7}{5} \cdot \frac{3}{3} = \frac{7}{5} \cdot 1 = \frac{7}{5}.$$

In general:

> **Multiplication Property of Fractions**
>
> For all real numbers a and nonzero real numbers b and c:
>
> $$\frac{ac}{bc} = \frac{a}{b}$$

When c is the greatest common factor of ac and bc in $\frac{ac}{bc}$, the fraction $\frac{a}{b}$ is said to be in **lowest terms**. Dividing the **numerator** (ac) and **denominator** (bc) of a fraction by their greatest common factor c is called **reducing** the fraction **to lowest terms**.

Example 1   Reduce $\dfrac{12x^2}{.\ 15x}$ to lowest terms, $x \neq 0$.

Solution $\dfrac{12x^2}{15x} = \dfrac{4x \cdot 3x}{5 \cdot 3x} = \dfrac{4x}{5}$, $x \neq 0$ *Answer*

Slant bars can be used to show the division operation in the reduction of fractions.

$$\dfrac{12x^2}{15x} = \dfrac{\overset{4\quad x}{\cancel{12x^2}}}{\underset{5\ 1}{\cancel{15x}}} = \dfrac{4x}{5}$$

Example 2   Simplify $\dfrac{5 - x}{x^2 - 3x - 10}$.

Solution

Factor numerator ⟶ $\dfrac{5 - x}{x^2 - 3x - 10} = \dfrac{5 - x}{(x + 2)(x - 5)}$
and denominator.

What values of x are excluded? The fraction is not defined for $x = -2$ and $x = 5$.

To show the common factor, express
the numerator as a product having -1 ⟶ $\dfrac{-1(x - 5)}{(x + 2)(x - 5)}$
as a factor.

Simplify: $\dfrac{-1\overset{1}{\cancel{(x - 5)}}}{(x + 2)\underset{1}{\cancel{(x - 5)}}} = \dfrac{-1}{x + 2}$, $x \neq -2$, $x \neq 5$ *Answer*

The fraction $\dfrac{-1}{x + 2}$ in Example 2 can also be written in the form

$-\dfrac{1}{x + 2}$, because

$$\dfrac{-1}{x + 2} = (-1)\dfrac{1}{x + 2} = -\dfrac{1}{x + 2}.$$

Caution! In a case like $\dfrac{7 + 9}{7}$, where 7 is *not* a factor of the numerator, the fraction cannot be reduced.

Oral Exercises

State any values of the variable for which the fraction is not defined.

1. $\dfrac{t}{t-2}$ $t=2$

2. $\dfrac{x}{4x+16}$ $x=-4$

3. $\dfrac{y}{2y-8}$ $y=4$

4. $\dfrac{a-3}{8a+16}$ $a=-2$

Reduce to lowest terms, noting the restrictions on the values of the variables.

5. $\dfrac{26}{6x}\ \dfrac{13}{3x}$, $x \neq 0$

6. $\dfrac{16x}{4}$ $4x$

7. $\dfrac{16ab}{8ab^2}\ \dfrac{2}{b}$, $a \neq 0, b \neq 0$

8. $\dfrac{-6mn^2}{18n}$ $-\dfrac{mn}{3}$, $n \neq 0$

9. $\dfrac{1}{c(c+2)}$ $\dfrac{1}{c(c+2)}$, $c \neq 0, -2$

10. $\dfrac{2}{x(x-3)}$ $\dfrac{2}{x(x-3)}$, $x \neq 0, 3$

Written Exercises

State any values of the variable for which the fraction is not defined.

A 1. $\dfrac{b-6}{10b-30}$ $b=3$

2. $\dfrac{a+7}{a^2-49}$ $a=7,-7$

3. $\dfrac{3}{x^2+5x-14}$ $x=-7,2$

4. $\dfrac{3y-7}{y^2+8y+12}$ $y=-6,-2$

Write each fraction in lowest terms, noting all necessary restrictions on values of the variables.

5. $\dfrac{21a^2}{7}$ $3a^2$

6. $\dfrac{15}{20b}\ \dfrac{3}{4b}$, $b \neq 0$

7. $\dfrac{6(y+2)}{9(y+2)}\ \dfrac{2}{3}$, $y \neq -2$

8. $\dfrac{3c+6}{3c-6}\ \dfrac{c+2}{c-2}$, $c \neq 2$

9. $\dfrac{5x-5y}{5x+5y}\ \dfrac{x-y}{x+y}$, $x \neq -y$

10. $\dfrac{8a-8b}{a^2-b^2}\ \dfrac{8}{a+b}$, $a \neq b, -b$

11. $\dfrac{d^2-4}{d-2}$ $d+2, d \neq 2$

12. $\dfrac{x^2-9}{3-x}\ \dfrac{-(x+3)}{},$ $x \neq 3$

13. $\dfrac{16-y^2}{y-4}$ $-(4+y)$, $y \neq 4$

14. $\dfrac{x^2+8x+16}{x^2-16}\ \dfrac{x+4}{x-4}$, $x \neq 4, -4$

15. $\dfrac{a^2+a-12}{12-4a}\ -\dfrac{a+4}{4}$, $a \neq 3$

16. $\dfrac{x^2-9}{x^2-x-6}\ \dfrac{x+3}{x+2}$, $x \neq 3, -2$

17. $\dfrac{-4a^2}{2a^2-4a^3}\ \dfrac{2}{2a-1}$, $a \neq 0, \frac{1}{2}$

18. $\dfrac{2d^2+6}{2d+6}\ \dfrac{d^2+3}{d+3}$, $d \neq -3$

19. $\dfrac{ab^2+a}{ab+a}\ \dfrac{b^2+1}{b+1}$, $a \neq 0\ b \neq -1$

20. $\dfrac{x^2-5x}{x^2-6x+5}\ \dfrac{x}{x-1}$, $x \neq 1, 5$

B 21. $\dfrac{5x^2+30x-35}{5x^2-5}\ \dfrac{x+7}{x+1}$, $x \neq 1, -1$

22. $\dfrac{x^2+10xy+25y^2}{x^2-25y^2}\ \dfrac{x+5y}{x-5y}$, $x \neq 5y, -5y$

23. $\dfrac{r^2+rs-12s^2}{r^2-9s^2}$

24. $\dfrac{a^2-2a-8}{a^2-4a}\ \dfrac{a+2}{a}$, $a \neq 0, 4$

25. $\dfrac{b^2-5b-6}{b^2-4b-12}\ \dfrac{b+1}{b+2}$, $b \neq 6, -2$

26. $\dfrac{y^2-2y-15}{y^2+10y+21}$

27. $\dfrac{x^2+x-6}{x^2-2x-15}\ \dfrac{x-2}{x-5}$, $x \neq -3, 5$

28. $\dfrac{z^2-4z-5}{z^2+4z-45}\ \dfrac{z+1}{z+9}$, $z \neq 5, -9$

29. $\dfrac{s^2+3s-10}{s^2+7s-18}$

30. $\dfrac{t^2+4t-5}{t^2+9t+20}\ \dfrac{t-1}{t+4}$, $t \neq -5, -4$

31. $\dfrac{p^2+2p-8}{p^2+13p-30}\ \dfrac{p+4}{p+15}$, $p \neq -15, 2$

32. $\dfrac{p^2+4p-32}{p^2+3p-28}$

23. $\dfrac{r+4s}{r+3s}$, $r \neq 3s, -3s$

26. $\dfrac{y-5}{y+7}$, $y \neq -7, -3$

29. $\dfrac{s+5}{s+9}$, $s \neq -9, 2$

32. $\dfrac{p+8}{p+7}$, $p \neq -7, 4$

C 33. $\dfrac{y^3 + 4y^2 - 12y}{y^3 - 3y^2 + 2y}$

34. $\dfrac{2a^3 + a^2 - 3a}{6a^3 + 5a^2 - 6a}$

35. $\dfrac{2r^3 + 10r^2 - 48r}{5r^3 + 30r^2 - 80r}$

36. $\dfrac{3b^3 + 2b^2 - 8b}{3b^4 - b^3 - 4b^2}$

37. $\dfrac{2x^3 + 24x^2 + 70x}{10x^3 + 40x^2 - 50x}$

38. $\dfrac{3c^4 + 27c^3 + 60c^2}{6c^2 + 6c - 72}$

39. $\dfrac{x^2 - 4x - 5}{x^2 + bx + x + b}$

40. $\dfrac{ab - cd - ac + bd}{ab - 2cd + 2bd - ac}$

41. $\dfrac{m^2 - mn - 6n^2}{m^2 - 2mn - 3n^2}$

42. $\dfrac{p^2 - pq - 2q^2}{p^3 + p^2q - pq^2 - q^3}$

43. $\dfrac{x^5 + 6x^4 - 4x - 24}{x^3 + 6x^2 - 2x - 12}$

44. $\dfrac{x^7 - 5x^6 - 9x + 45}{x^4 - 5x^3 + 3x - 15}$

Historical Note
Decimals

Computation with fractions has always presented problems. The Babylonians used a place value system partially based on 60, including fractions with denominators that were powers of 60. This system is reflected in our time measurements of minutes and seconds:

$$1 \text{ minute} = \frac{1}{60} \text{ hour}$$

$$1 \text{ second} = \frac{1}{60} \text{ minute} = \frac{1}{60^2} \text{ hour}$$

In 1579 Vieta (compare page 59) recommended using fractions with denominators that were powers of 10. The real impetus for the use of decimal fractions came with the explanation and notation presented by Simon Stevin (compare page 150) in a book published originally in Dutch in 1585. It was translated into English in 1608.

Stevin explained how, by using decimals, all computations could be done as if with whole numbers. He indicated the "decimal places" by using small numerals in circles. As one example, he showed the addition of numbers 27⓪8①4②7③, 37⓪6①7②5③, and 875⓪7①8②2③ as:

```
 ⓪①②③
 2 7 8 4 7                     27.847
 3 7 6 7 5   meaning   ⟹      37.675
 8 7 5 7 8 2                  875.782
─────────                    ────────
 9 4 1 3 0 4                  941.304
```

He wrote the sum as 941⓪3①0②4③.

The decimal point was soon introduced and then the small numerals in circles could be omitted.

33. $\dfrac{y + 6}{y - 1}, y \neq 0, 1, 2$

34. $\dfrac{a - 1}{3a - 2}, a \neq 0, -\dfrac{3}{2}, \dfrac{2}{3}$

35. $\dfrac{2(r - 3)}{5(r - 2)}, r \neq 0, -8, 2$

36. $\dfrac{b + 2}{b(b + 1)}, b \neq 0, -1,$

37. $\dfrac{x + 7}{5(x - 1)}, x \neq 0, 1, -5$

38. $\dfrac{c^2(c + 5)}{2(c - 3)}, c \neq 3, -4$

39. $\dfrac{x - 5}{x + b}, x \neq -b, -1$

40. $\dfrac{a + d}{a + 2d}, b \neq c, a \neq -$

41. $\dfrac{m + 2n}{m + n}, m \neq 3n, -n$

42. $\dfrac{p - 2q}{p^2 - q^2}, p \neq q, -q$

43. $x^2 + 2, x \neq -6, \sqrt{2},$

44. $x^3 - 3, x \neq 5, x^3 \neq -$

6-2 Ratios

> **OBJECTIVE** To learn how to express ratios of two quantities and to use ratios in solving problems.

To compare the populations of two cities, one having 80,000 residents and the other 20,000 residents, you can compute the quotient:

$$\frac{80,000}{20,000} = \frac{4}{1} = 4.$$

You may say that the first city has four times as many inhabitants as the second, or you may say that the populations are in the *ratio* 4 to 1.

> A **ratio** of one number to another (not zero) is the quotient of the first number divided by the second.

The ratio "4 to 1" may be expressed as the fraction $\frac{4}{1}$ or with the **ratio sign** as

$$4:1.$$

By the multiplication property of fractions (page 197),

$$\frac{6}{5} = \frac{12}{10} = \frac{18}{15} = \frac{-24}{-20} = \frac{6n}{5n}, \ n \neq 0,$$

and so the ratio 6:5 compares not only the numbers 6 and 5 but also the numbers 12 and 10, 18 and 15, and so on.

Quantities to be compared must be measured in the same units. If you wish to compare a 2-kilogram weight with a 10-gram weight, you must change the 2 kilograms to 2000 grams and then use the ratio $\frac{2000}{10}$ or 200:1. In general:

> To find the ratio of two quantities of the same kind:
>
> **1.** Find the measures in the same unit.
>
> **2.** Then divide these measures.

Example   The State Fish and Game Department stocked Lake Pierre with bass and catfish in the ratio of 5 to 3. If 2400 fish were released in the lake, how many of each kind of fish were placed in the lake?

Solution

Step 1   The problem asks for the number of bass and catfish in the lake.

Step 2   The ratio is $\dfrac{5}{3} = \dfrac{5n}{3n} = \dfrac{\text{number of bass}}{\text{number of catfish}}$ $(n \neq 0)$.

Step 3 $5n + 3n = 2400$

Step 4 $\qquad 8n = 2400$
$\qquad\quad n = 300$

$\therefore 5n = 1500$, the number of bass, and $3n = 900$, the number of catfish.

Step 5   *Check:* $\dfrac{1500}{900} = \dfrac{5}{3}$ and $1500 + 900 = 2400$ ✓

$\therefore$ the lake was stocked with 1500 bass and 900 catfish.   *Answer*

Oral Exercises

Give each ratio in its lowest terms. State restrictions.

1. $4:8$ 1:2   2. $6:36$ 1:6   3. $\dfrac{ab}{ac}$ $\dfrac{b}{c}, \begin{smallmatrix} a \neq 0 \\ c \neq 0 \end{smallmatrix}$ 4. $\dfrac{xyz}{ayz}$ $\dfrac{x}{a}, \begin{smallmatrix} a \neq 0 \\ y \neq 0 \\ z \neq 0 \end{smallmatrix}$ 5. $\dfrac{150}{5}$ $\dfrac{30}{1}$ 6. $\dfrac{90}{30}$

7. 6 meters to 18 meters   1:3   8. 7 kilograms to 21 kilograms   1:3   9. 3 days to 1 week   3:7

10. 2 minutes to 16 seconds   15:2   11. 6 kilograms to 3 grams   2000:1   12. 3 years to 3 months

Written Exercises

Give each ratio in its lowest terms.

A   1. The area of a rectangle measuring 5 by 3 centimeters to that of one 3 by 10 centimeters.   1:2

2. The area of a rectangle measuring 9 by 10 meters to that of one 3 by 15 meters.   2:1

3. The area of a rectangle measuring 3 millimeters by 5 centimeters to that of one 15 by 20 millimeters.   1:2

4. The area of a 6-centimeter square to that of a 0.6-meter square.   1:100

5. A basketball player's 27 free throws made to his 54 attempted.   1:2

6. 465 students to 15 teachers.   31:1

7. Girls to boys in a school of 3200 students with 1700 boys.   15:17

8. Wins to losses in a season of 36 games with 12 losses.   2:1

In Exercises 9–12, use the rule that in a triangle

$$\text{Area} = \tfrac{1}{2}(\text{Base} \times \text{Height}).$$

9. The area of a triangle with a 10-meter base and a 12-meter height to that of one with a 16-meter base and an 8-meter height.   15:16

10. The area of a triangle with a 4-meter base and a 6-meter height to that of one with a 12-meter base and an 18-meter height.   1:9

11. The area of a triangle with a 2-meter base and a 9-centimeter height to that of a rectangle measuring 10 by 12 centimeters.   15:2

12. The area of a triangle with a 1-meter base and a 20-centimeter height to that of a square measuring 40 centimeters on a side.   5:8

Find the ratio $x:y$ in each case.

Sample $3x = 4y$

Solution $3x = 4y$

$$\frac{3x}{3y} = \frac{4y}{3y}$$

$$\frac{x}{y} = \frac{4}{3} \quad \text{or} \quad x:y = 4:3 \quad \textit{Answer}$$

13. $6x = 9y$ 3:2   14. $3x = 3y$ 1:1   15. $8y = 16x$ 1:2   16. $5y = 25x$ 1:5

17. $3x - 7y = 0$ 7:3   18. $-7x + 4y = 0$ 4:7   19. $3x + 5y = 0$ $-5:3$ 20. $9x - 7y = 0$ 7:9

B 21. $\dfrac{x + y}{y} = \dfrac{5}{6}$ $-1:6$ 22. $\dfrac{7x - y}{y} = \dfrac{4}{3}$ 1:3   23. $\dfrac{2x + 3y}{3y} = \dfrac{5}{2}$ 9:4   24. $\dfrac{4x + 7y}{2y} = \dfrac{3}{7}$ $-43:28$

C 25. $\dfrac{x^2 + 2y^2}{y^2} = \dfrac{2x + y}{y}$ 1:1

26. $\dfrac{x^2 + 5y^2}{y^2} = \dfrac{y - 4x}{y}$ $-2:1$

Problems

Solve.

A 1. Find the greater of two numbers in the ratio of 7 to 9, whose difference is 10. **45**

2. Find the lesser of two numbers in the ratio of 2 to 11, whose sum is −65. **−55**

3. How many of the 33 members of the Ecology Club are boys if the ratio of girls to boys is 7 to 4? **12 boys**

4. A firm employs 656 people. If the ratio of the number of clerical and sales workers to the number of machine workers is 5 to 11, find the number of machine workers. **451 workers**

5. A 120-centimeter rope is cut into two pieces whose lengths are in the ratio of 6:14. How long is the shorter piece of rope? **36 cm**

6. A mutual fund invests in bonds and stocks in the ratio of 3 to 5. How much of $30,000 invested will go into bonds? **$11,250**

7. To help beautify Allentown, the people are planting shrubs and trees in the ratio of 11 to 2. How many of the 520 bought will be trees? **80 trees**

8. Pat types 2080 words in 40 minutes, while Leslie types 720 words in 18 minutes. Which one is the faster typist? **Pat**

B 9. Jack wishes to divide a board 154 centimeters long into three pieces whose lengths are in the ratios: longest to shortest; 4:1; middle to shortest, 2:1. Find the length of each piece. **22 cm, 44 cm, 88 cm**

10. The ratio of the length of a rectangle to its width is 7:2. If the perimeter of the rectangle is 396 centimeters, find its width. **44 cm**

★ Self-Test 1

Be sure that you understand these terms:

lowest terms (p. 197)
reducing to lowest terms (p. 197)

numerator (p. 197)
ratio (p. 201)

denominator (p. 197)

Be sure that you understand this symbol:

: (p. 201)

Write each fraction in lowest terms. State restrictions.

1. $\dfrac{x^2 - 16}{4 - x}$

2. $\dfrac{x^2 - 3x}{x^2 - 5x + 6}$

Objective 6-1, p. 197

Write each ratio in its lowest terms.

3. $(c + d):(c + d)^2$ 4. 6 years to 6 months

Objective 6-2, p. 201

5. The ratio of the length of a rectangle to its width is 6:5. If the perimeter of the rectangle is 44 centimeters, find its length.

Check your answers with those printed at the back of the book.

Multiplication and Division

6-3 Multiplying Fractions

> **OBJECTIVE** To learn how to multiply fractions.

When you read the property of quotients (page 145) from right to left
you have the following:

> **Rule for Multiplying Fractions**
>
> For any real numbers x and y and nonzero real numbers c and d:
>
> $$\frac{x}{c} \cdot \frac{y}{d} = \frac{xy}{cd}$$

Thus:

$$\frac{2}{3} \times \frac{4}{5} = \frac{8}{15},$$

$$(3v) \cdot \frac{8v}{u} = \frac{3v}{1} \cdot \frac{8v}{u} = \frac{24v^2}{u}, \, u \neq 0,$$

$$\frac{z}{(z-5)} \cdot \frac{(z+2)}{(z-1)} = \frac{z(z+2)}{(z-5)(z-1)} = \frac{z^2 + 2z}{z^2 - 6z + 5}, \, z \neq 1, z \neq 5$$

Products involving fractions should be reduced to lowest terms. Since the factors of the numerator and denominator of the factors of a product are the same as those of the product, common factors can be divided from the numerator and denominator either before or after the multiplication operation is performed. Slant bars can help keep track of such divisions.

Example 1 Express as a fraction in lowest terms:

$$\frac{2}{5} \times \frac{15}{8}$$

Solution $\quad \dfrac{2}{5} \times \dfrac{15}{8} = \dfrac{30}{40} = \dfrac{3}{4} \quad$ or $\quad \dfrac{\overset{1}{\cancel{2}}}{\underset{1}{\cancel{5}}} \times \dfrac{\overset{3}{\cancel{15}}}{\underset{4}{\cancel{8}}} = \dfrac{3}{4} \quad$ *Answer*

Example 2 Express as a fraction in lowest terms:

$$\frac{r^2 - 11r + 30}{r^2 - 6r + 9} \cdot \frac{r^2 - 3r}{r^2 - 5r}$$

Solution $\quad \dfrac{r^2 - 11r + 30}{r^2 - 6r + 9} \cdot \dfrac{r^2 - 3r}{r^2 - 5r} = \dfrac{(r - 5)(r - 6)}{(r - 3)(r - 3)} \cdot \dfrac{r(r - 3)}{r(r - 5)}$

$$= \frac{(r - 5)(r - 6)}{(r - 3)(r - 3)} \cdot \frac{r(r - 3)}{r(r - 5)}$$

$$= \frac{r - 6}{r - 3}, \ r \neq 0, \ r \neq 3, \ r \neq 5 \quad \textit{Answer}$$

Check by assigning to the variable a value other than 0 or 1 that will not make a denominator zero. For instance, let $r = 2$:

$$\frac{r^2 - 11r + 30}{r^2 - 6r + 9} = \frac{4 - 22 + 30}{4 - 12 + 9} = \frac{12}{1}$$

$$\frac{r^2 - 3r}{r^2 - 5r} = \frac{4 - 6}{4 - 10} = \frac{-2}{-6} = \frac{1}{3}$$

$$\left.\begin{array}{l}\end{array}\right\} \longrightarrow \frac{12}{1} \cdot \frac{1}{3} = 4$$

$$\frac{r - 6}{r - 3} = \frac{2 - 6}{2 - 3} = \frac{-4}{-1} = 4 \ \checkmark$$

Hereafter, it will be assumed that the replacement sets of the variables include no value for which the denominator is zero. **Hence, it will not be necessary to show excluded values of the variables involved.**

Oral Exercises

Express each product as a fraction in lowest terms.

1. $\dfrac{1}{3} \cdot \dfrac{1}{2} \quad \dfrac{1}{6}$ 　　2. $\dfrac{2}{5} \cdot \dfrac{3}{8} \quad \dfrac{3}{20}$ 　　3. $\left(-\dfrac{1}{2}\right)\left(\dfrac{7}{3}\right) \ -\dfrac{7}{6}$ 　　4. $\dfrac{2}{3}\left(-\dfrac{1}{9}\right) \ -\dfrac{2}{27}$

5. $\dfrac{c}{2} \cdot \dfrac{d}{3} \quad \dfrac{cd}{6}$ 　　6. $4 \cdot \dfrac{3}{7} \quad \dfrac{12}{7}$ 　　7. $p \cdot \dfrac{p}{q} \quad \dfrac{p^2}{q}$ 　　8. $\left(-\dfrac{1}{x}\right)\left(\dfrac{2}{y}\right) \ -\dfrac{2}{xy}$

9. $\left(-\dfrac{3}{b}\right)\left(-\dfrac{7}{c}\right) \ \dfrac{21}{bc}$ 　　10. $\dfrac{7a}{8b} \cdot \dfrac{a}{2} \ \dfrac{7a^2}{16b}$ 　　11. $\dfrac{g^2}{3z} \cdot \dfrac{g}{2z} \ \dfrac{g^3}{6z^2}$ 　　12. $\dfrac{p}{3q} \cdot \dfrac{5p^2}{7pr} \ \dfrac{5p^2}{21qr}$

Written Exercises

Express each product as a fraction in lowest terms. Check variable expressions by assigning values to the variables.

A 1. $\dfrac{2}{3} \cdot \dfrac{5}{13} \cdot 7$ $\dfrac{70}{39}$
  2. $\dfrac{1}{8} \cdot \dfrac{7}{3} \cdot (-5)$ $-\dfrac{35}{24}$
  3. $\dfrac{2}{6} \cdot \dfrac{3}{5}$ $\dfrac{1}{5}$
  4. $\dfrac{5}{8} \cdot \dfrac{6}{5}$ $\dfrac{3}{4}$

  5. $\dfrac{2}{4} \cdot \dfrac{4}{6} \cdot \dfrac{5}{13}$ $\dfrac{5}{39}$
  6. $\dfrac{3}{8} \cdot \dfrac{4}{6} \cdot \dfrac{16}{3}$ $\dfrac{4}{3}$
  7. $\dfrac{18}{33} \cdot \dfrac{20}{16} \cdot \dfrac{11}{2}$ $\dfrac{15}{4}$
  8. $\dfrac{9}{28} \cdot \dfrac{5}{3} \cdot \dfrac{4}{18}$ $\dfrac{5}{42}$

  9. $\dfrac{6a}{17b} \cdot \dfrac{34ab}{a}$ $12a$
  10. $\dfrac{-10ab}{2} \cdot \dfrac{12a}{9a^2b}$ $-\dfrac{20}{3}$
  11. $\dfrac{2}{5} \cdot \dfrac{15a^2}{6}$ a^2
  12. $8x^2y \cdot \dfrac{5}{4y}$ $10x^2$

  13. $\dfrac{-22cd^2}{2d} \cdot \dfrac{17c^2d}{17d}$ $-11c^3d$
  14. $\dfrac{24r^2s^2}{3s} \cdot \dfrac{-21s}{r}$ $-168rs^2$
  15. $\dfrac{6x + 18}{x} \cdot \dfrac{3x}{5x + 10}$ $\dfrac{18x + 54}{5x + 10}$

  16. $\dfrac{2t + 16}{4t} \cdot \dfrac{10t^2}{3t + 24}$ $\dfrac{5t}{3}$
  17. $\dfrac{y - 5}{8y - 4} \cdot \dfrac{10y - 5}{6y - 30}$ $\dfrac{5}{24}$
  18. $\dfrac{3z - 6}{4z + 8} \cdot \dfrac{z + 2}{z - 2}$ $\dfrac{3}{4}$

  19. $\dfrac{a + b}{a - b} \cdot \dfrac{a^2 - b^2}{a + b}$ $a + b$
  20. $\dfrac{c^2 - d^2}{c^2} \cdot \dfrac{c^4}{(c + d)^2}$ $\dfrac{c^3 - c^2d}{c + d}$
  21. $\dfrac{3x - xy}{6x^2y} \cdot \dfrac{3}{9 - y^2}$ $\dfrac{1}{6xy + 2xy^2}$

  22. $\dfrac{a^2 - 4}{a^2 - 1} \cdot \dfrac{a - 1}{a - 2}$ $\dfrac{a + 2}{a + 1}$
  23. $\dfrac{a^2 + b^2}{a^2 - b^2} \cdot \dfrac{a - b}{a + b}$ $\dfrac{a^2 + b^2}{(a + b)^2}$
  24. $\dfrac{m^2 - n^2}{m^2 - 4} \cdot \dfrac{m + 2}{m - n}$ $\dfrac{m + n}{m - 2}$

B 25. $\dfrac{2(x + 1)}{(x - 1)} \cdot \dfrac{x^2 + x - 2}{x^2 - x - 2}$ $\dfrac{2x + 4}{x - 2}$
  26. $\dfrac{y^2 + 5y + 6}{3y - 3} \cdot \dfrac{y^2 - y}{y + 2}$ $\dfrac{y^2 + 3y}{3}$
  27. $\dfrac{a^2 - 3a - 4}{a^2 - 2a} \cdot \dfrac{a - 2}{a - 4}$ $\dfrac{a + 1}{a}$

  28. $\dfrac{3x - 6}{6x + 6} \cdot \dfrac{x^2 + 3x + 2}{x^2 - 3x + 2}$ $\dfrac{x + 2}{2x - 2}$
  29. $\dfrac{2a^2 - a - 3}{6a^2 - 13a + 6} \cdot \dfrac{3a^2 - 2a}{2a - 3}$ $\dfrac{a^2 + a}{2a - 3}$
  30. $\dfrac{z^2 - 6z - 7}{z^2 + z} \cdot \dfrac{z^2 - z}{3z - 21}$ $\dfrac{z - 1}{3}$

  31. $\dfrac{c^2 - 6c - 16}{c^2 + 4c - 21} \cdot \dfrac{c^2 - 8c + 15}{c^2 + 9c + 14}$ $\dfrac{c^2 - 13c + 40}{c^2 + 14c + 49}$
  32. $\dfrac{x^2 + 9x + 18}{x^2 + 6x + 9} \cdot \dfrac{xy - 4y}{x^2 - 9x + 20}$ $\dfrac{xy + 6y}{x^2 - 2x - 15}$

  33. $\dfrac{h^2 - 2h - 3}{h^2 - 9} \cdot \dfrac{h^2 + 5h + 6}{h^2 - 1}$ $\dfrac{h + 2}{h - 1}$
  34. $\dfrac{a^2 + 10a + 21}{a^2 - 2a - 15} \cdot \dfrac{a^2 - 4a - 5}{a^2 + 6a - 7}$ $\dfrac{a + 1}{a - 1}$

  35. $\dfrac{x^2 - y^2}{x^2 + 4xy + 3y^2} \cdot \dfrac{x^2 + xy - 6y^2}{x^2 + xy - 2y^2}$ $\dfrac{x - 2y}{x + 2y}$
  36. $\dfrac{b^2 + 3b + 2}{b^2 + b} \cdot \dfrac{b^2 + 3b}{b^2 + 5b + 6}$ 1

C 37. $\dfrac{30 + y - y^2}{25 - y^2} \cdot \dfrac{y^2}{y^2 - 6y} \cdot \dfrac{y^2 - y - 12}{y^2 - 9}$ $\dfrac{y^2 - 4y}{y^2 - 8y + 15}$
  38. $\dfrac{12 + a - a^2}{9 - a^2} \cdot \dfrac{a + 2}{a^2 + a} \cdot \dfrac{3 + 2a - a^2}{8 + 2a - a^2}$ $\dfrac{1}{a}$

  39. $\dfrac{b^2 + 4b + 3}{b^2 - 8b + 7} \cdot \dfrac{35 + 2b - b^2}{b^2 - 7b - 8} \cdot \dfrac{b^2 - 9b + 8}{b^2 + 8b + 15}$ -1

  40. $\dfrac{2c^2 - c - 3}{4c^2 - 5c + 1} \cdot \dfrac{c^2 - 1}{(c + 1)^2} \cdot \dfrac{1 - 3c - 4c^2}{3 - 5c + 2c^2}$ $\dfrac{1 + c}{1 - c}$

6-4 Dividing Fractions

OBJECTIVE To learn how to divide fractions.

A quotient can be expressed as the product of the dividend and the reciprocal of the divisor (page 78). Thus:

$$15 \div 3 = 15 \times \frac{1}{3}; \quad 7 \div \frac{1}{8} = 7 \times 8; \quad \frac{3}{8} \div \frac{5}{9} = \frac{3}{8} \times \frac{9}{5}$$

Since the reciprocal of $\frac{c}{d}$ is $\frac{d}{c}$, you have the following:

Rule for Dividing Fractions

For any real number a and nonzero real numbers b, c, and d:

$$\frac{a}{b} \div \frac{c}{d} = \frac{a}{b} \cdot \frac{d}{c} = \frac{ad}{bc}$$

Thus, to divide fractions, multiply the dividend by the reciprocal of the divisor.

Example $\dfrac{y^2 - 9}{y^2 - 6y + 9} \div \dfrac{3y + 9}{7y - 21}$

Solution $\dfrac{y^2 - 9}{y^2 - 6y + 9} \div \dfrac{3y + 9}{7y - 21} = \dfrac{y^2 - 9}{y^2 - 6y + 9} \cdot \dfrac{7y - 21}{3y + 9}$

$$= \frac{(y - 3)(y + 3)}{(y - 3)(y - 3)} \cdot \frac{7(y - 3)}{3(y + 3)}$$

$$= \frac{\overset{1}{\cancel{(y - 3)}}\overset{1}{\cancel{(y + 3)}}}{\underset{1}{\cancel{(y - 3)}}\underset{1}{\cancel{(y - 3)}}} \cdot \frac{7\overset{1}{\cancel{(y - 3)}}}{3\underset{1}{\cancel{(y + 3)}}}$$

$$= \frac{7}{3} \quad \textit{Answer}$$

Oral Exercises

Simplify.

1. $\dfrac{2}{3} \div \dfrac{3}{4}$ $\dfrac{8}{9}$ 2. $\dfrac{8}{3} \div \dfrac{4}{5}$ $\dfrac{10}{3}$ 3. $\dfrac{-6}{7} \div \dfrac{3}{14}$ -4 4. $\dfrac{-2}{3} \div \dfrac{8}{-3}$ $\dfrac{1}{4}$ 5. $\dfrac{a^2}{b} \div \dfrac{a}{b}$ a 6. $\dfrac{rs}{p} \div \dfrac{ps}{r}$ $\dfrac{r^2}{p^2}$

Written Exercises

Simplify. Check variable expressions by assigning values to the variables.

A   1. $\dfrac{5}{8} \div \dfrac{3}{4}$ $\dfrac{5}{6}$ 2. $\dfrac{4}{15} \div \dfrac{2}{5}$ $\dfrac{2}{3}$ 3. $\dfrac{2a}{5b} \div \dfrac{3a}{5}$ $\dfrac{2}{3b}$ 4. $\dfrac{x^2}{y^2} \div \dfrac{x}{y^3}$ xy

5. $\dfrac{4lm^2}{9n^2} \div \dfrac{12m}{n}$ $\dfrac{lm}{27n}$ 6. $\dfrac{s^2}{r^3} \div \dfrac{6s}{r^4}$ $\dfrac{rs}{6}$ 7. $\dfrac{6t}{11u^2} \div \dfrac{12t^2}{22u}$ $\dfrac{1}{ut}$ 8. $\dfrac{12a^2b^2}{21xy^2} \div \dfrac{4ab^2}{7y^2}$ $\dfrac{a}{x}$

9. $(-16a^2) \div \dfrac{4a}{3}$ $-12a$ 10. $\dfrac{2ab}{5} \div (-12b^3)$ $-\dfrac{a}{30b^2}$ 11. $\dfrac{c+d}{15} \div \dfrac{c+d}{5}$ $\dfrac{1}{3}$ 12. $\dfrac{6z+1}{27} \div \dfrac{6z+1}{9}$ $\dfrac{1}{3}$

13. $\dfrac{a^2-4}{3a} \div (a+2)$ $\dfrac{a-2}{3a}$ 14. $\dfrac{x^2-x-6}{x^2} \div (x-3)$ $\dfrac{x+2}{x^2}$

15. $\dfrac{b+2}{b^2-9} \div \dfrac{1}{b-3}$ $\dfrac{b+2}{b+3}$ 16. $\dfrac{4a^2-1}{a^2-4} \div \dfrac{2a+1}{a-2}$ $\dfrac{2a-1}{a+2}$

17. $\dfrac{5}{a^2-9} \div \dfrac{5a-10}{a-3}$ $\dfrac{1}{a^2+a-6}$ 18. $\dfrac{c^2+2cd}{2cd+d^2} \div \dfrac{c^3+2c^2d}{cd+d^2}$ $\dfrac{c+d}{2c^2+cd}$

19. $\dfrac{2x}{3x+6} \div \dfrac{4x^2}{x^2-4}$ $\dfrac{x-2}{6x}$ 20. $\dfrac{y^2-4}{y^4} \div \dfrac{y^2-4y+4}{y^2}$ $\dfrac{y+2}{y^3-2y^2}$

21. $\dfrac{y^2-36}{y^2+12y+36} \div \dfrac{5y-30}{y^3+6y^2}$ $\dfrac{y^2}{5}$ 22. $\dfrac{x^2+3x^3}{4-x^2} \div \dfrac{x+4x^2+3x^3}{2x+x^2}$ $\dfrac{x^2}{2+x-x^2}$

23. $\dfrac{a^2+ab}{2a^2+3ab-2b^2} \div \dfrac{a^2}{2a^2+ab-b^2}$ $\dfrac{a^2+2ab+b^2}{a^2+2ab}$ 24. $\dfrac{y^3+2y}{4y^2-9} \div \dfrac{y^3+4y^2+3y}{2y^2-y-3}$ $\dfrac{y^2+2}{2y^2+9y+9}$

B   25. $\dfrac{a^2-a-20}{a^2+7a+12} \div \dfrac{a^2-7a+10}{a^2+9a+18}$ 26. $\dfrac{x^2-4}{x^2-5x+6} \div \dfrac{x^2+3x+2}{x^2-2x-3}$

27. $\dfrac{6a^2-a-2}{12a^2+5a-2} \div \dfrac{4a^2-1}{8a^2-6a+1}$ 28. $\dfrac{10b^2-13b-3}{2b^2-b-3} \div \dfrac{5b^2-9b-2}{3b^2+2b-1}$

29. $\dfrac{3n^2-75}{n^2+7n-8} \div \dfrac{12n^2+42n-90}{n^2+6n-7}$ 30. $\dfrac{2a^2-9a+9}{14-19a-3a^2} \div \dfrac{(a-3)^2}{(a+7)^2}$

31. $\dfrac{3r^2-14r+8}{2r^2-3r-20} \div \dfrac{6-25r+24r^2}{15-34r-16r^2}$ 32. $\dfrac{6x^2-5x-6}{3x^2-20x-7} \div \dfrac{12x^2+23x+10}{49-x^2}$

25. $\dfrac{a+6}{a-2}$ 26. 1 27. $\dfrac{3a-2}{3a+2}$ 28. $\dfrac{3b-1}{b-2}$

29. $\dfrac{n^2+2n-35}{4n^2+26n-48}$ 30. $\dfrac{2a^2+11a-21}{-(3a^2-11a+6)}$ 31. -1 32. $\dfrac{-(2x^2+11x-21)}{12x^2+19x+5}$

C 33. $\dfrac{ab - 6a + b - 6}{a - 3} \div \dfrac{ab - 6a + 3b - 18}{a^2 - 9}$ $\dfrac{a + 1}{a^2 - 9}$

34. $\dfrac{3rs + 9r + 2s + 6}{2r + 3} \div \dfrac{s + 3}{r - 1}$ $\dfrac{(3r + 2)(r - 1)}{2r + 3}$

35. $\dfrac{ac - bc + bt - at}{16x^3 - 4xy^2} \div \dfrac{ac - at}{y^2 - 4xy + 4x^2}$ $\dfrac{(a - b)(2x - y)}{4ax(2x + y)}$

36. $\dfrac{ab + 5ac - bd - 5cd}{b^2 + 3bc - 4c^2} \div \dfrac{a^2 + 2ad - 3d^2}{b^2 - c^2}$ $\dfrac{b^2 + 6bc + 5c^2}{(b + 4c)(a + 3d)}$

A **complex fraction** is a fraction whose numerator or denominator contains one or more fractions.

Simplify each complex fraction by doing the division.

Sample 1 $\dfrac{\dfrac{5}{6}}{\dfrac{3}{8}} = \dfrac{5}{6} \div \dfrac{3}{8} = \dfrac{5}{\cancel{6}} \cdot \dfrac{\overset{4}{\cancel{8}}}{3} = \dfrac{20}{9}$ *Answer*

Sample 2 $\dfrac{\dfrac{2 + 3t}{5t}}{\dfrac{1 - t}{3t^2}} = \dfrac{2 + 3t}{5t} \div \dfrac{1 - t}{3t^2} = \dfrac{2 + 3t}{\cancel{5t}} \cdot \dfrac{\overset{t}{\cancel{3t^2}}}{1 - t}$

$$= \dfrac{(2 + 3t)3t}{5(1 - t)} = \dfrac{6t + 9t^2}{5 - 5t} \quad Answer$$

A 37. $\dfrac{\dfrac{2}{3}}{\dfrac{5}{3}}$ $\dfrac{2}{5}$

38. $\dfrac{\dfrac{5}{36}}{\dfrac{7}{4}}$ $\dfrac{5}{63}$

39. $\dfrac{\dfrac{a}{b}}{\dfrac{a}{b}}$ 1

40. $\dfrac{\dfrac{x}{y^2}}{\dfrac{x}{y}}$ $\dfrac{1}{y}$

41. $\dfrac{\dfrac{14a^2b^2}{7a}}{\dfrac{7ab}{a^2}}$ $\dfrac{2a^2b}{7}$

42. $\dfrac{\dfrac{26c^2}{5c^2d}}{\dfrac{13c^3}{25d^3}}$ $\dfrac{10d^2}{c^3}$

43. $\dfrac{\dfrac{a + b}{c}}{\dfrac{a + b}{d}}$ $\dfrac{d}{c}$

44. $\dfrac{\dfrac{b + 3}{6a}}{\dfrac{b - 2}{3a^2}}$ $\dfrac{a(b}{2(b}$

B 45. $\dfrac{\dfrac{5}{4}}{\dfrac{15}{8}}$ $\dfrac{2}{3}$

46. $\dfrac{\dfrac{6}{5}}{\dfrac{16}{15}}$ $\dfrac{9}{8}$

47. $\dfrac{\dfrac{x^2 - 16}{x}}{\dfrac{x - 4}{x}}$ $\dfrac{x + 4}{x}$

48. $\dfrac{\dfrac{t^2 - 9}{t - 3}}{t}$ $t^2 -$

49. $\dfrac{\dfrac{y}{ay + b}}{a}$ $\dfrac{ay}{ay + b}$

50. $\dfrac{\dfrac{x + y}{xy}}{\dfrac{x - y}{xy}}$ $\dfrac{x + y}{x - y}$

51. $\dfrac{\dfrac{m + n}{x}}{\dfrac{m^2 - n^2}{x^2}}$ $\dfrac{x}{m - n}$

52. $\dfrac{\dfrac{cy - cz}{y^2 - z^2}}{\dfrac{y - c}{y + c}}$ $\dfrac{cy + c^2}{(y + z)(y - c)}$

6-5 Expressions Involving Multiplication and Division

> **OBJECTIVE** To learn how to simplify expressions involving multiplication and division of fractions.

In the absence of parentheses, the rule for order of performing multiplications and divisions (page 10) is applied to an expression containing fractions. *You replace only the fraction immediately following a division sign by its reciprocal.*

Example 1 Simplify $\dfrac{a^2}{a^2 - b^2} \cdot \dfrac{a + b}{a - b} \div \dfrac{a}{(a - b)^2}$.

Solution

$$\frac{a^2}{a^2 - b^2} \cdot \frac{a + b}{a - b} \div \frac{a}{(a - b)^2} = \frac{a^2}{a^2 - b^2} \cdot \frac{a + b}{a - b} \cdot \frac{(a - b)^2}{a}$$

$$= \frac{a^2}{(a - b)(a + b)} \cdot \frac{(a + b)}{(a - b)} \cdot \frac{(a - b)(a - b)}{a}$$

$$= \frac{\overset{a}{\cancel{a^2}}}{\cancel{(a - b)}\underset{1}{\cancel{(a + b)}}} \cdot \frac{\overset{1}{\cancel{(a + b)}}}{\underset{1}{\cancel{(a - b)}}} \cdot \frac{\overset{1}{\cancel{(a - b)}}\overset{1}{\cancel{(a - b)}}}{\underset{1}{\cancel{a}}}$$

$$= a \quad Answer$$

Example 2 Simplify $\dfrac{r}{r + 3} \div \dfrac{3r^2}{3r + 9} \cdot \dfrac{r^2 + 4r + 3}{r^2 - 9}$.

Solution

$$\frac{r}{r + 3} \div \frac{3r^2}{3r + 9} \cdot \frac{r^2 + 4r + 3}{r^2 - 9} = \frac{r}{r + 3} \cdot \frac{3r + 9}{3r^2} \cdot \frac{r^2 + 4r + 3}{r^2 - 9}$$

$$= \frac{r}{(r + 3)} \cdot \frac{3(r + 3)}{3r^2} \cdot \frac{(r + 1)(r + 3)}{(r - 3)(r + 3)}$$

$$= \frac{\overset{1}{\cancel{r}}}{\underset{1}{\cancel{(r + 3)}}} \cdot \frac{\overset{1}{\cancel{3}}\overset{1}{\cancel{(r + 3)}}}{\underset{1\ r}{\cancel{3r^2}}} \cdot \frac{(r + 1)\overset{1}{\cancel{(r + 3)}}}{(r - 3)\underset{1}{\cancel{(r + 3)}}}$$

$$= \frac{r + 1}{r(r - 3)} = \frac{r + 1}{r^2 - 3r} \quad Answer$$

Written Exercises

Simplify. Check by assigning values to the variables.

A 1. $\dfrac{2}{a^2} \cdot \dfrac{a}{4} \div \dfrac{5}{a}$ $\dfrac{1}{10}$

2. $\dfrac{b^3}{10} \cdot \dfrac{2}{b^4} \div \dfrac{1}{5b}$ 1

3. $\dfrac{cd^2}{g} \cdot \dfrac{cg}{d} \div \dfrac{c}{d}$ cd^2

4. $\dfrac{12xy^3}{5c^3} \cdot \dfrac{20c}{2y^2} \div \dfrac{y}{c}$ $\dfrac{24x}{c}$

5. $\dfrac{a^2 - 4}{b^2} \cdot \dfrac{b^2}{a + 2} \div \dfrac{a - 2}{b}$ b

6. $\dfrac{6x}{3x - 7} \cdot \dfrac{9x - 21}{21} \div \dfrac{x^2}{35}$ $\dfrac{30}{x}$

7. $\dfrac{2t + 3}{7st} \cdot \dfrac{14s^2t}{(2t + 3)(t - 1)} \div \dfrac{2}{t - 1}$ s

8. $\dfrac{a - 3b}{3a} \div \dfrac{8a - 24b}{9a^2} \cdot \dfrac{16b}{3a}$ $2b$

9. $\dfrac{c^2}{c^2 - d^2} \cdot \dfrac{c - d}{c + d} \div \dfrac{c}{(c + d)^2}$ c

10. $\dfrac{k^2 + 5k + 6}{6k} \cdot \dfrac{k - 2}{k + 3} \div \dfrac{k - 2}{12k^3}$ $2k^3 + 4k^2$

11. $\dfrac{a}{(a + 1)} \div \dfrac{5a^2}{6a + 18} \cdot \dfrac{5a^3 + 5a^2}{a^2 - 9}$ $\dfrac{6a}{a - 3}$

12. $\dfrac{r^2 - rs}{rs} \div \dfrac{2r - 2s}{rs} \cdot \dfrac{17}{r^3}$ $\dfrac{17}{2r^2}$

B 13. $\dfrac{x^2 - x - 6}{x^2 + 2x - 15} \cdot \dfrac{x^2 - 25}{x^2 - 4x - 5} \div \dfrac{x^2 + 5x + 6}{x^2 - 1}$ $\dfrac{x - 1}{x + 3}$

14. $\dfrac{a^2 + 3a - 10}{a^2 + 3a - 18} \cdot \dfrac{a^2 - 3a}{a^2 - 2a} \div \dfrac{a^2 + 7a + 10}{a^2 + 5a - 6}$ $\dfrac{a - 1}{a + 2}$

15. $\dfrac{y^2 - yd - 2d^2}{10y + 5d} \cdot \dfrac{4y^2 - d^2}{3y - 6d} \div \dfrac{y^2 - d^2}{15y - 15d}$ $2y - d$

16. $\dfrac{s^2 - 2s}{s^2 - 3s - 4} \cdot \dfrac{s^2 + 2s + 1}{s^2 + 5s} \div \dfrac{s^2 - 4s - 5}{s^2 - 25}$ $\dfrac{s - 2}{s - 4}$

C 17. $\dfrac{x^2 - 4x + 3}{x^2} \div \dfrac{x^2 - 6x + 9}{x^2 + x} \div \dfrac{x^2 - 2x - 3}{x^2 - x - 6}$ $\dfrac{x^2 + x - 2}{x^2 - 3x}$

18. $\dfrac{a^2 + 11a + 18}{a^2 + 4a - 5} \div \dfrac{a^2 + 8a + 12}{a^2 - 6a - 7} \div \dfrac{a^2 - 7a - 8}{a^2 + 2a - 15}$ $\dfrac{(a + 9)(a - 7)(a - 3)}{(a - 1)(a + 6)(a - 8)}$

★ *Self-Test 2*

Express each as a fraction in lowest terms.

1. $\dfrac{4 + 6x}{x^2 - 1} \cdot \dfrac{x + 1}{8}$

2. $\dfrac{y^2 + 5y - 14}{y^2 - 4} \cdot \dfrac{y^2 + 6y + 8}{y^2 + 4y - 21}$ Objective 6-3, p. 205

3. $\dfrac{y^2 - 16}{y^4} \div \dfrac{y + 4}{y^4}$

4. $\dfrac{2x^2 + x - 1}{x^2 - x - 6} \div \dfrac{2x^2 - 7x + 3}{x^2 + x - 2}$ Objective 6-4, p. 208

5. $\dfrac{x + y}{4} \div \dfrac{x + y}{2}$

6. $\dfrac{a^2 - b^2}{b^4} \div (a + b)$

7. $\dfrac{x^2 - 4}{x + 2} \cdot \dfrac{y^4}{y^2 - 1} \div \dfrac{y^2}{y + 1}$

8. $\dfrac{3x - 3y}{x^2 + 2x + 1} \div \dfrac{6x - 6y}{x + 2} \cdot \dfrac{2(x + 1)}{x + 2}$ Objective 6-5, p. 211

Check your answers with those printed at the back of the book.

Consumer Note $$$$$$$$$$$$$$$$$$$$$$$$$$$$$$$$$$$$$
Estimating a Grocery Bill

You can estimate the cost of a number of grocery items by rounding (page 99) the cost of each to the nearest 10¢ and adding the rounded values.

Here is a computer program in BASIC that will help you to practice this kind of estimating. You may wish to start with only two or three items and work up to a larger number. That is, you might start with line 50 changed to:

50 FOR N=1 TO 2 or 50 FOR N=1 TO 3

```
10   PRINT "ROUND EACH NUMBER TO THE NEAREST TENTH."
20   PRINT "FIND THE SUM OF THE ROUNDED VALUES."
30   LET S=0
40   LET S1=0
50   FOR N=1 TO 5
60   LET A=INT(200*RND(1)+1)/100
70   PRINT A
80   LET S=S+A
90   LET A1=INT(10*A+.5)/10
100  LET S1=S1+A1
110  NEXT N
120  PRINT "WHAT IS YOUR ROUNDED SUM";
130  INPUT T
140  IF T=INT(10*S1+.5)/10 THEN 170
150  PRINT "MY ROUNDED SUM = ";S1
160  GOTO 180
170  PRINT "CORRECT!"
180  PRINT "ACTUAL SUM = ";S
190  END
```

You can estimate the result of any arithmetic computation by rounding the numbers involved and doing the operations on the rounded numbers. In some cases, you might want to round numbers to the nearest integers.

Sums and Mixed Expressions

6-6 Adding and Subtracting Fractions

> **OBJECTIVE** To learn how to add and subtract fractions.

Consider these sums:

$$\frac{3}{7} + \frac{2}{7}$$ $$\frac{a}{b} + \frac{c}{b}$$

By the rule for division (page 78):

$$\frac{3}{7} = 3\left(\frac{1}{7}\right) \text{ and } \frac{2}{7} = 2\left(\frac{1}{7}\right)$$ $$\frac{a}{b} = a\left(\frac{1}{b}\right) \text{ and } \frac{c}{b} = c\left(\frac{1}{b}\right)$$

By the distributive axiom:

$$3\left(\frac{1}{7}\right) + 2\left(\frac{1}{7}\right) = (3 + 2)\left(\frac{1}{7}\right)$$ $$a\left(\frac{1}{b}\right) + c\left(\frac{1}{b}\right) = (a + c)\left(\frac{1}{b}\right)$$

$$\therefore \frac{3}{7} + \frac{2}{7} = (3 + 2)\left(\frac{1}{7}\right)$$ $$\therefore \frac{a}{b} + \frac{c}{b} = (a + c)\left(\frac{1}{b}\right)$$

$$= \frac{3 + 2}{7} = \frac{5}{7}$$ $$= \frac{a + c}{b}$$

Similarly: $\frac{3}{7} - \frac{2}{7} = \frac{3 - 2}{7} = \frac{1}{7}$ $\qquad \frac{a}{b} - \frac{c}{b} = \frac{a - c}{b}$

These chains of equalities suggest the following theorem:

> **Rule for Adding and Subtracting Fractions
> with Equal Denominators**
>
> For any real numbers a and c and nonzero real number b:
>
> $$\frac{a}{b} + \frac{c}{b} = \frac{a + c}{b} \text{ and } \frac{a}{b} - \frac{c}{b} = \frac{a - c}{b}$$

Example 1 $\quad \dfrac{5}{17} + \dfrac{3}{17} - \dfrac{11}{17} = \dfrac{5 + 3 - 11}{17} = \dfrac{-3}{17} = -\dfrac{3}{17}$ *Answer*

Example 2
$$\frac{3xy}{x + 2y} + \frac{x^2 + y^2}{x + 2y} + \frac{y^2}{x + 2y} = \frac{3xy + x^2 + y^2 + y^2}{x + 2y}$$

$$= \frac{x^2 + 3xy + 2y^2}{x + 2y} = \frac{(x + y)(\overset{1}{\cancel{x + 2y}})}{\underset{1}{\cancel{(x + 2y)}}} = x + y \quad Answer$$

If the denominators are not equal, you use the multiplication property of fractions (page 197) to change the fractions so that the denominators will be equal. As a common denominator, you may use any positive integer having the denominators as factors.

Example 3 $\dfrac{2}{5} + \dfrac{7}{9} = \dfrac{2 \cdot 9}{5 \cdot 9} + \dfrac{7 \cdot 5}{9 \cdot 5} = \dfrac{18}{45} + \dfrac{35}{45} = \dfrac{18 + 35}{45} = \dfrac{53}{45}$ *Answer*

Example 4 $\dfrac{3}{8} - \dfrac{5}{12} = \dfrac{3 \cdot 12}{8 \cdot 12} - \dfrac{5 \cdot 8}{12 \cdot 8} = \dfrac{36 - 40}{96}$

$$= \frac{-4}{96} = \frac{-1}{24}, \text{ or } -\frac{1}{24} \quad Answer$$

However, for convenience you usually seek the **least common denominator** (L.C.D.). If the denominators have a common factor, the L.C.D. will be less than the product of the denominators.
    For example, to find the L.C.D. for

$$\frac{3}{8} \quad \text{and} \quad \frac{5}{12}$$

systematically, you write 8 and 12 as products of primes (page 140). Then you take each factor the greatest number of times it appears in any one denominator:

$$8 = \underbrace{2 \cdot 2 \cdot 2} \qquad 12 = 2 \cdot 2 \cdot \underbrace{3}$$

$$\therefore \text{ the L.C.D.} = 2 \cdot 2 \cdot 2 \cdot 3 = 24.$$

Then:
$$\frac{3}{8} - \frac{5}{12}$$

$$= \frac{3}{8} \cdot \frac{3}{3} - \frac{2}{2} \cdot \frac{5}{12} \qquad \boxed{\begin{array}{l} 24 \div 8 = 3 \\ 24 \div 12 = 2 \end{array}}$$

$$= \frac{9}{24} - \frac{10}{24} = \frac{-1}{24}$$

Example 5 Simplify $\dfrac{7}{12} + \dfrac{5}{18} - \dfrac{11}{30}$.

Solution To find the L.C.D., factor each denominator:

$$\left.\begin{array}{l} 12 = 2^2 \cdot 3 \\ 18 = 2 \cdot 3^2 \\ 30 = 2 \cdot 3 \cdot 5 \end{array}\right\} \quad \therefore \text{L.C.D.} = 2^2 \cdot 3^2 \cdot 5 = 4 \cdot 9 \cdot 5 = 180.$$

$$\frac{7}{12} + \frac{5}{18} - \frac{11}{30} = \frac{7}{12} \cdot \frac{15}{15} + \frac{5}{18} \cdot \frac{10}{10} - \frac{11}{30} \cdot \frac{6}{6}$$

$$= \frac{105 + 50 - 66}{180} = \frac{89}{180} \quad \textit{Answer}$$

Example 6 Simplify $\dfrac{6t - 3}{t^2 - 5t + 6} - \dfrac{5}{t - 3}$.

Solution To find the L.C.D., factor each denominator:

$$\left.\begin{array}{l} t^2 - 5t + 6 = (t - 3)(t - 2) \\ t - 3 = (t - 3) \end{array}\right\} \quad \therefore \text{L.C.D.} = (t - 3)(t - 2).$$

$$\frac{6t - 3}{(t - 3)(t - 2)} - \frac{5}{(t - 3)} = \frac{6t - 3}{(t - 3)(t - 2)} - \frac{5(t - 2)}{(t - 3)(t - 2)}$$

$$= \frac{(6t - 3) - 5(t - 2)}{(t - 3)(t - 2)} = \frac{6t - 3 - 5t + 10}{(t - 3)(t - 2)}$$

$$= \frac{t + 7}{t^2 - 5t + 6} \quad \textit{Answer}$$

Oral Exercises

Find the sum or difference, in lowest terms, for each expression.

1. $\dfrac{3}{10} + \dfrac{4}{10} \quad \dfrac{7}{10}$

2. $\dfrac{6}{13} + \dfrac{2}{13} \quad \dfrac{8}{13}$

3. $\dfrac{4}{7} - \dfrac{3}{7} \quad \dfrac{1}{7}$

4. $\dfrac{7}{2} - \dfrac{6}{2} \quad \dfrac{1}{2}$

5. $\dfrac{2}{x} - \dfrac{7}{x} \quad -\dfrac{5}{x}$

6. $\dfrac{7}{r} - \dfrac{3}{r} \quad \dfrac{4}{r}$

7. $\dfrac{x}{3y} + \dfrac{x}{3y} \quad \dfrac{2x}{3y}$

8. $\dfrac{a}{5b} + \dfrac{4a}{5b} \quad \dfrac{a}{b}$

9. $\dfrac{x}{6} + \dfrac{4y}{6} \quad \dfrac{x + 4y}{6}$

10. $\dfrac{h}{9} - \dfrac{3t}{9} \quad \dfrac{h - 3t}{9}$

11. $\dfrac{x + y}{3} - \dfrac{y}{3} \quad \dfrac{x}{3}$

12. $\dfrac{t - u}{4} + \dfrac{t}{4} \quad \dfrac{2t - u}{4}$

State the L.C.D. of the following denominators.

13. $2, 3$ 6 14. $4, 8$ 8 15. $2, x$ $2x$ 16. $5, y$ $5y$ 17. $13, 3$ 39 18. $10, 2$ 10

19. ab, ac abc 20. b^2d, bd b^2d 21. ab, bc, ac abc 22. x, y, xyz xyz 23. $a + b, b + a$ $a + b$ 24. $a - b, b - a$ $-(a - b)$

Written Exercises

Simplify. Check by assigning values to the variables.

A 1. $\dfrac{5}{19} + \dfrac{3}{19}$ $\dfrac{8}{19}$

2. $\dfrac{5}{27} + \dfrac{22}{27}$ 1

3. $\dfrac{3}{5} + \dfrac{3}{5} - \dfrac{4}{5}$ $\dfrac{2}{5}$

4. $\dfrac{3}{10} - \dfrac{2}{10} + \dfrac{7}{10}$ $\dfrac{4}{5}$

5. $\dfrac{5}{7x} - \dfrac{6}{7x} + \dfrac{1}{7x}$ 0

6. $\dfrac{8}{11z} + \dfrac{9}{11z} - \dfrac{18}{11z}$ $-\dfrac{1}{11z}$

7. $\dfrac{x + 3}{3} + \dfrac{2x - 1}{3}$ $\dfrac{3x + 2}{3}$

8. $\dfrac{2z}{7} + \dfrac{3z + 1}{7}$ $\dfrac{5z + 1}{7}$

9. $\dfrac{4c}{c + d} + \dfrac{4d}{c + d}$ 4

10. $\dfrac{a}{a - b} - \dfrac{b}{a - b}$ 1

11. $\dfrac{b^2}{b - c} - \dfrac{c^2}{b - c}$ $b + c$

12. $\dfrac{g^2}{g + 2} - \dfrac{4}{g + 2}$ $g - 2$

13. $7 + \dfrac{2}{3}$ $7\dfrac{2}{3}$

14. $8 - \dfrac{3}{5}$ $7\dfrac{2}{5}$

15. $\dfrac{3}{a} + \dfrac{1}{2}$ $\dfrac{6 + a}{2a}$

16. $\dfrac{1}{7} - \dfrac{a}{b}$ $\dfrac{b - 7a}{7b}$

17. $\dfrac{a + 2}{6} + \dfrac{2}{12}$ $\dfrac{a + 3}{6}$

18. $\dfrac{5}{11} - \dfrac{x + 1}{22}$ $\dfrac{9 - x}{22}$

19. $\dfrac{2x + 1}{4} - \dfrac{x - 1}{8}$ $\dfrac{3x + 3}{8}$

20. $\dfrac{a + 2b}{6} + \dfrac{a + b}{2}$ $\dfrac{4a + 5b}{6}$

21. $\dfrac{3a + 2b}{3b} - \dfrac{a + 2b}{6a}$

22. $\dfrac{2x - y}{2y} + \dfrac{x + y}{x}$ $\dfrac{2x^2 + xy + 2y^2}{2xy}$

23. $\dfrac{1}{x} + \dfrac{2}{x^2} - \dfrac{1}{x^3}$ $\dfrac{x^2 + 2x - 1}{x^3}$

24. $\dfrac{3}{a^3} - \dfrac{1}{a^2} + \dfrac{2}{a^3}$ $\dfrac{5 - a}{a^3}$

21. $\dfrac{6a^2 + 3ab - 2b^2}{6ab}$

B 25. $\dfrac{x + 1}{x + 2} - \dfrac{x + 2}{x + 3}$ $\dfrac{-1}{x^2 + 5x + 6}$

26. $\dfrac{y - 1}{y + 1} - \dfrac{y + 1}{y - 1}$ $\dfrac{-4y}{y^2 - 1}$

27. $\dfrac{2x}{x^2 - 5x + 6} + \dfrac{3}{x - 2}$ $\dfrac{5x - 9}{x^2 - 5x + 6}$

28. $\dfrac{2z - 3}{z^2 - 3z - 18} + \dfrac{2}{z - 6}$ $\dfrac{4z + 3}{z^2 - 3z - 18}$

29. $\dfrac{2a - 1}{12a^2} - \dfrac{3 - a}{2a} + \dfrac{a}{4}$ $\dfrac{3a^3 + 6a^2 - 16a - 1}{12a^2}$

30. $\dfrac{2}{16y^2} - \dfrac{y + 3}{8y} + \dfrac{y - 2}{2y}$ $\dfrac{3y^2 - 11y + 1}{8y^2}$

31. $\dfrac{1}{a^2 - a - 2} + \dfrac{1}{a^2 + 2a + 1}$

32. $\dfrac{8}{c^2 - 4} + \dfrac{2}{c^2 - 5c + 6}$ $\dfrac{10}{c^2 - c - 6}$

33. $\dfrac{3x}{x^2 + 3x + 2} - \dfrac{3x - 6}{x^2 + 4x + 4}$

34. $\dfrac{5}{a^2 - 25} + \dfrac{1}{a + 5} + \dfrac{a + 2}{5 - a}$ $\dfrac{-a^2 - 6a - 10}{a^2 - 25}$

C 35. $a - \dfrac{2a}{a^2 - 1} + \dfrac{3}{a + 1}$ $\dfrac{a^3 - 3}{a^2 - 1}$

36. $\dfrac{x}{x^2 - 16} + \dfrac{6}{4 - x} - \dfrac{1}{x - 4}$ $\dfrac{-6x - 28}{x^2 - 16}$

31. $\dfrac{2a - 1}{(a - 2)(a + 1)^2}$

33. $\dfrac{9x + 6}{(x + 2)^2(x + 1)}$

6-7 Mixed Expressions

> **OBJECTIVE** To learn how to change mixed expressions to fractions and fractions to mixed expressions.

A **mixed numeral** like $3\frac{2}{5}$ denotes the sum of an integer and a fraction. When you transform it into a fraction, you write the integer as a fraction with denominator 1 and add the fractions.

Example 1 $\quad 5\frac{3}{7} = \frac{5}{1} + \frac{3}{7} = \frac{35}{7} + \frac{3}{7} = \frac{38}{7} \qquad (-5\frac{3}{7} \text{ means } -(5 + \frac{3}{7}) \text{ or } -\frac{38}{7})$

The sum or difference of a polynomial and a fraction is called a **mixed expression**. A mixed expression can be written as a single fraction.

Example 2 $\quad x + \dfrac{3}{x} = \dfrac{x}{1} + \dfrac{3}{x} = \dfrac{x^2}{x} + \dfrac{3}{x} = \dfrac{x^2 + 3}{x}$

Example 3 $\quad 7 - \dfrac{2a - b}{a + b} = \dfrac{7}{1} - \dfrac{2a - b}{a + b} = \dfrac{7(a + b)}{a + b} - \dfrac{2a - b}{a + b}$

$$= \dfrac{7a + 7b - 2a + b}{a + b} = \dfrac{5a + 8b}{a + b}$$

You can change a fraction to a mixed expression by dividing.

Example 4 $\quad \dfrac{24}{5} = 4\dfrac{4}{5}$ $\qquad$ **Example 5** $\quad \dfrac{30t^2 - 7}{6t} = 5t - \dfrac{7}{6t}$

Oral Exercises

State each expression as a fraction in lowest terms.

1. $2\dfrac{1}{4}$ $\quad \dfrac{9}{4}$ $\qquad$ 2. $5\dfrac{1}{6}$ $\quad \dfrac{31}{6}$ $\qquad$ 3. $-1\dfrac{1}{5}$ $\quad -\dfrac{6}{5}$ $\qquad$ 4. $-7\dfrac{3}{8}$ $\quad -\dfrac{59}{8}$

5. $a + \dfrac{2}{b}$ $\quad \dfrac{ab + 2}{b}$ $\qquad$ 6. $3 - \dfrac{c}{d}$ $\quad \dfrac{3d - c}{d}$ $\qquad$ 7. $x - \dfrac{37}{5x}$ $\quad \dfrac{5x^2 - 37}{5x}$ $\qquad$ 8. $p + \dfrac{7}{2p}$ $\quad \dfrac{2p^2 + 7}{2p}$

9. $6 + \dfrac{y}{y + 1}$ $\quad \dfrac{7y + 6}{y + 1}$ $\qquad$ 10. $4 - \dfrac{a}{b - 1}$ $\quad \dfrac{4b - 4 - a}{b - 1}$ $\qquad$ 11. $8 + \dfrac{x}{y + z}$ $\quad \dfrac{8y + 8z + x}{y + z}$ $\qquad$ 12. $5 - \dfrac{ab}{a - b}$ $\quad \dfrac{5a - 5b - ab}{a - b}$

State each fraction as a mixed expression.

13. $\dfrac{b^2 - 2}{b}$ $b - \dfrac{2}{b}$

14. $\dfrac{c^3 + 7}{c}$ $c^2 + \dfrac{7}{c}$

15. $\dfrac{b^2 + 2b - 1}{b}$ $b + 2 - \dfrac{1}{b}$

16. $\dfrac{7t^2 + t - 3}{t}$ $7t + 1 - \dfrac{3}{t}$

Written Exercises

Answers on page A2 at the back of the book.
Express each mixed expression as a fraction in lowest terms.

A

1. $b + \dfrac{6}{b - 1}$

2. $a + \dfrac{2b}{b + a}$

3. $3 + \dfrac{a + 2b}{a - b}$

4. $10 + \dfrac{2a - 3b}{a + b}$

5. $x - y + \dfrac{1}{x + y}$

6. $h + 1 - \dfrac{1}{h - 1}$

7. $\dfrac{5}{x + 2} + 1$

8. $\dfrac{3}{m - 2} - 1$

9. $7 + \dfrac{3}{a} + \dfrac{6}{b}$

10. $\dfrac{m}{n} + 3 + \dfrac{n}{m}$

11. $d + 3 + \dfrac{2d - 1}{d - 2}$

12. $h + 2 - \dfrac{h + 1}{h - 1}$

Change each fraction to a mixed expression.

13. $\dfrac{17}{3}$ $5\dfrac{2}{3}$

14. $\dfrac{129}{12}$ $10\dfrac{3}{4}$

15. $\dfrac{21 + 14a^2}{7}$ $3 + 2a^2$

16. $\dfrac{6 + 8b^2}{2b}$ $\dfrac{3}{b} + 4b$

17. $\dfrac{10a^3 - 3}{5a^2}$ $2a - \dfrac{3}{5a^2}$

18. $\dfrac{22x^4 - 33x}{11x^2}$ $2x^2 - \dfrac{3}{x}$

19. $\dfrac{16c^2d^2 + 12cd}{16cd}$ $cd + \dfrac{3}{4}$

20. $\dfrac{20xy^2 + 10x}{2xy}$ $10y + \dfrac{5}{y}$

Just for Fun

1, 3, 6, 10, 15, . . . are called triangular numbers because they can be represented by dots arranged to form triangles:

   1   3   6   10   15   and so on

Note that: $1 + 2 = 3$
                $1 + 2 + 3 = 6$
                $1 + 2 + 3 + 4 = 10$
                $1 + 2 + 3 + 4 + 5 = 15$

1. Find and draw diagrams for the next five triangular numbers.   21, 28, 36, 45, 55

2. If n represents the number of the triangular number in the list ($n = 1$ for 1, $n = 2$ for 3, and so on), verify for the first ten triangular numbers that

the nth triangular number $= \dfrac{n(n + 1)}{2}$. $\dfrac{1(1 + 1)}{2} = 1$; $\dfrac{2(2 + 1)}{2} = 3$; $\dfrac{3(3 + 1)}{2} = 6$;

$\dfrac{4(4 + 1)}{2} = 10$; $\dfrac{5(5 + 1)}{2} = 15$; $\dfrac{6(6 + 1)}{2} = 21$; $\dfrac{7(7 + 1)}{2} = 28$; $\dfrac{8(8 + 1)}{2} = 36$;

$\dfrac{9(9 + 1)}{2} = 45$; $\dfrac{10(10 + 1)}{2} = 55$

6-8 Dividing a Polynomial by a Polynomial

OBJECTIVE To learn how to divide a polynomial by a polynomial.

Compare these divisions:

Step 1
$$16\overline{)375}$$
with quotient 2, 320, remainder 55

Step 1
$$2x+1\overline{)6x^2+7x+5}$$
with quotient $3x$, $6x^2+3x$, remainder $4x+5$

Step 2
$$16\overline{)375}$$
with quotient 23, 320, 55, 48, $7 \longleftarrow$ Remainder

Step 2
$$2x+1\overline{)6x^2+7x+5}$$
with quotient $3x+2$, $6x^2+3x$, $4x+5$, $4x+2$, $3 \longleftarrow$ Remainder

Thus: $\dfrac{375}{16} = 23\dfrac{7}{16}$

Thus: $\dfrac{6x^2+7x+5}{2x+1} = 3x+2+\dfrac{3}{2x+1}$

In both cases:

$$\frac{\text{Dividend}}{\text{Divisor}} = \text{Quotient} + \frac{\text{Remainder}}{\text{Divisor}}$$

or

$$\text{Dividend} = \text{Quotient} \times \text{Divisor} + \text{Remainder}$$

You use the second equation to check a division exercise. If the remainder is zero, the divisor and quotient are factors of the dividend.

When you divide polynomials, write the terms of the divisor and dividend in order of *decreasing* degree in a chosen variable.

Example 1 Divide $12x^2 - x - 6$ by $2 + 3x$.

Solution

$$\begin{array}{r} 4x - 3 \\ 3x + 2 \overline{)12x^2 - x - 6} \\ 12x^2 + 8x \\ \hline -9x - 6 \\ -9x - 6 \\ \hline 0 \end{array}$$

$$\frac{12x^2 - x - 6}{3x + 2} = 4x - 3$$

Check: $(3x + 2)(4x - 3) = 12x^2 - x - 6$ ✓

In Example 1, the remainder is zero, and so $3x + 2$ and $4x - 3$ are factors of $12x^2 - x - 6$.

Example 2 shows how to insert missing terms by using 0 as a coefficient.

Example 2 $t^2 + 2t - 3 \overline{)t^3 + 1}$

Solution

$$\begin{array}{r} t - 2 \\ t^2 + 2t - 3 \overline{)t^3 + 0t^2 + 0t + 1} \\ t^3 + 2t^2 - 3t \\ \hline -2t^2 + 3t + 1 \\ -2t^2 - 4t + 6 \\ \hline 7t - 5 \end{array}$$

$$\frac{t^3 + 1}{t^2 + 2t - 3} = t - 2 + \frac{7t - 5}{t^2 + 2t - 3}$$

Check: $(t - 2)(t^2 + 2t - 3) + (7t - 5) = t^3 + 1$ ✓

The division process ends when the remainder is 0 or the degree of the remainder is less than that of the divisor.

Written Exercises

Write each quotient as a polynomial or a mixed expression. Check.

A 1. $\dfrac{x^2 + 4x + 3}{x + 1}$ $x + 3$

2. $\dfrac{t^2 - 3t + 2}{t - 1}$ $t - 2$

3. $\dfrac{u^2 - 6u + 8}{u - 2}$ $u - 4$

4. $\dfrac{y^2 + 4y + 3}{y + 3}$ $y + 1$

5. $\dfrac{s^2 + 3s - 4}{4 + s}$ $s - 1$

6. $\dfrac{z^2 + 3z - 10}{5 + z}$ $z - 2$

7. $\dfrac{a^2 + 2a + 3}{a + 3}$ $a - 1 + \dfrac{6}{a + 3}$

8. $\dfrac{v^2 + 3v + 4}{v + 1}$ $v + 2 + \dfrac{2}{v + 1}$

Answers to Exs. 9–24 on page A3 at the back of the book.

9. $\dfrac{7 - 4x + x^2}{x - 3}$ 10. $\dfrac{1 - 3r + r^2}{r - 4}$ 11. $\dfrac{t^2 - 16}{t + 4}$ 12. $\dfrac{m^2 - 25}{m - 5}$

13. $\dfrac{x^2 + 4}{x - 2}$ 14. $\dfrac{d^2 + 12}{d + 3}$ 15. $\dfrac{2x^2 - 5x - 2}{2x + 1}$ 16. $\dfrac{3c^2 + 8c + 4}{3c + 2}$

17. $\dfrac{6r^2 + r - 5}{2r - 3}$ 18. $\dfrac{6a^2 + 4a + 3}{3a - 1}$ 19. $\dfrac{9t^2 + 1}{3t + 2}$ 20. $\dfrac{4s^2 + 1}{2s + 1}$

21. $\dfrac{6x^2 + ax - 2a^2}{2x + a}$ 22. $\dfrac{2u^2 - 3uv - 9v^2}{u - 3v}$ 23. $\dfrac{3s^2 + 2st - 6t^2}{s + 2t}$ 24. $\dfrac{6c^2 - ac + a^2}{2c + a}$

B 25. $\dfrac{x^3 - a^3}{x - a}$ $\quad x^2 + ax + a^2$ 26. $\dfrac{x^3 + a^3}{x + a}$ $\quad x^2 - ax + a^2$ 27. $\dfrac{z^3 + z^2 - 3z + 9}{z + 3}$ $\quad z^2 - 2z$

28. $\dfrac{r^3 - 19r + 12}{r - 4}$ $\quad r^2 + 4r - 3$ 29. $\dfrac{6x^3 + 5x^2 + 9}{2x + 3}$ $\quad 3x^2 - 2x + 3$ 30. $\dfrac{6s^3 - 8s^2 - 7s + 2}{3s - 1}$

31. $\dfrac{2y^3 + 5y^2 + 7y + 6}{y^2 + y + 2}$ $\quad 2y + 3$ 32. $\dfrac{3u^3 - 4u^2 + 2u + 4}{u^2 - 2u + 2}$ $\quad 3u + 2$ 33. $\dfrac{t^4 - 2t^3 + 6t + 9}{t^2 - 3}$

34. $\dfrac{z^4 - 2z^3 - 4z - 4}{z^2 - 2z - 2}$ $\quad z^2 + 2$

30. $2s^2 - 2s - 3 - \dfrac{1}{3s - 1}$

35. One factor of $a^6 - 1$ is $a^2 - 1$. Find the other factor. $\quad a^4 + a^2 + 1$ 33. $t^2 - 2t + 3 + \dfrac{18}{t^2 - 3}$

36. One factor of $3x^3 + 2x^2 + 2x - 1$ is $3x - 1$. Find the other factor. $\quad x^2 + x + 1$

C 37. Find the number c for which $x + 2$ is a factor of $2x^2 + x + c$. $\quad c = -6$

38. Find the number c for which $3x - 2$ is a factor of $6x^2 - 10x + c$. $\quad c = 4$

Just for Fun

Recall (page 219) that the triangular numbers are:

$$1,\ 3,\ 6,\ 10,\ 15,\ \text{and so on}$$

The square numbers are:

$$1,\ 4,\ 9,\ 16,\ 25,\ \text{and so on}$$

1. Verify that each square number from 4 to 100 is the sum of two consecutive triangular numbers. *(below)*

2. Illustrate Exercise 1 by dividing the square array of dots shown at the right into two triangular arrays.

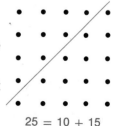

1. $4 = 1 + 3$; $9 = 3 + 6$; $16 = 6 + 10$; $25 = 10 + 15$; $36 = 15 + 21$;
$49 = 21 + 28$; $64 = 28 + 36$; $81 = 36 + 45$; $100 = 45 + 55$

$25 = 10 + 15$

★ *Self-Test 3*

Be sure that you understand these terms:

least common denominator (p. 215)   mixed numeral (p. 218)
mixed expression (p. 218)

Write each as a fraction in lowest terms.

1. $\dfrac{12}{7x} + \dfrac{x-1}{7x}$ 2. $\dfrac{2x}{x-y} - \dfrac{x+2y}{x-y}$ Objective 6-6, p. 214

3. $\dfrac{5}{x^2-4} + \dfrac{3}{x-2}$ 4. $\dfrac{9}{x^2-x-2} + \dfrac{6}{x^2+2x+1}$

5. $8 + \dfrac{2a-7b}{a+b}$ 6. $\dfrac{11}{y-3} - 13$ Objective 6-7, p. 218

7. Divide $4x^2 + 4x - 15$ by $2x - 3$.   Objective 6-8, p. 220

Check your answers with those printed at the back of the book.

Historical Note
An Ancient Equation

Equations have been used for thousands of years. We know something about the equations used by the ancient Egyptians from manuscripts that have been preserved from about 1900 B.C. One problem is:

> A quantity and its $\frac{1}{5}$ added together become 21.
> What is the quantity?

You can write the equation

$$x + \tfrac{1}{5}x = 21$$

and solve it by the methods you have studied. However, the Egyptians used a proportion to solve it (although they did not write it the way we do):

Let $x = 5$.
Then $5 + 1 = 6$. But the sum is to be 21.
Therefore, the correct value of x can be found from:

$$\frac{x}{5} = \frac{21}{6}$$

$$x = \frac{5}{2} \cdot 7 = \frac{35}{2} = 17\frac{1}{2}$$

Compare this solution with the one you used.

Fractions and Equations

6-9 Solving Equations with Fractional Coefficients

> **OBJECTIVE** To learn how to solve equations in which the numerical coefficients are fractions.

To solve an equation in which the coefficients are fractions, begin by multiplying both members by the L.C.D. of the fractions.

Example 1 Solve $\frac{1}{5}x - \frac{2}{3}x + \frac{3}{10}x = 1$.

Solution The L.C.D. is 30.

$$30\left(\frac{1}{5}x - \frac{2}{3}x + \frac{3}{10}x\right) = 30(1)$$
$$6x - 20x + 9x = 30$$
$$-5x = 30$$
$$x = -6$$

The check is left to you.
The solution is -6. *Answer*
$\frac{1}{5}(-6) - \frac{2}{3}(-6) + \frac{3}{10}(-6) = -\frac{6}{5} + 4 - \frac{9}{5} = 1 \checkmark$

Example 2 Solve $\frac{x}{6} - \frac{20 - x}{8} = 1$.

Solution The L.C.D. is 24.

$$24\left(\frac{x}{6} - \frac{20 - x}{8}\right) = 24(1)$$
$$4x - 3(20 - x) = 24$$
$$4x - 60 + 3x = 24$$
$$7x = 84$$
$$x = 12$$

The check is left to you.
The solution is 12. *Answer*
$\frac{12}{6} - \frac{20 - 12}{8} = 2 - 1 = 1 \checkmark$

Example 3 Solve $0.14x + 0.25(100 - x) = 36$.

Solution The L.C.D. is 100. Multiply both members by 100.

$$14x + 25(100 - x) = 3600$$

Complete the solution and check your result.
$$14x + 2500 - 25x = 3600$$
$$-11x = 1100$$
$$x = -100$$
$$0.14(-100) + 0.25(100 + 100) = -14 + 50 = 36$$

Written Exercises

Solve.

A 1. $\frac{x}{2} + \frac{x}{4} = 3$ 4

2. $\frac{a}{3} - \frac{a}{9} = 2$ 9

3. $\frac{5b}{6} - b = \frac{4}{6}$ -4

4. $\dfrac{7d}{10} - \dfrac{d}{5} = \dfrac{3}{2}$ 3

5. $\dfrac{6}{7}y - \dfrac{1}{2}y = 5$ 14

6. $\dfrac{2}{3}x - \dfrac{5}{9}x = -1$ −9

7. $0.04b - 0.01b = 0.3$ 10

8. $0.7a - 0.2a = 2.5$ 5

9. $\dfrac{2}{5}x - \dfrac{3}{4}x = \dfrac{1}{20}$ $-\dfrac{1}{7}$

10. $\dfrac{1}{3}z + \dfrac{2}{5}z = \dfrac{11}{15}$ 1

11. $\dfrac{3}{4}b - \dfrac{5}{8}b = \dfrac{1}{2}$ 4

12. $\dfrac{5}{12}c = \dfrac{2}{3} + \dfrac{1}{3}c$ 8

B 13. $\dfrac{d}{3} = \dfrac{5 - d}{4}$ $\dfrac{15}{7}$

14. $\dfrac{4r - 3}{7} = 3$ 6

15. $\dfrac{y + 2}{2} = \dfrac{2y}{3}$ 6

16. $\dfrac{2x - 1}{5} = \dfrac{x + 1}{2}$ −7

17. $\dfrac{x + 1}{5} - \dfrac{3}{2} = \dfrac{3x - 6}{10}$ −7

18. $\dfrac{a}{7} - \dfrac{12 + a}{8} = 1$ 140

19. $\dfrac{2x - 15}{6} = \dfrac{x}{9} + \dfrac{3x}{4}$ $-\dfrac{90}{19}$

20. $\dfrac{5x - 1}{2} + \dfrac{2x + 4}{4} = 8$ $\dfrac{5}{2}$

21. $\dfrac{1}{2}(2x - 3) - \dfrac{2}{5}(x + 1) = \dfrac{1}{10}$ $\dfrac{10}{3}$

22. $\dfrac{1}{3}(x - 2) + \dfrac{3}{5}(x + 9) = \dfrac{14}{15}$ $-\dfrac{57}{14}$

23. $0.08x + 0.12(10{,}000 - x) = 960$ 6000

24. $0.04x + 0.03(1000 - x) = 20$ −1000

C 25. $\dfrac{2x + 5}{15} - \dfrac{x - 2}{9} = \dfrac{4x + 1}{3} - x$ $\dfrac{5}{7}$

26. $y + \dfrac{3y - 5}{7} + \dfrac{5y - 1}{3} = 20$ $6\dfrac{4}{5}$

27. $\dfrac{3t}{4} - \dfrac{t + 1}{2} = \dfrac{5t - 5}{3}$ $\dfrac{14}{17}$

28. $\dfrac{2x}{5} - \dfrac{x + 2}{2} = 13 - \dfrac{4x - 1}{7}$ 30

29. $0.10x - 0.01(x - 2) = 0.02x - 0.04(x - 6)$ 2

30. $0.06y - 0.03(3 - y) = 0.06 - 0.03(y + 2)$ $\dfrac{3}{4}$

Puzzle Time

Diophantus was a famous Greek mathematician, who lived and worked in Alexandria, Egypt, probably in the third century A.D. After he died, someone described his life in this puzzle:

> He was a boy for $\frac{1}{6}$ of his life.
> After $\frac{1}{12}$ more, he acquired a beard.
> After another $\frac{1}{7}$, he married.
> In the fifth year after his marriage
>   his son was born.
> The son lived half as many years as
>   his father.
> Diophantus died 4 years after his son.

How old was Diophantus when he died? Write an equation and solve it.

If $x =$ his age at death, then $\frac{1}{6}x + \frac{1}{12}x + \frac{1}{7}x + 5 + \frac{1}{2}x + 4 = x$; $x = 84$, so he was 84 years old at death.

6-10 Fractional Equations

> **OBJECTIVE** To learn how to solve fractional equations.

An equation which has a variable in the denominator of one or more terms is called a **fractional equation.**

Example Solve $\dfrac{2}{x^2 - x} - \dfrac{2}{x - 1} = 1$.

Solution Factor the denominators: $\dfrac{2}{x(x - 1)} - \dfrac{2}{x - 1} = 1$.

$$\text{L.C.D.} = x(x - 1); \ x \neq 0, \ x \neq 1$$

$$x(x - 1)\left(\frac{2}{x(x - 1)}\right) - x(x - 1)\left(\frac{2}{x - 1}\right) = x(x - 1)(1)$$

$$2 - 2x = x(x - 1)$$
$$2 - 2x = x^2 - x$$
$$0 = x^2 + x - 2$$
$$0 = (x + 2)(x - 1)$$
$$x = -2 \text{ or } x = 1$$

1 is excluded above; thus it is not a root of the original equation.

Now check -2 in the original equation:

$$\frac{2}{(-2)^2 - (-2)} - \frac{2}{-2 - 1} \overset{?}{=} 1$$

$$\frac{2}{4 + 2} - \frac{2}{-3} \overset{?}{=} 1$$

$$\frac{2}{6} + \frac{2}{3} \overset{?}{=} 1$$

$$\frac{1}{3} + \frac{2}{3} \overset{?}{=} 1$$

$$1 = 1 \ \checkmark$$

$\therefore$ the solution is -2. *Answer*

In the preceding Example, notice that multiplying the equation by $x(x - 1)$ led to an equation that was *not equivalent* to the given one. This new equation had the extra root 1, a number for which the multiplier $x(x - 1)$ represents *zero*.

Caution: Multiplying an equation by a variable expression which can represent zero may produce an equation having roots not satisfying the original equation. **Only values producing true statements when substituted in the original equation belong to the solution set.**

Written Exercises

Solve.

A 1. $\dfrac{18}{x} = \dfrac{3 + 3x}{x}$ 5

2. $\dfrac{1 + m}{m} = \dfrac{3}{m}$ 2

3. $\dfrac{n - 1}{n} - \dfrac{5}{3n} = \dfrac{1}{4}$ $3\dfrac{5}{9}$

4. $\dfrac{4}{5b} + \dfrac{b - 2}{b} = -\dfrac{1}{5}$ 1

5. $\dfrac{a}{a + 3} = \dfrac{2}{5}$ 2

6. $\dfrac{d}{d - 2} = \dfrac{4}{3}$ 8

7. $\dfrac{6 - x}{6x} = \dfrac{1}{x + 1}$ $-3, 2$

8. $\dfrac{x - 3}{4x} = \dfrac{2}{x + 3}$ 9, -1

9. $\dfrac{6y}{2y + 1} - \dfrac{3}{y} = -1 - \dfrac{3}{8}$ 1

10. $\dfrac{7}{x} - \dfrac{4x}{2x - 3} = -2$ $2\dfrac{5}{8}$

11. $\dfrac{1}{a^2 - a} = \dfrac{3}{a} - 1$ 2

12. $2 + \dfrac{4}{b - 1} = \dfrac{4}{b^2 - b}$ -2

B 13. $\dfrac{x}{x - 2} = \dfrac{2}{x - 2} + 3$ no solution

14. $\dfrac{r}{r - 2} - \dfrac{2}{r - 2} = 2$ no solution

15. $\dfrac{2x - 3}{x - 3} - 2 = \dfrac{12}{x + 3}$ 5

16. $\dfrac{2r - 5}{r - 2} - 2 = \dfrac{3}{r + 2}$ 1

17. $\dfrac{z + 3}{z - 1} + \dfrac{z + 1}{z - 3} = 2$ 2

18. $\dfrac{x + 2}{x - 2} - \dfrac{2}{x + 2} = -\dfrac{7}{3}$ $\dfrac{2}{5}, -1$

C 19. $\dfrac{1}{c - 4} + \dfrac{2}{c^2 - 16} = \dfrac{3}{c + 4}$ 9

20. $\dfrac{a + 3}{a^2 - 1} + \dfrac{a - 3}{a^2 - a} = \dfrac{2a}{a^2 + a}$

21. $\dfrac{8}{h - 1} + \dfrac{30}{1 - h^2} = \dfrac{6}{h + 1}$ 8

22. $\dfrac{b}{b + 1} - \dfrac{b + 1}{b - 4} = \dfrac{5}{b^2 - 3b - 4}$

20. and 22. no solution

23. $\dfrac{x - 4}{2x^2 + 5x - 3} = \dfrac{4x - 1}{4x^2 + 13x + 3} - \dfrac{2x + 7}{8x^2 - 2x - 1}$ 4, -2

24. $\dfrac{2x}{2x^2 + 5x + 2} = \dfrac{3x}{3x^2 + 7x + 2} - \dfrac{3x + 2}{6x^2 + 5x + 1}$ $-\dfrac{4}{3}, -1$

6-11 Ratios and Percents; Proportions

OBJECTIVE To learn how to solve problems involving percents.

The ratio of one number to another is often expressed as a *percent*. Percent is a notation for a ratio with the denominator 100. For example,

$\dfrac{25}{100}$ is called "25 percent" and written 25%.

Example 1 Express the ratio $\dfrac{3}{4}$ as a percent.

Solution Write the equation: $\dfrac{3}{4} = \dfrac{r}{100}$

and solve for r: $\qquad r = \dfrac{3}{4} \cdot 100 = 75$

Check: $\dfrac{\overset{3}{\cancel{75}}}{\underset{4}{\cancel{100}}} = \dfrac{3}{4} \checkmark$

$\therefore \dfrac{3}{4} = \dfrac{75}{100}$ or 75%. **Answer**

An equation stating that two ratios are equal is called a **proportion.**

Example 2 Find 25% of $240.

Solution Let P = the desired portion.

Then: $\qquad \dfrac{P}{240} = \dfrac{25}{100}$

$P = \dfrac{25}{100} \cdot 240 = \dfrac{1}{4} \cdot 240 = 60$

$\therefore$ 25% of $240 is $60. **Answer**

Example 3 If 20% of a number is 32, what is the number?

Solution Let B = the desired number.

$$\frac{32}{B} = \frac{20}{100}$$

$$20B = 3200$$

$$B = 160$$

∴ 32 is 20% of 160. *Answer*

The proportions used in Examples 1–3 can be combined into a formula as follows:

$$\frac{P}{B} = \frac{r}{100}$$

If we use R for $\dfrac{r}{100}$, we have the formula

$$\frac{P}{B} = R$$

or

$$P = RB.$$

The number B is called the **base,** R is called the **rate,** and the number P is called the **percentage.** Thus:

Percentage = Rate × Base

$$P = RB$$

Percents may also be written as decimals. For example:

$$1\% = \frac{1}{100} = 0.01 \qquad 56\% = 0.56$$

$$100\% = 1 \qquad 115\% = 1.15$$

Example 4 How much money did Dr. Stevens save if she purchased an $840 microscope at a discount of 30%?

Solution

Step 1 The problem asks for the amount of the discount.

Step 2 Let P = the amount of the discount.

Step 3 $P = RB$ or $\dfrac{P}{B} = \dfrac{r}{100}$

$\qquad R = 30\% = 0.3 \qquad\qquad r = 30$

$\qquad B = 840 \qquad\qquad\qquad B = 840$

$\qquad P = 0.3(840) \quad$ or $\quad \dfrac{P}{840} = \dfrac{30}{100}$

Steps 4–5 Complete the solution and check. $\quad P = 252$; she saved \$252.

$$\frac{252}{840} = \frac{3}{10} = \frac{30}{100}\ \checkmark$$

Written Exercises

Copy and complete this table.

Sample 1 Change $12\frac{1}{2}\%$ to a fraction. **Sample 2** Change $\frac{1}{3}$ to a percent.

Solution $\quad \dfrac{12\frac{1}{2}}{100} = \dfrac{25}{2} \times \dfrac{1}{100}$ $\qquad\qquad$ *Solution* $\quad \dfrac{1}{3} = \dfrac{r}{100}; r = \dfrac{100}{3} = 33\frac{1}{3}$

$\qquad\qquad = \dfrac{25}{200} = \dfrac{1}{8}$ *Answer* $\qquad\qquad \therefore \frac{1}{3} = 33\frac{1}{3}\%.$ *Answer*

A

	Fraction	Percent	Decimal
1.	$\frac{1}{100}$	? 1%	? 0.01
2.	? $\frac{1}{50}$	2%	? 0.02
3.	? $\frac{1}{25}$	? 4%	0.04
4.	$\frac{1}{50}$	? 2%	? 0.02
5.	? $\frac{1}{10}$	10%	? 0.1
	$\frac{1}{8}$	$12\frac{1}{2}\%$	0.125
6.	? $\frac{1}{6}$	? $16\frac{2}{3}\%$	$0.16\frac{2}{3}$
7.	$\frac{1}{5}$	? 20%	? 0.2
8.	? $\frac{1}{4}$	25%	? 0.25

	Fraction	Percent	Decimal
	$\frac{1}{3}$	$33\frac{1}{3}\%$	$0.33\frac{1}{3}$
9.	? $\frac{1}{2}$	? 50%	0.5
10.	$\frac{2}{3}$	? $66\frac{2}{3}\%$	? ← $0.66\frac{2}{3}$
11.	? $\frac{3}{4}$	75%	? 0.75
12.	? $\frac{4}{5}$	? 80%	0.8
13.	$\frac{5}{6}$	? $83\frac{1}{3}\%$	? ← $0.83\frac{1}{3}$
14.	? $\frac{7}{8}$	$87\frac{1}{2}\%$	? ← $0.87\frac{1}{2}$
15.	? $\frac{9}{10}$	? 90%	0.9
16.	$\frac{19}{20}$	? 95%	? 0.95

Problems

Solve.

A

1. Out of 1250 persons surveyed, 32% felt that the most serious problem facing the world today is environmental pollution. How many people gave this reply? **400 people**

2. If the sightseeing boat, Merry II, was filled to 75% of capacity, how many of the 160 seats were occupied? **120 seats**

3. How many minutes of an hour's TV special are taken up by commercials if 16% of the program is allotted to commercials? **9.6 min**

4. A jacket, which had an original cost of $32, is being offered at a 20% discount. Find the amount of the discount. **$6.40**

5. The extra equipment on a new car cost $330. If this represents 11% of the price of the car, what was the price of the car? **$3000**

6. When the United Fund Drive at Washington High School had received $819, it had reached 65% of its goal. What was its goal? **$1260**

7. The Mantz Company has 78 female employees, which represents 52% of the total work force of the company. How many employees does the company have? **150 employees**

8. A real estate broker receives a commission of 15% for selling a house. If she received $3750 as commission for a sale, what was the price of the house? **$25,000**

9. If 160 kilograms of an alloy contain 76.8 kilograms of copper, what percent of the alloy is copper? **48%**

10. The sales tax on $320 is $19.20. What is the rate of sales tax? **6%**

11. Gil Garcia receives $850 per month as salary. If she pays $153 rent each month, what percent of her salary is spent for rent? **18%**

12. The list price of a typewriter is $140. If a discount of $10.50 is given for cash, what percent of the list price is the discount? **7.5%**

B

13. The price of one share of Alcron Trucking Company stock rose from $55.20 to $57.96. By what percent of the first price did the price of the stock increase? **5%**

14. An article is marked $36 and a 16% discount on that price is given. What profit is made if the article cost $15? **$15.24**

15. In an election, 10% of the voters voted for candidate Smith, 30% for candidate Sims, 20% for candidate Holsom, and the remaining 120 voted for candidate Field. How many votes were cast in all? **300 votes**

16. A dealer pays $180 for a TV set. She has overhead totaling 10% of the selling price and wishes to make 35% profit on the selling price. What price should she charge for the set? **$327.27**

C

17. A customer received a 20% discount on a suit during a sale. He also received a 4% discount on the sale price for paying cash. If he paid $80.25 for the suit, what was the regular price of the suit? **$104.49**

18. In a mental arithmetic contest, 40% of the contestants were eliminated the first day. Of those remaining, $14\frac{2}{7}$% won prizes. If 12 prizes were awarded, how many students had entered the contest? **140 students**

Career Note
Pharmacist

The primary responsibility of a pharmacist is to prepare and dispense medicine prescribed by doctors. Pharmacists are experts in the use, composition, and effect of drugs. Occasionally, they are required to "compound" or mix ingredients for a prescription, but most medicines are now prepared by manufacturers rather than by pharmacists.

Many pharmacies offer more than medical and health supplies. An individual owning such a pharmacy orders and sells merchandise, supervises personnel, and handles the finances of the business.

At least five years of study beyond high school are required to graduate from a college of pharmacy. During the first few years of study, mathematics and basic science courses are emphasized.

 Self-Test 4

Be sure that you understand these terms:

fractional equation (p. 226) proportion (p. 228)

Solve.

1. $\dfrac{r}{8} = \dfrac{r}{12} + \dfrac{1}{3}$

2. $\dfrac{x + 1}{6} = \dfrac{x + 2}{9}$ Objective 6-9, p. 224

3. $\dfrac{1}{4}(x - 1) + \dfrac{3}{5}(x + 2) = \dfrac{7}{20}$

4. $\dfrac{5}{x} + 3 = 8$

5. $\dfrac{6}{y + 3} = \dfrac{10}{y}$ Objective 6-10, p. 226

6. $\dfrac{s}{s - 1} = \dfrac{3}{s - 1} + 4$

7. $\dfrac{6}{3a} + \dfrac{3}{3a + 1} = -6$

8. What percent of 900 is 3? Objective 6-11, p. 228

9. A pair of slacks, which had an original price of $27, is being offered at a 15% discount. Find the amount of the discount.

Check your answers with those printed at the back of the book.

Mid-Chapter Test

Write in lowest terms.

6-1 1. $\dfrac{a^2 - 3a - 10}{a^2 + 4a + 4}$ $\dfrac{a - 5}{a + 2}$ 2. $\dfrac{3x^2 - 27}{3x^2 + 18x + 27}$ $\dfrac{x - 3}{x + 3}$

6-2 3. Give the ratio of 4 months to 1 year in lowest terms. 1:3

Express the product as a fraction in lowest terms.

6-3 4. $\dfrac{2m}{n} \cdot \dfrac{mn}{8m^2}$ $\dfrac{1}{4}$ 5. $\dfrac{a^2 - 4b^2}{ab + b^2} \cdot \dfrac{2b}{3a + 6b}$ $\dfrac{2a - 4b}{3a + 3b}$

Simplify.

6-4 6. $\dfrac{5z + 10}{8} \div \dfrac{5}{2z + 2}$ $\dfrac{z^2 + 3z + 2}{4}$ 7. $\dfrac{x^2 - x - 12}{x^2 - 1} \div \dfrac{x^2 + 8x + 15}{x^2 + 2x + 1}$ $\dfrac{x^2 - 3x - 4}{x^2 + 4x - 5}$

6-5 8. $\dfrac{a^2 - 9}{b} \cdot \dfrac{b^2}{a + 3} \div \dfrac{a - 2}{b}$ $\dfrac{ab^2 - 3b^2}{a - 2}$

6-6 9. $\dfrac{x + 3}{2} + \dfrac{x - 1}{3}$ $\dfrac{5x + 7}{6}$ 10. $\dfrac{x + 2y}{2x} - \dfrac{3x + y}{4y}$ $\dfrac{-3x^2 + xy + 4y^2}{4xy}$

Express as a fraction in lowest terms.

6-7 11. $c + \dfrac{5}{c + 2}$ $\dfrac{c^2 + 2c + 5}{c + 2}$ 12. $\dfrac{a}{b} + 1 + \dfrac{a}{a + b}$ $\dfrac{a^2 + 3ab + b^2}{ab + b^2}$

Write the quotient as a polynomial or mixed expression.

6-8 13. $\dfrac{2x^2 + 13x + 15}{x + 5}$ $2x + 3$ 14. $\dfrac{6z^2 + 5z - 4}{2z - 1}$ $3z + 4$

Solve.

6-9 15. $\dfrac{a}{2} + \dfrac{a}{6} = 2$ 3   16. $\dfrac{3m}{4} - \dfrac{2m}{3} = 1$ 12

6-10 17. $\dfrac{d - 2}{d} = \dfrac{1}{d}$ 3   18. $\dfrac{y}{3y + 2} + \dfrac{2}{y} = -1$ -1

6-11 19. Change $\dfrac{17}{20}$ to a percent.   20. Change $62\frac{1}{2}\%$ to a fraction. $\dfrac{5}{8}$
     85%

Looking Ahead

You have now learned the methods of operating with fractions in algebra and of solving fractional equations. In the remaining sections of this chapter, you will learn how to apply these skills to problem solving.

Applications of Fractions

6-12 Percent-Mixture Problems

> **OBJECTIVE** To learn how to solve percent-mixture problems.

Example How many grams of a 55% acid solution must be added to 20 grams of a 10% acid solution to produce a 50% acid solution?

Solution

Step 1 The problem asks for the number of grams of 55% solution to be added.

Step 2 Let x = number of grams of 55% solution to be added. Make a table:

	Weight of acid	Total weight
10% solution	(0.1)(20)	20
55% solution	(0.55)x	x
Mixture	(0.1)(20) + (0.55)x	20 + x

Step 3 In mixture, the acid is to be (0.5)(total weight):

$$(0.1)(20) + (0.55)x = (0.5)(20 + x)$$

Step 4 Multiply both members by 100:

$$(10)(20) + 55x = 50(20 + x)$$
$$200 + 55x = 1000 + 50x$$
$$5x = 800$$
$$x = 160$$

Step 5 The check is left to you. $(0.1)(20) + (0.55)(160) = 2 + 88 = 90$
$(0.5)(20 + 160) = 90$

∴ 160 grams of 55% solution are to be added. *Answer*

Problems

Solve.

A
1. How many kilograms of water must be added to 20 kilograms of a 10% salt solution to produce a 5% solution? **20 kg**

2. How many grams of water must be added to 6 grams of a 40% antiseptic solution to produce a 30% solution? **2 g**

3. How many kilograms of water must be added to 60 kilograms of an 80% acid solution to produce a 70% acid solution? **8⅔ kg**

4. How many grams of water must be added to 12 grams of a 30% antifreeze solution to produce a 20% solution? **6 g**

5. How many kilograms of water must be evaporated from 60 kilograms of a 5% salt solution to produce a 25% solution? **48 kg**

6. How many kilograms of water must be evaporated from 100 kilograms of a 6% brine (salt and water) to obtain a 20% brine? **70 kg**

B
7. A druggist has 20 grams of a 10% solution of alcohol. How many grams of a 6% alcohol solution must be added to form an 8% alcohol solution? **20 g**

8. A certain alloy contains 75% copper and a second alloy 35% copper. How many kilograms of the second alloy must be added to 62 kilograms of the first to form an alloy that is 50% copper? **103¼ kg**

9. How many kilograms of milk testing 5% butterfat and how many kilograms of cream testing 25% butterfat should be mixed to give 100 kilograms testing 20% butterfat? *(below)*

10. How many kilograms of a 25% silver alloy must be melted with how many kilograms of a 55% silver alloy to obtain 30 kilograms of a 32% silver alloy? **23 kg of 25% alloy, 7 kg of 55% alloy**

9. 25 kg of milk, 75 kg of cream

Biographical Note
Robert Hutchings Goddard

Robert H. Goddard (1882–1945) held more than two hundred patents in the field of rocket engineering. In 1926 he designed, built, and launched the first liquid-fuel rocket near Worcester, Massachusetts. He patented the idea of a multi-stage rocket, without which a moon landing would not have been possible. He also made innovations in fuel-injection and guidance systems. Throughout the 1930's Goddard conducted test flights near Roswell, New Mexico.

In a paper published in 1919, he had suggested that jet propulsion could be used to reach escape velocity, the velocity at which a body must travel to overcome the force of earth's gravity. Forty years later the first satellite escaped earth's gravitational force and went into orbit around the sun.

6-13 Investment Problems

> **OBJECTIVE** To learn how to solve some problems involving investments.

The general percentage formula is:

Percentage = Rate × Base

The amount of interest, *I* dollars, paid for one year on an investment of the principal, *P* dollars, at the interest rate, *R*, for one year is found from:

Interest = Rate × Principal

To find **simple interest** for *T* years, you multiply the interest by *T*. The formula is usually given in the form:

> Interest = Principal × (Rate per year) × (Time in years)
>
> $I = PRT$

Thus, the simple interest on $1000 at 5% a year for 3 months in dollars is:

$$(1000)(0.05)(\tfrac{3}{12}) = 50(\tfrac{1}{4}) = 12.50$$

Example A total of $10,000 is invested, part in a savings and loan association at 6% and the remainder in municipal bonds that pay 4% annual interest. If the yearly return from both investments is $508, how much is invested at each rate?

Solution

Step 1 The problem asks for the amount that is invested at each rate.

Step 2 Let x = number of dollars invested at 6%.
Then $10,000 - x$ = number of dollars invested at 4%.

Step 3

	Principal	Interest
Invested at 6%	x	$(0.06)x$
Invested at 4%	$10,000 - x$	$(0.04)(10,000 - x)$
Total	$10,000$	508

The statements about the total interest make this equation:

$$(0.06)x + (0.04)(10,000 - x) = 508$$

Step 4 $6x + 4(10,000 - x) = 50,800$
$6x + 40,000 - 4x = 50,800$
$2x = 10,800$ ⟶ $\begin{cases} x = 5,400 \\ 10,000 - x = 4,600 \end{cases}$

Step 5 The check is left for you.

$(0.06)(5400) + (0.04)(4600) = 324 + 184 = 508$ ✓

Problems

Solve.

A 1. If $900 is invested at $4\frac{1}{2}\%$ per year, how much simple interest is earned in 3 years? **$121.50**

2. What is the simple interest for 2 years on $3000 invested at 5% per year? **$300**

3. What sum of money invested at 4% will yield $110 in simple interest annually? **$2750**

4. Maria and Mike Gomez invested a specific amount of money on which they received 5% annually. At the end of each year, for 4 consecutive years, they withdrew the interest. If the total interest was $240, what sum did they invest? **$1200**

5. The Hairstons wanted to improve their property. They borrowed $1200 from their parents at simple interest of 3% per year. Two years later they paid back the $1200, together with the amount of interest. What was the total amount they paid? **$1272**

6. The local bank offers $5\frac{1}{2}\%$ interest on savings, while a certain savings and loan company pays $6\frac{1}{2}\%$. How much less (simple)

interest over a 5-year period, on $2500, would you receive from the local bank? **$125**

7. A certain sum is invested at 4% annual interest. If $1400 is added to the account, the annual interest will amount to $196. How much was originally invested? **$3500**

8. The Stanford Company had $6800 in an account at 4% annual interest. They withdrew some money to buy furniture, and the remaining funds drew $172 annual interest. How much did they withdraw? **$2500**

9. The Downeys invested part of $7000 at 4% and the remainder at 5%. Their annual income from the two investments was $330. Find the amount they invested at each rate. *(below)*

10. A sum of money was invested at 6% per year, and 5 times as much at 4% per year. How much was invested at each rate if the annual return totaled $312? **$1200 at 6%, $6000 at 4%**

(*See page 479 for additional problems.*)

9. $2000 at 4%, $5000 at 5%

Consumer Note $$$$$$$$$$$$$$$$$$$$$$$$$$$$$$$$$$$$$
How Banks Compute Interest

If $100 (principal) were left in a bank that paid 6% interest a year, the amount at the end of 1 year would be

$$A = P + R \times P = \$100 + (0.06)(\$100), \text{ or } \$106.$$

The next year, the "principal" on which interest is to be computed would be $106, and the amount at the end of 2 years would be

$$\$106 + (0.06)(\$106), \text{ or } \$112.36.$$

This is called **compounding interest annually**. The **compound interest** in this case is $12.36. The simple interest would have been just $12.

However, most banks compound interest more often than once a year. Suppose that the bank compounded interest quarterly (four times a year). If the annual rate is 6%, the rate per quarter is 0.06/4, or 0.015. Then, by quarters we have:

```
100 + ( .015)( 100)            = 100 + 1.5         = 101.5
101.5 + ( .015)( 101.5)        = 101.5 + 1.5225    = 103.023
103.023 + ( .015)( 103.023)    = 103.023 + 1.54534 = 104.568
104.568 + ( .015)( 104.568)    = 104.568 + 1.56852 = 106.136
```

Thus, at the end of 1 year, the amount is $106.14 and the interest is $6.14, instead of just $6. At the end of two years the interest would be $12.65.

Study the series of computations that are used in the preceding table. Notice the steps that repeat:

Compute A from P and R.
Give P the value of A.
Compute A with this value of P.
Repeat the number of times specified.

This pattern is illustrated by the partial flowchart at the right.

A computer is especially useful in doing such repetitive calculations. If you have access to a computer that will accept BASIC, type in the following program:

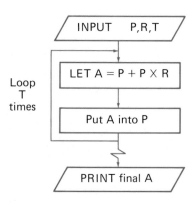

```
10   PRINT "AMOUNT AT R PER YEAR ON";       90   LET I=P*R1
20   PRINT "$100 COMPOUNDED N TIMES";       100  LET A=P+I
30   PRINT "A YEAR FOR Y YEARS"             110  PRINT P;" + (";R1;")(";P;")";
40   LET P=100                              120  PRINT TAB(30);"=";P;" +";I;
50   PRINT "WHAT ARE R, N, Y";              130  PRINT TAB(51);"=";A
60   INPUT R,N,Y                            140  LET P=A
70   LET R1=R/N                             150  NEXT J
80   FOR J=1 TO N*Y                         160  END
```

Notice Step 140 LET P = A. That means "Give P the value of A." *It is not an equation.*

RUN the preceding program for .06, 4, 1 and .06, 4, 2 to verify the results stated on page 238. If you RUN it for .06, 12, 1, and .06, 12, 2, you will find that the amounts are $106.17 and $112.72 respectively.

Many banks now compound interest daily, and many use a special method for this. This method is to divide the annual rate by 360, but to compound it 365 times a year (366 for leap years). Before trying the program for such large numbers, change it to PRINT only the final amount:

Delete lines 110, 120, 130 and add: 155 PRINT A

You can then check the results in the table shown below. (There may be some variation in the last digit.) For the last row use

80 FOR J = 1 TO 365*Y

for the first two entries and

80 FOR J = 1 TO 365*Y + 2

for the last one (to account for the two leap years in 10 years).

Even if you do not have access to a computer, you can study the table and answer the questions.

Principal = $100   R = 0.06

Times per Year \ Years	1	2	10
1	106	112.36	179.08
4	106.14	112.65	181.40
12	106.17	112.72	181.94
365/360	106.27	112.94	183.79

1. How much does $100 amount to at simple interest for 10 years? $160

2. If the interest is compounded annually, how much more than the amount in Exercise 1 is the final amount in 10 years? $19.08

3. What is the increase caused by compounding daily over compounding monthly for 10 years? $1.85

When banks are compounding daily, they often quote a rate called the **effective annual yield.** For example, in the table above the interest on $100 compounded daily for a year is $6.27. This gives an effective annual yield of 6.27/100, or 6.27%.

6-14 Uniform-Motion Problems

> **OBJECTIVE** To learn how to solve problems involving uniform motion.

An object which moves without changing its speed, or rate, is said to be in **uniform motion**. The basic formula to be used in solving uniform-motion problems is:

$$\text{Distance} = \left(\begin{array}{c}\text{Rate per}\\\text{unit of time}\end{array}\right) \times \left(\begin{array}{c}\text{Number of units}\\\text{of time}\end{array}\right)$$

$$D = RT$$

You may also use this formula for *average* rates.

Example 1 (Objects moving in the same direction) A truck enters Interstate 5 and drives north at 90 km/h (kilometers per hour). At the same time a Highway Patrol car 40 kilometers south of the truck starts north at 110 km/h. How long will it take the patrol car to pass the truck?

Solution

Step 1 The problem asks for the length of time it will take the patrol car to pass the truck.

Step 2 Let t = number of hours required to pass the truck.

Step 3

	R	T	D
Truck	90	t	$90t$
Patrol Car	110	t	$110t$

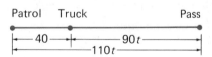

$$\underbrace{110t}_{\substack{\text{Patrol car's}\\\text{distance}}} = \underbrace{90t}_{\substack{\text{Truck's}\\\text{distance}}} + \underbrace{40}_{+\ 40}$$

Step 4
$$20t = 40$$
$$t = 2$$

Step 5 *Check:* In 2 hours, the truck traveled $2 \cdot 90 = 180$ km.

In 2 hours, the patrol car traveled $2 \cdot 110 = 220$ km.

$220 - 180 = 40$ ✓

∴ the patrol car will pass the truck in 2 hours. *Answer*

Example 2 (Objects moving in opposite directions) At noon a jetliner left New York for Los Angeles, 4000 km away. At 1 P.M. New York time a jetliner, flying 10 km/h faster than the first, left Los Angeles for New York. The planes passed each other at 3:00 P.M. New York time. Find their speeds.

Solution

Step 1 The problem asks for the speeds of the planes.

Step 2 Let x = speed of slower plane in km per hour.
Then $x + 10$ = speed of faster plane in km per hour.

Step 3

	R	T	D
Slower	x	3	$3x$
Faster	$x + 10$	2	$2(x + 10)$

$$\underbrace{\text{Distance of slower plane}}_{3x} + \underbrace{\text{Distance of faster plane}}_{2(x + 10)} = \frac{4000}{= 4000}$$

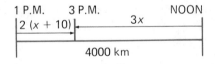

Steps 4 and 5 are left for you. You should find that the speeds of the planes are 796 km/h and 806 km/h.

$$3x + 2x + 20 = 4000$$
$$5x = 3980$$
$$x = 796$$
$$x + 10 = 806$$
$$3(796) + 2(806)$$
$$= 2388 + 1612$$
$$= 4000 ✓$$

Example 3 (Round Trip) While training for a bicycle race, Charles rode up a mountain road at 12 km/h and then back down at 30 km/h. If the round trip took $3\frac{1}{2}$ hours, how long did the uphill trip take, and how many kilometers was it?

Solution

Step 1 The problem asks for the time and the distance.

Step 2 Let t = time in hours to ride uphill.

Since the time for the round trip was $3\frac{1}{2}$ or $\frac{7}{2}$ hours, $\frac{7}{2} - t$ = time in hours to ride downhill.

Step 3

	R	T	D
Uphill	12	t	$12t$
Downhill	30	$\frac{7}{2} - t$	$30(\frac{7}{2} - t)$

$$\underbrace{\text{Distance up}}_{12t} \stackrel{\downarrow}{=} \underbrace{\text{Distance down}}_{30(\frac{7}{2} - t)}$$

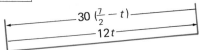

Steps 4 and 5 are left for you. You should find that the uphill trip took $2\frac{1}{2}$ hours, and that the distance uphill was 30 km.

$12t = 105 - 30t$
$42t = 105$
$t = 2\frac{1}{2}, 12t = 30$
$30(\frac{7}{2} - \frac{5}{2}) = 30 = 12(2\frac{1}{2})$ ✓

Problems

Solve.

A

1. Two jets leave Chicago at the same time, one flying due west at 750 km/h, the other flying due east at 850 km/h. After how long will the planes be 4000 km apart? **2.5 hours**

2. A police car passed a truck which was traveling at 80 km/h and 6 minutes ($\frac{1}{10}$ hour) later was 3 km ahead of the truck. What was the speed of the police car? **110 km/h**

3. Joe drove 210 km at 70 km/h and then another 210 km at 105 km/h. It took Bill the same length of time to drive the entire 420 km at constant speed. What was Bill's speed? **84 km/h**

4. A motorist driving at 100 km/h can go from Wilton to Stockton in 2 hours less time than can a train which averages 75 km/h. How far apart are the two towns? **600 km**

5. Anne Jones and Rita Sanchez left downtown Hillsboro at the same time and arrived in downtown Central City at the same time. Anne took a train which averaged 120 km/h.

Rita took a plane which averaged 480 km/h but spent $2\frac{1}{2}$ hours in going to and from airports. How far apart are Hillsboro and Central City? **400 km**

6. Two bicyclists started at the same time from towns 84 km apart and rode toward each other. Because one of them rode downhill, his speed was twice as great as that of the other. Find both speeds if they meet after two hours. **14 km/h and 28 km/h**

7. At 8:00 A.M. Jill and Tom start on a hike at 4 km/h. At 11:00 A.M. their mother discovered that they had forgotten their lunches and started after them in her car at 64 km/h. When does she overtake them? **11:12 A.M.**

8. A power boat can travel upstream on a river at 24 km/h and downstream at 30 km/h. How far upstream can it go if the round trip is to take 3 hours? **40 km**

B

9. The Thompsons averaged 60 km/h in driving from their house to the airport, but they arrived 10 minutes late. If they had averaged 96 km/h, they would have been five minutes early. Find the distance from their house to the airport. **40 km**

10. A car and a train leave St. Louis at the same time, bound for Hillsboro. The train averages 75 km/h, and the car 100 km/h. The driver of the car stopped for a 2-hour dinner, and arrived in Hillsboro 1 hour after the train. How long did the train trip last? **4 hours**

(*See pages 479–481 for additional problems.*)

6-15 Rate-of-Work Problems

> **OBJECTIVE** To learn how to solve some problems that deal with the rate of doing things.

To solve problems about the rate of doing things, you use this formula:

$$\begin{pmatrix} \text{Amount of} \\ \text{work done} \end{pmatrix} = \begin{pmatrix} \text{Rate per} \\ \text{unit of time} \end{pmatrix} \times \begin{pmatrix} \text{Number of units} \\ \text{of time} \end{pmatrix}$$

$$W = RT$$

Notice that the sum of the fractional parts of a job must be 1.

Example 1 It takes 12 hours for one spillway to lower the water level in Lake San Marcos by 40 centimeters while a second spillway takes 8 hours to lower the water level by the same amount. How long would it take to lower the water level 40 centimeters if both spillways are open at once?

Solution

Step 1 The problem asks for the number of hours it will take both spillways to lower the water level.

Step 2 Let x = number of hours for both spillways to lower the water level 40 cm.
Then $\frac{1}{12}x$ = fractional part of job done by first spillway;
$\frac{1}{8}x$ = fractional part of job done by second spillway.

Step 3 $\underbrace{\text{Part of job done} \atop \text{by first spillway}}_{\frac{1}{12}x} + \underbrace{\text{Part of job done} \atop \text{by second spillway}}_{\frac{1}{8}x} = \underbrace{\text{Whole job done} \atop \text{together}}_{1}$

Step 4 L.C.D. = 24 $24(\frac{1}{12}x + \frac{1}{8}x) = 24(1) \longrightarrow 5x = 24$
$2x + 3x = 24 \longrightarrow x = \frac{24}{5} = 4\frac{4}{5}$

Step 5 *Check:* In $\frac{24}{5}$ hours, the first spillway finishes $\frac{1}{12}(\frac{24}{5})$, or $\frac{2}{5}$ of the job.

In $\frac{24}{5}$ hours, the second spillway finishes $\frac{1}{8}(\frac{24}{5})$, or $\frac{3}{5}$ of the job.

Does $\frac{2}{5} + \frac{3}{5} = 1$? Yes ✓

∴ it takes $4\frac{4}{5}$ hours for both spillways working together. *Answer*

Sometimes the participants in accomplishing a job do not work for the same length of time. In such a case, the values substituted for time in the equation may differ.

Example 2 How long would it take to lower the water level in Example 1 if the spillways were opened together, but the first spillway was shut off after 4 hours?

Solution

Step 1 The problem asks for the length of time it would take to lower the water level if the first spillway were shut off after 4 hours.

Step 2 Let x = the number of hours the second spillway is open.

Step 3 The first spillway runs for 4 hours. $\frac{1}{12}(4) + \frac{1}{8}x = 1$

Steps 4 and 5 are left for you. It would take $5\frac{1}{3}$ hours. *Answer*

$8 + 3x = 24$
$x = 5\frac{1}{3}$
$\frac{1}{3} + \frac{1}{8} \cdot \frac{16}{3} = 1$ ✓

Problems

Solve.

A 1. Working alone, a painter can paint a small apartment in 10 hours. Her helper can paint the same apartment in 15 hours. How long would it take the painter and her helper to complete the job if they work together? **6 hours**

2. Pete can do a job in 50 minutes while his brother Jim can do it in $\frac{1}{2}$ the time. How long will it take them to do the job working together? **$16\frac{2}{3}$ minutes**

3. Pearson College owns a tabulator that can process registration data in 6 hours. Wanting to speed up the processing, the school authorized the purchase of a second tabu-

lator that can do the job in 8 hours. How many hours will it take the two tabulators working together to process all the data? **$3\frac{3}{7}$ hour**

4. A tank can be emptied by one pipe in 40 minutes and by another in 30 minutes. If the tank is $\frac{7}{8}$ full, how long will it take to empty it when both pipes are open? **15 minutes**

5. Shelley can keypunch 300 cards in one hour. When she and Linda work together, they can complete the job in 24 minutes. How long would it take Linda to keypunch 300 cards if she worked alone? **40 minutes**

6. With drain pipes *A* and *B* open, the Vista swimming pool can be emptied in one hour and thirty minutes. If drain pipe *A* can empty the pool in 3 hours, how long would it take drain pipe *B* to empty the pool? 3 hours

7. A bank teller can count a certain amount of money in 15 minutes, but if she is helped by another teller, they can count the money in 10 minutes. Find the amount of time it would take the second teller to count the money alone. 30 minutes

8. One pipe can fill a tank in 4 hours. A second pipe can also do it in 4 hours, but a third needs 6 hours. How long would it take to fill the tank if all three pipes were open? $1\frac{1}{2}$ hours

B 9. It takes one man 10 hours to do a certain job. After he has been at work for 4 hours, another man is sent to help. The two men then complete the job in 2 more hours. How long would the second man have taken to do the job alone? 5 hours

10. Maria can paint the walls of an apartment in 8 hours. After she has worked 3 hours, Pat joins her and they finish the job in 2 hours more. How long would it take Pat to do the whole job without the aid of Maria? $5\frac{1}{3}$ hours

11. A filler pipe can fill a tank in 12 hours, while an outlet pipe can empty the tank in 18 hours. How long would it take to fill the empty tank with both pipes operating? 36 hours

12. A tank is fitted with two pipes. One can fill it in 8 hours. After it has been open 2 hours, the second pipe is opened and the tank is filled in 2 hours more. How long would it take the second pipe alone to fill the tank? 4 hours

(*See page 481 for additional problems.*)

 # Self-Test 5

Be sure that you understand these terms:

simple interest (p. 236)   uniform motion (p. 240)

Solve.

1. How many kilograms of pure acid must be added to 4 kilograms of a 40% acid solution to produce a 50% solution? Objective 6-12, p. 234

2. If $1300 is invested at 4% per year, how much simple interest is earned in 2 years? Objective 6-13, p. 236

3. A total of $7000 is invested, part at an interest rate of 4% and the remainder at 5%. How much is invested at each rate if the annual interest from both investments amounts to $337?

4. One man drives 50 kilometers in the same length of time a second man drives 70 kilometers. If the speed of the first driver is 20 kilometers per hour slower, find the speed of each. Objective 6-14, p. 240

5. Fran Gerner can wash and wax her car in 3 hours while it takes her daughter 4 hours to do the same job. How long would it take them if they worked together? Objective 6-15, p. 243

Check your answers with those printed at the back of the book.

Chapter Summary

1. Factoring is used in multiplying and dividing fractions.
2. Factoring is used in finding the least common denominator when necessary in adding or subtracting fractions.
3. Operations on fractions are used in solving equations that involve fractions.
4. Problems dealing with investments, uniform motion, or rate of work often require the use of equations involving fractions.

Chapter Test

6-1   1. For what values of x is $\dfrac{x-2}{x^2-1}$ not defined? $x = 1, -1$

Reduce to lowest terms.

2. $\dfrac{6x+4y}{2x-8y}$ $\dfrac{3x+2y}{x-4y}$ 3. $\dfrac{7-x}{x^2-5x-14}$ $\dfrac{-1}{x+2}$ 4. $\dfrac{a^2+4a-5}{a^2+5a-6}$ $\dfrac{a+5}{a+6}$

6-2   5. Express the ratio of 3 centimeters to 8 millimeters in lowest terms.   15:4

6. If a 20-centimeter string is cut into two pieces whose lengths are in the ratio 3:2, how long is each piece?   12 cm and 8 cm

Express as a single fraction in lowest terms.

6-3   7. $\dfrac{10x}{15x^4} \cdot \dfrac{5x^3}{6x}$ $\dfrac{5}{9x}$ 8. $\dfrac{a^2-b^2}{c^2-d^2} \cdot \dfrac{c+d}{a+b}$ $\dfrac{a-b}{c-d}$

6-4   9. $\dfrac{12r-4s}{16} \div \dfrac{c^2-d^2}{4c-4d}$ $\dfrac{3r-s}{c+d}$ 10. $\dfrac{n^3+2n^2+n}{2n^2+7n+6} \div \dfrac{n^2+2n+1}{2n^2+n-3}$ $\dfrac{n^2-n}{n+2}$

11. $\dfrac{9x^2y}{10z} \div \dfrac{18xy}{15z^2}$ $\dfrac{3xz}{4}$ 12. $\dfrac{a+1}{a-1} \div \dfrac{2a+2}{a^2-1}$ $\dfrac{a+1}{2}$

6-5   13. $\dfrac{2x-1}{x^2-x} \cdot \dfrac{x}{2x^2+5x-3} \div \dfrac{1}{x^2+4x+3}$ $\dfrac{x+1}{x-1}$

6-6 14. $\dfrac{2a - 2b}{8ab} - \dfrac{2a + 2b}{8ab} + \dfrac{6b - 3a}{8ab}$ $\dfrac{-3a + 2b}{8ab}$

15. $\dfrac{a + b}{11} - \dfrac{2a + b}{22}$ $\dfrac{b}{22}$ 16. $\dfrac{1}{x^2 - y^2} + \dfrac{y}{x + y}$ $\dfrac{1 + xy - y^2}{x^2 - y^2}$

6-7 17. $8 - \dfrac{cd}{c + d}$ $\dfrac{8c + 8d - cd}{c + d}$ 18. $x + 3 + \dfrac{2x - 1}{x + 1}$ $\dfrac{x^2 + 6x + 2}{x + 1}$

19. Change to a mixed expression: $\dfrac{6n^2 + 4n + 12}{2n}$ $3n + 2 + \dfrac{6}{n}$

6-8 20. Divide $u^3 + u^2 - 8u + 4$ by $u - 2$. $u^2 + 3u - 2$

Solve.

6-9 21. $x - \dfrac{2x}{7} = \dfrac{5}{21}$ $\dfrac{1}{3}$ 22. $\dfrac{2x - 7}{5} = \dfrac{x}{6} - \dfrac{2x}{5}$ $2\dfrac{4}{19}$

6-10 23. $\dfrac{4r}{r - 3} - 3 = \dfrac{3r - 1}{r + 3}$ $12, -1$ 24. $\dfrac{5}{x - 1} + \dfrac{60}{1 - x^2} = \dfrac{10}{x + 1}$ -9

6-11 25. What would be the sale price on an item regularly priced at $10.50 if a 30% discount is given?   **$7.35**

6-12 26. How many kilograms of water must be evaporated from 50 kilograms of a 10% salt solution to produce a 25% solution?   **30 kg**

27. How many kilograms of a 35% silver alloy must be melted with how many kilograms of a 65% silver alloy to obtain 20 kilograms of a 50% silver alloy?   **10 kg of each**

6-13 28. A sum of money was invested at 4% per year, and a sum twice that amount at 5% per year. How much was invested at each rate if the annual return totaled $70?   **$500 at 4%, $1000 at 5%**

6-14 29. Henry can row 12 kilometers downstream in the same length of time it takes him to row 5 kilometers upstream. If the current in the river flows at 6 kilometers per hour, how fast does Henry row in still water?   **$14\frac{4}{7}$ km/h**

6-15 30. It takes one printing press 7 hours to do a certain job. After the first press has been at work for 4 hours, another press is put to work. The two presses then complete the job in 1 hour more. How long would it take the second press to do the job working by itself?   **$3\frac{1}{2}$ hours**

248 *Chapter 6*

Programmed Chapter Review

6-1   1. $\dfrac{ac}{bc} = \dfrac{a}{b}$, provided $c \neq$ __?__, $b \neq$ __?__. $0, 0$

2. In simple form, $\dfrac{15}{10b} =$ __?__. $\dfrac{3}{2b}$

3. In simple form, $\dfrac{2c + 6}{2c - 6} =$ __?__. $\dfrac{c + 3}{c - 3}$

6-2   4. The ratio of 10 kilograms to 25 kilograms is __?__. $\frac{2}{5}$ or 2:5

5. The ratio of the area of a 2-cm square to the area of a 4-cm square is __?__. $\frac{1}{4}$ or 1:4

6-3   6. $\dfrac{x}{3} \cdot \dfrac{6}{y} \cdot \dfrac{y^4}{10}$ written as a single fraction in lowest terms is __?__. $\dfrac{xy^3}{5}$

7. In simple form, $\dfrac{y - 2}{6y - 12} \cdot \dfrac{10y - 5}{15y - 10}$ is __?__. $\dfrac{2y - 1}{6(3y - 2)}$

6-4   8. To divide fractions, multiply the dividend by the reciprocal of the __?__.   divisor

9. In simple form, $\dfrac{a^2 - b^2}{2b} \div \dfrac{a + b}{4b^2}$ is __?__. $2b(a - b)$

10. In simple form, $\dfrac{x - y}{x} \div \dfrac{x + y}{2x} =$ __?__. $\dfrac{2(x - y)}{x + y}$

6-5   11. In simple form, $\dfrac{a^2}{b^2} \div \dfrac{a^3}{b^4} \cdot \dfrac{a - b}{b - a} =$ __?__. $-\dfrac{b^2}{a}$

12. In simple form, $\dfrac{r^2 + r}{r^3} \cdot \dfrac{r + 1}{r} \div \dfrac{(r + 1)^2}{r - 1} =$ __?__. $\dfrac{r - 1}{r^3}$

6-6   13. When written as a single fraction in lowest terms, $\dfrac{10}{7a} - \dfrac{13}{7a} + \dfrac{5}{7a} =$ __?__. $\dfrac{2}{7a}$

14. When written as a single fraction in lowest terms, $\dfrac{x^2 + y^2}{x + y} + \dfrac{2xy}{x + y} = \underline{\;?\;}$.

$x + y$

15. In simple form, $\dfrac{a - 4}{5} - \dfrac{a - 1}{6} = \underline{\;?\;}$.

$\dfrac{a - 19}{30}$

16. In simple form, $\dfrac{6x}{x^2 - 9} + \dfrac{3}{x + 3} = \underline{\;?\;}$.

$\dfrac{9(x - 1)}{x^2 - 9}$

6-7 17. Written as a mixed expression, $\dfrac{10 + 16a^2}{2a} = \underline{\;?\;}$.

$\dfrac{5}{a} + 8a$

18. Written as a reduced fraction, $x - 3 + \dfrac{5x - 6}{x - 2} = \underline{\;?\;}$.

$\dfrac{x^2}{x - 2}$

6-8 19. When you divide $6x^2 - 3x + 2$ by $2x - 1$, the first term in the quotient is $\underline{\;?\;}$.

$3x$

20. Before dividing $4 + 7x - 3x^2 + 8x^3$ by $2x^2 + 3$, you rearrange the terms of the dividend in order of $\underline{\;?\;}$ degree in x.

decreasing

21. The division process ends when the remainder is $\underline{\;?\;}$ or the degree of the remainder is $\underline{\;?\;}$ the degree of the divisor.

0
less than

22. If the remainder is 0, the divisor and the quotient are $\underline{\;?\;}$ of the dividend.

factors

6-9 23. To solve $\dfrac{6x}{11} - \dfrac{4x}{3} = 5$, you must first multiply all its terms by $\underline{\;?\;}$.

33

24. The solution of $\dfrac{2}{5}x - \dfrac{1}{6}x = \dfrac{21}{30}$ is $\underline{\;?\;}$.

3

25. The solution of $\dfrac{2r}{3} - \dfrac{r + 4}{2} = \dfrac{3r - 1}{4}$ is $\underline{\;?\;}$.

-3

6-10 26. An equation which has a variable in the denominator of one or more terms is called a $\underline{\;?\;}$ equation.

fractional

27. To solve $\dfrac{5}{t} = \dfrac{t - 3}{2}$, you must first multiply all its terms by $\underline{\;?\;}$.

$2t$

28. The solution set of $a - \dfrac{2}{a-3} = \dfrac{a-1}{3-a}$ is __?__ .

$\{-1\}$

29. The solution set of $\dfrac{60}{b^2 - 36} + 1 = \dfrac{5}{b-6}$ is __?__ .

$\{-1\}$

6-11 30. A percentage is a number equal to the product of the rate and another number, called the __?__ .

base

31. 21% of 123 is __?__ .

25.83

32. 120 is 40% of __?__ .

300

33. 50 is __?__ % of 150.

$33\frac{1}{3}\%$

6-12 34. The equation used to solve the problem "How many grams of water must be added to 12 grams of an 8% salt solution to produce a 6% solution?" is __?__ .

$(0.08)(12)$
$= (0.06)(x + 12)$

35. The solution to Problem 34 is __?__ .

4 grams

6-13 36. An equation used to solve the problem "The Adams family invested three times as much money at 4% per year as they did at 5%. If their yearly income from these investments is $357, find the amounts invested at each rate." is __?__ .

$0.05x + (0.04)(3x)$
$= 357$

37. In Problem 36, the amount invested at 4% is __?__ , and the amount invested at 5% is __?__ .

$6300,
$2100

6-14 38. An equation used to solve the problem "An express train required 3 hours longer to travel 500 kilometers than a plane required to travel 2000 kilometers. If the plane travels 8 times as fast as the train, find the speed of the train." is __?__ .

$\dfrac{500}{x} = \dfrac{2000}{8x} + 3$

39. The solution to Problem 38 is __?__ .

$83\frac{1}{3}$ km/h

6-15 40. An equation used to solve the problem "One bulldozer can clear a certain area in 6 days. Another takes 5 days to clear the same area. How long would it take two of the slower and three of the faster bulldozers to clear the area?" is __?__ .

$\dfrac{2x}{6} + \dfrac{3x}{5} = 1$

41. The solution to Problem 40 is __?__ .

$1\frac{1}{14}$ days

Cumulative Review, Chapters 1-6

Simplify each expression.

1. $3(19 - 11)$ 24

2. $4(-2) + 8$ 0

3. $-11 + (-15) + 20$ -6

4. $(-3)^2(-2) + 4$ -14

5. $\dfrac{12 - 18}{-2} + 3(5)$ 18

6. $(-6)^2 + 3(-2) + 4$ 34

If $x = 3$, $y = -2$, $z = 0$, and $w = 4$, evaluate each expression.

7. $2x + w$ 10

8. $3y - 2z$ -6

9. xy^2 12

10. $wx - 2y^3$ 28

11. $xz^2 + 2wy$ -16

12. $xw + 6y + 3z$ 0

13. $\dfrac{xy - w}{5}$ -2

14. $\dfrac{-7wy}{x^2w + y^3}$ 2

Solve each equation.

15. $2y - 3 = -7$ -2

16. $3r + 2 = r + 8$ 3

17. $3(x - 1) + 4(x + 2) = 33$ 4

18. $5(t + 2) = 2t - 5$ -5

19. $4x + 2 - 6x + 5 = x - 2$ 3

20. $7 - 5n + 3 = 2n - 6 + n$ 2

21. $14t - 12 + t = 3(t - 4)$ 0

22. $15 - 17z + 21 = 5(3 - z) + 3$ $\frac{3}{2}$

Simplify each expression.

23. $(3x^2 - 2x + 7) + (x^2 - 3x - 4)$ $4x^2 - 5x + 3$

24. $(2n^2 - 5n + 3) - (n^2 - 5n + 1)$ $n^2 + 2$

25. $(2x^2y)(-4xy^3)$ $-8x^3y^4$

26. $(3m^2)^2(2m^3)$ $18m^7$

27. $-3z(2z + 5)$

28. $4t(3t - 8)$ $12t^2 - 32t$

29. $3n^2(5n^2 - 2n + 3)$ $15n^4 - 6n^3 + 9n^2$

30. $4r^3(6 - 7r + 2r^2)$

31. $(x - 3)(x + 1)$ $x^2 - 2x - 3$

32. $(y - 3)(y + 8)$ $y^2 + 5y - 24$

33. $(2n - 3)(2n + 3)$

34. $(4r - 5)(2r + 3)$ $8r^2 + 2r - 15$

35. $(3x + 2)(3x + 1)$ $9x^2 + 9x + 2$

36. $(4y - 3)(5y - 2)$

27. $-6z^2 - 15z$ 30. $24r^3 - 28r^4 + 8r^5$ 33. $4n^2 - 9$ 36. $20y^2 - 23y + 6$

Factor completely.

37. $14r^2s + 28rs - 21rs^2$ $7rs(2r + 4 - 3s)$

38. $t^2 - 5t + 4$ $(t - 4)(t - 1)$

39. $3x^2 - 20x + 12$ $(3x - 2)(x - 6)$

40. $12x^2 - 2x - 24$ $2(3x + 4)(2x - 3)$

41. $36m^2 - 49n^2$ $(6m + 7n)(6m - 7n)$

42. $xt - 2yt + xr - 2yr$ $(t + r)(x - 2y)$

Solve.

43. $4t^2 = 12t$ $\{0, 3\}$

44. $(k + 2)(2k - 1) = 0$ $\{-2, \frac{1}{2}\}$

45. $18x^2 = 48x$ $\{0, \frac{8}{3}\}$

46. $y^2 - 4y = 21$ $\{-3, 7\}$

Simplify to a single fraction in lowest terms.

47. $\dfrac{2a^2 - 2b^2}{6a + 6b} \quad \dfrac{a - b}{3}$

48. $\dfrac{2}{5} - \dfrac{3}{n^2} + \dfrac{5}{2} \quad \dfrac{29n^2 - 30}{10n^2}$

49. $\dfrac{3r - 2s}{4r + 4s} \cdot \dfrac{(r + s)^2}{3r^2 + rs - 2s^2} \quad \dfrac{1}{4}$

50. $\dfrac{y^2 - 9}{2y + 6} \div \dfrac{y - 3}{y + 2} \quad \dfrac{y + 2}{2}$

51. $\dfrac{c^2 - 1}{3c + 3} - \dfrac{c^2 - 1}{4c + 4} \quad \dfrac{c - 1}{12}$

52. $\dfrac{27}{x^2 - 81} + \dfrac{3}{2x + 18} \quad \dfrac{3}{2x - 1}$

Solve.

53. $\dfrac{4}{3z - 2} + \dfrac{1}{3z} = \dfrac{1}{z} - \dfrac{2}{3}$

54. $\dfrac{3x - 4}{x - 1} = 2 + \dfrac{x + 4}{x + 1} \quad \dfrac{1}{2}$

55. Find three consecutive even integers whose sum is 78.   **24, 26, 28**

56. Find two consecutive even integers the sum of whose squares is 164.   **−10 and −8, or 8 and 10**

57. If a rectangle has an area of 35 square centimeters and if its length is 3 centimeters less than twice its width, what are its dimensions?   **5 cm by 7 cm**

58. A negative integer is 5 greater than 2 times another negative integer. If the difference of the squares of the integers is 13, what are the integers?   **−6 and −7**

59. If Charlotte had $1000 less invested at 5% than she now does at 4%, her annual return would be the same. How much does she now have invested at 4%?   **$5000**

60. How many grams of an alloy containing 10% copper must be melted with how many grams of an alloy containing 60% copper to make 250 grams of an alloy containing 50% copper?   **50 g of 10% alloy, 200 g of 60% alloy**

61. In still water Kenneth's motorboat is 6 kilometers per hour faster than Martin's. In a current flowing at 4 kilometers per hour, Kenneth can travel 78 kilometers upstream in the same length of time Martin goes 84 kilometers downstream. What is the speed of Martin's boat in still water?   **24 km/h**

Looking Ahead

You have now studied how to use one variable in polynomials and fractions to solve problems. In the next three chapters, you will learn how to extend your skills in several ways:

(a) You will study how to work with inequalities as well as equations.

(b) You will learn what "relations" and "functions" are and how to use them.

(c) You will learn how to use two variables to solve more kinds of problems.

Maintaining Skills

Remember how?

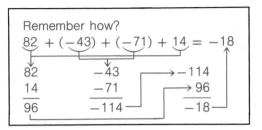

$$82 + (-43) + (-71) + 14 = -18$$

82	−43	→ −114
14	−71	→ 96
96	−114	−18

Now practice:

1. $23 + (-81) + 64 + (-8) =$ __?__ −2
2. $-105 + 67 + (-18) + 84 =$ __?__ 28
3. $143 + (-212) + 87 + (-14) =$ __?__ 4
4. $-92 + (-312) + (-11) + 500 =$ __?__ 85

5.	−821	6.	308	7.	−432	8.	1240	9.	2307	10.	4020
	423		− 67		− 65		−823		− 421		1311
	212		− 14		391		−614		203		−3198
	−104		−221		48		212		−1295		− 207
	−290		6		−58		15		794		1926

Now practice:

11. $7 + (15 - 3) - 2 =$ __?__ 17
12. $12 - (15 + 3) + 18 =$ __?__ 12
13. $-6 + (-5 + 2) - 3 =$ __?__ −12
14. $14 + (-2 - 8) - 5 =$ __?__ −1

Remember how?

$$14 - (2 - 5) + 3 = 20$$
$$14 - (-3) \quad + 3$$
$$14 \quad + 3 \quad + 3 = 20$$

15. $6 + [3 - (2 - 5) + 3] - 1 =$ __?__ 14
16. $12 + [5 - (7 + 2) - 1] =$ __?__ 7
17. $3 + [(2 - 6) - (4 + 1)] + 3 =$ __?__ −3
18. $14 - [(8 - 2) + (-6 + 1)] + 3 =$ __?__ 16
19. $[2 - (6 + 5)] - [3 + (2 - 5)] =$ __?__ −9
20. $[3 - (12 - 3)] + [-5 - (2 + 7)] =$ __?__ −20

Remember how?

$$3 \times [4 - (2 + 3)] - 3 \times (5 - 1) = -15$$
$$3 \times [4 \quad - \quad 5] \quad - 3 \times \quad (4)$$
$$3 \times \quad (-1) \quad - 3 \times \quad (4)$$
$$-3 \quad - \quad 12 \quad = -15$$

Now practice:

21. $5 \times (6 - 3) + 4$ 19
22. $(7 + 2) \times (-1) + 18$ 9
23. $3 \times (5 - 6) + (8 \div 2)$ 1
24. $-4 \times (8 - 5) + (-3) \times (-2 + 8)$ −30

25. $6 \times (-12 \div 3) \div (4 - 2)$ −12
26. $12 \div (-8 \div 4) \times (3 - 1)$ −12
27. $-15 + 2 \times (6 - 10) + (14 \div 2)$ −16
28. $[24 \div (8 - 5)] \times [6 \div (-2)]$ −24
29. $\left[\dfrac{4 \times (8 - 3)}{12 - 2} \right] \times [(-4) \div 4]$ −2
30. $\left[\dfrac{3 \times (12 \div 4)}{8 + 1} \right] \times \left[\dfrac{-8 + (2 \times 4)}{3} \right]$ 0

Inequalities

Life Science The barrel cactus stores water in its thick stems. Botanists call desert plants xerophytes, from the Greek words meaning "dry plant."

7

Order and Inequalities

7-1 Order and Betweenness

OBJECTIVE To learn how to express the order of real numbers.

You know that 3 is less than 5 and 5 is greater than 3. We use these symbols to describe the *order* of real numbers:

$<$ means "is less than"

$>$ means "is greater than."

Thus,

"$3 < 5$" and "$5 > 3$."

You can avoid confusing the symbols "$<$" and "$>$" by thinking of them as arrowheads pointing (in a true statement) toward the numeral naming the smaller number. Notice that

"$3 < 5$" and "$5 > 3$"

give the same information.

Any sentence including $\neq$, $<$, or $>$ is called an **inequality.**

To extend the idea of order to negative numbers, we study graphs on the number line. Suppose that a horizontal number line has the positive direction to the right. Then if the graph of one number lies to the left of the graph of a second number, the first number is *less than* the second number, and the second number is *greater than* the first.

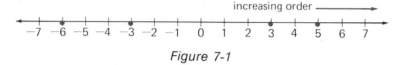

Figure 7-1

The graph in Figure 7-1 pictures

$$3 < 5$$

and also

$$-6 < -3.$$

(Contrast this with "$|-6| > |-3|$." Recall absolute value, page 39.)

The statement "5 is **between** 3 and 6" means that

"$3 < 5$ and $5 < 6$"   or   "$6 > 5$ and $5 > 3$."

Each pair of statements may be written compactly as follows:

"$3 < 5 < 6$"   means   "$3 < 5$ and $5 < 6$."
"$6 > 5 > 3$"   means   "$6 > 5$ and $5 > 3$."

These statements may also be read as

"5 is greater than 3 and less than 6."

Example   Write the integers between -3 and 2.

Solution   From Figure 7-1 we see that -2, -1, 0, and 1 are the integers between -3 and 2.

Oral Exercises

Translate the following symbolic statements into words.

1. $1 < 4$

2. $0 < 7$

3. $-5 < -2$

4. $-8 < 0$

5. $4 > 2$

6. $5 > 0$

7. $-1 > -3$

8. $0 > -2$

9. $-200 < -1$

10. $\frac{1}{8} > \frac{1}{10}$

11. $0.125 > 0.1$

12. $\frac{2}{3} < \frac{3}{4}$

1. 1 is less than 4.
4. -8 is less than 0.
7. -1 is greater than -3.
10. $\frac{1}{8}$ is greater than $\frac{1}{10}$.

2. 0 is less than 7.
5. 4 is greater than 2.
8. 0 is greater than -2.
11. 0.125 is greater than 0.1.

3. -5 is less than -2.
6. 5 is greater than 0.
9. -200 is less than -1.
12. $\frac{2}{3}$ is less than $\frac{3}{4}$.

Tell whether the following statements are true or false.

13. $-7 > 2$ F   14. $7 > 2$ T   15. $16 < 19$ T   16. $-16 < -21$ F

17. $|-7| < 2$ F   18. $|-8| > -2$ T   19. $|-8| < |-21|$ T 20. $|-19| > |17|$ T

21. $-6 < 2 < 9$ T   22. $-21 < 0$ and $0 > -2$ T   23. $7 > 0 > -5$ T   24. $6 < 7$ and $7 < 6$ F

Written Exercises

Replace each __?__ with one of the symbols $<$ or $>$ to make a true statement.

A 1. $-6 \underline{?} 0$ $<$ 2. $0 \underline{?} -8$ $>$ 3. $7 \underline{?} 8 + 2$ $<$ 4. $3 - 1 \underline{?} 1 + 3$ $<$

5. $2 \times 7 \underline{?} 3 \times 5$ $<$ 6. $6 \times 2 \underline{?} 1 \times 3$ $>$ 7. $4 \underline{?} 2 + 3$ $<$ 8. $8 + 1 \underline{?} -1$ $>$

Translate these statements into symbols.

9. 5 is less than 10. $5 < 10$ 10. -8 is less than -4. $-8 < -4$

11. -3 is greater than -7. $-3 > -7$ 12. 12 is greater than 0. $12 > 0$ $-1 < 0 < 1$

13. 6 is greater than 4 and less than 8. $4 < 6 < 8$ 14. 0 is greater than -1 and less than 1.

15. -16 is between -10 and -20.   16. 21 is between 17 and 24. $17 < 21 < 24$
$-20 < -16 < -10$

Write each statement as two statements joined by *and*. Answers on page A3 at the back of the book.

17. $-5 < -4.5 < 4$ 18. $-1.5 < 0 < 25$ 19. $6 < 8.5 < 10.25$

20. $25 < 145 < 1000$ 21. $7 > 1 > -25$ 22. $8 > -7 > -32$

23. $-2.5 < -2 < -1.75$ 24. $-25 > -1007 > -1100$ 25. $7.5 < 8.2 < 9.5$

26. $-7.5 > -8.2 > -9.5$ 27. $0 > -2 > -150$ 28. $0 < 25 < 150$

List the integers between the numbers given.

29. 1, 5   30. $-5, -1$ 31. 0, 4   32. $-4, 0$ 33. $-100, -95$ 34. 25, 30

2, 3, 4 $-4, -3, -2$ 1, 2, 3 $-3, -2, -1$ $-99, -98, -97, -96$ 26, 27, 28, 29

Historical Note
Greater than—less than

The symbols for "greater than" and "less than" were invented by Thomas Harriot (1560–1621), an English mathematician and astronomer. They appeared in his algebra book, which was published in 1631, ten years after his death. He also used Recorde's symbol of equality (page 9). Harriot was appointed geographer for Sir Walter Raleigh's expedition to Roanoke, Virginia, in 1585–1586. His report of that trip was included in Hakluyt's *Voyages,* published in 1600.

7-2 Subsets and Betweenness

> **OBJECTIVE** To learn how to interpret and graph subsets of the real numbers.

For numbers, we have the relations "equals," "is less than," and "is greater than." For sets, we have the relations "equals" and "is a subset of."

> Equal sets have the same members: $\{1, 2, 3\} = \{2, 1, 3\}$

Sometimes we give names to sets we are working with, as, for example: Let $M = \{1, 2, 3\}$; let $N = \{2, 1, 3\}$. Then $M = N$.

> If every member of a set B is also a member of a set A, then B is a **subset** of A, written
>
> $B \subset A$.

"$\{3\} \subset \{1, 2, 3\}$" is read, "The set whose member is 3 **is a subset of** the set whose members are 1, 2, and 3.

Remember (page 17) that

"$3 \in \{1, 2, 3\}$" is read, "3 *is a member of* the set whose members are 1, 2, and 3."

Any set is considered to be a subset of itself.

A set whose members can be counted is called a **finite set**. For example,

$E = \{$the integers between -2 and $3\}$

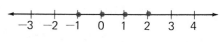

Figure 7-2

is a finite set (Figure 7-2).

A set for which the counting of members would never end is called an **infinite set**. An example of one kind of infinite set is the set of integers: $\{\ldots, -2, -1, 0, 1, 2, 3, \ldots\}$.

An example of another kind of infinite set is

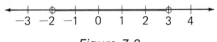

F = {the real numbers between −2 and 3}.

Figure 7-3

F is an infinite set because the graphs of the members completely fill the segment between the graphs of −2 and 3 except the end points, and cannot be counted (Figure 7-3). Notice that the open circles indicate that −2 and 3 are not included.

   The empty set, Ø (page 107), is considered to be finite.
   Note that *E* and *F* are subsets of {the real numbers}.
   Ø is considered to be a subset of every set.

Oral Exercises

Answers on page A3 at the back of the book.
Translate the following symbolic statements into words.

1. 2 ∈ {1, 2, 3}

2. {2} ⊂ {2, 4, 6}

3. {−3, −2, −1} ⊂ {the negative integers}

4. {the odd integers} ⊂ {the integers}

5. {the prime numbers} ⊂ {the positive integers}

6. {the negative integers} ⊂ {the integers}

7. If *A* ⊂ *B* and *B* ⊂ *C*, then *A* ⊂ *C*.

8. If *A* ⊂ *B* and *B* ⊂ *A*, then *A* = *B*.

Describe the set whose graph is shown. There may be more than one correct description.

Sample 1
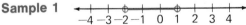

Solution   {the real numbers between −2 and 1} or {the real numbers greater than −2 and less than 1}

Sample 2
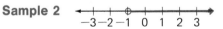

Solution   {the real numbers greater than −1}

9.
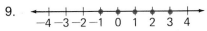

{the integers between −2 and 4}

10.
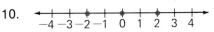

{the even integers between −3 and 3}

11.
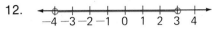

{the real numbers greater than −2}

12.
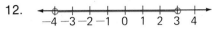

{the real numbers between −4 and 3}

13.
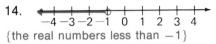

{the real numbers between −3 and 2}

14.
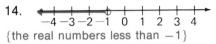

{the real numbers less than −1}

State whether the given set is finite or infinite.

15. {the whole numbers less than 10}   finite

16. {the odd natural numbers greater than 4}   infinite

17. {the negative integers greater than −100}

18. {the real numbers between −8 and 3}   infinite

19. Are all integers real numbers?   yes   finite

20. Are all real numbers integers?   no

Written Exercises

Replace each __?__ with one of the symbols $\in$, $\subset$, $<$, or $>$ to make a true statement.

A 1. 3 __?__ {the odd natural numbers} $\in$ 2. {7} __?__ {the real numbers} $\subset$

3. 5 __?__ 4 − 1 $>$ 4. 8 + 3 __?__ 9 + 4 $<$

5. {5} __?__ {the odd natural numbers} $\subset$ 6. 24 __?__ {the even integers} $\in$

Graph each set.

7. {the odd natural numbers less than 10}   8. {the even integers between −3 and 5}

9. {the real numbers greater than 2}   10. {the real numbers less than 2}

11. {the real numbers between −1 and 3}   12. {the real numbers between −5 and −2}

 Self-Test 1

Be sure that you understand these terms:

inequality (p. 255)   between (p. 256)   equal sets (p. 258)
subset (p. 258)   finite set (p. 258)   infinite set (p. 258)

Be sure that you understand these symbols:

$<$ (p. 255) $>$ (p. 255) $\subset$ (p. 258)

Replace each __?__ with $<$ or $>$ to make a true statement.

1. 2 __?__ −1   2. −3 __?__ 2   Objective 7-1, p. 255

Translate into words.

3. −3 < 4   4. 0 > −7
5. −2 < 0 < 3   6. 7 > 3 > −1

Replace each __?__ with $\subset$ or $\in$ to make a true statement.

7. {2, 3} __?__ {1, 2, 3, 4}   8. 3 __?__ {1, 3, 5}   Objective 7-2, p. 258

Is the set finite or infinite?

9. {−1, 0, 1, 2}   10. {the integers}

Check your answers with those printed at the back of the book.

Solving Inequalities

7-3 Transforming Inequalities

> **OBJECTIVE** To learn how to transform inequalities and find their solution sets.

You can see that only the first of the following statements is true:

$$-7 < 1; \qquad -7 = 1; \qquad 1 < -7$$
$$\text{TRUE} \qquad \text{FALSE} \qquad \text{FALSE}$$

In general, the following basic assumption is made:

> ### Axiom of Comparison
> For all real numbers a and b, one and only one of the following statements is true:
> $$a < b, \qquad a = b, \qquad b < a.$$

Figure 7-4 shows:
  The graph of a to the left of the graph of b: $a < b$
  The graph of b to the left of the graph of c: $b < c$
  The graph of a to the left of the graph of c: $a < c$

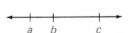

Figure 7-4

In general, the following assumption is made:

> ### Transitive Axiom of Order
> For all real numbers a, b, and c:
> **1.** If $a < b$ and $b < c$, then $a < c$;
> **2.** If $c > b$ and $b > a$, then $c > a$.

The transitive axiom of order corresponds to the transitive axiom of equality (page 88). There are no reflexive and symmetric properties of order.

Inequalities can be transformed by operating on both members.

What happens when a real number is added to each member of the inequality "$-5 < 2$"? Study Figures 7-5 and 7-6.

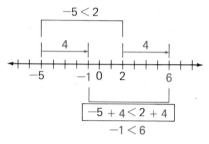

Figure 7-5

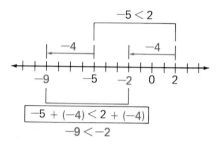

Figure 7-6

The statements in Figures 7-5 and 7-6 suggest the next assumption:

> **Addition Axiom of Order**
>
> For all real numbers a, b, and c:
>
> **1.** If $a < b$, then $a + c < b + c$; similarly:
>
> **2.** If $a > b$, then $a + c > b + c$.

What happens when each member of the inequality "$-5 < 2$" is multiplied by a nonzero real number? Study Figures 7-7 and 7-8.

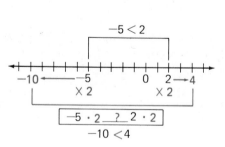

Figure 7-7

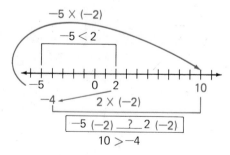

Figure 7-8

The statements in Figures 7-7 and 7-8 suggest the next assumption:

> **Multiplication Axiom of Order**
>
> For all real numbers a, b, and c:
>
> **1.** If $a < b$ and $c > 0$, then $ac < bc$; similarly,
> if $a > b$ and $c > 0$, then $ac > bc$.
> **2.** If $a < b$ and $c < 0$, then $ac > bc$; similarly,
> if $a > b$ and $c < 0$, then $ac < bc$.

Notice that multiplying each member of a *directed inequality* by a *negative number reverses* the direction of the inequality.

The axioms that have been stated guarantee that the following transformations of a given inequality always produce an **equivalent inequality,** that is, one with the same solution set.

> **Transformations That Produce an Equivalent Inequality**
>
> **1.** Substituting for either member of the inequality an expression equivalent to that member.
> **2.** Adding to (or subtracting from) each member the same real number.
> **3.** Multiplying (or dividing) each member by the same positive number.
> **4.** Multiplying (or dividing) each member by the same negative number and reversing the direction of the inequality.

As was noted in the development of transformations that produce equivalent equations, transformation by subtraction is a special kind of transformation by addition (page 56) and transformation by division is a special case of transformation by multiplication (page 82).

You use these transformations to find solution sets of open inequalities, as shown in the Example on the next page.

Example   Solve $3(1 - x) - 1 < 8 - x$ over the set of real numbers, and graph the solution set.

Solution

	$3(1 - x) - 1 < 8 - x$
1. Use the distributive axiom to simplify the left member.	$3 - 3x - 1 < 8 - x$
	$-3x + 2 < 8 - x$
2. Subtract 2 from each member.	$-3x + 2 - 2 < 8 - x - 2$
	$-3x < 6 - x$
3. Add x to each member.	$-3x + x < 6 - x + x$
	$-2x < 6$
4. Divide each member by -2. [Note change from $<$ to $>$.]	$\dfrac{-2x}{-2} > \dfrac{6}{-2}$
	$x > -3$

$\therefore$ the solution set is {all real numbers greater than -3}. The graph of the solution set is:

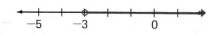

$$-5 \qquad -3 \qquad\qquad 0 \qquad\qquad \textit{Answer}$$

Oral Exercises

Tell how to transform the first inequality to obtain the second one. Then describe the solution set of the given inequality.   A. = Add, S. = Subtract, M. = Multiply, D. = Divide

Sample $-3z < 6; \; z > -2$

Solution   Divide each member by -3 and reverse the direction of the inequality. The solution set is all real numbers greater than -2.

1. $x - 2 < 3; \; x < 5$ A. 2
2. $t + 5 < 7; \; t < 2$ S. 5
3. $u + 7 > 0; \; u > -7$ S
4. $y - 6 > -4; \; y > 2$ A. 6
5. $2z < 12; \; z < 6$ D. by 2
6. $3n < -18; \; n < -6$ D
7. $-2 > \dfrac{x}{2}; \; -4 > x$ M. by 2
8. $\dfrac{v}{5} > 2; \; v > 10$ M. by 5
9. $1 < \dfrac{t}{4}; \; t > 4$ M. by 4
10. $2k > \dfrac{1}{3}; \; k > \dfrac{1}{6}$ D. by 2
11. $-3x < 12; \; x > -4$ and reverse   D. by -3
12. $-2s > -6; \; s < 3$ and reve   D.

Tell how to transform the given inequality into an equivalent one in which one member is a variable and the other is a numeral for a specific number. State the transformed inequality.   A = Add; S. = Subtract; M. = Multiply; D. = Divide

13. $x + 5 > 7$ S. 5 $x > 2$
14. $z - 4 > -1$ A. 4 $z > 3$
15. $2z < 6$ D. by 2 $z < 3$
16. $4t < 20$ D. b $t < 5$
17. $\dfrac{s}{3} < -1$ M. by 3 $s < -3$
18. $\dfrac{y}{4} > -2$ M. by 4 $y > -8$
19. $2 - t > 6$ A. t, S. 6 $-4 > t$
20. $3 - u < 1$ A. u, S. 1 $2 < u$

Written Exercises

Solve each inequality. In Exercises 1–12, also graph the solution set.

A 1. $z - 5 < 15$ $z < 20$ 2. $x + 4 > 24$ $x > 20$ 3. $4z > 36$ $z > 9$ 4. $16t < 32$ $t < 2$

5. $3y + 1 < 13$ $y < 4$ 6. $2u - 3 > 7$ $u > 5$ 7. $\frac{s}{2} + 1 > 2$ $s > 2$ 8. $2 + \frac{n}{3} < 5$ $n < 9$

9. $-5k < 30$ $k > -6$ 10. $-6t > -24$ $t < 4$ 11. $3 - 2x > 17$ $x < -7$ 12. $1 - 6m \leq 25$ $m > -4$

13. $2x < x + 9$ $x < 9$ 14. $3r - 1 > 2r + 3$ $r > 4$ 15. $1 - 2t > t + 10$ $t < -3$

16. $2t + 2 < 14 - 2t$ $t < 3$ 17. $\frac{z}{2} + 1 < \frac{3}{2}$ $z < 1$ 18. $2 > \frac{2}{3} - \frac{x}{3}$ $x > -4$

19. $1 - v > 2 + v$ $v < -\frac{1}{2}$ 20. $t - 1 > 2 - t$ $t > \frac{3}{2}$ 21. $2(x - 2) > 4$ $x > 4$

22. $6 < 3(1 - s)$ $s < -1$ 23. $2(t - 3) < 3(t + 2)$ $t > -12$ 24. $3(3 + y) < 5(5 + y)$ $y > -8$

B 25. $\frac{1}{2}x > 2(x - 6)$ $x < 8$ 26. $x - \frac{3}{2} > \frac{1}{2}(x + 4)$ $x > 7$

27. $2(t + 3) + 3(t + 2) > 2$ $t > -2$ 28. $4(1 - z) + 6(1 + z) < 0$ $z < -5$

29. $3(r - 2) - 2(r - 3) < 4 + 2r$ $r > -4$ 30. $2(3x - 1) + 3(1 - x) > 2(x + 1)$ $x > 1$

31. $5(2 - a) - 4(2a - 1) > 3(3 - a)$ $a < \frac{1}{2}$ 32. $4(2n - 3) + 2(1 - 2n) < 2n - 5$ $n < 2\frac{1}{2}$

Biographical Note
Florence Rena Sabin

Florence Rena Sabin (1871–1953) made important contributions to the study of anatomy. She was born in Central City, Colorado, and was educated at Smith College and the Johns Hopkins University School of Medicine. Her first major research project was a study of the lymphatics, the vessels that carry lymph through the body. Her work led to the discovery of the origin and processes of the body's lymphatic system. Florence Sabin next turned to a study of the red and white blood corpuscles. In the course of this research, she perfected a new technique for studying living blood cells. In 1925 she joined the staff of the Rockefeller Institute for Medical Research in New York. There she continued her study of the blood, applying her previous results to research on a cure for tuberculosis. She was elected to the National Academy of Sciences in 1925.

Extra for Experts ExtraExtraExtraExtraExtraExt
Binary System of Numeration

We are so used to using ten as the base for writing numbers that it is hard to think of other bases. However, any integer greater than 1 can be used as a base. Compare:

Decimal Notation (Base Ten)
Digits: 0, 1, 2, 3, 4, 5, 6, 7, 8, 9

Binary Notation (Base Two)
Digits: 0, 1

Places

...	(Ten)^2	(Ten)	(Unit)

Places

...	(Two)^2	(Two)	(Unit)

The base of a numeration system is always written as 10.

The binary system is especially useful in the construction of computers because the digits can be represented by switches in "ON" or "OFF" positions.

Study these numerals:

Decimal	Binary	Decimal	Binary	Decimal	Binary
1	1	9	1001	$0.5 = \frac{1}{2}$	0.1 (Two)$^{-1}$
2	10	10	1010		
3	11	11	1011	$\frac{1}{4}$	0.01 (Two)$^{-2}$
4	100 (Two)^2	12	1100		
5	101	13	1101	$\frac{1}{8}$	0.001 (Two)$^{-3}$
6	110	14	1110		
7	111	15	1111	$\frac{1}{16}$	0.0001 (Two)$^{-4}$
8	1000 (Two)^3	16	10000 (Two)^4		

Translate these binary numerals into decimal numerals:

Sample 1 $1011 = 1(\text{Two})^3 + 0(\text{Two})^2 + 1(\text{Two}) + 1 = 8 + 2 + 1 = 11$

Sample 2 $0.11 = 1(\text{Two})^{-1} + 1(\text{Two})^{-2} = \frac{1}{2} + \frac{1}{4} = \frac{3}{4} = 0.75$

1. 10100 20 2. 0.101 $\frac{5}{8}$ 3. 11100 28 4. 0.111 $\frac{7}{8}$ 5. 10.111 2$\frac{7}{8}$ 6. 0.1011 $\frac{11}{16}$

Translate these decimal numerals into binary numerals:

Sample 3 $20 = 16 + 4 = 10100$

Sample 4 $\frac{3}{8} = \frac{1}{4} + \frac{1}{8} = 0.011$

7. 24 11000 8. 32 100000 9. $\frac{5}{16}$ 0.0101 10. $\frac{7}{8}$ 0.111 11. 1$\frac{1}{2}$ 1.1 12. 2$\frac{5}{8}$ 10.101

7-4 Using Inequalities to Solve Problems

> **OBJECTIVE** To learn how to solve problems involving inequalities.

Example Find all sets of three consecutive positive odd integers such that the sum of the integers in the set is greater than four times the least integer in the set.

Solution

Step 1 The problem asks us to find all sets of three consecutive positive odd integers such that the sum of the integers in the set is greater than four times the least integer in the set.

Step 2 Let k = the least integer in the set.

Then $k + 2$ and $k + 4$ are the other integers in the set.

Step 3 The sum of the integers is greater than four times the least.

$$k + (k + 2) + (k + 4) \quad > \quad 4k$$

Step 4
$$3k + 6 > 4k$$
$$3k + 6 - 3k > 4k - 3k$$
$$6 > k$$

The only positive odd integers less than 6 are 1, 3, and 5. The corresponding sets having these as their least members are

$$\{1, 3, 5\}, \{3, 5, 7\}, \text{ and } \{5, 7, 9\}.$$

Step 5 *Check:*

Set	Sum of the Integers > 4 × (least integer)?
$\{1, 3, 5\}$	$1 + 3 + 5 > 4 \cdot 1$ ✓
$\{3, 5, 7\}$	$3 + 5 + 7 > 4 \cdot 3$ ✓
$\{5, 7, 9\}$	$5 + 7 + 9 > 4 \cdot 5$ ✓

$\therefore$ the required sets are $\{1, 3, 5\}, \{3, 5, 7\}$, and $\{5, 7, 9\}$. *Answer*

Problems

Solve.

A 1. Of all pairs of consecutive even integers whose sum is less than 50, find the pair whose sum is greatest.   **22 and 24**

2. Of all pairs of consecutive odd integers whose sum is greater than 75, find the pair whose sum is least.   **37 and 39**

3. Three times the smaller of two consecutive odd integers is less than twice the larger integer. What are the largest possible values for the integers?   **3 and 5**

4. The sum of three consecutive integers diminished by 15 is greater than the largest of the three. What are the smallest possible values for the integers?   **8, 9, and 10**

5. Find all sets of four consecutive positive odd integers such that their sum is greater than five times the smallest of them.   (*below*)

6. Find all sets of four consecutive positive even integers such that the largest integer in the set is greater than twice the smallest.   **{2, 4, 6, 8}**
{4, 6, 8, 10}

5. {1, 3, 5, 7}, {3, 5, 7, 9}, {5, 7, 9, 11}, {7, 9, 11, 13},
{9, 11, 13, 15}, {11, 13, 15, 17}

Applications
Electrical Power and Energy

Power is associated with the flow of an electric current in a circuit. Electrical power is measured in watts. The amount of power that is used depends on the voltage of the source of electricity and on the current. Current is the rate of flow of electrical charge, measured in amperes. Most household appliances (with the exception of large ones, such as stoves or clothes dryers) operate at between 115 and 125 volts. Look at some electrical appliances in your home. The voltage and power are usually labeled.

The watt, ampere, and volt are units in the metric system. Using these units of measurement, power (P) is related to voltage (V) and current (I) by the formula

$$P = VI.$$

Example 1 If current from a 120-volt source flows through a 100-watt light bulb, find the amount of current flowing in the circuit.

Solution You are given $V = 120$ and $P = 100$. Use the formula:

$$P = VI$$
$$100 = 120 \cdot I$$
$$I = \frac{100}{120} = \frac{5}{6}$$

$$I = \frac{5}{6} \text{ or about 0.83 ampere } \textit{Answer}$$

When P watts of power are used for t hours, the energy (e) consumed, measured in watt-hours (Wh), is

$$e = Pt.$$

Electric companies base their charge to their customers on a larger unit, the kilowatt-hour (1 kilowatt-hour = 1000 watt-hours). The symbol for kilowatt-hour in the metric system is kWh.

Example 2 A room air conditioner uses about 860 watts. If the average cost of electricity is 5.4¢ per kilowatt-hour, how much does it cost to operate the air conditioner for 6 hours?

Solution Using the formula for energy, find the amount of energy consumed.

$$e = Pt$$
$$e = 860 \cdot 6$$
$$e = 5160 \text{ Wh or } 5.160 \text{ kWh}$$

To compute the cost:

$$\text{cost} = 5.4 \times 5.160$$
$$= 27.864$$

∴ the cost of energy is about 28¢. *Answer*

1. A desk calculator operates at 115 volts with a current of 0.14 amperes. How much power in watts is used by the calculator? **16.1 watts**

2. A toaster uses about 1150 watts. If it operates at 120 volts, how much current in amperes flows through the wiring? **about 9.58 amperes**

3. A 1000-watt hair dryer operates on a current of 8.33 amperes. What is the voltage in the circuit? **about 120 volts**

4. A solid-state color television uses 200 watts. Assuming the cost of electricity is 5.4¢ per kilowatt-hour, how much does it cost to watch a 3-hour movie? **about 3¢**

5. The oven in an electric range uses 12,200 watts. At 5.4¢ per kilowatt-hour, how much does it cost to roast a turkey for 5 hours? **about $3.29**

Puzzle Time

An article was on sale at 25% discount off the original price. The employees were allowed a 20% discount off the sale price. If an employee paid $60 for the article, what was the original price? **$100**

7-5 Intersection and Union of Sets

OBJECTIVE To learn how to find unions and intersections of sets.

Figure 7-9 shows relationships among the sets:

$$H = \{0, 3, 5, 6, 9\}$$
$$K = \{3, 4, 9\}$$
$$L = \{1, 8\}$$

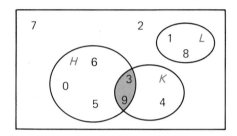

Do you see that the set represented by shading,

$$\{3, 9\},$$

consists of the members that sets

Figure 7-9

$$H = \{0, 3, 5, 6, 9\} \quad \text{and} \quad K = \{3, 4, 9\}$$

have in common? You call $\{3, 9\}$ the *intersection* of $\{0, 3, 5, 6, 9\}$ and $\{3, 4, 9\}$ and write

$$\{0, 3, 5, 6, 9\} \cap \{3, 4, 9\} = \{3, 9\}$$

or

$$H \cap K = \{3, 9\}.$$

The latter is read, "The intersection of H and K is $\{3, 9\}$."
  In general:

> For any two sets A and B, the set consisting of all members belonging to *both* A and B is called the **intersection** of A and B, written $A \cap B$.

A representation of sets like that shown in Figure 7-9 is called a **Venn diagram** in honor of the English mathematician John Venn (1834–1923).
  In Figure 7-9, the regions representing H and L do not overlap. Two sets, like H and L, which have no members in common are called **disjoint sets**. Their intersection has no members. The set with no members is the empty set, $\emptyset$. Thus,

$$H \cap L = \emptyset.$$

Figure 7-10 again shows the sets *H*, *K*, and *L* discussed on page 270. Now the set represented by the shaded region,

$$\{0, 3, 4, 5, 6, 9\},$$

consists of the members which belong to *at least one* of the sets

$$H = \{0, 3, 5, 6, 9\} \quad \text{and} \quad K = \{3, 4, 9\}.$$

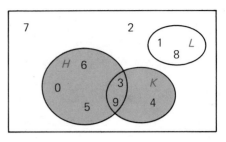

Figure 7-10

You call it the *union* of *H* and *K*, and write

$$\{0, 3, 5, 6, 9\} \cup \{3, 4, 9\} = \{0, 3, 4, 5, 6, 9\}$$

or

$$H \cup K = \{0, 3, 4, 5, 6, 9\}.$$

The latter is read, "**The union of** *H* **and** *K* **is** {0, 3, 4, 5, 6, 9}."

In general:

> For any two sets *A* and *B*, the set consisting of all members belonging to *at least one* of the sets *A* and *B* is called the **union** of *A* and *B*, written *A* ∪ *B*.

Do you see that in Figure 7-10, $K \cup L = \{1, 3, 4, 8, 9\}$?

You usually represent sets of real numbers as graphs on a number line rather than as Venn diagrams.

Example Let $E = \{$the real numbers less than 2$\}$
$F = \{$the real numbers between -1 and 4$\}$
Graph: $E, \quad F, \quad E \cup F, \quad E \cap F$

Solution

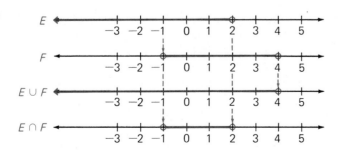

Note that for any set *A*

$$A \cup \emptyset = A \quad \text{and} \quad A \cap \emptyset = \emptyset.$$

Oral Exercises

Refer to the adjoining diagram and list the members
of each of the following sets.
{0, 1, 2, 3, 5, 6, 7, 8, 9}

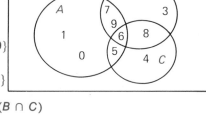

1. *A* ∪ *B*
2. *A* ∩ *B* {6, 7, 9}
3. *B* ∩ *C* {6, 8}
4. *B* ∪ *C* {2, 3, 4, 5, 6, 7, 8, 9}
5. *A* ∩ (*B* ∩ *C*) {6}
6. (*A* ∩ *B*) ∪ *C* {4, 5, 6, 7, 8, 9}
7. (*A* ∪ *B*) ∩ *C* {5, 6, 8}
8. (*A* ∪ *B*) ∪ *C*
   {0, 1, 2, 3, 4, 5, 6, 7, 8, 9}
9. (*A* ∩ *B*) ∪ (*A* ∩ *C*) {5, 6, 7, 9}
10. Express {6, 7, 8, 9} in terms of *A*, *B*, and *C*. (*A* ∩ *B*) ∪ (*B* ∩ *C*)

In Exercises 11–18, refer to the number line diagram
at the right and describe each set.

D = {the real numbers greater than −2}
E = {the real numbers between −3 and 3}
F = {the real numbers less than 1}

11. *D* ∪ *F*
12. *D* ∪ *E*
13. *D* ∩ *E*
14. *D* ∩ *F*
15. *E* ∪ *F*
16. *E* ∩ *F*
17. *D* ∩ (*E* ∩ *F*)
18. (*D* ∩ *E*) ∪ *F*

11. {real nos.}
12. {real nos. > −3}
13. {real nos. betw. −2 and 3}
14. {real nos. betw. −2 an
15. {real nos. < 3}
16. {real nos. betw. −3 and 1}
17. {real nos. betw. −2 and 1}
18. {real nos. < 3}

Written Exercises

Specify the union and intersection of the given sets. If the sets are
disjoint, say so. Answers to Exs. 1–8 below.

A

1. {0, 1, 2, 3}, {2, 3, 4}
2. {−3, −2, −1, 0}, {−1, 0, 1}
3. {2, 4, 6}, {1, 3, 5}
4. {2, 4}, {1, 2, 3, 4, 5}
5. {2, 3, 5, 7, 11}, {1, 3, 5, 7, 9}
6. {−6, −5, −4}, {−3, −2, −1}
7. {the natural numbers}, {the even integers}
8. {the odd integers}, {the whole numbers}
9. {the positive real numbers}, {the negative real numbers} {real nos. except 0}; ∅ (disjoint)
10. {0}, ∅ {0}; ∅ (disjoint)

In Exercises 11–22, graph each set, their union, and their intersection.

11. {the natural numbers less than 6}
    {−2, −1, 0, 1, 2}
12. {the whole numbers less than 6}
    {the even natural numbers less than 9}
13. {the negative integers greater than −6}
    {the odd integers between −4 and 4}
14. {the even whole numbers less than 7}
    {the first five even natural numbers}

1. {0, 1, 2, 3, 4}; {2, 3}
2. {−3, −2, −1, 0, 1}; {−1, 0}
3. {1, 2, 3, 4, 5, 6}; ∅ (disjoint)
4. {1, 2, 3, 4, 5}; {2, 4}
5. {1, 2, 3, 5, 7, 9, 11}; {3, 5, 7}
6. {−6, −5, −4, −3, −2, −1}; ∅ (disjoint)
7. {natural nos. and non-positive even integers}; {even natural integers}
8. {whole nos. and negative odd integers}; {odd whole nos.}

15. {the real numbers less than 4}
{the real numbers greater than 1}

16. {the real numbers between 0 and 5}
{the real numbers between 2 and 6}

B 17. {the positive real numbers}
{the real numbers between -2 and 3}

18. {the real numbers less than 3}
{the real numbers between 0 and 6}

19. {the real numbers between -2 and 4}
· {the real numbers between -4 and 2}

20. {the real numbers between 1 and 5}
{the real numbers between -4 and 2}

21. {the real numbers less than 1}
{the real numbers less than -2}

22. {the real numbers greater than -3}
{the real numbers greater than 2}

Draw a Venn diagram to illustrate the statement.

23. If $A \subset B$, then $A \cup B = B$.

24. If $A \subset B$, then $A \cap B = A$.

For each of Exercises 25 and 26, make two copies of the Venn diagram shown at the right. On your copies shade the regions representing the sets named.

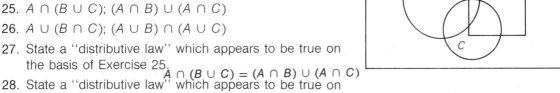

C 25. $A \cap (B \cup C)$; $(A \cap B) \cup (A \cap C)$

26. $A \cup (B \cap C)$; $(A \cup B) \cap (A \cup C)$

27. State a "distributive law" which appears to be true on the basis of Exercise 25. $A \cap (B \cup C) = (A \cap B) \cup (A \cap C)$

28. State a "distributive law" which appears to be true on the basis of Exercise 26. $A \cup (B \cap C) = (A \cup B) \cap (A \cup C)$

Draw a Venn diagram showing relationships among the given sets. List the members of set F.

29. $E = \{4, 5, 6\}$, $E \cup F = \{2, 3, 4, 5, 6\}$, $E \cap F = \{4, 6\}$ $F = \{2, 3, 4, 6\}$

30. $E = \{-1, -2, -4\}$, $E \cup F = \{-1, -2, -3, -4, -5\}$, $E \cap F = \{-1\}$ $F = \{-1, -3, -5\}$

Puzzle Time

Copy the diagram at the right and write in the remaining members of these sets:

$A = \{1, 2, 3, 4, 5, 6, 7\}$
$B = \{1, 3, 5, 7, 9\}$
$C = \{3, 4, 5, 6, 7\}$
$D = \{-3, -1, 1, 3, 4\}$

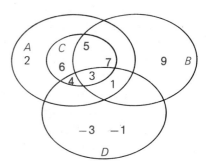

7-6 Solving Combined Inequalities

> **OBJECTIVE** To learn about combined inequalities and how to find their solution sets.

Sometimes inequalities are combined.

> A sentence formed by joining two sentences by the word *and* is called a **conjunction.**

For a conjunction of statements to be true, *both* statements must be true. For example,

"$5 > 3$ and $6 > 7$" is false because "$6 > 7$" is false.

The solution set of a conjunction of open sentences is the set of values that make *both* of the joined sentences true. Thus, the graph of such a conjunction is the *intersection* of the graphs of its parts. For example, the graph of

"$-4 < y$ and $y < 5$"

is the intersection of the graphs of "$-4 < y$, and "$y < 5$" (Figure 7-11).

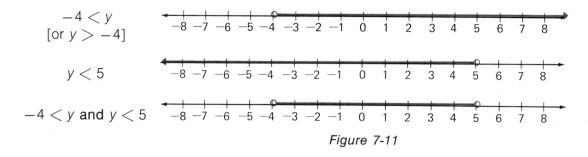

$-4 < y$
[or $y > -4$]

$y < 5$

$-4 < y$ and $y < 5$

Figure 7-11

The conjunction "$-4 < y$ and $y < 5$" is usually written in the compact form:

"$-4 < y < 5$"

> A sentence formed by joining two sentences by the word *or* is called a **disjunction.**

For a disjunction of statements to be true, *at least one* of the statements must be true. For example,

"$5 > 3$ or $6 > 7$" is true because "$5 > 3$" is true.

The solution set of a disjunction of open sentences is the set of values that make *at least one* of the joined sentences true. Thus, the graph of such a disjunction is the *union* of the graphs of its parts. For example, the graph of

"$y < -3$ or $y > 3$"

is the union of the graphs of "$y < -3$" and "$y > 3$" (Figure 7-12).

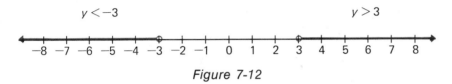

Figure 7-12

The disjunction

"$y = 2$ or $y > 2$"

is written

"$y \geq 2$."

Similarly,

"$y \leq 2$" means "$y < 2$ or $y = 2$."

Example 1   The solution set of "$x < 2$ and $x \geq 2$" is the empty set.

Example 2   The solution set of "$x < 2$ or $x \geq 2$" is the set of all the real numbers.

You can use the transformations listed on page 263 to solve more complicated open sentences of this kind as shown in Example 3 on the next page.

Example 3   Find the solution set of the open sentence

$$-4 < x - 3 \le 2,$$

and graph it.

Solution   The inequality $-4 < x - 3 \le 2$ means the conjunction

$$
\begin{array}{ccc}
-4 < x - 3 & \text{and} & x - 3 \le 2 \\
-4 + 3 < x - 3 + 3 & \text{and} & x - 3 + 3 \le 2 + 3 \\
-1 < x & \text{and} & x \le 5 \\
& -1 < x \le 5 &
\end{array}
$$

∴ the solution set is {5 and all real numbers between -1 and 5}. The graph of the solution set is:

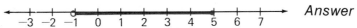   *Answer*

You can shorten the work in Example 3 as follows:

$$
\begin{array}{c}
-4 < x - 3 \le 2 \\
-4 + 3 < x - 3 + 3 \le 2 + 3 \\
-1 < x \le 5
\end{array}
$$

Example 4   Solve the open sentence and draw its graph:

$$2z - 1 < -5 \quad \text{or} \quad 2z - 1 > 5$$

Solution   Copy the joined inequalities and transform them as follows:

$$
\begin{array}{ccc}
2z - 1 < -5 & \text{or} & 2z - 1 > 5 \\
2z - 1 + 1 < -5 + 1 & \text{or} & 2z - 1 + 1 > 5 + 1 \\
2z < -4 & \text{or} & 2z > 6 \\
\dfrac{2z}{2} < \dfrac{-4}{2} & \text{or} & \dfrac{2z}{2} > \dfrac{6}{2} \\
z < -2 & \text{or} & z > 3
\end{array}
$$

∴ the solution set is

{all real numbers that are less than -2 or greater than 3}.

The graph of the solution set is

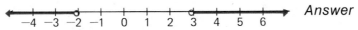   *Answer*

Oral Exercises

Tell whether the given statement is true or false. Give a reason for your answer.

Sample $1 > 4$ or $2 > -3$

Solution True. Although "$1 > 4$" is a false statement, "$2 > -3$" is true, and a disjunction is true if at least one of the joined statements is true.

1. $6 < 1$ or $6 < 5$ F   2. $2 < 5$ and $3 < 2$ F   3. $-2 < -1$ and $1 < 2$ T   4. $3 < 7$ or $-7 < 0$ T

5. $6 < 1$ and $6 < 5$ F   6. $3 < 1$ or $-1 < -3$ F   7. $2 < 1$ or $2 \geq 1$ T   8. $3 > 2$ and $3 < 0$ F

In Exercises 9–14, match each graph with one of the open sentences given in a–f.

9. c

10. e

11. f

12. a

13. b

14. d

a. $x > 2$

b. $x < 1$ or $x > 6$

c. $0 < x < 4$

d. $x < 0$ or $3 < x$

e. $x \leq 2$

f. $-1 \leq x \leq 5$

Written Exercises

Solve each open sentence and graph each solution set which is not empty.

A   1. $-1 < x - 2 < 4$ $1 < x < 6$ 2. $2 \leq y + 3 \leq 6$ $-1 \leq y \leq 3$ 3. $0 \leq 4 + t < 4$ $-4 \leq t < 0$

4. $-3 < -6 + z \leq 3$ $3 < z \leq 9$ 5. $-5 \leq 2r + 1 \leq 7$ $-3 \leq r \leq 3$ 6. $-2 < 3t - 2 < 10$ $0 < t < 4$

7. $x + 1 \leq -3$ or $x + 1 \geq 3$ $x \leq -4$ or $x \geq 2$ 8. $s - 4 < -2$ or $s - 4 > 2$ $s < 2$ or $s > 6$

9. $2u - 3 < -3$ or $3 < 2u - 3$ $u < 0$ or $3 < u$ 10. $2x + 1 \leq -5$ or $2x + 1 \geq 5$ $x \leq -3$ or $x \geq 2$

11. $-2 < -x < 3$ $2 > x > -3$

12. $-6 \le -2z \le 4$ $3 \ge z \ge -2$

13. $-3t < -9$ or $-3t > 9$ $t > 3$ or $t < -3$

14. $-5t < -10$ or $10 < -5t$ $t > 2$ or $-2 > t$

B 15. $-1 < 3 - 2t < 5$ $2 > t > -1$

16. $-2 < -v - 3 < 2$ $-1 > v > -5$

17. $6 - t \le 2$ or $t - 6 < 2$ all real nos.

18. $1 - 2t > 7$ or $1 - 2t < -1$ $t < -3$ or $t > 1$

19. $u + 2 \le -4$ and $u + 2 > 4$ $\emptyset$

20. $s - 3 < 1$ and $s - 3 \ge -1$ $2 \le s < 4$

21. $2r - 1 < 1$ or $2r - 1 \ge -7$ all real nos.

22. $6 - r \le 5$ or $6 - r > 4$ all real nos.

23. $3z - 5 > 2z$ and $3z - 5 < -2z$ $\emptyset$

24. $2x - 6 < x$ or $2x - 6 > -x$ all real nos.

25. $3v + 1 > 1 + v$ or $v + 3 > 3 - v$ $v > 0$

26. $3y < 4y + 1$ and $3 - y < 1$ $y > 2$

C 27. $3x - 1 < 3x + 1 \le 3x + 5$ all real nos.

28. $2t - 1 \le 1 + 2t < 2t$ $\emptyset$

29. $2z < 2z + 1 \le z + 5$ $z \le 4$

30. $2(1 - s) \ge 1 - 2s$ or $3s - 6 < 2 - s$ all real

Career Note
Statistician

Planning surveys, designing experiments, and analyzing data are the major concerns of statisticians. In preparing a survey for a television rating service, for example, statisticians first decide how many viewers to contact and how to contact them. The statisticians then prepare a list of questions for the poll, being careful that all the questions are impartial. Finally, they transmit instructions to workers who will tabulate the information.

In designing experiments, statisticians research the factors involved and formulate mathematical equations or "models" to develop or test theories.

Finally, statisticians analyze data they have obtained and present it in reports. They often use tables and graphs to give a clear picture of their results.

A very strong background in mathematics is important for a career in this field. The minimum educational background may be a bachelor's degree with a major in mathematics or statistics, or a major in some field using statistics with a minor in statistics.

Computer Activity

If you have access to a computer that will accept BASIC, try this program that will find some solutions of the inequality of the Example on page 264:

$$3(1 - x) - 1 < 8 - x.$$

```
10  FOR X=-10 TO 10
20  LET Y1=3*(1-X)-1
30  LET Y2=8-X
40  PRINT Y1,Y2,
50  IF Y1<Y2 THEN 80
60  PRINT X;" IS NOT A SOLUTION."
70  GOTO 90
80  PRINT X;" IS A SOLUTION."
90  NEXT X
100 END
```

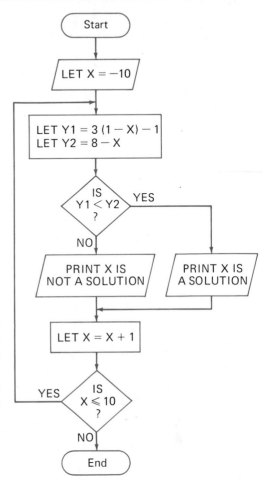

Compare this program with the flowchart at the right. Notice that the IF . . . THEN statement in line 50 corresponds to the first decision (diamond-shaped) box in the flowchart. The second decision box controls the loop that is the FOR . . . NEXT loop in the program.

This program may be used to find some values in the solution set of any of the inequalities in the Written Exercises on page 265.

To use this program for other inequalities, LET

$$Y1 = \text{(the left member)}$$

and

$$Y2 = \text{(the right member)},$$

and experiment with values of X in line 10. Change line 50 if necessary. For example, to find some values in the solution set of Exercise 14, page 265, use

$$3x - 1 > 2x + 3$$

and make these changes in the program:

```
20  LET Y1=3*X-1
30  LET Y2=2*X+3
50  IF Y1>Y2 THEN 80
```

Extra for Experts ExtraExtraExtraExtraExtraExt
Equations and Inequalities
Involving Absolute Value

Equations and inequalities involving absolute value (Section 2-3) occur frequently in higher mathematics.

Consider the following sentences and their graphs:

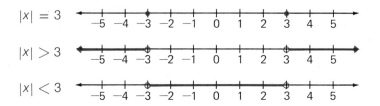

From these graphs, you can see that

$$\text{``}|x| = 3\text{'' means ``}x = 3 \text{ or } x = -3\text{'';}$$
$$\text{``}|x| > 3\text{'' means ``}x > 3 \text{ or } x < -3\text{'';}$$
$$\text{``}|x| < 3\text{'' means ``}x < 3 \text{ and } x > -3\text{'';}$$
$$\text{that is, ``}-3 < x < 3.\text{''}$$

Example 1 Solve $|2t - 5| = 3$.

Solution $|2t - 5| = 3$ means the *disjunction:*

$$
\begin{array}{lcl}
2t - 5 = 3 & \text{or} & 2t - 5 = -3 \\
2t = 8 & \text{or} & 2t = 2 \\
t = 4 & \text{or} & t = 1
\end{array}
$$

$\therefore$ the solution set is $\{1, 4\}$. ***Answer***

Example 2 Solve $|2t - 5| > 3$.

Solution $|2t - 5| > 3$ means the *disjunction:*

$$2t - 5 > 3 \qquad \text{or} \qquad 2t - 5 < -3$$

Completing the solution is left to you. You should find that the solution set is

$$
\begin{array}{l}
2t > 8 \text{ or } 2t < 2 \\
t > 4 \text{ or } t < 1
\end{array}
$$

$\{$all real numbers that are less than 1 or greater than 4$\}$. ***Answer***

Example 3 Solve $|2t - 5| < 3$.

Solution $|2t - 5| < 3$ means the *conjunction:*

$$-3 < 2t - 5 < 3$$
$$2 < 2t < 8$$
$$1 < t < 4$$

∴ the solution set is

{all real numbers between 1 and 4}. *Answer*

State a conjunction or a disjunction which is equivalent to the given open sentence. Answers on page A3 at the back of the book.

1. $|x - 3| = 2$ 2. $|t + 1| = 5$ 3. $|z| \leq 7$ 4. $|u| > 3$
5. $|s + 2| < 1$ 6. $|y - 3| \leq 4$ 7. $|2 - t| \geq 3$ 8. $|6 - t| > 2$
9. $|3 + 2a| = 1$ 10. $|2s + 3| = 3$ 11. $|2x - 7| < 3$ 12. $|-1 - 3r| \geq 2$

13–24. Solve each of the open sentences in Exercises 1–12, and graph the solution set if it is not empty. Answers on page A3 at the back of the book.

Solve, and graph the solution set if it is not empty.

25. $|x - 3| + 3 < 5$ $1 < x < 5$
26. $|(x - 3) + 3| < 5$ $-5 < x < 5$
27. $|1 - 2(1 - z)| \geq 1$ $z \geq 1$ or $z \leq 0$
28. $|y - 3| + 1 \geq |2 - 3|$ all real nos.
29. $3 + 2(1 - |t|) = 1$ $t = 2$ or $t = -2$
30. $1 - (|u - 1| - 1) \leq 0$ $u \geq 3$ or $u \leq -1$
31. $|2y - 1| = y - 2$ ∅
32. $|x - 2| = x - 2$ $x \geq 2$
33. $|z - 3| = z - 1$ $z = 2$
34. $|x - 2| > x - 2$ $x < 2$
35. $|z - 3| > z - 1$ $z < 2$
36. $|x - 2| < x - 2$ ∅

Puzzle Time ∘∘ ◯◯◯ ◯◯ ∘∘∘∘ ◯◯ ∘◯◯◯◦

What's wrong?

$$a > 3$$
$$3a > 3(3)$$
$$3a - a^2 > 9 - a^2$$
$$a(3 - a) > (3 - a)(3 + a)$$
$$a > 3 + a$$
$$∴ 0 > 3.$$

$a(3 - a) > (3 - a)(3 + a)$ is equivalent to $a > 3 + a$ only if $3 - a > 0$ or $3 > a$. But we are given $a > 3$.

★ *Self-Test 2*

Be sure that you understand these terms:

axiom of comparison (p. 261) transitive axiom of order (p. 261) equivalent inequalities (p. 263)
intersection of sets (p. 270) disjoint sets (p. 270) union of sets (p. 271)
Venn diagram (p. 270) conjunction (p. 274) disjunction (p. 275)

Solve each inequality and graph its solution set.

1. $2x - 1 < 5$ 2. $3(t - 2) > t + 2$ Objective 7-3, p. 261

Solve.

3. Find all sets of three consecutive positive even integers whose sum de- Objective 7-4, p. 267
   creased by 10 is less than twice the greatest of the three integers.

Given $A = \{1, 2, 3, 4, 5\}$, $B = \{4, 5, 6, 7\}$, and $C = \{6, 7, 8\}$, identify:

4. $A \cap B$ 5. $B \cup C$ 6. $A \cap C$ Objective 7-5, p. 270

Solve each inequality and graph its solution set.

7. $-2 < x - 2 \le 3$ 8. $2t - 1 > 5$ or $1 - t > 0$ Objective 7-6, p. 274

Check your answers with those printed at the back of the book.

Chapter Summary

1. To compare numbers, $<$ (is less than) and $>$ (is greater than) are used. $-3 < 1 < 4$ (or $4 > 1 > -3$) means that 1 is between -3 and 4.
2. Special symbols are used to describe relationships between sets:
   $\{1, 2\} \subset \{1, 2, 3\}$ means that $\{1, 2\}$ is a subset of $\{1, 2, 3\}$.
   $\{1, 2\} \cup \{2, 3, 4\} = \{1, 2, 3, 4\}$ means that the union of $\{1, 2\}$ and $\{2, 3, 4\}$ is $\{1, 2, 3, 4\}$.
   $\{1, 2\} \cap \{2, 3, 4\} = \{2\}$ means that the intersection of $\{1, 2\}$ and $\{2, 3, 4\}$ is $\{2\}$.
3. Open inequalities can be solved by applying transformations to obtain simpler equivalent inequalities.
4. Sentences joined by *and* form a conjunction. Sentences joined by *or* form a disjunction.

Chapter Test

Insert a symbol to make a true statement.

7-1 1. $-7 \underline{\quad?\quad} -6$ $<$ 2. $-5 \underline{\quad?\quad} -8$ $>$

7-2 3. $\{1, 3\} \underline{\quad?\quad} \{1, 3, 5, 7, 11\}$ $\subset$

7-3 4. Solve and graph the solution set of $3x - 1 < x + 7.$ $x < 4$

Solve.

7-4 5. Find all sets of four consecutive positive integers such that their sum
     is less than three times the greatest of the set of integers. $\{1, 2, 3, 4\}, \{2, 3, 4, 5\}$

7-5 6. If $A = \{0, 2, 4, 6\}$ and $B = \{1, 3, 5\}$, find $A \cup B$ and $A \cap B.$ $A \cup B = \{0, 1, 2, 3, 4, 5, 6\}$
     $A \cap B = \emptyset$

7-6 7. Solve and graph the solution set of $-1 < 2x - 3 \leq 3.$
     $1 < x \leq 3$

Programmed Chapter Review

7-1 1. A sentence containing $<$ or $>$ or $\neq$ is called an $\underline{\quad?\quad}$.   inequality

2. The integers between -1 and 3 are $\underline{\quad?\quad}$.   0, 1, 2

3. The sentence "$3 < 7 < 10$" means that 7 is $\underline{\quad?\quad}$ than 3 and   greater
   7 is $\underline{\quad?\quad}$ than 10.   less

7-2 4. $\{2, 3, 4\} \underline{\quad?\quad} \{1, 2, 3, 4, 5\}$ $\subset$ (is a subset of)
     (or $\neq$)

5. $\{2, 3, 4\}$ is a $\underline{\quad?\quad}$ set.   finite

6. $\{\ldots, -1, 0, 1, \ldots\}$ is an $\underline{\quad?\quad}$ set.   infinite

7-3 7. Of the three statements "$a > 0$," "$a = 0$," and "$a < 0$," how
     many are true for a given real number a?   one

8. If $6x < 5x$, then x is $\underline{\quad?\quad}$.   negative (or less than 0)

9. If $3z - 2 > 4$, then $z > \underline{\quad?\quad}$.   2

7-4 10. Three consecutive integers are between 1 and 7. Possible sets
     are $\underline{\quad?\quad}$, $\underline{\quad?\quad}$, and $\underline{\quad?\quad}$. $\{2, 3, 4\}, \{3, 4, 5\},$
     $\{4, 5, 6\}$

11. The sum of three consecutive positive integers decreased by 4
    is less than twice the largest. That is:
    $$(n - 1) + n + (n + 1) - 4 < 2(\underline{\quad?\quad})$$ $n + 1$

12. From $3n - 4 < 2n + 2$, you find $n < \underline{\quad?\quad}$.   6

13. Possible positive integral values for $\{n - 1, n, n + 1\}$ when $n < 6$ are:

$\{\underline{\ ?\ }\}, \{\underline{\ ?\ }\}, \{\underline{\ ?\ }\}, \{\underline{\ ?\ }\}$

$\{1, 2, 3\}, \{2, 3, 4\},$
$\{3, 4, 5\}, \{4, 5, 6\}$

7-5 14. $\{3, 7, 9\} \cap \{3, 5, 7\} = \underline{\ ?\ }$

$\{3, 7\}$

15. $\{3, 7, 9\} \cup \{3, 5, 7\} = \underline{\ ?\ }$

$\{3, 5, 7, 9\}$

16. If $E \cap F = \emptyset$, then E and F are said to be $\underline{\ ?\ }$ sets.

disjoint

7-6 17. If $1 < x + 2 < 4$, then $\underline{\ ?\ } < x < \underline{\ ?\ }$.

$-1, 2$

18. If $2t - 1 > 5$ or $-3t > -6$, then $t > \underline{\ ?\ }$ or $t < \underline{\ ?\ }$.

$3, 2$

19. Two simple sentences joined by *or* form a $\underline{\ ?\ }$

disjunction

20. Two simple sentences joined by *and* form a $\underline{\ ?\ }$.

conjunction

Consumer Note $$
Using Labels

Labels give information that helps you select the product that best meets your needs for the least cost. The labels on sacks of grass seed, for example, are required to report: (1) the kind and type (coarse or fine) of seed, (2) the purity (what percent of the package weight is actually good seed—not dirt, chaff, or weed seed), and (3) the germination at a given date (what percent of the good seed in the package will actually sprout). Lawn seed mixtures usually contain some fine and some coarse varieties of grass, as this gives a lawn that is both durable and attractive.

Complete the computations for the sample label shown below to calculate the actual value of a seed purchase.

Lawn Seed Mixture	Percent of Total Weight	Germination (%)	Germinating Seed as a Percent of Total	
Fine: Kentucky Bluegrass	6	75	75% of 6% = $\underline{\ ?\ }$	4.5%
Red Fescue	6	75	75% of 6% = $\underline{\ ?\ }$	4.5%
Coarse: Annual Ryegrass	83	85	$\dfrac{\underline{\ ?\ }}{85\%}$ of $\dfrac{\underline{\ ?\ }}{83\%}$ = $\underline{\ ?\ }$	70.55%
Other: Dirt, weed seeds	5		(Total = $\underline{\ ?\ }$)	79.55%

If you buy this mixture for $6 per kilogram, the price per kilogram of seed which actually germinates is $6 \div 0.8 = \$\underline{\ ?\ }$.   7.50

Maintaining Skills

Remember how?

$3x + 2 - 2x + 3 = x + 5$

$(3x - 2x) + (2 + 3)$

$x + 5$

Now practice:

1. $4t - 5 + t - 2 = $ _?_ $5t - 7$

2. $-3a - 2 + 5 + 6a = $ _?_ $3a + 3$

3. $15x + 2y - 3x - y = $ _?_ $12x + y$

4. $41b + 21c - 3c + b = $ _?_ $42b + 18c$

5. $2x^2 - 3x + 5 - x + 3 + x^2 = $ _?_

6. $3r^2 - 2r + 5 - r^2 - r + 2 = $ _?_

7. $2 - 4t^2 + 3t - t^2 - 7 - 3t = $ _?_

8. $3u^2 - 3 + 5u^2 - 2u + 5 = $ _?_

9. $7b^3 - 3b^2 + 2b - 3 + 5b^2 - 3b = $ _?_

10. $11y^3 + 5y - 3y^2 + 2y^2 - 5y - 11y^2 = $ _?_

5. $3x^2 - 4x + 8$

6. $2r^2 - 3r + 7$

7. $-5t^2 - 5$

8. $8u^2 - 2u + 2$

9. $7b^3 + 2b^2 - b - 3$

10. $11y^3 - 12y^2$

Remember how?

$4(x - 7) - 3(2x + 1) = -2x - 31$

$4x - 28 - 6x - 3$

$-2x - 31$

Now practice:

11. $6(2y + 3) - 4(3y + 9) = $ _?_ -18

12. $-3(7 - 2x) + 5(2x + 4) = $ _?_ $16x - 1$

13. $12(7 + 5b) - 10(7b - 6) = $ _?_ $144 - 10b$

14. $-8(3r - 10) + 6(4 - 2r) = $ _?_ $104 - 36r$

15. $-7(4t + 3) + 6(5t - 2) = $ _?_ $2t - 33$

16. $12(-3t + 1) - 8(5 + 4t) = $ _?_ $-68t - 28$

17. $3(2s + 3 - s) - 4(5s + 2) = $ _?_ $-17s + 1$

18. $-4(3 - 2x + 5) + 3(4x - 2) = $ _?_ $20x - 38$

19. $2z(z - 3) - 4(z^2 + 3z) = $ _?_ $-2z^2 - 18z$

20. $-3y(4 - y) + 2(3y^2 + 4) = $ _?_ $9y^2 - 12y + 8$

Remember how?

$(2n - 1)(n - 3) = 2n^2 - 7n + 3$

$2n(n - 3) - 1(n - 3)$

$2n^2 - 6n - n + 3$

Now practice:

21. $(x - 3)(x + 2) = $ _?_ $x^2 - x - 6$

22. $(y + 4)(y + 3) = $ _?_ $y^2 + 7y + 12$

23. $(2a - 1)(a + 3) = $ _?_ $2a^2 + 5a - 3$

24. $(r - 5)(3r - 1) = $ _?_ $3r^2 - 16r + 5$

$4k^2 - 1$

$9b^2 + 12b + 4$

$6x^2 - 5x - 6$

25. $(2k - 1)(2k + 1) = $ _?_

26. $(3b + 2)(3b + 2) = $ _?_

27. $(2x - 3)(3x + 2) = $ _?_

28. $(4c - 3)(2c + 5) = $ _?_

29. $(5m - 1)(2m - 3) = $ _?_

30. $(10t - 3)(2t + 1) = $ _?_

$8c^2 + 14c - 15$

$10m^2 - 17m + 3$

$20t^2 + 4t - 3$

285

Functions and
Relations

Life Science An electroencephalograph (EEG) traces a record of a person's brain waves. If the nerve centers are injured, the traces become more jagged.

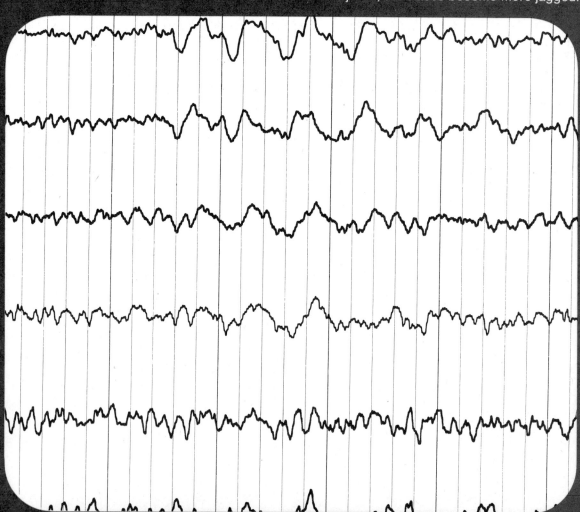

8

Graphing Functions and Relations

8-1 Functions Defined by Equations

OBJECTIVE To learn what a function is and how to find its values.

Look at the diagram in Figure 8-1. It illustrates a **correspondence** between the members of set D and the members of set R in which each member of D is matched (by an arrow) with *exactly one* member of R. Such a correspondence is called a *function*. In general:

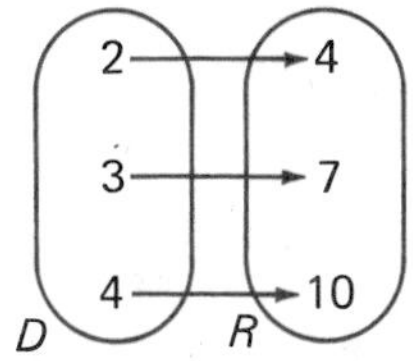

Figure 8-1

A **function** consists of two sets, the **domain** and the **range,** together with a *rule* which assigns to each member of the domain exactly one member of the range. Each member of the range must be assigned to at least one member of the domain.

In Figure 8-1, set D is the *domain* and set R is the *range*.

One way of defining a function is by using an equation as the rule. For example, if the domain is $\{2, 3, 4\}$,

then the equation

$$y = 3x - 2$$

makes the assignments, or pairings, shown at the right. Do you see that the given equation pairs each member of {2, 3, 4} with a single member of {4, 7, 10}?

$$
\begin{array}{l}
x \longrightarrow 3x - 2 \ = y \\
2 \longrightarrow 3 \cdot 2 - 2 = 4 \\
3 \longrightarrow 3 \cdot 3 - 2 = 7 \\
4 \longrightarrow 3 \cdot 4 - 2 = 10
\end{array}
$$

Single letters, such as f, g, F, and h, are often used to name functions. The **arrow notation**

$$f: x \longrightarrow 3x - 2$$

is read "the function f that pairs x with $3x - 2$." To specify a function completely, you must also describe the domain of the function. The numbers assigned by the rule form the range.

Example 1 List the members of the range of

$$h: x \longrightarrow 3 + 2x - x^2, D = \{0, 1, 2, 3\}.$$

Solution In

$$3 + 2x - x^2,$$

replace x by each member of D to find the members of the range, R, as shown at the right.

$\therefore R = \{0, 3, 4\}$ *Answer*

x	$3 + 2x - x^2$
0	$3 + 2 \cdot 0 - 0^2 = 3$
1	$3 + 2 \cdot 1 - 1^2 = 4$
2	$3 + 2 \cdot 2 - 2^2 = 3$
3	$3 + 2 \cdot 3 - 3^2 = 0$

Notice that the function h in Example 1 assigns the number 3 to both 0 and 2. However, in specifying a set you list a given member only once.

> Members of the range are called **values** of the function.

Thus, in Example 1, the values of h are 0, 3, and 4. To indicate that

$$h: x \longrightarrow 3 + 2x - x^2$$

assigns to the number 2 the value 3, you write

$$h(2) = 3,$$

which may be read "h of two equals 3" or "the value of h at 2 is 3."

CAUTION! $h(2)$ is *not* the product of h and 2; instead, it represents the *number* that h assigns to 2.

Example 2 Given $F: t \rightarrow t^3 + 1$, with domain the set of real numbers. Find $F(1)$, $F(-1)$, and $F(2)$.

Solution First, write the equation: $\qquad\qquad F(t) = t^3 + 1$

Then, replace t by each value specified:

$$F(1) = 1^3 + 1 = 2$$
$$F(-1) = (-1)^3 + 1 = 0$$
$$F(2) = 2^3 + 1 = 9$$

$\therefore F(1) = 2, F(-1) = 0, F(2) = 9.$ *Answer*

The variable used in defining a function does not matter. For instance,

$$G: z \longrightarrow z^3 + 1, \text{ with domain the set of real numbers,}$$

is the same function as F in Example 2. Both F and G assign to each real number its cube increased by 1.

Unless otherwise stated, you may assume that each domain is the set of real numbers.

Oral Exercises

State the range of the given function.

Sample 1 $g: x \rightarrow 2x + 1$, $D = \{0, 1, 2\}$ $\qquad$ *Solution* $\{1, 3, 5\}$ is the range. *Answer*

1. $f: z \rightarrow 3z$, $D = \{0, 1, 2\}$ $\quad \{0, 3, 6\}$
2. $T: x \rightarrow x - 2$, $D = \{1, 2, 3\}$ $\quad \{-1, 0, 1\}$
3. $s: t \rightarrow t^2$, $D = \{1, 2, 3\}$ $\quad \{1, 4, 9\}$
4. $H: y \rightarrow y^2$, $D = \{-1, 0, 1\}$ $\quad \{0, 1\}$
5. $g: x \rightarrow x^2 - 1$, $D = \{0, 1, 2\}$ $\quad \{-1, 0, 3\}$
6. $k: u \rightarrow u^2 - u$, $D = \{0, 1, 2\}$ $\quad \{0, 2\}$

Let $f(x) = 2x - 1$. State the given value of f.

Sample 2 $f(-3)$ $\qquad$ *Solution* $f(-3) = 2(-3) - 1 = -7$ *Answer*

7. $f(1)$ $\quad$ 1
8. $f(0)$ $\quad$ -1
9. $f(3)$ $\quad$ 5
10. $f(-1)$ $\quad$ -3
11. $f(5)$ $\quad$ 9
12. $f(-4)$ $\quad$ -9

Complete the following statements about the function $G: x \rightarrow x^2$.

13. The value of G at 3 is __?__. $\quad$ 9
14. The value of G at -3 is __?__. $\quad$ 9
15. The value of G at __?__ is 0. $\quad$ 0
16. The value of G at both __?__ and __?__ is 1. $\quad$ 1; -1

Written Exercises

Find the range of each function.

A 1. $g: x \rightarrow 3x + 2$, $D = \{-1, 0, 1\}$ $\{-1, 2, 5\}$ 2. $f: x \rightarrow 2x - 5$, $D = \{1, 2, 3\}$ $\{-3, -1, 1\}$

3. $h: t \rightarrow 3 - 2t$, $D = \{-2, 0, 2\}$ $\{7, 3, -1\}$ 4. $g: t \rightarrow -1 - 3t$, $D = \{-3, -1, 1\}$ $\{8, 2, -4\}$

5. $F: x \rightarrow 2x^2 - 3$, $D = \{-1, 1, 2\}$ $\{-1, 5\}$ 6. $H: u \rightarrow 4 - u^2$, $D = \{-1, 1, 2\}$ $\{3, 0\}$

7. $r: x \rightarrow \dfrac{6}{x}$, $D = \{1, 2, 3\}$ $\{6, 3, 2\}$ 8. $k: t \rightarrow \dfrac{12}{t + 1}$, $D = \{1, 2, 3\}$ $\{6, 4, 3\}$

9. $f: z \rightarrow z^2 - 3z + 2$, $D = \{1, 2, 3\}$ $\{0, 2\}$ 10. $h: x \rightarrow x^3 - 3x^2 + 2x$, $D = \{0, 1, 2\}$ $\{0\}$

11. $G: t \rightarrow (t - 1)(t - 2)$, $D = \{-1, 0, 1\}$ 12. $p: y \rightarrow y(y + 2)$, $D = \{0, 2, 4\}$ $\{0, 8, 24\}$
$\{6, 2, 0\}$

Given that $f(x) = x - x^2$, find:

13. $f(0)$ 0   14. $f(2)$ −2   15. $f(1)$ 0   16. $f(-2)$ −6   17. $f(-1)$ −2   18. $f(3)$ −6

Given $g: t \rightarrow (t + 1)^2$, find:

19. $g(0)$ 1   20. $g(2)$ 9   21. $g(-1)$ 0   22. $g(-2)$ 1   23. $g(-3)$ 4   24. $g(1)$ 4

Given $h: z \rightarrow (2 - z^2)^2$, find:

B 25. $h(0)$ 4   26. $h(1)$ 1   27. $h(2)$ 4   28. $h(3)$ 49   29. $h(-2)$ 4   30. $h(-3)$ 49

Given $k: x \rightarrow (x^2 - 2x)^2$, find:

31. $k(0)$ 0   32. $k(1)$ 1   33. $k(2)$ 0   34. $k(3)$ 9   35. $k(-2)$ 64   36. $k(-3)$ 22

If $f(x) = x^2 - 4$ and $g(t) = t + 1$, find:

37. $f(3)$ 5   38. $g(3)$ 4   39. $f(3) + g(3)$ 9   40. $f(3) - g(3)$ 1

If $f(x) = 3x + 1$ and $g(z) = z - 2$, find:

C 41. $f(g(4))$ [Hint: First find $g(4)$.] 7   42. $g(f(4))$ 11   43. $f(g(1))$ −2   44. $g(f(1))$ 2

Historical Note
Function Notation

Leonhard Euler* (1707–1783) was a Swiss mathematician who taught and wrote about mathematics in both St. Petersburg, Russia, and Berlin, Germany. He made contributions to many branches of mathematics and was particularly successful in devising useful notations. Among his notations was the $f(x)$ notation to represent the value of a function.

* Pronounced *Oi*-ler.

8-2 Functions Defined by Different Rules

> **OBJECTIVE** To learn other ways of defining functions.

In Section 8-1 the rules for functions were given as equations such as

$$y = 2x - 3 \quad \text{or} \quad f(x) = 2x - 3$$

or with arrow notation as

$$f\colon x \longrightarrow 2x - 3.$$

Sometimes functions are defined by simply giving a table of corresponding values as the "rule" part of the definition. The table below shows the enrollments of the four high schools in Central City. The contents of this table can also be presented as a correspondence or as a list (set) of **ordered pairs,** as shown below.

High School Enrollment in Central City

Table

School	Enrollment
Amelia Earhart	950
Thomas A. Edison	1175
Enrico Fermi	1700
Harriet Tubman	1050

Correspondence

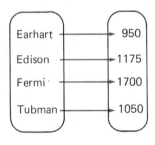

Ordered Pairs

(Earhart, 950)
(Edison, 1175)
(Fermi, 1700)
(Tubman, 1050)

Corresponding to each school listed in the table above there is one and only one enrollment. Therefore, the table describes a *function.* The *domain* is

$$D = \{\text{Earhart, Edison, Fermi, Tubman}\}$$

and the *range* is

$$R = \{950, 1175, 1700, 1050\}.$$

It is easier to compare the enrollments if the facts are presented in a bar graph as in Figure 8-2. It is clear from the graph that the school with the greatest enrollment is Fermi, and the one with the least enrollment is Earhart.

High School Enrollment in Central City

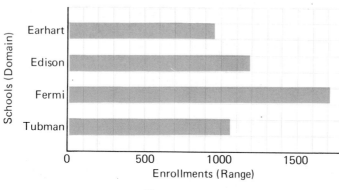

Figure 8-2

Some functions have dates as members of the domain. For such a function you may use a broken-line graph such as the one shown in Figure 8-3.

Enrollment in Thomas A. Edison High School

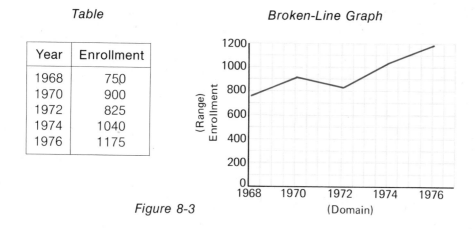

Table

Year	Enrollment
1968	750
1970	900
1972	825
1974	1040
1976	1175

Broken-Line Graph

Figure 8-3

Notice that the graph in Figure 8-3 does not show the number of students enrolled in the "in-between" years. However, such a graph clearly shows the changes or trends over periods of time.

The paired numbers in the function pictured in Figure 8-3 can be displayed as a *set of ordered pairs:*

{(1968, 750), (1970, 900), (1972, 825), (1974, 1040), (1976, 1175)}

In an ordered pair of numbers such as (1968, 750), you call

the first number, 1968, the **first component,**

and

the second number, 750, the **second component.**

Thus, the domain of the function is the set of first components, and the range is the set of second components.

Oral Exercises

Read the ordered pairs. List the domain. List the range.

1.

Number (domain)	Cost (range)
1	$2
2	$4
3	$6
4	$8
5	$10
6	$12

2.

Time (domain)	Temperature (range)
7 A.M.	15 °C
9 A.M.	20 °C
11 A.M.	25 °C
1 P.M.	30 °C
3 P.M.	32 °C
5 P.M.	31 °C

3.

Student (domain)	Height (range)
Anna	150 cm
Bob	190 cm
Charles	185 cm
Roberto	180 cm
Susan	160 cm
Tanya	155 cm

4.

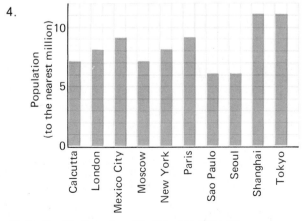

(Calcutta, 7), (London, 8), (Mexico City, 9), (Moscow, 7), (New York, 8), (Paris, 9), (Sao Paulo, 6), (Seoul, 6), (Shanghai, 11), (Tokyo, 11)

5.

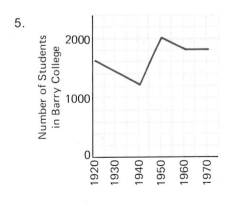

(1920, 1600), (1930, 1400), (1940, 1200), (1950, 2000), (1960, 1800), (1970, 1800)

Written Exercises

Make a bar graph for the facts shown in each table. Give the graph a title. List the domain and the range.

A 1.

Continent	Approximate Highest Elevation
Africa	5900 m
Asia	8800 m
Australia	2200 m
Europe	5600 m
North America	6200 m
South America	6900 m

      domain   range

2.

Lake	Approximate Area
Superior (N. America)	82,000 km²
Victoria (Africa)	69,000 km²
Aral Sea (Asia)	66,000 km²
Huron (N. America)	60,000 km²
Michigan (N. America)	58,000 km²
Tanganyika (Africa)	33,000 km²

      domain   range

Make a broken-line graph for the facts shown in each table. Give the graph a title. List the domain and the range.

   domain   range

3.

Year	Approximate Length of Railroad Track
1860	50,000 km
1880	150,000 km
1900	320,000 km
1920	410,000 km
1940	380,000 km
1960	350,000 km

   domain   range

4.

Time	Distance Traveled
8 A.M.	0 km
9 A.M.	5 km
10 A.M.	10 km
11 A.M.	15 km
12 Noon	20 km

APPROXIMATE AVERAGE MONTHLY TEMPERATURE (CELSIUS)

	City	Jan.	Feb.	Mar.	Apr.	May	June	July	Aug.	Sept.	Oct.	Nov.	Dec.
5.	Chicago	−3°	−2°	2°	9°	16°	22°	24°	23°	19°	13°	4°	−2°
6.	Montreal	−10°	−9°	−2°	6°	13°	18°	21°	20°	15°	9°	2°	−7°
7.	Los Angeles	13°	14°	15°	17°	18°	20°	23°	23°	22°	19°	17°	14°
8.	Calgary	−11°	−7°	−4°	3°	9°	13°	17°	15°	11°	6°	−3°	−8°

   domain   range

Computer Activity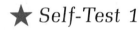

If you have access to a computer that will accept BASIC, try this program:

```
10  PRINT "X ---> 3X+2"
20  FOR X=-1 TO 1
30  PRINT X;" --->";3*X+2
40  NEXT X
50  END
```

You will find that it will print the values of the function in Exercise 1, page 290. You can use it to verify other answers by changing lines 10, 20, and 30 as needed. For example, to check Exercise 10, change these lines to:

```
10  PRINT "X ---> X↑3 - 3X↑2 + 2X"
20  FOR X=0 TO 2
30  PRINT X;" --->";X↑3-3*X↑2+2*X
```

★ *Self-Test 1*

Be sure that you understand these terms:

correspondence (p. 287) function (p. 287) domain (p. 287)
range (p. 287) arrow notation (p. 288) values of the function (p. 288)
ordered pairs (p. 291) first component (p. 293) second component (p. 293)

Be sure that you understand this symbol: (a, b) (p. 291)

1. Given $f: x \rightarrow 1 + x^2, x \in \{-2, 0, 2\}$, find the range of f. Objective 8-1, p. 287
2. If $g(x) = (x - 1)(x^2 - 4)$, find $g(3)$.
3. Draw a bar graph for the table given below. Objective 8-2, p. 291

Ex. 3

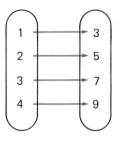

Ex. 5

4. List the ordered pairs in the table of Exercise 3.
5. List the ordered pairs in the correspondence shown above.

Check your answers with those printed at the back of the book.

8-3 Coordinates in a Plane

> **OBJECTIVE** To learn how to graph ordered pairs of numbers in a coordinate plane, and how to read coordinates of points on a graph.

The functions that you deal with most often have sets of numbers as domains and ranges. Thus, they are made up of sets of ordered pairs of numbers. *Ordered pairs of numbers can be graphed as points in a plane.*

Recall that in Section 2-1 you learned how to construct a number line. You now mark off the plane as follows:

1. Draw a horizontal number line, called the **horizontal axis.**

2. Draw a second number line intersecting the first at right angles such that both number lines have the same zero point. The common zero point is called the **origin** (*O*), and the second number line is called the **vertical axis.**

3. Indicate the positive direction on each axis by a *single* arrowhead. The positive direction is usually to the right on the horizontal axis and upward on the vertical axis (Figure 8-4).

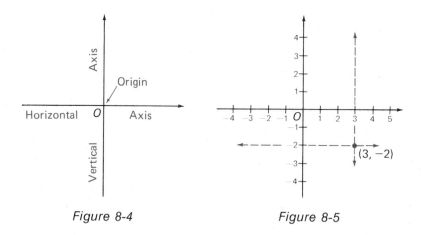

Figure 8-4   Figure 8-5

You locate the graph of the ordered pair (3, −2) as follows:

1. Find the graph (page 32) of 3 on the horizontal axis (Figure 8-5), and draw a vertical line through it.

2. Find the graph of -2 on the vertical axis, and draw a horizontal line through it.

3. Mark the point of intersection of these lines with a dot. It is the graph of $(3, -2)$.

Locating a point in this way is called **plotting the point.**

It is convenient to draw the axes on squared paper, using the length of the side of a square as the unit on each axis (Figure 8-6).

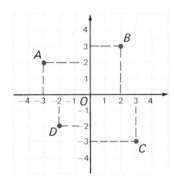

Figure 8-6

You find the ordered pair of numbers corresponding to a point as follows:

1. From point A in Figure 8-6, draw a vertical line segment to meet the horizontal axis. The coordinate (page 32) of the point where it meets this axis is called the **abscissa** (ab-*sis*-a) of A, -3.

2. Draw a horizontal line segment from A to meet the vertical axis. The coordinate of this meeting point is called the **ordinate** (*or*-din-et) of A, 2.

Together, the abscissa and ordinate of A are called the **coordinates** of A. The coordinates are written as an ordered pair, with the abscissa first, $(-3, 2)$.

Verify the coordinates of the other points graphed in Figure 8-6:

$$B(2, 3), \quad C(3, -3)$$
$$D(-2, -2), \quad O(0, 0)$$

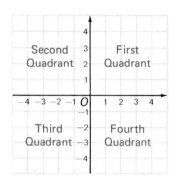

The axes separate the plane into four regions, called quadrants, numbered as shown in Figure 8-7.

Figure 8-7

Notice that

    in the *first quadrant,* both coordinates are positive;

    in the *second quadrant,* the abscissa is negative but the ordinate is positive;

    in the *third quadrant,* both coordinates are negative;

    in the *fourth quadrant,* the abscissa is positive but the ordinate is negative.

> When a coordinate system is set up on a plane as we have just done, the axes are called **coordinate axes,** and the plane is called a **coordinate plane.**

In working with a coordinate plane, you take the following facts for granted:

> **1.** There is exactly one point in the coordinate plane paired with each ordered pair of real numbers.
>
> **2.** There is exactly one ordered pair of real numbers paired with each point in the coordinate plane.

Thus, there is a *one-to-one correspondence* (page 33) between ordered pairs of real numbers and points of a coordinate plane. This correspondence is called a plane rectangular coordinate system.

Oral Exercises

1–20. Give the coordinates of each point designated by a letter (*A–T*).

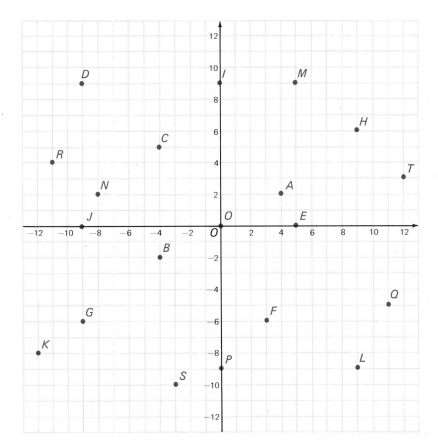

1. *A*(4, 2)
2. *B*(−4, −2)
3. *C*(−4, 5)
4. *D*(−9, 9)
5. *E*(5, 0)
6. *F*(3, −6)
7. *G*(−9, −6)
8. *H*(9, 6)
9. *I*(0, 9)
10. *J*(−9, 0)
11. *K*(−12, −8)
12. *L*(9, −9)
13. *M*(5, 9)
14. *N*(−8, 2)
15. *O*(0, 0)
16. *P*(0, −9)
17. *Q*(11, −5)
18. *R*(−11, 4)
19. *S*(−3, −10)
20. *T*(12, 3)

In each of Exercises 21–30, name the quadrants containing the specified points.

21. The ordinate is 7.   I, II   22. The ordinate is −6.   III, IV   23. The abscissa is 3.   I, IV
24. The abscissa is −1.   II, III   25. The ordinate is positive.   I, II   26. The ordinate is negative. III, IV
27. The abscissa is negative. II, III   28. The abscissa is positive.   I, IV

29. The ordinate equals the abscissa. I, III   30. The ordinate equals the negative of the abscissa. II, IV
31. (0.75, 1.5)   I   32. (−0.7, 1)   II
33. (2.7, −1)   IV   34. (−3.8, −9.4)   III

Written Exercises

Plot the graph of each ordered pair.

A   1. $(5, 9)$ 2. $(-5, -9)$ 3. $(-5, 9)$ 4. $(5, -9)$ 5. $(0, -3)$ 6. $(7, 0)$

   7. $(8, 8)$ 8. $(2.5, 3)$ 9. $(-6, -11)$ 10. $(-1, -3\frac{1}{2})$ 11. $(2, 2.5)$ 12. $(0, -1)$

Use the graph from the Oral Exercises on page 299 to name the letter(s) of the point(s) whose coordinates have the given property.

B   13. The sum of the abscissa and the ordinate is 6.   *A, Q*

   14. The sum of the abscissa and the ordinate is 15.   *H, T*

   15. The sum of the abscissa and the ordinate is -3.   *F*

   16. The difference of the ordinate and the abscissa is 4.   *K, M*

   17. The ordinate is greater than the abscissa.   *B, C, D, G, I, J, K, M, N, R*

   18. The ordinate is less than the abscissa.   *A, E, F, H, L, P, Q, S, T*

   19. The product of the ordinate and the abscissa is 8.   *A, B*

   20. The abscissa divided by the ordinate is undefined.   *E, J, O*

Each of Exercises 21–23 lists three vertices of a parallelogram. Graph these, determine the coordinates of a fourth vertex, and sketch the resulting parallelogram.   (See below.)

   21. $(0, 0), (4, 0), (2, 2)$ 22. $(-2, 0), (-6, 0), (-5, -3)$ 23. $(4, -2), (3, -2), (7, -3)$

C   24. How many answers are possible for each of Exercises 21–23?   3

21. $(-2, 2), (2, -2),$ or $(6, 2)$ **23.** $(6, -3), (8, -3),$ or
22. $(-1, -3), (-3, 3),$ or $(-9, -3)$ $(0, -1)$

Historical Note
Coordinates

Like many ideas in mathematics, the idea of coordinates was approached by many mathematicians even as far back as the ancient Greeks. In the fourteenth century, Nicole Oresme (pronounced Ni-coal O-raim), a French mathematician, who died in 1382, used coordinates that he called longitude and latitude.

René Descartes (Day-cart) (1596–1650) shown below and Pierre de Fermat (de Fer-mah) (1601–1665) shown above used a version of coordinates in their work. Fermat's work was not published until after his death. Descartes published his ideas in *La géométrie* in 1637. The plane coordinate system described in Section 8-3 is sometimes called a rectangular Cartesian coordinate system in honor of Descartes, although he did not use the grid style of graph.

8-4 Relations

> **OBJECTIVE** To learn what relations are and how to graph them on a coordinate plane.

The diagram at the left below shows how each number in the set

$$D = \{0, 1, 2, 3\}$$

is paired with one or more numbers in the set

$$R = \{1, 2, 3, 4\}.$$

The same pairing is shown in the adjoining table, and in the listing of the set of ordered pairs of numbers.

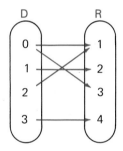

0	1
0	3
1	2
2	1
3	4

$\{(0, 1), (0, 3), (1, 2), (2, 1), (3, 4)\}$

Does this pairing define a function with domain D and range R? No! In a function, each member of the domain is assigned *exactly one* partner in the range. The given pairing, however, assigns to the number 0, two range members, namely, 1 and 3. This pairing is an example of a *relation*.

> A **relation** is any set of ordered pairs. The set of first components in the ordered pairs is called the **domain** of the relation, and the set of second components is called the **range.**

The domain of the relation described above is the set D, and the range is the set R. Recall (page 288) that no member of a set is listed more than once.

Figure 8-8 shows the graphs of all the ordered pairs that form the relation described on page 301. We call this set of points the **graph of the relation**. Notice that domain members are shown along the horizontal axis and range members along the vertical axis.

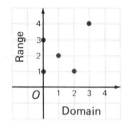

Figure 8-8

You now see that a function is a special kind of relation.

> A function is a relation such that each member of the domain is paired with one and only one member of the range.

In the graph of a function, there will be only one point plotted for each value in the domain.

Oral Exercises

State the domain and the range for each relation below. Is the relation a function?

1. {(3, 5), (2, 4), (3, 7), (2, 6)} $D = \{2, 3\}$; $R = \{4, 5, 6, 7\}$; no
2. {(1, 3), (2, 3), (3, 2), (4, 3)} $D = \{1, 2, 3, 4\}$; $R = \{2, 3\}$; yes
3. {(2, 6), (3, 5), (4, 5), (5, 7)} $D = \{2, 3, 4, 5\}$; $R = \{5, 6, 7\}$; yes
4. {(1, 2), (2, 3), (3, 4), (4, 5)} $D = \{1, 2, 3, 4\}$; $R = \{2, 3, 4, 5\}$; yes
5. {(7, 1), (7, 2), (7, 3), (6, 1)} $D = \{6, 7\}$; $R = \{1, 2, 3\}$; no
6. {(4, 1), (4, 2), (5, 0), (5, 3)} $D = \{4, 5\}$; $R = \{0, 1, 2, 3\}$; no

List the members of the set of ordered pairs in the relation graphed in each diagram. Give the domain and the range of the relation. Is the relation a function?

7. (1, 2), (2, 3), (3, 2), (4, 3)

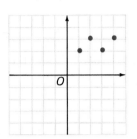

$D = \{1, 2, 3, 4\}$; $R = \{2, 3\}$; yes

8. (0, −2), (0, −1), (0, 0),
    (0, 1), (0, 2), (0, 3)

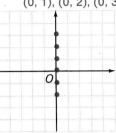

$D = \{0\}$; $R = \{−2, −1, 0, 1, 2, 3\}$; no

9. (−1, 1), (−1, −2), (2, 0),
    (3, 1), (3, −2)

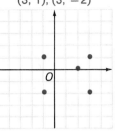

$D = \{−1, 2, 3\}$;
$R = \{−2, 0, 1\}$; no

10.

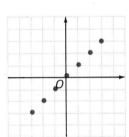

(−3, −3), (−2, −2), (−1, −1), (0, 0),
(1, 1), (2, 2), (3, 3)
$D = R = \{−3, −2, −1, 0, 1, 2, 3\}$; yes

11.

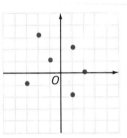

(−3, 2), (−2, 1), (−1, 0), (0, −1), (1, 0)
(2, 1), (3, 2)
$D = \{−3, −2, −1, 0, 1, 2, 3\}$
$R = \{−1, 0, 1, 2\}$; yes

12.

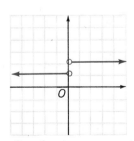

(−3, −1), (−2, 3), (−1, 1),
(1, 2), (1, −2), (2, 0)
$D = \{−3, −2, −1, 1, 2\}$
$R = \{−2, −1, 0, 1, 2, 3\}$; no

Give the domain and the range of each relation. Is the relation a function?

Sample

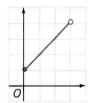

Solution $D = \{$all real numbers ≥ 0 and $< 3\}$

$R = \{$all real numbers ≥ 1 and $< 4\}$

The relation is a function.

13.

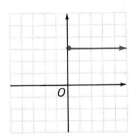

$D = \{$real nos. $\geq 0\}$
$R = \{3\}$
yes

14.

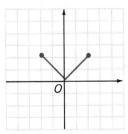

$D = \{$real nos. $\geq −2$ and $\leq 2\}$
$R = \{$real nos. ≥ 0 and $\leq 2\}$
yes

15.

$D = \{$real nos. except $0\}$
$R = \{1, 2\}$
yes

Written Exercises

Graph the relation whose ordered pairs are shown in the given table or list. State the domain and the range of the relation. Indicate if the relation is a function.

A 1.

1	2
2	3
3	5
4	6
7	8

2.

5	6
5	5
4	3
4	7
3	2

3.

1	0
2	3
3	4
1	5

4.

0	1
1	2
2	3
3	4
4	5

5.

−2	2
−1	1
0	0
1	1
2	2

6.

−2	4
−1	1
0	0
1	2
2	4
3	9
4	5

7.

−2	−6
−1	−1
0	0
1	1
2	8
3	16
4	18

8.

0	0
0	1
0	2
1	0
1	1
1	2
2	0
2	1
2	2

9. $\{(-4, 1), (-1, 2), (4, 3), (4, -3), (-1, -2), (-4, -1), (-5, 0)\}$
10. $\{(0, -1), (1, -2), (2, -3), (3, -4), (-1, 2), (-2, 3), (-3, 4)\}$
11. $\{(-3, 2), (0, 1), (3, 2), (3, -2), (0, -1), (-3, 0), (-4, 1)\}$
12. $\{(-2, 3), (1, 4), (2, 5), (6, -1), (1, 0), (-2, 1), (-3, 2)\}$
13. $\{(-2, -1), (-1, 0), (0, 3), (1, 8), (-3, 0), (-4, 3), (-5, 8)\}$
14. $\{(1, 2), (2, 3), (3, 6), (4, 1), (0, 3), (1, 6), (-2, 11)\}$

1. $D = \{1, 2, 3, 4, 7\}$
   $R = \{2, 3, 5, 6, 8\}$
   function
2. $D = \{3, 4, 5\}$
   $R = \{2, 3, 5, 6, 7\}$
   not a function
3. $D = \{1, 2, 3\}$
   $R = \{0, 3, 4, 5\}$
   not a function
4. $D = \{0, 1, 2, 3, 4\}$
   $R = \{1, 2, 3, 4, 5\}$
   function
5. $D = \{-2, -1, 0, 1, 2\}$
   $R = \{0, 1, 2\}$
   function
6. $D = \{-2, -1, 0, 1, 2,$
   $R = \{0, 1, 2, 4, 5, 9\}$
   function
7. $D = \{-2, -1, 0, 1, 2,$
   $R = \{-6, -1, 0, 1, 8,$
   $16, 18\}$ function
8. $D = \{0, 1, 2\}$
   $R = \{0, 1, 2\}$
   not a function
9. $D = \{-5, -4, -1, 4\}$
   $R = \{-3, -2, -1, 0,$
   $2, 3\}$; not a function
10. $D = \{-3, -2, -1, 0,$
    $R = \{-4, -3, -2, -$
    $3, 4\}$ function
11. $D = \{-4, -3, 0, 3\}$
    $R = \{-2, -1, 0, 1, 2\}$
    not a function
12. $D = \{-3, -2, 1, 2, 6\}$
    $R = \{-1, 0, 1, 2, 3, 4,$
    not a function
13. $D = \{-5, -4, -3, -$
    $-1, 0\}$ $R = \{-1, 0, 3$
    function
14. $D = \{-2, 0, 1, 2, 3, 4$
    $R = \{1, 2, 3, 6, 11\}$
    not a function

Consumer Note $$
Nutrition Labeling

Have you noticed the nutrition information that is printed on the labels of many canned foods? For example, a can of corn has:

Nutrition Information per Serving

Calories 230	Carbohydrates 50 grams
Protein 4 grams	Fat 2 grams

Percentage of U.S. Recommended Daily Allowance (U.S. RDA)
per Serving

Protein	6	Riboflavin (B_2)	6
Vitamin A	4	Niacin	8
Vitamin C	20	Calcium	Less than 2
Thiamin (B_1)	2	Iron	4

The information on the can of corn tells us that 1 serving contains 6% of the recommended daily allowance of protein. The amount of protein is 4 grams. Thus: $0.06A = 4$ and $A = \dfrac{400}{6} \doteq 67$. The recommended daily allowance of protein is about 67 grams. Refer to the following table to answer the questions below.

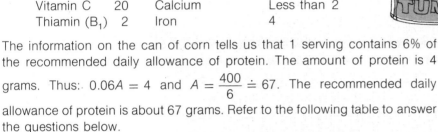

Percentage of U.S. Recommended Daily Allowance (U.S. RDA) per Serving				
	Beans	Zucchini	Vegetable Juice	Grade A Milk
Protein	4	2	2	20
Vitamin A	15	20	40	10
Vitamin C	40	4	45	4
Thiamin (B_1)	4	6	4	6
Riboflavin (B_2)	10	4	2	25
Niacin	4	4	6	0
Calcium	4	2	2	30
Iron	8	8	2	0

1. Find the percent of the U.S. RDA of vitamin C that one would get from a serving of corn, a serving of beans, and a serving of vegetable juice. **105%**

2. What percent of vitamin A would be obtained from the servings in Exercise 1? **59%**

3. A serving each of corn and zucchini would provide what percent of the U.S. RDA of iron? **12%**

4. A serving each of corn, beans, and milk would provide what percent of the U.S. RDA of riboflavin (B_2)? **41%**

8-5 Open Sentences in Two Variables

> **OBJECTIVE** To learn how to find solution sets of open sentences in two variables with given replacement sets for the variables.

Open sentences such as

$$3x + 2y = 10 \quad \text{and} \quad 2x - 3y \geq 6$$

are called open sentences in two variables.

> An ordered pair of values for which the sentence in two variables becomes a true statement is called a **solution** of the sentence.

For example $(x, y) = (2, 3)$ *is not* a solution of $3x + 2y = 10$, because

$$3(2) + 2(3) = 6 + 6 \neq 10.$$

On the other hand $(x, y) = (4, -1)$ *is* a solution because

$$3(4) + 2(-1) = 12 - 2 = 10.$$

> The set of all solutions of an open sentence is called the **solution set** of the sentence. Finding the solution set is called **solving** the sentence.

To see how to find solutions for such a sentence, study the following examples.

Example 1 Find the solution set of $3x + 2y = 10$ if the replacement set of both x and y is the set of whole numbers.

Solution

1. Solve the given sentence for y in terms of x.

$$3x + 2y = 10$$
$$2y = 10 - 3x$$
$$y = 5 - \tfrac{3}{2}x$$

2. Replace x with successive members of its replacement set and determine the corresponding values of y.

3. If the value of y determined by step 2 belongs to the replacement set of y, then the pair of corresponding values is a solution of the sentence.

x	$y = 5 - \frac{3}{2}x$	Solution
0	$5 - 0 = 5$	$(0, 5)$
1	$5 - \frac{3}{2}(1) = 3\frac{1}{2}$	Not a solution
2	$5 - \frac{3}{2}(2) = 2$	$(2, 2)$
3	$5 - \frac{3}{2}(3) = \frac{1}{2}$	Not a solution
4	$5 - \frac{3}{2}(4) = -1$	Not a solution

Values of x greater than 3 produce negative values of y.

$\therefore$ the solution set is $\{(0, 5), (2, 2)\}$. *Answer*

Notice that $(4, -1)$ is a solution of $3x + 2y = 10$ if the replacement set of y is the set of integers, but it is not a solution if the replacement set of y is the set of whole numbers.

Do you see that the solution set of the equation in Example 1 is a function with domain $\{0, 2\}$ and range $\{2, 5\}$? In Example 2, below, the solution set of the open sentence is a relation that is *not* a function.

In general:

> The solution set of any open sentence in two variables is a relation.

Example 2 Find the solution set of $2x - 3y \geq 6$ if $x \in \{-3, 0, 3\}$ and $y \in \{-5, -3, -1, 1, 3\}$.

Solution

$2x - 3y \geq 6$

$-3y \geq 6 - 2x$

$y \leq -2 + \frac{2}{3}x$

$y \leq \frac{2}{3}x - 2$

x	$\frac{2}{3}x - 2$	$y \leq \frac{2}{3}x - 2$	Solutions
-3	$\frac{2}{3}(-3) - 2 = -4$	$y \leq -4$	$(-3, -5)$
0	$\frac{2}{3}(0) - 2 = -2$	$y \leq -2$	$(0, -5), (0, -3)$
3	$\frac{2}{3}(3) - 2 = 0$	$y \leq 0$	$(3, -5), (3, -3), (3, -1)$

$\therefore$ the solution set is
$\{(-3, -5), (0, -5), (0, -3), (3, -5), (3, -3), (3, -1)\}$. *Answer*

Oral Exercises

Assume that the replacement set of each variable is the set of real numbers. Determine whether the given ordered pair of numbers is a solution of the open sentence.

Sample 1 $8x - y > -1$; $(1, -9)$

Solution Yes, it is a solution, because $8 + 9 > -1$. *Answer*

1. $x + y = 6$; $(4, 2)$ yes
2. $2x - y = 10$; $(2, 1)$ no
3. $x + 3y = 20$; $(2, 6)$ ye
4. $4x + 3y = 31$; $(0, 9)$ no
5. $-2x - y = -6$; $(2, 2)$ yes
6. $7x + 3y = 63$; $(6, 6)$ r
7. $x^2 + y^2 = 25$; $(3, 4)$ yes
8. $x - y^2 = 0$; $(1, 1)$ yes
9. $xy = 16$; $(4, 4)$ yes
10. $x - xy = 10$; $(10, 10)$ no
11. $x^2 + xy - 6 = 0$; $(2, 1)$ yes
12. $2x^2 - xy = 1$; $(1, 2)$ ne

Transform each open sentence into an equivalent one having y as one member.

Sample 2 $x + 3y = 6$ *Solution* $3y = 6 - x$; $y = 2 - \frac{1}{3}x$ *Answer*

13. $4x - y = 5$ $y = 4x - 5$
14. $x - 2y = -6$ $y = \frac{1}{2}x + 3$
15. $2x + 3y = 9$ $y = 3 - \frac{2}{3}$
16. $2x - 3y = 9$ $y = \frac{2}{3}x - 3$
17. $x + y \le 3$ $y \le 3 - x$
18. $x - 2y \ge 8$ $y \le \frac{1}{2}x - 4$

State which of the following ordered pairs are solutions of the equation $y = x + 2$ and which are not.

19. $(1, 3)$ yes   20. $(-1, 1)$ yes   21. $(0, -2)$ no   22. $(2, 5)$ no   23. $(-6, -8)$ no   24. $(6, 8)$ ye

Written Exercises

Find the missing values.

A
1. $y = x + 4$; $(2, \underline{\ ?\ })$, $(3, \underline{\ ?\ })$, $(0, \underline{\ ?\ })$ 6; 7; 4
2. $y = 3x$; $(0, \underline{\ ?\ })$, $(-1, \underline{\ ?\ })$, $(7, \underline{\ ?\ })$ 0; -3; 21
3. $y = x - 2$; $(4, \underline{\ ?\ })$, $(-3, \underline{\ ?\ })$, $(0, \underline{\ ?\ })$ 2; -5; -2
4. $y = 5 - 4x$; $(5, \underline{\ ?\ })$, $(1, \underline{\ ?\ })$, $(-1, \underline{\ ?\ })$ -15; 1; 9
5. $y = \dfrac{3}{x - 2}$; $(5, \underline{\ ?\ })$, $(-1, \underline{\ ?\ })$, $(8, \underline{\ ?\ })$ 1; -1; $\dfrac{1}{2}$
6. $y = \dfrac{-3}{x - 4}$; $(1, \underline{\ ?\ })$, $(7, \underline{\ ?\ })$, $(-2, \underline{\ ?\ })$ 1; -1; $\dfrac{1}{2}$
7. $2x + y = 6$; $(2, \underline{\ ?\ })$, $(0, \underline{\ ?\ })$, $(1, \underline{\ ?\ })$ 2; 6; 4
8. $3x + y = 10$; $(1, \underline{\ ?\ })$, $(0, \underline{\ ?\ })$, $(2, \underline{\ ?\ })$ 7; 10; 4

9. $x - y = 5$; $(6, \underline{\ ?\ })$, $(3, \underline{\ ?\ })$, $(-1, \underline{\ ?\ })$ $1; -2; -6$
10. $2x - y = 7$; $(3, \underline{\ ?\ })$, $(5, \underline{\ ?\ })$, $(-3, \underline{\ ?\ })$ $-1; 3; -13$
11. $x + 2y = 5$; $(1, \underline{\ ?\ })$, $(-1, \underline{\ ?\ })$, $(-3, \underline{\ ?\ })$ $2; 3; 4$
12. $2x - 3y = 6$; $(0, \underline{\ ?\ })$, $(-3, \underline{\ ?\ })$, $(3, \underline{\ ?\ })$ $-2; -4; 0$

Find the solution set of each equation given that $\{-1, 0, 1\}$ is the re-placement set of x, and the set of real numbers is the replacement set of y.

$\{(-1, 1), (0, 2), (1, 3)\}$ $\{(-1, -2), (0, -3), (1, -4)\}$ $\{(-1, -\frac{3}{2}), (0, 0), (1, \frac{3}{2})\}$ $\{(-1, 0), (0, 3), (1, 6)\}$
13. $y = x + 2$ 14. $y = -x - 3$ 15. $y = \frac{3}{2}x$ 16. $y = 3x + 3$

17. $y = x^2$ 18. $y = x^2 + 2$ 19. $y = x^2 - 2x$ 20. $y = x^2 + 4x$
$\{(-1, 1), (0, 0), (1, 1)\}$ $\{(-1, 3), (0, 2), (1, 3)\}$ $\{(-1, 3), (0, 0), (1, -1)\}$ $\{(-1, 3), (0, 0), (1, 5)\}$

Find the solution set of each equation given that the replacement set of both x and y is the set of whole numbers.   Answers on page A3 at the back of the book.

21. $x + y = 4$ 22. $2x + y = 8$ 23. $x + 2y = 7$ 24. $x + 3y = 12$
25. $2x + 3y = 20$ 26. $3x + 4y = 25$ 27. $2x + 3y = 12$ 28. $3x + 5y = 30$

Find the solution set of each inequality given that $\{-1, 0, 1\}$ is the replacement set of x and $\{-2, -1, 0, 1, 2\}$ is the replacement set of y. Graph the solution set.   Answers on pages A3 and A4 at the back of the book.

B 29. $y > -x$ 30. $y < 2x$ 31. $y - 1 \leq 4x$ 32. $1 - y \leq 2x$
33. $x + y > x - 2$ 34. $2 - y \leq x + 2$ 35. $3x + 2y \leq 12$ 36. $3x - 2y \geq 2$

Find the solution set over the given replacement sets for x and y.

C 37. $y = x^2 - 4x + 3$; $x \in$ {the real numbers}; $y \in \{0, -1, 3\}$ $\{(1, 0), (3, 0), (2, -1), (0, 3), (4, 3)\}$
38. $y = x^2 - 6x$; $x \in$ {the real numbers}; $y \in \{0, -5\}$ $\{(0, 0), (6, 0), (1, -5), (5, -5)\}$

★ *Self-Test 2*

Be sure that you understand these terms:

horizontal axis (p. 296)   origin (p. 296)   vertical axis (p. 296)
graph of an ordered pair   plotting a point (p. 297)   abscissa (p. 297)
  of numbers (p. 297)
ordinate (p. 297)   coordinates (p. 297)   quadrant (p. 298)

coordinate axes (p. 298)   coordinate plane (p. 298)
plane rectangular coordinate system (p. 298)   relation (p. 301)
graph of a relation (p. 302)   open sentence in two variables (p. 306)
solution set (p. 306)   solving an open sentence (p. 306)

1. In what quadrant does the point (5, −6) lie?   Objective 8-3, p. 296
2. Does the point (−3, 0) lie on the vertical axis or the horizontal axis?
3. What is the name of the point (0, 0)?

4. The set of first components in a set of ordered pairs is called the __?__   Objective 8-4, p. 301
   of a relation, and the set of second components is called the __?__ .
5. When is a relation a function?

6. Transform the equation "$x + 4y = 8$" into an equivalent equation having   Objective 8-5, p. 306
   "y" as one member.
7. Find the solution set for "$y = 2x − 1$" if $x \in \{0, 1, 2\}$ and $y \in \{$the real
   numbers$\}$.

Check your answers with those printed at the back of the book.

Career Note
Photographer

Photographers use cameras and other equipment to record images on film. There are several stages involved in this process. First a camera, filters, lenses, and film are selected according to the type of picture required and the available light. If the picture is to be taken indoors or after dark, special lighting may be necessary. After the picture has been taken, the photographer uses chemical and mechanical processes to develop, enlarge, and print the picture.

Many photographers specialize in areas such as portrait, aerial, and educational photography. Photography is an essential part of advertising, journalism, and many areas of scientific research.

Some people prepare for a career in photography by attending college or art school. Others train for two to three years at a commercial studio. To become a skilled photographer a person should have manual dexterity and a good eye for detail.

Linear Equations and Functions

8-6 The Graph of a Linear Equation in Two Variables

> **OBJECTIVE** To learn how to graph a linear equation in two variables.

When graphing the solution set of an equation in variables x and y, it is customary to take the horizontal axis as the x-axis and the vertical axis as the y-axis.

Every solution of the equation

$$-x + 2y = 4$$

is an ordered pair of numbers represented by (x, y). The graph of one such solution, $(0, 2)$, is the point P in Figure 8-9. To find other solutions of this equation, substitute values for x and obtain corresponding values for y, as shown in the table below. These solutions are also graphed in Figure 8-9.

$$-x + 2y = 4 \quad \text{or} \quad y = \tfrac{1}{2}x + 2$$

x	$y = \tfrac{1}{2}x + 2$	Solutions
-4	$\tfrac{1}{2}(-4) + 2 = 0$	$(-4, 0)$
-2	$\tfrac{1}{2}(-2) + 2 = 1$	$(-2, 1)$
0	$\tfrac{1}{2}(0) + 2 = 2$	$(0, 2)$
2	$\tfrac{1}{2}(2) + 2 = 3$	$(2, 3)$
4	$\tfrac{1}{2}(4) + 2 = 4$	$(4, 4)$

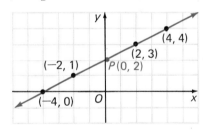

Figure 8-9

Figure 8-9 suggests that the points corresponding to these solutions lie on a straight line, part of which is shown in the diagram. In fact, if the set of real numbers is the replacement set for both x and y, then each solution of the equation does give the coordinates of a point on this line, and the coordinates of each point of the line satisfy the equation.

Because this line is the set of all those points and only those points whose coordinates satisfy the equation, the line is called the **graph of the equation** in the coordinate plane, and

$$-x + 2y = 4$$

is called **an equation of the line.**

In general:

> In the coordinate plane, the graph of any equation equivalent to one of the form
>
> $$Ax + By = C, \; x \text{ and } y \in \{\text{the real numbers}\},$$
>
> where A, B, and C are real numbers with A and B not both zero is a straight line. Any such equation is called a **linear equation in two variables,** x and y. If A, B, and C are integers, the equation is said to be in **standard form.**

Notice that in a linear equation, each term is a constant or a monomial of degree 1. Thus,

$$\text{``}3x - 2y = 1\text{''} \text{ is linear,}$$

but

$$\text{``}x + \frac{2}{y} = 5,\text{''} \; \text{``}x^2 + y^2 = 3,\text{''} \text{ and ``}xy = 7,\text{''} \text{ are not linear.}$$

Although you need plot only two points to graph a linear equation, it is good practice to plot a third point as a check. Sometimes it is helpful to find solutions of the form

$$(0, b) \text{ and } (a, 0),$$

the points where the graph crosses the axes. You obtain the latter by replacing y with "0" and finding the corresponding value of x.

In the following examples and throughout the rest of this book, you may assume, unless otherwise directed, that the replacement set for each variable in an open sentence in two variables is the set of real numbers.

Example 1 Graph $x + 3y = 6$ in the coordinate plane.

Solution

$x + 3y = 6$

$3y = 6 - x$

$y = 2 - \frac{1}{3}x$

When $y = 0$, $x = 6$.

When $x = 0$, $y = 2$.

When $x = 3$, $y = 1$.

Solutions

$(6, 0)$

$(0, 2)$

$(3, 1)$

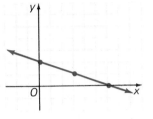

Example 2 Graph $x = -2$ in the coordinate plane.

Solution Since the equation places no restriction on y, every point having abscissa -2 corresponds to a solution regardless of its second coordinate.

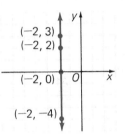

A function whose ordered pairs satisfy a linear equation is called a **linear function**. Thus,

$$f\colon x \longrightarrow 2x - 4$$

is a linear function. This function may be said to be *defined by* the linear equation

$$y = 2x - 4.$$

Oral Exercises

State whether or not the equation is linear.

1. $x + y = 6$ yes

2. $xy = 10$ no

3. $\frac{x}{3} - 4y = 1$ yes

4. $2x - y = 0$ yes

5. $x^2 + y^2 = 1$ no

6. $x = 0$ yes

7. $y = 2$ yes

8. $4x - \frac{6}{y} = 21$ no

9. $y - x^2 = 1$ no

10. $\frac{1}{3}x + \frac{3}{4}y = x^2$ no

11. $\frac{1}{x} + \frac{1}{y} = 4$ no

12. $\frac{x}{2} + \frac{y}{2} = 4$ yes

13. Describe the graph of $y = 2$.   A line 2 units above and parallel to the x-axis.

Written Exercises

Tell whether each of the following points is above, on, or below the graph of $y + 3 = 0$.

A
1. $(1, -2)$
   above
2. $(1, 6)$
   above
3. $(0, -3)$
   on
4. $(-7, 7)$
   above
5. $(1, -5)$
   below
6. $(-21, -3)$
   on

Tell whether each of the following points lies to the left of, on, or to the right of the graph of $x = 5$.

7. $(-1, 2)$
   left
8. $(5, 1)$
   on
9. $(6, 2)$
   right
10. $(-2, -3)$
    left
11. $(5, -1)$
    on
12. $(6, 11)$
    right

Find the coordinates of the points where the graph of each equation crosses (a) the x-axis and (b) the y-axis.

13. $6x + 7y = 42$ $(7, 0)$
    $(0, 6)$
14. $5x - 4y = 20$ $(4, 0)$
    $(0, -5)$
15. $3x = 11y$ $(0, 0)$
    $(0, 0)$
16. $4y = -13x$ $(0, 0$
    $(0, 0$

Graph each equation in the coordinate plane.

17. $x = 2$
18. $y = -3$
19. $x = -5$
20. $y = 5$

21. $y = x + 2$
22. $y = x - 1$
23. $3x + y = 7$
24. $2x + y = 5$

25. $3x - y = 9$
26. $2x - 3y = 4$
27. $3x + 4y = 12$
28. $2x + 5y = 15$

Graph each of the following functions.

29. $f: x \rightarrow x$
30. $g: x \rightarrow x + 3$
31. $h: x \rightarrow 2x$
32. $F: x \rightarrow 2x + 3$

Graph each pair of equations on the same set of axes. Name the coordinates of the point where the graphs intersect, and show that the coordinates satisfy both equations.

B
33. $x + y = 12;\ 2x - y = 3$ $(5, 7)$
34. $2x + y = 4;\ y = x + 1$ $(1, 2)$

35. $2x + y = -2;\ x + 3y = 9$ $(-3, 4)$
36. $5x + y = 4;\ x - 2y = 3$ $(1, -1)$

Just for Fun

On a piece of graph paper, graph the following line segments:

$x = 0,\ 2 \le y \le 7$
$x + 3y = 6,\ 0 \le x \le 6$
$x - 3y = 6,\ 6 \le x \le 18$
$5x + 3y = 45,\ 3 \le x \le 6,$

$x = 6,\ 0 \le y \le 5$
$x + 3y = 21,\ 0 \le x \le 6$
$x - 3y = -9,\ 6 \le x \le 18$
$5x + 3y = 117,\ 15 \le x \le 18$

$x = 18,\ 4 \le y \le 9$
$x - y = -7,\ 0 \le x \le 3$
$x - 3y = -27,\ 3 \le x \le 15$

8-7 Slope of a Line

> **OBJECTIVE** To learn how to find the slope of a line given the graph of the line or an equation of the line or two points on the line.

To describe the steepness, or pitch, of a roof, you determine the vertical rise for every meter of horizontal run. For example, if a roof rises 20 centimeters for every meter (100 centimeters) of horizontal distance, its pitch is the ratio

$$\frac{20}{100} \quad \text{or} \quad 20\%$$

as shown in Figure 8-10.

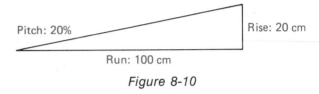

Pitch: 20%   Run: 100 cm   Rise: 20 cm

Figure 8-10

Similarly, to describe the steepness, or *slope* of a straight line, you choose two points on it and compute the quotient:

> **slope** $= \dfrac{\text{rise}}{\text{run}} = \dfrac{\text{vertical change}}{\text{horizontal change}} = \dfrac{\text{difference of ordinates}}{\text{difference of abscissas}}$

Example 1 Find the slope of the straight line through points $(-3, 3)$ and $(3, 1)$.

Solution Sketch a graph. Then you have from the formula above:

$$\text{slope} = \frac{\text{difference of ordinates } (y\text{'s})}{\text{difference of abscissas } (x\text{'s})}$$

$$= \frac{3 - 1}{-3 - 3} = \frac{2}{-6} = -\frac{1}{3} \quad \left[\text{or } \frac{1 - 3}{3 - (-3)} = \frac{-2}{6} = -\frac{1}{3} \right]$$

Check by counting units in the rise and run: $\dfrac{\text{rise}}{\text{run}} = \dfrac{-2}{6} = -\dfrac{1}{3}$

$\therefore$ slope $= -\dfrac{1}{3}$. *Answer*

Example 2 Find the slope of the line with equation $2x - 3y = 6$.

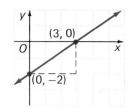

Solution Find two points on the line (page 312):

$$(0, -2) \text{ and } (3, 0)$$

Then the slope $= \dfrac{0 - (-2)}{3 - 0} = \dfrac{2}{3}.$ *Answer*

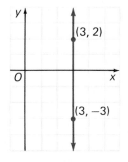

If you use the formula on page 315 to try to compute the "slope" of the line pictured in Figure 8-11, you find

$$\frac{2 - (-3)}{3 - 3} = \frac{5}{0}.$$

Since you cannot divide by 0, the formula does not apply, and this line, like every vertical line, **has no slope.**

Figure 8-11

> A basic property of a line is that its slope is constant.

Thus, you may use any two of its points in computing its slope.

Example 3 Determine whether or not the points in each table lie on a line. If they do, find the slope of the line.

a.

x	y
0	3
1	4
2	5
3	6

b.

x	y
0	6
1	4
2	2
3	0

c.

x	y
0	0
1	1
2	3
3	6

Solution

a. There are equal changes in x and y, and so the points lie on a line. The slope is $\dfrac{1}{1}$, or 1. *Answer*

b. There are equal changes in x and y, and so the points lie on a line. The slope is $\frac{-2}{1}$, or -2. *Answer*

c. There are equal changes in x, but the changes in y are not equal. Therefore, the points do not lie on a line. *Answer*

Oral Exercises

Find the slope of each line.

1. 1

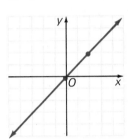

2. no slope

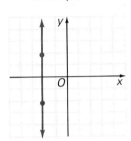

3. 0

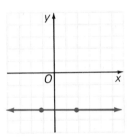

4. $\frac{3}{2}$

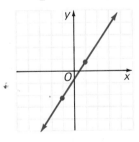

5. -3

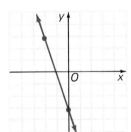

6. 2

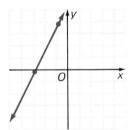

Written Exercises

Find the slope of the straight line through the two points whose coordinates are given.

A 1. $(-1, 5), (3, -2)$ $-\frac{7}{4}$ 2. $(2, 3), (7, 6)$ $\frac{3}{5}$ 3. $(-4, -5), (0, -2)$ $\frac{3}{4}$ 4. $(0, 0), (3, 5)$ $\frac{5}{3}$

5. $(2, 0), (3, 7)$ 7   6. $(3, 2), (2, -5)$ 7   7. $(-5, -5), (0, 0)$ 1   8. $(2, 5), (-1, -3)$ $\frac{8}{3}$

9. $(-1, -2); (-5, -6)$ 1   10. $(4, 2); (-3, 2)$ 0   11. $(a, 4), (2, 2)$ $\frac{2}{a-2}$ 12. $(a, b), (c, d)$ $\frac{d-b}{c-a}$

Find the slope of the line having the given equation.

13. $x + 2y = 6$ $-\frac{1}{2}$ 14. $2x - y = 4$ 2   15. $x - 4y = 8$ $\frac{1}{4}$ 16. $4x + y = 12$ -4

17. $4x + 5y = 20$ $-\frac{4}{5}$ 18. $5x - 4y = 20$ $\frac{5}{4}$ 19. $3x - y = 9$ 3   20. $2x + 5y = 10$ $-$

21. $x - 2y = 5$ $\frac{1}{2}$ 22. $x + 3y = 4$ $-\frac{1}{3}$ 23. $2x + 3y = 8$ $-\frac{2}{3}$ 24. $2x - y = 7$ 2

Determine whether or not the points in each table lie on a line. If they do, find the slope.

25. yes; 3

x	y
0	0
1	3
2	6
3	9

26. no

x	y
0	3
1	6
2	7
3	10

27. yes; 1

x	y
2	−1
3	0
4	1
5	2

28. no

x	y
0	−2
1	0
2	4
3	6

29. yes; −1

x	y
0	1
−1	2
−2	3
−3	4
−4	5

30. yes; −1

x	y
0	−1
1	−2
2	−3
3	−4
4	−5

31. no

x	y
0	−1
1	−2
2	−4
3	−8
4	−12

32. yes; 2

x	y
−3	−6
−2	−4
−1	−2
0	0
1	2

Through the given point, draw a line with the given slope.

Sample $(-3, 1)$; slope, $\frac{3}{4}$

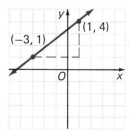

Solution   First, plot the point $(-3, 1)$. From the point, measure 4 units to the right and 3 units up. Connect the 2 points to determine the line.

33. $(5, 3)$; slope, 2   34. $(1, -2)$; slope, 3   35. $(1, 4)$; slope, 0   36. $(-3, 2)$; slope, -1

37. $(3, -4)$; slope, $-\frac{1}{2}$ 38. $(-4, 5)$; slope, $\frac{2}{3}$ 39. $(-1, -1)$; slope, -2 40. $(-2, -1)$; slope, $\frac{1}{3}$

B 41. Show by means of a graph that the line passing through the points $(-3, 4)$ and $(0, 6)$ has the same slope as the line passing through the points $(1, 3)$ and $(4, 5)$.

42. Do the points $(0, 0)$, $(1, 2)$, and $(2, 4)$ lie on the same line? How can you use the idea of slope to show this? Yes; show that any 2 pairs of points give the same slope.

43. Find the slope of the line which passes through the points $(1, 4)$ and $(2, 5)$. If point $(x, 6)$ lies on that line, find the value of x. $1; x = 3$

44. The slope of a line through point $(0, 2)$ is $\frac{2}{3}$. If point $(3, y)$ lies on that line, find the value of y. $y = 4$

Determine a value for b so that the slope of the line through each pair of points has the given value. Check your solution by graphing.

C 45. $(5, 1)$, $(b, 4)$; slope, $-\frac{3}{2}$ 3   **46.** $(0, 5)$, $(2, b)$; slope, $\frac{1}{2}$ 6   **47.** $(b, 5)$, $(2, 0)$; slope, 1 7

48. $(2, b)$, $(0, 1)$; slope, -2 -3 **49.** $(8, 3b)$, $(b, 3)$; slope, $\frac{1}{2}$ 2   **50.** $(b, 6)$, $(2b, 10)$; slope, 1 4

Biographical Note
Richard Courant

Richard Courant (1888–1972) was recognized as a leading authority on the application of mathematical methods to physics. He was born in Germany and studied at Göttingen with the mathematician David Hilbert. They developed the methods of applying the theories of quantum mechanics proposed in the 1920's. The quantum theory is a way of explaining the change in energy levels of atomic particles.

In 1953 Courant was one of the founders of the Institute of Mathematical Sciences of New York University, which was later named after him. The activities of the Courant Institute have included research on radar and communications, the mathematics of atomic-reactor design, the control of nuclear energy for the production of power, and the development of theories in meteorology.

Courant tried to emphasize the humanistic aspects of mathematics. In 1941, he and Herbert Robbins published *What Is Mathematics?*, a book which has remained a widely used source for people without specialized training in higher mathematics.

8-8 The Slope-Intercept Form of a Linear Equation

> **OBJECTIVE** To learn how to use the slope-intercept form of an equation of a straight line.

The graph of

$$y = 2x$$

is the straight line (Figure 8-12) containing the points whose coordinates are given in the table. Do you see that when the abscissas of two points on the line differ by 1, their ordinates differ by 2, the slope of the line? Notice that the line passes through the origin.

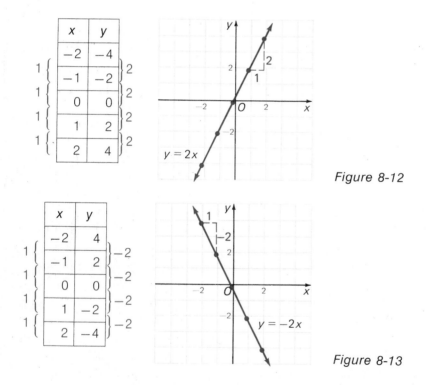

Figure 8-12

Figure 8-13

Can you guess the slope of the line whose equation is "$y = -2x$" (Figure 8-13)? It is -2, because an increase of 1 in the abscissa produces a change of -2 in the ordinate. This line also contains the origin.

In general:

> For every real number m, the graph in the coordinate plane of the equation
>
> $$y = mx$$
>
> is the line that has slope m and passes through the origin.

In Figure 8-14, compare the graphs of "$y = 2x + 4$" and "$y = 2x$." They have equal slopes, but they cross the y-axis at different points. The *ordinate* of the point where a line crosses the y-axis is called the line's **y-intercept**. To determine the y-intercept, replace x with "0" in the equation of each line:

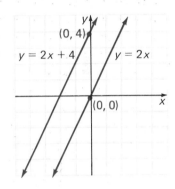

Figure 8-14

$y = 2x$ $y = 2x + 4$

$y = 2 \cdot 0$ $y = 2 \cdot 0 + 4$

$y = 0$ ⟵ y-intercepts ⟶ $y = 4$

If you write

"$y = 2x$"   as   "$y = 2x + 0$,"

you can see that the constant term in these equations is the y-intercept of each graph:

$y = 2x + 0$ and $y = 2x + 4$.

In general:

> For all real numbers m and b, the graph in the coordinate plane of the equation
>
> $$y = mx + b$$
>
> is the line whose slope is m and y-intercept is b. This is called the **slope-intercept form** of an equation of a straight line.

One way to describe a straight line is to write its equation in the slope-intercept form and then read off the values of the slope m and the y-intercept b. To transform an equation in standard form (page 312) to slope-intercept form, solve for y.

Standard Form	Transforming to $y = mx + b$	Describing the line	
		Slope	y-intercept
$x + 2y = 4$	$2y = -x + 4,\ y = -\frac{1}{2}x + 2$	$-\frac{1}{2}$	2
$6x - 3y = 8$	$3y = 6x - 8,\ y = 2x - \frac{8}{3}$	2	$-\frac{8}{3}$
$2y = 10$	$y = 0x + 5$	0	5

Example Sketch the line with $m = -\dfrac{1}{2}$ and $b = \dfrac{1}{4}$, and then find an equation for the line.

Solution The y-intercept is $\dfrac{1}{4}$; so you label $\left(0, \dfrac{1}{4}\right)$. Since the slope

is $-\dfrac{1}{2}$, you move 2 units to the right of $\left(0, \dfrac{1}{4}\right)$ and then 1 unit

down to find another point, $\left(2, -\dfrac{3}{4}\right)$, on the line. Sketch the line

containing these two points. From $y = mx + b$ an equation is

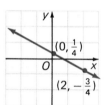

$$y = -\frac{1}{2}x + \frac{1}{4}. \quad \textit{Answer}$$

Or changed to standard form:

$$4y = -2x + 1$$
$$2x + 4y = 1 \quad \textit{Answer}$$

Oral Exercises

For each of the following linear equations, find the slope and the y-intercept.

1. $y = 3x + 5$ 3; 5   2. $y = x - 4$ 1; -4 3. $y = -x - 6$ -1; -6 4. $y = -\dfrac{1}{2}x + 2$

$-\dfrac{1}{2}$; 2

5. $y - 5 = 0$ 0; 5   6. $y + 3 = 0$ 0; -3 7. $2y = 5x + 4$ $\frac{5}{2}$; 2   8. $2y = 6x + 5$ 3; $\frac{5}{2}$

9. $5 - 3x = y$ -3; 5   10. $4 + \frac{1}{3}x = y$ $\frac{1}{3}$; 4   11. $5x - 5y = 11$; $-\frac{1}{5}$ 12. $3x - 2y = 6$ $\frac{3}{2}$; -3

Written Exercises

Write a linear equation in standard form whose graph has the given slope and *y*-intercept.   Answers below.

A 1. $m = 1, b = 4$ 2. $m = -2, b = 1$ 3. $m = -3, b = -2$ 4. $m = 5, b = -2$

5. $m = \frac{1}{2}, b = 6$ 6. $m = -\frac{1}{4}, b = 3$ 7. $m = 0, b = 2$ 8. $m = 0, b = -5$

9. $m = -\frac{2}{3}, b = -\frac{1}{7}$ 10. $m = -\frac{5}{6}, b = \frac{5}{12}$ 11. $m = \frac{4}{5}, b = -20$ 12. $m = \frac{7}{3}, b = -4$

Change each equation to the **slope-intercept** form, and draw the graph. Answers below.

13. $x - y = 7$ 14. $y - 2x = -4$ 15. $2x - y = 5$ 16. $2x + y = 1$

17. $-x - y = 5$ 18. $-3x + y = 0$ 19. $2x - 3y = 0$ 20. $5x + 5y + 4 = 0$

21. $3y + 5 = 0$ 22. $5x + 3y = 0$ 23. $4x - 4y = 8$ 24. $4y - 7 = 0$

B 25. Write an equation of the line having *y*-intercept 3 and which has the same slope as the line whose equation is $y = 3x - 5$. $y = 3x + 3$

26. What do the lines with equations $y = -2x, y = 3x, y = -x,$ and $y = \frac{1}{3}x$

have in common?   Each has a *y*-intercept of 0.

27. What do the lines with equations $x + 2y = 6, 2x = -4y + 10,$ and $y = -\frac{1}{2}x + 5$ have in common? Support your answer by drawing the graphs.   Each has slope $-\frac{1}{2}$.

28. In the equation $2y + ax = 10$, for what value of *a* does the graph of the equation have a slope of 1? Of -1? $a = -2; a = 2$

29. In the equation $by - 3x = 6$, for what value of *b* does the graph of the equation have a slope of 1? Of 3? $b = 3; b = 1$

C 30. Using the standard form of a linear equation,

$$Ax + By = C,$$

find a formula for the slope and a formula for the *y*-intercept in terms of the coefficients, assuming that $B \neq 0$.   slope: $-\frac{A}{B}$

y-intercept: $\frac{C}{B}$

1. $x - y = -4$
2. $2x + y = 1$
3. $3x + y = -2$
4. $5x - y = 2$
5. $x - 2y = -12$
6. $x + 4y = 12$
7. $y = 2$
8. $y = -5$
9. $14x + 21y = -3$
10. $10x + 12y = 5$
11. $4x - 5y = 100$
12. $7x - 3y = 12$
13. $y = x - 7$
14. $y = 2x - 4$
15. $y = 2x - 5$
16. $y = -2x + 1$
17. $y = -x - 5$
18. $y = 3x$
19. $y = \frac{2}{3}x$
20. $y = -x - \frac{4}{5}$
21. $y = -\frac{5}{3}$
22. $y = -\frac{5}{3}x$
23. $y = x - 2$
24. $y = \frac{7}{4}$

8-9 Finding an Equation of a Line, y-intercept Not Given

> **OBJECTIVE** To learn how to find an equation of a line given the slope and one point on the line, or two points on the line.

Example 1 Find an equation in standard form of a line through point $(-1, -1)$ with slope $\frac{2}{3}$.

Solution The slope-intercept form of the equation is

$$y = \frac{2}{3}x + b.$$

Since $(-1, -1)$ is on the line, its coordinates must satisfy the equation; that is:

$$-1 = \frac{2}{3}(-1) + b$$

$$-1 = -\frac{2}{3} + b$$

$$-\frac{1}{3} = b$$

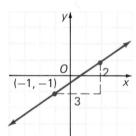

Thus, an equation of the line is

$$y = \frac{2}{3}x - \frac{1}{3}.$$

A standard form is found as:

$$3y = 2x - 1$$
$$2x - 3y = 1 \quad \textit{Answer}$$

To determine an equation of a line containing two given points, find the slope of the line, and then find the y-intercept, as above. The following example illustrates the method.

Example 2 Find an equation in standard form of the line containing the points $(5, 3)$ and $(-3, 1)$.

Solution Slope $= m = \dfrac{3-1}{5-(-3)} = \dfrac{2}{8} = \dfrac{1}{4}$

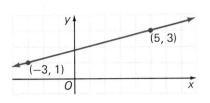

The slope-intercept form of the equation is

$$y = \frac{1}{4}x + b.$$

Choose one point, say (5, 3). Since it lies on the line:

$$3 = \frac{1}{4}(5) + b$$

$$12 = 5 + 4b$$

$$\frac{7}{4} = b$$

Thus, an equation of the line is

$$y = \frac{1}{4}x + \frac{7}{4}.$$

A standard form is found as:

$$4y = x + 7$$
$$x - 4y = -7 \quad \text{Answer}$$

Written Exercises

1. $3x - y = 1$
2. $2x - y = -1$
3. $2x + y = -1$
4. $4x + y = 7$
5. $3x - 4y = 3$
6. $5x - 4y = 15$
7. $x + 2y = 6$
8. $2x + 3y = 0$
9. $x + y = 5$
10. $2x - y = -8$
11. $4x + y = -7$
12. $y = -1$

Write an equation in standard form of the line passing through the given point and having the given slope.

A 1. (1, 2); 3

2. (1, 3); 2

3. (−2, 3); −2

4. (3, −5); −4

5. (1, 0); $\dfrac{3}{4}$

6. (−1, −5); $\dfrac{5}{4}$

7. (0, 3); $-\dfrac{1}{2}$

8. (0, 0); $-\dfrac{2}{3}$

9. (5, 0); −1

10. (−2, 4); 2

11. (−1, −3); −4

12. $\left(\dfrac{3}{4}, -1\right)$; 0

Write an equation in standard form of the line passing through the given points.

13. (1, 2), (0, 4)

14. (3, −1), (4, 5)

15. (0, −2), (3, 4)

16. (0, 4), (−3, 0)

17. (−1, 2), (2, 5)

18. (4, −3), (0, 3)

19. (5, −1), (3, 2)

20. (6, 3), (4, −2)

21. (−2, −3), (−1, 2)

22. (−2, 4), (3, −1)

23. (−3, −1), (1, −4)

24. (2, −1), (−3, 4)

13. $2x + y = 4$
14. $6x - y = 19$
15. $2x - y = 2$
16. $4x - 3y = -12$
17. $x - y = -3$
18. $3x + 2y = 6$
19. $3x + 2y = 13$
20. $5x - 2y = 24$
21. $5x - y = -7$
22. $x + y = 2$
23. $3x + 4y = -13$
24. $x + y = 1$

8-10 Direct Variation and Proportions

> **OBJECTIVE** To learn what direct variations are and how to use them to solve problems.

The table below shows the cost, c dollars, of a number, n, of rolls of film at $2 each.

Number n	Cost each (in dollars) 2	Total cost, c (in dollars) 2n
1	2	2
2	2	4
3	2	6
4	2	8
5	2	10

You can see that

$$c = 2n$$

and that this equation defines a function. In this case, the domain is {the whole numbers}. See the graph in Figure 8-15.

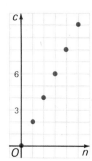

Figure 8-15

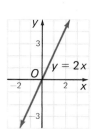

Figure 8-16

If the domain is {the real numbers}, the equation

$$y = 2x$$

defines a function whose graph is a straight line through the origin with slope 2 (Figure 8-16). This is a special kind of linear function, called a *linear direct variation*.

In general:

> A **linear direct variation** (or simply a **direct variation**) is a function defined by an equation of the form
>
> $$y = kx, \text{ where } k \text{ is a nonzero constant.}$$

You can say that

y varies directly as x

or

y varies with x.

The constant k is called the **constant of variation.**

Example 1   Given that d varies directly as t, and that $d = 120$ when $t = 4$, find:

a. the constant of variation.　　　b. the value of d when the value of t is 6.

Solution   Let $d = kt$.

a. $d = 120$ when $t = 4$.

$120 = k(4)$

$\therefore k = \dfrac{120}{4} = 30.$ *Answer*

b. $d = 30t$

$t = 6$

$\therefore d = 30(6) = 180.$ *Answer*

If one ordered pair of a direct variation is

$$(x_1, y_1) \text{ (read ''x sub 1, y sub 1'')}$$

and another of the same function is

$$(x_2, y_2)$$

and neither is $(0, 0)$, then

$$y_1 = kx_1 \quad \text{and} \quad y_2 = kx_2.$$

From these equations you can find the ratios

$$\frac{y_1}{x_1} = k \quad \text{and} \quad \frac{y_2}{x_2} = k.$$

Since each ratio equals k, the ratios are equal:

$$\frac{y_1}{x_1} = \frac{y_2}{x_2}, \ (x_1, y_1) \neq (0, 0), (x_2, y_2) \neq (0, 0)$$

The equality of ratios is called a *proportion* (page 228). Therefore, k is sometimes called the **constant of proportionality,** and y may be said to be **directly proportional to** x.

This proportion may be read

"y_1 is to x_1 as y_2 is to x_2."

x_1 and y_2 are called the **means** of the proportion, and y_1 and x_2 are called the **extremes.**

Multiplying both members of

$$\frac{y_1}{x_1} = \frac{y_2}{x_2}, \ (x_1, y_1) \neq (0, 0), (x_2, y_2) \neq (0, 0)$$

by $x_1 x_2$ gives:

$$y_1 x_2 = y_2 x_1, \ (x_1, y_1) \neq (0, 0), (x_2, y_2) \neq (0, 0)$$

Thus, in any proportion, *the product of the means equals the product of the extremes.*

Example 2 The amount of money that Universal Magazine pays for an article varies directly as the number of words in the article. If the magazine pays $240 for a 1200-word article, how much will be paid for an article of 1500 words?

Solution

Step 1 The problem asks for the amount to be paid for a 1500-word article.

Step 2 Let c be the amount paid for n words.

$$\frac{c_1}{n_1} = \frac{c_2}{n_2} \qquad \begin{aligned} c_1 &= 240 & c_2 &= \underline{\ ?\ } \\ n_1 &= 1200 & n_2 &= 1500 \end{aligned}$$

Step 3 $\dfrac{240}{1200} = \dfrac{c_2}{1500}$

Step 4 $240(1500) = 1200c_2$

$1200c_2 = 360{,}000$

$c_2 = \dfrac{360{,}000}{1200} = 300$

Or:
$$
\left[
\begin{array}{l}
\dfrac{240}{1200} = \dfrac{c_2}{1500} \\[2mm]
\dfrac{20}{1} = \dfrac{c_2}{15} \\[2mm]
c_2 = 20(15) = 300
\end{array}
\right.
$$

Step 5 The check is left to you. $\dfrac{240}{1200} = \dfrac{1}{5} = \dfrac{300}{1500}\;\checkmark$

$\therefore$ the magazine will pay \$300 for a 1500-word article. *Answer*

Dividing both members of $y_1 x_2 = y_2 x_1$ by $x_2 y_2$ gives the form:

$$\frac{y_1}{y_2} = \frac{x_1}{x_2},\ (x_1, y_1) \neq (0, 0),\ (x_2, y_2) \neq (0, 0)$$

You may use whichever proportion is more convenient for a problem.

Oral Exercises

State whether or not each formula expresses direct variation. For each direct variation, state the constant of variation.

1. $y = 3x$ yes; 3
2. $p = 4s$ yes; 4
3. $st = 6$ no
4. $C = 2\pi r$ yes; 2π
5. $3y = x$ yes; $\dfrac{1}{3}$
6. $d = 1.5t$ yes; 1.5
7. $q = 7.5p$ yes; 7.5
8. $mn = 24$ no
9. $c = \dfrac{1}{3}d$ yes; $\dfrac{1}{3}$
10. $\dfrac{a}{b} = 3$ yes; 3
11. $x = \dfrac{1}{y}$ no
12. $\dfrac{x}{y} = 10$ yes; $\dfrac{1}{10}$

Which of these sets of ordered pairs are direct variations?

Sample $\{(1, 3), (4, 12), (-3, -9)\}$

Solution $\dfrac{3}{1} = 3, \dfrac{12}{4} = 3, \dfrac{-9}{-3} = 3$

Since all these ratios equal 3, the function is a direct variation. *Answer*

13. $\{(1, 2), (2, 4), (3, 6)\}$ yes
14. $\{(4, 3), (12, 9), (24, 18)\}$ yes
15. $\{(3, 5), (5, 7), (7, 9)\}$ no
16. $\{(0, 1), (0, 3), (1, 6)\}$ no
17. $\{(12, 8), (6, 4), (8, 3)\}$ no
18. $\{(-1, 2), (3, -6), (9, -18)\}$ yes

Written Exercises

In Exercises 1–6, find the constant of variation.

A   1. y varies directly as x and $y = 9$ when $x = 3$.   3

2. y varies directly as x and $y = 2$ when $x = 6$. $\frac{1}{3}$

3. s varies directly as t and $s = 6$ when $t = 12$. $\frac{1}{2}$

4. m varies directly as n and $m = -10$ when $n = -2$.   5

5. a varies directly as b and $a = 56$ when $b = 14$.   4

6. d varies directly as f and $d = 76.2$ when $f = 152.4$. $\frac{1}{2}$

7. If w varies directly as x and $w = 9$ when $x = 3$, find w when $x = 4$. $w = 12$

8. If s varies directly as r and $s = 12$ when $r = 4$, find s when $r = 5$. $s = 15$

9. If v varies directly as w and $v = 2500$ when $w = 4$, find v when $w = 5.5$. $v = 3437.5$

10. If p varies directly as q and $p = 2000$ when $q = 200$, find p when $q = 300$. $p = 3000$

In each direct variation, find the missing value.

11. $x_2 = 25$, $y_1 = 100$, $x_1 = 20$, $y_2 = $ _?_   125   12. $x_1 = 10$, $x_2 = 2$, $y_2 = 5$, $y_1 = $ _?_   25

13. $s_2 = 4.8$, $s_1 = 2.4$, $m_1 = 1$, $m_2 = $ _?_   2   14. $y_1 = 64$, $x_1 = 24$, $y_2 = 8$, $x_2 = $ _?_   3

15. $s_1 = \frac{1}{2}$, $r_1 = \frac{2}{3}$, $r_2 = \frac{1}{6}$, $s_2 = $ _?_ $\frac{1}{8}$ 16. $u_1 = \frac{2}{3}$, $v_1 = \frac{1}{6}$, $u_2 = \frac{4}{5}$, $v_2 = $ _?_ $\frac{1}{5}$

Solve.

17. $\dfrac{x}{8} = \dfrac{5}{4}$ $x = 10$ 18. $\dfrac{7}{8} = \dfrac{2}{x}$ $x = \dfrac{16}{7}$ 19. $\dfrac{2y}{3} = \dfrac{8}{7}$ $y = \dfrac{12}{7}$ 20. $\dfrac{3y}{4} = \dfrac{5}{12}$ $y = \dfrac{5}{9}$

21. $\dfrac{x}{7 - x} = \dfrac{1}{3}$ $x = \dfrac{7}{4}$ 22. $\dfrac{3s}{s + 2} = \dfrac{5}{2}$ $s = 10$ 23. $\dfrac{6r}{r + 7} = \dfrac{9}{5}$ $r = 3$ 24. $\dfrac{3x}{10x + 2} = \dfrac{2}{7}$ $x = 4$

Translate into formulas expressing direct variation. Use k as the constant of variation.

Sample   The tension, T, on a spring varies directly as the distance, d, it is stretched (within certain limits).

Solution $T = kd$ or $\dfrac{T_1}{d_1} = \dfrac{T_2}{d_2}$

25. The perimeter of a square is directly proportional to the length of a side. $p = ks$

26. The weight, w, of an astronaut on the moon is directly proportional to the weight, W, on the earth. $w = kW$

27. The amount of interest (at a fixed rate) on a bank account varies directly as the amount of money on deposit. $I = km$

28. The distance traveled (at a fixed rate) varies directly as the time spent. $d = kt$

Problems

Solve.

$95\frac{5}{21}$ g

A 1. An employee's wages are directly proportional to the time worked. If the salary is $200 for 5 days, how much will it be for 18 days? **$720**

2. A certain car consumes 60 liters of gasoline in 3 hours. If the rate of gasoline consumption is constant, how much gasoline will the car use on a 35-hour trip? **700 liters**

3. A weight of 40 kilograms causes a beam to bend 10 millimeters. If the bending varies directly as the weight, how much will the beam bend with a weight of 60 kilograms? **15 mm**

4. The amount of extension on a wire spring is directly proportional to the amount of weight hung on it. A weight of 40 grams causes an extension of 8.4 centimeters. How much weight causes an extension of 20 centimeters?

5. If the Dorsey corporation paid a total dividend of $25 on 350 shares of its stock, how much of a dividend did it pay on 1050 shares? **$75**

6. An automatic doughnut machine can produce 1000 doughnuts in 6 hours. How long would it take the machine to make 300 doughnuts? **1.8 h**

B 7. Rod A has 180 equal divisions, and rod B has 100. Both rods have the same length. A length equal to 66.6 divisions on rod A is equal to a length of how many divisions on rod B?
37 divisions

8. When an electric current is 10 amperes, the electromotive force is 50 volts. Find the force when the current is 25 amperes if the force is proportional to the current. **125 volts**

★ Self-Test 3

Be sure that you understand these terms:

graph of an equation (p. 312)   equation of a line (p. 312)
linear equation in two variables (p. 312)
standard form of a linear equation (p. 312)   linear function (p. 313)
slope (p. 315)   y-intercept (p. 321)   direct variation (p. 327)
constant of variation (p. 327)   constant of proportionality (p. 328)
directly proportional (p. 328)   means (p. 328)   extremes (p. 328)

1. Select the equations which are linear.   Objective 8-6, p. 311
   a. $x - y = 5$ b. $y = 7$ c. $x^2 + y^2 = 9$
2. Graph the equation $y = x + 3$.
3. Determine the slope of a line passing through the points (1, 2) and (3, 5).   Objective 8-7, p. 315
4. From the equation $y = -\frac{2}{3}x + 1$, determine the slope and y-intercept of   Objective 8-8, p. 320
   the line.
5. Write an equation in standard form of a line through point (1, 2) with   Objective 8-9, p. 324
   slope 1.
6. Write an equation in standard form of a line through points (−5, 0) and
   (0, 5).
7. If x varies directly as y, and $x = 3$ when $y = 6$, find x when $y = 18$.   Objective 8-10, p. 326

Check your answers with those printed at the back of the book.

Chapter Summary

1. A function can be defined by an equation or a table or a correspondence or a set of ordered pairs.
2. The value of the function $f: x \rightarrow 3x + 2$ for $x = 2$ is denoted by $f(2)$. Thus, $f(2) = 3(2) + 2 = 8$.
3. Ordered pairs of real numbers can be graphed as points on a coordinate plane.
4. A relation is any set of ordered pairs. A function is a relation such that each member of the domain is paired with one and only one member of the range.
5. The solution set of an open sentence in two variables is a relation and can be graphed on a coordinate plane.
6. An equation of a straight line can be found from:
   a. the slope and the y-intercept
   b. the slope and any point on the line
   c. two points on the line
7. Direct variation is a linear function defined by an equation of the form $y = kx$, $k \neq 0$.

Chapter Test

8-1   1. Find the range of the function $f: x \rightarrow x^2 - 2x$ if the domain is $\{0, 2, 4\}$. $\{0, 8\}$

2. Given $g: t \rightarrow \dfrac{6}{t - 1}$, find $g(4)$.   2

8-2   3. Make a broken-line graph from the table:

Time of Day	6:00 A.M.	10:00 A.M.	2:00 P.M.	6:00 P.M.	10:00 P.M.
Temperature	7 °C	10 °C	24 °C	18 °C	10 °C

4. Write the set of ordered pairs given in the table at the right. $\{(1, 2), (2, 4), (3, 6)\}$

D	R
1	2
2	4
3	6

In the number pair $(3, -2)$:

8-3   5. Name the abscissa. **3**   6. Name the ordinate. **−2**

7. Name the quadrant in the coordinate plane in which its graph lies. **fourth**

8-4   8. The graph of a relation is shown at the right. Is the relation a function? **yes**

8-5   9. Is the number pair $(3, 1)$ a solution of the equation

$$x - y = -2? \quad \textbf{no}$$

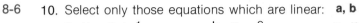

Ex. 8

8-6   10. Select only those equations which are linear: **a, b**
    a. $y = x + 1$ b. $y = 0$ c. $x - y^2 = 1$ d. $x^2 + y^2 = 1$

11. Graph $y = x - 2$ in the coordinate plane.

8-7   12. Find the slope of the straight line passing through the points whose coordinates are $(2, 4)$ and $(-1, 7)$. **−1**

8-8   13. Find the slope and y-intercept of the line having the equation $y + 6 = x$. **1; −6**

8-9   14. Write an equation in standard form of the line passing through the points $(2, -1)$ and $(-3, 4)$. **$x + y = 1$**

8-10   15. If y varies directly as x, and $y = 21$ when $x = 7$, find the constant of variation. **3**

Programmed Chapter Review

8-1   1. If a function g is defined by the equation

$$y = 4x + 3,$$

the arrow notation for the function is $g: \underline{\ ?\ } \to 4x + 3$. x

2. If the domain of $f: x \to 4 - x^2$ is $\{-2, -1, 0, 1, 2\}$, the range is $\underline{\ ?\ }$. $\{0, 3, 4\}$

3. The members of the range are called the $\underline{\ ?\ }$ of the function.   values

4. If $g(t) = 2t - 3$, then $g(2) = \underline{\ ?\ }$.   1

8-2   5. The first component of the ordered pair $(-1, 4)$ is $\underline{\ ?\ }$. -1

6. In a function there is one and only one member of the $\underline{\ ?\ }$ corresponding to each member of the $\underline{\ ?\ }$.   range domain

8-3   7. On the coordinate plane, the horizontal axis and vertical axis intersect at a point called the $\underline{\ ?\ }$.   origin

8. The quadrant containing an ordered number pair in which the abscissa is -3 and the ordinate is 2 is quadrant _?_ .

2

8-4

9. A _?_ is any set of ordered pairs of elements.

relation

10. The relation $\{(6, 1), (6, 2), (6, 3), (7, 1)\}$ has $\{\_?\_\}$ as domain, $\{\_?\_\}$ as range, and _?_ (is/is not) a function.

$\{6, 7\}$
$\{1, 2, 3\}$, is not

8-5

11. If the replacement set of both x and y is the set of whole numbers, the solution set of $2x + y = 8$ is $\{\_?\_\}$.

$\{(0, 8), (1, 6), (2, 4), (3, 2), (4, 0)\}$

12. The ordered pair $(6, 2)$ _?_ (is/is not) a solution of

$$x - y = 4.$$

is

8-6

13. A function whose ordered pairs satisfy a linear equation is called a _?_ function.

linear

14. When solved for y in terms of x, the equation $x + 3y = 9$ takes the form _?_ .

$y = -\dfrac{1}{3}x + 3$

15. The point $(1, 1)$ lies (above/below) _?_ the graph of $y = -2$.

above

8-7

16. The slope of the line shown on the coordinate plane at the right is _?_ .

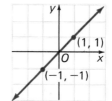

1

8-8

17. The ordinate of the point where a line crosses the y-axis is called the line's _?_ .

y-intercept

18. The slope and y-intercept of the graph of the equation $2y - 8 = 0$ are _?_ and _?_ .

0, 4

19. A linear equation whose graph has the slope $-\dfrac{1}{3}$ and y-intercept 2 is _?_ .

$y = -\dfrac{1}{3}x + 2$

8-9

20. An equation in standard form of the line passing through the points $(0, 3)$ and $(3, 0)$ is _?_ .

$x + y = 3$

8-10

21. If $y = kx$, and $y = 9$ when $x = 2$, then when $x = 3$, $y = \_?\_$.

13.5

22. In U.S. Grant High School the girls outnumber the boys 5 to 4. If there are 212 boys in the school, then there are _?_ girls.

265

Maintaining Skills

Now practice:

$x(a + b + 2)$
1. $ax + bx + 2x = \underline{}$

2. $3x^2 - 3xy + 3x = \underline{}$
$3x(x - y + 1)$
3. $x^3 - x^2 + x = \underline{}$
$x(x^2 - x + 1)$
4. $ay^2 + aby + ab = \underline{}$
$a(y^2 + by + b)$

5. $24t^2 + 12t - 6 = \underline{}\ 6(4t^2 + 2t - 1)$

6. $12x^2 - 18x^4 + 6x = \underline{}$
$6x(2x - 3x^3 + 1)$

7. $15r^2s^3 + 24r^2s^6 - 18r^2s^2 = \underline{}$

8. $25a^2b^2 - 15a^2b^3 + 20a^2b = \underline{}\ 5a^2b(5b - 3b^2 + 4)$

9. $36rs^2 + 18r^2s - 12r^2s^2 = \underline{}$

10. $18p^2q^2 - 9p^2q^3 + 27p^3q^2 = \underline{}\ 9p^2q^2(2 - q + 3p)$

7. $3r^2s^2(5s + 8s^4 - 6)$ 9. $6rs(6s + 3r - 2rs)$

Now practice:
11. $n^2 - 4 = \underline{}(n + 2)(n - 2)$

12. $16r^2 - 1 = \underline{}(4r + 1)(4r - 1)$

13. $n^2 + 10n + 25 = \underline{}(n + 5)^2$

14. $r^2 - 12r + 36 = \underline{}(r - 6)^2$

$(5 + 3a)(5 - 3a)$
15. $25 - 9a^2 = \underline{}$

$(6 + 7r)(6 - 7r)$
16. $36 - 49r^2 = \underline{}$

$(y - 9)^2$
17. $y^2 - 18y + 81 = \underline{}$

18. $9r^2 - 6r + 1 = \underline{}$
$(3r - 1)^2$

19. $4t^2 - 12t + 9 = \underline{}$
$(2t - 3)^2$

20. $25a^2 - 30a + 9 = \underline{}$
$(5a - 3)^2$

Now practice:
21. $n^2 - 8n + 7 = \underline{}$
$(n - 7)(n - 1)$

22. $r^2 + 6r + 5 = \underline{}(r + 5)(r + 1)$

23. $y^2 + 2y - 35 = \underline{}$
$(r + 7)(r - 5)$

24. $z^2 - 2z - 15 = \underline{}$
$(z - 5)(z + 3)$

$(t - 8)(t + 1)$
25. $t^2 - 7t - 8 = \underline{}$

$(n - 5)(n + 2)$
26. $n^2 - 3n - 10 = \underline{}$

27. $x^2 - 9xy + 20y^2 = \underline{}$
$(x - 4y)(x - 5y)$

28. $a^2 + 11ab + 18b^2 = \underline{}$
$(a + 9b)(a + 2b)$

29. $p^2 - 15pq + 26q^2 = \underline{}$
$(p - 13q)(p - 2q)$

30. $14 + 9t + t^2 = \underline{}$
$(7 + t)(2 + t)$

Now practice:
31. $3b^2 + 4b + 1 = \underline{}$
$(3b + 1)(b + 1)$

32. $3n^2 - 7n + 2 = \underline{}$
$(3n - 1)(n - 2)$

33. $4y^2 + 4y + 1 = \underline{}\ (2y + 1)^2$

34. $4k^2 + 12k + 9 = \underline{}(2k + 3)^2$

$(2t + 1)(t - 1)$
35. $2t^2 - t - 1 = \underline{}$

$(3s + 1)(s - 4)$
36. $3s^2 - 11s - 4 = \underline{}$

$(4c + 5)(c - 1)$
37. $4c^2 + c - 5 = \underline{}$

38. $6x^2 - x - 1 = \underline{}$
$(3x + 1)(2x - 1)$

39. $16m^2 - 16m - 5 = \underline{}$
$(4m + 1)(4m - 5)$

40. $16z^2 - 11z - 5 = \underline{}$
$(16z + 5)(z - 1)$

Systems of
Open Sentences
in Two Variables

Life Science This cross section of a branch of red oak shows the pattern of annual
rings and xylem rays.

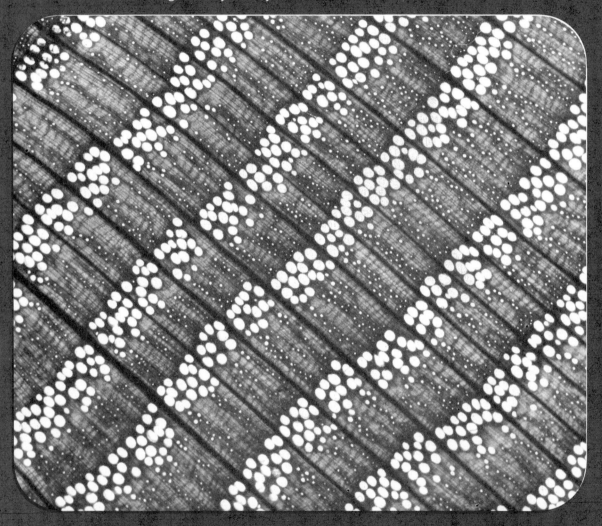

9

Solving Systems of Linear Equations

9-1 Solution by the Graphic Method

> **OBJECTIVE** To learn how to use graphs to find the solutions of pairs of linear equations in two variables.

Because *two* equations impose *two* conditions on the variables at the same time, they are called a **system of simultaneous equations.**

> A **solution** of a system of two equations in two variables is an ordered pair of numbers that satisfies both equations. The set of all solutions is called the **solution set** of the system.

You saw in Section 8-6 that the graph of a linear equation in two variables is a straight line. When two such lines *intersect,* as in Figure 9-1, the coordinates of the *point of intersection* satisfy the equations of *both* lines:

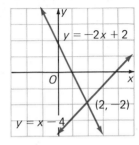

$$y = -2x + 2 \qquad y = -2x + 2 \qquad \Big| \qquad y = x - 4$$
$$y = x - 4 \qquad -2 \overset{?}{=} -2(2) + 2 \Big| -2 \overset{?}{=} 2 - 4$$
$$-2 = -2 \checkmark \qquad \Big| \qquad -2 = -2 \checkmark$$

One solution

Figure 9-1

No other ordered pair satisfies both equations because no point other than the point $(2, -2)$ lies on both graphs.

The graphs in Figure 9-2 do not inter-sect. The lines *are parallel.* Parallel lines are lines that lie in the same plane but have no point in common. Parallel lines have the same slope.

The graphs in Figure 9-3 *coincide. Every* solution of either equation is a solution of the other. The equations are equivalent. (Divide both members of the second equation by 3.)

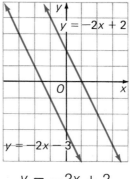

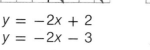

$$y = -2x + 2$$
$$y = -2x - 3$$

No solution

Figure 9-2

$$y = -2x + 2$$
$$3y = -6x + 6$$

Infinite set of solutions

Figure 9-3

> A pair of linear equations can be solved by graphing the equations in the same coordinate system and determining the coordinates of all points common to the graphs.

Oral Exercises

State the solution of each system.

1.
(1, 3)

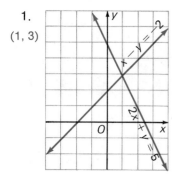

2.
(2, −4)

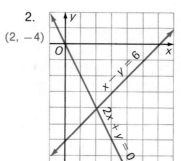

3.
(−2, 2)

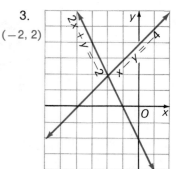

4.
(−2, 0)

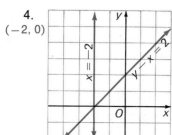

5.
(0, 2)

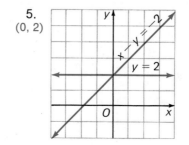

6.
(−1, −3)

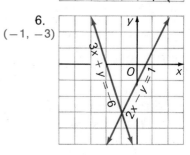

7. Given a system of linear equations that has no solution, how are the graphs of the equations related? They are parallel lines.

8. Given a system of linear equations that has at least two solutions, how are the graphs of the equations related? They coincide.

Written Exercises

Solve each system by graphing.

A 1. $x + y = 6$ (4, 2)
$x - y = 2$

2. $x - y = 1$ (2, 1)
$x + y = 3$

3. $x + y = 9$ (3, 6)
$y = 2x$

4. $y = 4 - x$ Ø
$y = -x$

5. $x - 2y = 0$ (4, 2)
$x + 2y = 8$

6. $x + y = 2$ (2, 0)
$x - 2y = 2$

7. $y = x - 4$ (3, −1)
$2x + y = 5$

8. $x - 6 = y$ (2, −4)
$2x - y = 8$

9. $x = 4 - y$ (1, 3)
$y = x + 2$

10. $x = y + 1$ Ø
$y = x + 1$

11. $3x + 4y = 10$ (2, 1)
$x - y = 1$

12. $y = \frac{1}{2}x + 1$ all real nos.
$x + 2 = 2y$

Write an equation of a line parallel to the line with the given equation, having the given value as *y*-intercept.

13. $y = \frac{1}{2}x + 2$; -2
$y = \frac{1}{2}x - 2$

14. $y = -\frac{2}{3}x + 1$; 0
$y = -\frac{2}{3}x$

15. $y = -\frac{4}{3}x - 1$; 3
$y = -\frac{4}{3}x + 3$

16. $y = \frac{3}{2}x - 4$; -1
$y = \frac{3}{2}x - 1$

In Exercises 17–20, solve graphically and estimate the coordinates of the point of intersection to the nearest $\frac{1}{2}$ unit.

B 17. $x + y = 1 \left(1\frac{1}{2}, -\frac{1}{2}\right)$
$x - y = 2$

18. $2x + y = 7\left(3\frac{1}{2}, -\frac{1}{2}\right)$
$x - 3y = 5$

19. $3x + 5y = 17\left(3, 1\frac{1}{2}\right)$
$15x - 15y = 29$

20. $y - \frac{2}{3}x = 2\left(2\frac{1}{2}, 3\frac{1}{2}\right)$
$y = -\frac{2}{3}x + 5$

21. Where on the graph of $x - 2y = 6$ is the abscissa equal to the ordinate? (−6, −6)

22. Where on the graph of $2y = -x + 7$ is the ordinate three times the abscissa? (1, 3)

C 23. Find the area of the triangle whose vertices are determined by the graphs of $2x + y = 5$, $y = x - 4$, $y = 5$. 27 square units

24. Find the area of the trapezoid whose vertices are determined by the graphs of $y = 0$, $y = 3$, $x = y$, $y = -\frac{3}{2}x + 12$. $16\frac{1}{2}$ square units

9-2 Solution by the Substitution Method

> **OBJECTIVE** To learn how to use the substitution method to find the solutions of pairs of linear equations in two variables.

In Figure 9-4 you can see that $(2, -2)$ is the common solution of any pair of linear equations whose graphs pass through the point that is its graph. In particular, the pair of heavy red lines represent the equations

$$x = 2$$
$$y = -2$$

whose common solution is $(2, -2)$.

Because this system of equations has the same solution set as the system

$$y = -2x + 2$$
$$y = x - 4$$

these systems are said to be **equivalent systems**. The system

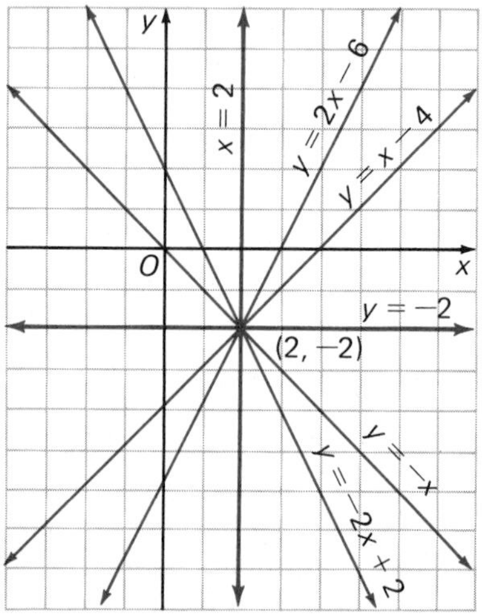

$$x = 2$$
$$y = -2$$

Figure 9-4

is also equivalent to the systems

$y = -2x + 2$	$y = 2x - 6$	$y = -2x + 2$	
$y = -x$	$y = x - 4$	$y = 2x - 6$	and so on.

To find the solution of a pair of linear equations written in slope-intercept form:

$$\begin{cases} y = -2x + 2 \\ y = -x \end{cases}$$

Substitute "$-x$" for "y" in the first equation:

$$-x = -2x + 2$$
$$x = 2$$

Solve the resulting equation:

Obtain the corresponding value of y by replacing "x" with "2" in either of the given equations:

$$y = -x = -2$$

Check in the other equation:

$$-2x + 2 = (-2)(2) + 2 = -2 \checkmark$$

The resulting equivalent system is $\begin{matrix} x = 2 \\ y = -2 \end{matrix}$ and the solution is $(2, -2)$.

It is not necessary to have both equations in slope-intercept form. You can put one into slope-intercept form and then substitute the resulting expression (substitution principle, page 2) in the other equation.

Example   Solve: $3x - 4y = -15$
$5x + y = -2$

Solution

1. Solve for y in the second equation (since its coefficient is 1).

$$5x + y = -2$$
$$y = -5x - 2$$

2. Substitute this expression for y in the first equation.

$$3x - 4y = -15$$
$$3x - 4(-5x - 2) = -15$$

3. Solve for x.

$$3x + 20x + 8 = -15$$
$$23x = -23$$
$$x = -1$$

4. Find the corresponding value of y.

$$y = -5x - 2 = -5(-1) - 2$$
$$= 5 - 2$$
$$y = 3$$

Check:

$3x - 4y = -15$	$5x + y = -2$
$3(-1) - 4(3) \overset{?}{=} -15$	$5(-1) + (3) \overset{?}{=} -2$
$-3 - 12 \overset{?}{=} -15$	$-5 + 3 \overset{?}{=} -2$
$-15 = -15$ ✓	$-2 = -2$ ✓

$\therefore$ the solution is $(-1, 3)$.   *Answer*

Of course, you can equally well solve first for x whenever that will result in less computation.

In general:

> To find the solution of a pair of linear equations by the **substitution method:**
>
> **1.** Solve *one* equation for *one* of the variables.
>
> **2.** Substitute the resulting expression in the *other* equation.
>
> **3.** Solve this derived equation.
>
> **4.** Find the corresponding value of the other variable.

Written Exercises

Solve each system of equations, using the substitution method. Give the value of the first variable in the first equation as the first component in the ordered pair.

A 1. $2x + y = 6$ (2, 2)
$y = x$

2. $a + 4r = 2$ (−2, 1)
$a = −2r$

3. $z + t = −4$ (−3, −1)
$−z + t = 2$

4. $x − 3y = −4$ (2,
$2x + y = 6$

5. $r + s = 2$ (1, 1)
$3r + 2s = 5$

6. $2a + b = 4$ (3, −2)
$b = 1 − a$

7. $3r − s = 5$ (2, 1)
$5r − 2s = 8$

8. $u + 5v = −17$
$3u − 4v = 6$ (−2,

9. $4c − 3d = 9$ (3, 1)
$2c − d = 5$

10. $a = 2 + 4b$ (6, 1)
$2b = a − 4$

11. $g = 3 − 3h$ (−3, 2)
$4h = g + 11$

12. $a − 2y = 0$ (6, 3)
$4a − 3y = 15$

B 13. $\frac{1}{3}(x + y) = 6$ (11, 7)
$\frac{1}{2}(x − y) = 2$

14. $\frac{a}{5} − b = −4$ (15, 7)
$a − b = 8$

15. $r + s = 18$ (16, 2)
$r − \frac{s}{2} = 15$

16. $x − y = −15$ (−1(
$\frac{1}{5}(x + y) = −1$

17. $\frac{x}{2} + \frac{y}{2} = 7$ (20, −6)
$3x + 2y = 48$

18. $\frac{1}{6}(x + y) = 2$ (10, 2)
$\frac{1}{4}(x − y) = 2$

19. $\frac{r}{2} + \frac{s}{3} = 1$ (4, −3)
$\frac{r}{4} + \frac{2s}{3} = −1$

20. $\frac{c}{2} − \frac{d}{5} = −4$ (−6,
$\frac{2c}{3} − \frac{3d}{5} = −7$

Applications
Scale Drawings and Maps

A scale drawing is a drawing that is drawn in proportion to the object that it represents. The constant of proportionality, or scale is often given as a ratio.

For example, the rectangle at the right represents the outline of a room. It is drawn to the scale 1:100. This means that 1 millimeter on the drawing represents 100 millimeters in the room. The dimensions printed on the diagram are the dimensions of the room. You can also think of the scale 1:100 as meaning 1 centimeter represents 1 meter.

1. Find the dimensions of the room above in meters.

2. At the right is a scale drawing of a house lot. The scale is

1:500.

Use a metric ruler and measure the length and width on the drawing. Then compute the actual length and width of the lot in meters.

4 m by 3 m

35 m by 20 m

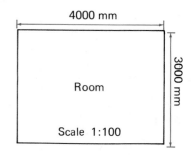

4000 mm

3000 mm

Room

Scale 1:100

house lot

Scale 1:500

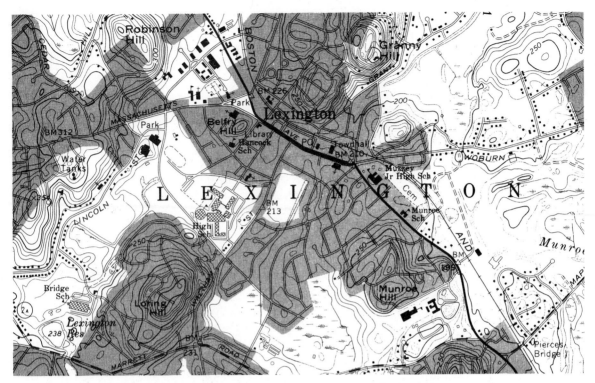

Above is a copy of a portion of one of the maps in the 7.5-minute series published by the United States Geological Survey. (Such a map represents a region that is 7.5 minutes of longitude by 7.5 minutes of latitude.) Its scale is 1:24,000.

3. What distance does 1 centimeter on the above map represent? 24,000 cm, or 240 m

4. What is the distance between the Library and the fork in the road northwest of Muzzey Junior High School? 720 m

Atlases give maps with a variety of ratios. Find the distance in kilometers represented by 1 centimeter on each of these maps.

5. North America, 1:40,000,000 400 km

6. Asia, 1:16,000,000 160 km

7. Australia and New Zealand, 1:15,000,000 150 km

8. Canada and Arctic America, 1:12,500,000 125 km

9. United States, 1:12,000,000 120 km

10. Southeastern United States, 1:4,000,000 40 km

11. Great Lakes, 1:2,500,000 25 km

12. San Francisco Bay Area, 1:1,000,000 10 km

13. Washington, D.C., 1:250,000 2.5 km

14. Quebec and vicinity, 1:100,000 1 km

9-3 Solving Problems with Two Variables

> **OBJECTIVE** To learn how to use pairs of linear equations in two variables to solve problems.

Problems involving two numbers can be solved by using either one or two variables. A solution using two variables is often more direct.

Example Together, two scientists devoted 28 hours to testing water samples for pollution. If the first scientist spent 4 hours more than the second, how many hours did each spend?

Solution

Step 1 The problem asks for the number of hours each scientist spent.

Step 2 Let x = number of hours spent by first scientist, and y = number of hours spent by second scientist.

Step 3 $x + y = 28$ (Total time spent)
$x - y = 4$ (Difference in time spent)

Step 4 From the second equation: $y = x - 4$
From the first equation: $x + (x - 4) = 28$
$2x = 32$ → $y = x - 4 = 16 - 4$
$x = 16$ $y = 12$

Step 5 The check is left to you. $16 + 12 = 28$; $16 - 12 = 4$ √

∴ the first scientist spent 16 hours; the second spent 12 hours. *Answer*

Oral Exercises

Translate into a system of equations in two variables.

1. The sum of two numbers is 42 and their difference is 14. $x + y = 42$; $x - y = 14$

2. The sum of two numbers is 40, and one number is three times the other. $x + y = 40$;
$x = 3y$

3. One number is 6 less than another, and their sum is 22.　$x = y - 6;\ x + y = 22$

4. One number is twice another, and their difference is 11.　$x = 2y;\ x - y = 11$

5. On a mathematics test Sandy scored 14 points more than Leslie. The sum of their scores was 160.　$S = L + 14;\ S + L = 160$

6. In a school ecology project, the ninth-grade class collected 25 more bags of aluminum cans than the tenth-grade class. The sum of their collections was 65 bags.　$n = t + 25;\ n + t = 65$

7. The forest service stocked Lake Crewel with 8000 bass and catfish. There were 2200 more catfish than bass.　$b + c = 8000;\ c - b = 2200$

8. A realtor sold a total of 120 homes and avocado groves last year. The number of homes exceeded the number of groves by 30.　$h + g = 120;\ h - g = 30$

Problems

Solve, using a system of two equations in two variables and the substitution method.

A 1. The perimeter of a rectangle is 54 centimeters. Two times the altitude is 3 centimeters more than the base. What is the area of the rectangle?　**170 cm²**

2. The manager of a theater knows that 900 tickets were sold for a certain performance. If orchestra tickets sold for $3 each and balcony tickets for $2 each, and if the total receipts were $2300, how many of each kind of ticket were sold?　**500 $3-tickets, 400 $2-tickets**

3. An engineer worked for 6 days and an assistant worked for 7 days investigating the effects of manufacturing processes which contribute to air pollution. Together they received a salary of $450. The following week, the engineer worked 5 days and the assistant worked 3 days for a combined salary of $290. Find the daily wages of each.　**eng.: $40; ass't.: $30**

4. A chemist has two acid solutions: one is 20% acid and the other 45% acid. How many kilograms of each must be used in order to produce 50 kilograms of a solution that is 30% acid?　**30 kg of 20%, 20 kg of 45%**

5. The sum of twice one number and five times a second number is 95. The difference between seven times the first number and three times the second number is 25. Find the numbers.　**10 and 15**

B 6. Two weights balance when placed 3 meters and 4 meters from the fulcrum of a lever. If the positions of the weights are interchanged, the smaller one would have to be increased by 7 kilograms in order to maintain balance. Find each weight.　**9 kg and 12 kg**

7. Marsha scored 85 on her first test in mathematics. The average of her first two tests was 9 less than her score on the third test. The average of all three tests was 83. What did she score on the second and third tests?
75 on second, 89 on third

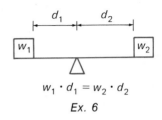

$$w_1 \cdot d_1 = w_2 \cdot d_2$$

Ex. 6

8. The average of two numbers is $\frac{7}{24}$. One fourth of their difference is $\frac{1}{48}$. Find both numbers.　**$\frac{1}{3}$ and $\frac{1}{4}$**

9-4 Solution by the Addition-or-Subtraction Method

> **OBJECTIVE** To learn how to use the addition-or-subtraction method to find the solutions of pairs of linear equations in two variables.

The addition-or-subtraction method is convenient when the coefficients of a pair of corresponding terms have the same absolute value.

Example 1 Solve: $x - 2y = -6$
$x + y = 6$

Solution

1. To obtain an equation that does not involve x, subtract (add the opposite of) each member of the second equation from the corresponding member of the first equation. Solve the resulting equation for y.

$$\begin{array}{r} x - 2y = -6 \\ x + y = 6 \\ \hline -3y = -12 \\ y = 4 \end{array}$$

2. Now replace y with "4" in either of the original equations. Solve the resulting equation for x.

$$\begin{array}{r} x + y = 6 \\ x + 4 = 6 \\ x = 2 \end{array}$$

3. The check is left for you.

∴ the solution is (2, 4). *Answer*
↳ $2 - 2 \cdot 4 = -6; 2 + 4 = 6$ ✓

Example 2 Solve: $4r - 3s = -10$
$2r + 3s = 4$

Solution

1. To obtain an equation that does not involve s, add the corresponding members of the given equations. Solve the resulting equation for r.

$$\begin{array}{r} 4r - 3s = -10 \\ 2r + 3s = 4 \\ \hline 6r = -6 \rightarrow r = -1 \end{array}$$

2. Replace r with "-1" in one of the original equations. Solve the resulting equation for s.

$$\begin{array}{r} 2r + 3s = 4 \\ 2(-1) + 3s = 4 \\ -2 + 3s = 4 \rightarrow s = 2 \end{array}$$

3. The check is left for you.

∴ the solution is (−1, 2). *Answer*
↳ $4(-1) - 3(2) = -10; 2(-1) + 3(2) = 4$ ✓

Written Exercises

Solve by addition or subtraction.

$\left(5, -\dfrac{25}{2}\right)$

A   1. $x + y = 6$ (5, 1)   2. $r - s = -3$ (3, 6)   3. $a + 2b = 1$ (3, −1)   4. $c + 2n = -20$
  $x - y = 4$ $r + s = 9$ $a - b = 4$ $c - 2n = 30$

5. $2r + s = -6$ (−4, 2)   6. $8w - z = 20$ (4, 12)   7. $2u + v = 0$ (−1, 2)   8. $5m - 6n = 16 \left(\dfrac{4}{5}, -2\right)$
  $3r + s = -10$ $-5w + z = -8$ $2u - 3v = -8$ $5m + n = 2$

9. $3x + 2y = 13$ (5, −1) 10. $2x - y = 0$ (7, 14)   11. $x - 11y = -2$ 12. $5a + 3b = 10$ (2, 0)
  $3x - 4y = 19$ $4x - y = 14$ $4x - 11y = -8$ (−2, 0) $2a - 3b = 4$

13. $12m + 3n = 51$ 14. $15 = 3s - 7t$ (5, 0)   15. $2 = 2a - 3b$ (4, 2)   16. $25x + 16y = 91$
  $7m - 3n = 44$ (5, −3) $15 = 3s + 2t$ $26 = 5a + 3b$ $16x + 16y = 64$
                                                                                      (3, 1)

Clear the equations of fractions before adding or subtracting.

B 17. $\dfrac{1}{5}(x - y) = 1$ 18. $2y - x = 6$ 19. $x - \dfrac{3}{2}y = 10$ 20. $\dfrac{2a}{3} - \dfrac{b}{5} = 2$

  $x + y = 9$ $\dfrac{1}{4}(3y - x) = 1$ $\dfrac{1}{3}x - y = \dfrac{13}{3}$ $\dfrac{2a}{3} + b = -1$

  (7, 2)   (−10, −2)   (7, −2) $\left(\dfrac{9}{4}, -\dfrac{5}{2}\right)$

Problems

Use two variables and a system of two equations to solve each problem.

A   1. The sum of two numbers is 34 and their difference is 4. Find the numbers. 19, 15

2. A total of 60 kiloliters of fuel is to be allotted to two rockets. One rocket is to receive 12 kiloliters less than the other. How many kiloliters will be allotted to each? 24 kl, 36 kl

3. The sum of two numbers is 56. The larger exceeds twice the smaller by 2. Find the numbers. 18, 38

4. Two numbers are such that their sum is 40, and their difference is 4 more than the smaller. Find the numbers. 12, 28

5. The larger of two numbers is 16 more than the smaller. Their sum is 6 less than three times the smaller. Find the numbers. 22, 38

6. Rudy is 5 years older than his brother. Three years ago he was twice as old. How old is each? Rudy: 13; brother: 8

B   7. Large cans of a certain kind of cream sell for 54¢ and small cans for 21¢. Roberta bought several cans for a total of $2.46. If she spent 78¢ more for the large cans than for the small cans, how many cans of each size did she buy? 3 large, 4 small

8. A store manager has $520 in one-dollar and five-dollar bills. If there are 5 times as many one-dollar bills as five-dollar bills, how many of each kind are there? 260 one-dollar, 52 five-dollar

9. At a joint conference of psychologists and sociologists, there were 24 more psychologists than sociologists. If there were 90 participants, how many were from each profession? 57 psychologists, 33 sociologists

10. During a holiday, the number of campers admitted to Laguna State Beach was 3 less than twice the number of trailers. If a total of 51 vehicles were admitted during the holiday, how many were there of each kind? 33 campers, 18 trailers

Applications
Solving Real Problems

To translate a situation into the form of a problem that can be solved, you must be sure that you have information relating to it that is *consistent* and *sufficient*.

To illustrate what we mean, we show two "textbook type" problems that cannot be solved.

Example 1 Find three consecutive integers whose sum is 26.

Solution

Step 1 The problem asks us to find three consecutive integers whose sum is 26.

Step 2 Let x = smallest of the integers.
Then the other two integers are $x + 1$ and $x + 2$.

Step 3 The sum of the integers is 26.
$$x + (x + 1) + (x + 2) \stackrel{\downarrow}{=} 26$$

Step 4 $3x + 3 = 26$; $3x = 23$; $x = 7\frac{2}{3}$
Since $7\frac{2}{3}$ is not an integer, the problem has no solution.

From the first statement of Step 4 you can see that the sum of any 3 consecutive integers, $3x + 3$ or $3(x + 1)$, must be a multiple of 3. But 26 is *not* a multiple of 3. Thus, the conditions of the problem do not fit with each other. That is, they are *not consistent*.

Example 2 How much coffee worth 75¢ per pound must be mixed with coffee worth $1.20 per pound to produce a mixture worth $1.00 per pound?

Solution

Step 1 The problem asks us to find the amount of 75¢ coffee.

Step 2 Let x = number of pounds of 75¢ coffee.
Let y = number of pounds of $1.20 coffee.
$0.75x + 1.20y = (x + y)1.00$ We cannot find a specific answer because the total amount is not given.

The information in Example 2 is *not sufficient*.

In the following problems, solve the problem if possible. If it is not possible, explain why and describe any additional information that may be needed.

1. A number of nickels and dimes have a total value of 65¢. How many dimes are there?   Not possible; need the total number of coins.

2. How many quarters make up a value of $1.20? Not possible; 120 is not a multiple of 25.

3. Four coins, dimes and quarters, have a total value of 70¢. How many of each are there? 2 dimes, 2 quarters

Consider these situations.

4. Tri-bar Company advertises a superwidget for $10 down and $2 a week. If you wanted to buy a superwidget, what else would you want to know about the cost? the number of weekly payments of $2

5. A record album is advertised on the radio: "Telephone in your order and pay the mail carrier $4.98 plus C.O.D. charges." What else would you like to know? the C.O.D. charges

6. You want to make some salad dressing that is to have $\frac{1}{3}$ vinegar and $\frac{2}{3}$ oil. How do you decide how much of each to use? decide how much dressing you want

7. Suppose that you have invited 8 friends for a cookout. You want to find out how many bags of rolls to buy. What information do you need?

the number of rolls per bag

Biographical Note
Louise Arner Boyd

Louise Arner Boyd (1887–1972) was a geographer and polar explorer. She was born and educated in California. Her first expedition was a trip to Greenland in 1926. On succeeding expeditions she explored East Greenland, Northeast and West Greenland, and eastern arctic Canada. Her research in these areas included the collection of data for maps and studies of the geology, botany, and meteorology of the regions. While preparing for an expedition in 1928, she learned that the explorer Roald Amundsen had disappeared and she joined in the search. Though Amundsen was never found, Louise Boyd was honored by the governments of Norway and France for her efforts.

During World War II, Louise Boyd served as a consultant to the United States government. She studied radio and magnetic phenomena in the ocean surrounding Greenland and other arctic areas, and supplied maps, photographs, and firsthand geographic information about strategic areas of the arctic. In 1955 one of her childhood dreams was realized; she made a successful flight over the North Pole. Among her many honors was her election to the council of the American Geographical Society in 1960.

9-5 Multiplication in the Addition-or-Subtraction Method

> **OBJECTIVE** To learn how to extend the addition-or-subtraction method for solving pairs of linear equations in two variables.

Sometimes the coefficients of a pair of corresponding terms in a pair of linear equations in two variables do not have the same absolute value. You then can use the multiplication property of equality (page 74) as shown in the following example.

Example Solve: $2r + 5s = 11$
$3r - 2s = -12$

Solution

1. To obtain an equation that does not involve *r*, multiply both members of the first equation by 3 and both members of the second equation by 2.

$$3(2r + 5s) = 3(11)$$
$$2(3r - 2s) = 2(-12)$$

2. Subtract the second equation from the first and solve the resulting equation for *s*.

$$6r + 15s = 33$$
$$6r - 4s = -24$$
$$19s = 57 \rightarrow s = 3$$

3. Replace *s* with "3" in either of the original equations. Then solve for *r*.

$$2r + 5s = 11$$

$$2r + 5(3) = 11 \rightarrow r = -2$$

4. The check is left for you. $2(-2) + 5(3) = 11; 3(-2) - 2(3) = -12 \checkmark$

∴ the solution is $(-2, 3)$. *Answer*

An alternative solution for the Example would be to obtain first an equation that does not involve *s*. Namely, multiply both members of the first equation by 2 and both members of the second by 5. Add the resulting equations and solve for *r*. Then continue as outlined above.

When you find an equation that involves only one variable, you may say that you have *eliminated* the other variable.

> To find the solution of a pair of linear equations by the addition-or-subtraction method:
>
> 1. Eliminate one variable by adding or subtracting corresponding members of the given equations. (Use multiplication if necessary to obtain coefficients of equal absolute values.)
> 2. Solve the resulting equation to find the value of the other variable.
> 3. Replace this variable with that value in either original equation.
> 4. Solve the resulting equation to find the value of the first variable.

Oral Exercises

Determine a number which can be used to multiply one equation in each pair so that one variable can be eliminated. F. = first equation, S. = second equation

1. $3x + 2y = 14$ S. by 2
   $2x + y = 6$

2. $2x + 3y = 2$ S. by 3
   $3x - y = 14$

3. $4a - 3b = 1$ S. by 4
   $a - 4b = 6$

4. $3t + 5w = 14$ S. by 5
   $2t - w = -1$

Determine a number which you would use to multiply each equation in the system to eliminate a variable. (You have two choices.)

5. $5x - 2y = 1$
   $3x - 7y = -18$
   F. by 3, S. by 5

6. $4a - 5b = 26$
   $3a - 6b = 15$
   F. by 3, S. by 4

7. $3x + 2y = 19$
   $4x - 3y = 7$
   F. by 4, S. by 3

8. $2p + 9q = 20$
   $9p + 2q = 13$
   F. by 9, S. by 2

Written Exercises

Solve each system of equations, using the addition-or-subtraction method.

A

1. $a + b = 3$ $(4, -1)$
   $3a - 5b = 17$

2. $3x - y = 3$ $(2, 3)$
   $x + 3y = 11$

3. $2c - d = -1$ $\left(-\dfrac{3}{2}, -2\right)$
   $4c + 3d = -12$

4. $2u - w = -1$ $(2, 5)$
   $u + 3w = 17$

5. $3x + 2y = -17$
   $x - 3y = 9$ $(-3, -4)$

6. $7m - 5n = 11$
   $3m + n = -11$
   $(-2, -5)$

7. $4x + 3y = 1$
   $6x - 2y = 21$
   $\left(\dfrac{5}{2}, -3\right)$

8. $3a + 4b = -25$
   $2a - 3b = 6$ $(-3, -4)$

Sample

$\dfrac{x}{3} + \dfrac{y}{2} = -1$

$\dfrac{x}{6} - \dfrac{y}{8} = 1$

Solution

$6\left(\dfrac{x}{3} + \dfrac{y}{2}\right) = 6(-1) \longrightarrow 2x + 3y = -6$

$24\left(\dfrac{x}{6} - \dfrac{y}{8}\right) = 24(1) \longrightarrow \dfrac{4x - 3y = 24}{6x \qquad = 18}$

$x = 3$

$\dfrac{x}{3} + \dfrac{y}{2} = -1$

$\dfrac{3}{3} + \dfrac{y}{2} = -1$

$y = -4$

9. $\dfrac{x}{6} + \dfrac{y}{4} = \dfrac{3}{2}$ (3, 4)   10. $\dfrac{m}{5} + \dfrac{3n}{5} = 2$ (4, 2)   11. $\dfrac{5a}{4} + b = \dfrac{11}{2}$ (2, 3)   12. $2x - \dfrac{5y}{2} = 13$ (4,

$\dfrac{2x}{3} - \dfrac{y}{2} = 0$ $\dfrac{m}{2} - n = 0$ $a + \dfrac{b}{3} = 3$ $\dfrac{x}{3} + \dfrac{y}{5} = \dfrac{14}{15}$

Note that the equations in Exercises 13–16 are not linear in the original variables.

B 13. $\dfrac{1}{a} + \dfrac{1}{b} = 7$ $\left[\text{*Hint:* 1. Let } x = \dfrac{1}{a} \text{ and } y = \dfrac{1}{b}.\quad \text{2. Rewrite: } \begin{array}{l} x + y = 7 \\ 2x + 3y = 16 \end{array} \right.$

$\dfrac{2}{a} + \dfrac{3}{b} = 16$ 3. Solve for x and y. Then $a = \dfrac{1}{x}$ and $b = \dfrac{1}{y}$. $\Big]$

$\left(\dfrac{1}{5}, \dfrac{1}{2}\right)$

14. $\dfrac{3}{r} + \dfrac{3}{s} = -4$ $\left(6, -\dfrac{2}{3}\right)$ 15. $\dfrac{1}{x} + \dfrac{1}{y} = 18$ $\left(\dfrac{1}{8}, \dfrac{1}{10}\right)$ 16. $\dfrac{5}{a} - \dfrac{6}{b} = -3$ (−

$\dfrac{6}{r} - \dfrac{4}{s} = 7$ $\dfrac{2}{x} - \dfrac{1}{y} = 6$ $\dfrac{10}{a} + \dfrac{9}{b} = 1$

Problems

Solve by using a system of two equations in two variables.

A 1. Four times the smaller of two numbers is equal to three times the larger. When the larger is doubled, it exceeds their original sum by 5. Find the numbers. 15 and 20

2. The larger of two numbers is 16 more than the smaller. When added together, their sum is 6 less than three times the smaller. What are the numbers? 22 and 38

3. A family has $1200 more invested at 5% than at 4%. They receive $108 more per year from the money invested at the higher rate. How much has been invested at each rate? (*below*)

4. To join a nature study club, there is an initiation fee and monthly dues. At the end of 6 months, a member will have paid $37 to the club. At the end of 10 months, $45 will have been paid. What are the monthly dues and the initiation charge? $25 initiation fee, $2 dues

5. Four liters of oil and 40 liters of gasoline cost $9.20. Six liters of oil and 52 liters of gasoline cost $12.60. Find the cost of a liter of oil and a liter of gasoline. oil: 80¢; gasoline: 15¢

6. The principal of a school is taking a group of students to lunch for having participated in a project called Operation–Cleanup. If 10 students have hot dogs and 20 students have hamburgers, the bill will total $20.00. However, if 20 students have hot dogs and 10 students have hamburgers, the bill will be only $17.50. What is the cost of each hot dog and each hamburger? (*below*)

7. An investment counselor has an income of $280 per year from two stocks. Stock A pays dividends at the rate of 5% and stock B at the rate of 6%. If the total investment is $5000, how much is invested in each stock? $2000 in A, $3000 in B

3. $6000 at 5%, $4800 at 4%

6. hot dog: 50¢; hamburger: 75¢

B 8. The owner of a candy shop wants to mix mints worth 50¢ a kilogram with chocolates worth 80¢ a kilogram to produce a mixture to sell at 70¢ a kilogram. How many kilograms of each variety should be used for a 30 kilogram mix? **10 kg of 50¢, 20 kg of 80¢**

9. A company takes loans from two banks. It borrows $300 more from the bank which charges 7% interest than from the bank which charges 8% interest. If the interest payments for one year are $126, how much does the company borrow at each rate?

10. Rose's mother is 4 years younger than her father. When they were married, she was $\frac{5}{6}$ as old as her husband. How old was each when they married? **mother: 20; father: 24**

9. $1000 at 7%, $700 at 8%

Computer Activity

Computers cannot solve problems. However, if you can translate the solution of a problem into a formula or a systematic process, called an **algorithm**, a computer can be programmed to do the computation for you.

To find a formula for solving a pair of linear equations in two variables, solve this general pair:

$$Ax + By = C \qquad E(Ax + By) = E(C)$$
$$Dx + Ey = F \longrightarrow B(Dx + Ey) = B(F)$$

$$\begin{array}{l} AEx + BEy = CE \\ BDx + BEy = BF \\ \hline (AE - BD)x = CE - BF \end{array}$$

$$x = \frac{CE - BF}{AE - BD}$$

$$Ax + By = C$$
$$A\left(\frac{CE - BF}{AE - BD}\right) + By = C$$
$$A(CE - BF) + B(AE - BD)y = C(AE - BD)$$
$$y = \frac{ACE - BCD - ACE + ABF}{B(AE - BD)} = \frac{AF - CD}{AE - BD}$$

$\therefore$ If $AE - BD \neq 0$, the solution is $\left(\dfrac{CE - BF}{AE - BD}, \dfrac{AF - CD}{AE - BD}\right)$.

If you have access to a computer that will accept BASIC, type in the following program. It will enable you to find solutions of pairs of linear equations in two variables.

```
10   PRINT "INPUT A,B,C,D,E,F";
20   INPUT A,B,C,D,E,F
30   LET D1=A*E-B*D
40   IF D1=0 THEN 70
50   PRINT "SOLUTION IS (";(C*E-B*F)/D1;",","(A*F-C*D)/D1;")."
60   STOP
70   PRINT "NO UNIQUE SOLUTION"
80   END
```

Only one question mark will be printed.
Type in all 6 numbers, separated by commas.

★ *Self-Test 1*

Be sure that you understand these terms:

system of simultaneous equations (p. 337)
solution of a system of two equations in two variables (p. 337)
parallel lines (p. 338)   equivalent systems (p. 340)
substitution method (p. 341)   addition-or-subtraction method (p. 346)

1. Solve this system graphically: $y = -2x + 8$ Objective 9-1, p. 337
   $$-2x + y = -4$$

2. Solve this system by the substitution method: $d = 2c + 4$ Objective 9-2, p. 340
   $$3c + d = 9$$

3. Use a system of two equations in two variables to solve this problem: The   Objective 9-3, p. 344
   perimeter of a rectangle is 60 meters. The length equals twice the width.
   Find the dimensions of the rectangle.

Solve each system by the addition-or-subtraction method.

4. $a - b = 4$ Objective 9-4, p. 346
    $4a - b = -2$

5. $2x + 3y = 1$ Objective 9-5, p. 350
    $3x - 4y = 10$

Check your answers with those printed at the back of the book.

Career Note
Landscape Architect

Landscape architects design the arrangement of flowers, trees, shrubbery, and walkways for building projects such as apartment complexes, college campuses, parks and playgrounds, shopping centers, hotels and resorts, or highways. They prepare working drawings for a site and sometimes supervise the grading, construction, and planting. A landscape architect may be employed by a private architectural or engineering firm or by a government agency involved in city planning.

The educational requirement is a bachelor's degree in landscape architecture. High school courses in art, botany, and mathematics are good preparation for the college program. Courses at the college level include surveying, landscape and architectural design, and horticulture.

Special Kinds of Problems

9-6 Puzzle Problems

> **OBJECTIVE** To learn how to use systems of equations to solve certain kinds of puzzle problems.

Digit Problems

All two-digit decimal numerals have the same form in general:

$$\left.\begin{array}{l} 76 = 7\cdot 10 + 6\cdot 1 \\ 67 = 6\cdot 10 + 7\cdot 1 \end{array}\right] \longrightarrow 10t + u, \text{ where } \longrightarrow \left[\begin{array}{l} t \in \{1, 2, 3, 4, 5, 6, 7, 8, 9\} \quad \text{and} \\ u \in \{0, 1, 2, 3, 4, 5, 6, 7, 8, 9\}. \end{array}\right.$$

Example The sum of the digits in a two-digit numeral is 10. The number represented when the digits are reversed is 16 times the original tens digit. Find the original two-digit number.

Solution

Step 1 The problem asks us to find the original number.

Step 2 Let t = the tens digit in the original numeral and u = the units digit in the original numeral.

Step 3

	Tens	Units	Value
Original number	t	u	$10t + u$
New number	u	t	$10u + t$

The sum of the digits of the original number is 10: $t + u = 10$

The new number is 16 times the original tens digit:

$$10u + t = 16t \longrightarrow 10u - 15t = 0$$

Step 4 $10(t + u) = 10(10) \longrightarrow$

$$\begin{array}{r} 10t + 10u = 100 \\ -15t + 10u = 0 \\ \hline 25t \qquad = 100 \\ t = 4 \end{array}$$

$$\begin{array}{l} t + u = 10 \\ 4 + u = 10 \\ u = 6 \end{array}$$

Step 5 *Check:* Is the sum of the digits of the original number 10?

$6 + 4 = 10$ ✓   Is $64 = 16\cdot 4$? $64 = 64$ ✓

∴ the original number is 46. *Answer*

Solve each problem, assuming that each number is a two-digit number.

A 1. A number is 6 times the sum of its digits. The units digit is 1 less than the tens digit. Find the number.   54

2. A number is 8 times the sum of its digits. The tens digit is 5 greater than the units digit. Find the number.   72

3. The sum of the digits is 9. If the digits are reversed, the number is increased by 45. What is the original number?   27

4. The sum of the digits is 13. If the number represented by reversing the digits is subtracted from the original number, the result is 27. Find the original number.   85

5. The tens digit is twice the units digit. If 36 is subtracted from the number, the digits will be interchanged. Find the original number.   84

6. The sum of the digits is 9. The number is diminished by 45 when the digits are reversed. What is the original number?   72

Age Problems

Example   Two years ago, Carol's age was 1 year less than twice Wanda's. Four years from now, Carol will be 8 years more than half Wanda's age. How old is Carol now?

Solution

Step 1   The problem asks us to find Carol's age now.

Step 2   Let x = Carol's age now and y = Wanda's age now.

Step 3

Time	Carol	Wanda
Now	x	y
2 years ago	$x - 2$	$y - 2$	$\rightarrow x - 2 = 2(y - 2) - 1$
4 years from now	$x + 4$	$y + 4$	$\rightarrow x + 4 = \frac{1}{2}(y + 4) + 8$

Step 4
$$\begin{array}{r} x - 2y = -3 \\ 4x - 2y = 24 \\ \hline -3x = -27 \\ x = 9 \\ y = 6 \end{array}$$

Step 5
$9 - 2 = 7 = 2(6 - 2) - 1$
$9 + 4 = 13 = \frac{1}{2}(6 + 4) + 8$

Steps 4 and 5 are left to you.
You should find that Carol is now 9 years old.   *Answer*

Solve.

A 1. Julian is 2 years older than his brother. Twelve years ago, he was twice as old. How old is each?   Julian: 16; brother: 14

2. Five years ago, Janet was only $\frac{1}{5}$ of the age of her mother. Now she is $\frac{1}{3}$ of her mother's age. Find their ages.   Janet: 10; mother: 30

3. In four years Bruce will be as old as John is now. Eight years ago, the sum of their ages was 16. Find their ages.   Bruce: 14; John: 18

4. Kathy's mother is 4 years younger than her father. When they were married, she was $\frac{6}{7}$ as old as her husband. At what age were they married?   mother: 24; father: 28

5. A father, being asked his age and that of his son said, "If you add 4 to my age and divide the sum by 4, you will have my son's age. But 6 years ago I was $7\frac{1}{2}$ times as old as my son." Find their ages.   father: 36; son: 10

Fraction Problems

Example The denominator of a fraction is 2 more than the numerator. If 1 is subtracted from each, then the value of the resulting fraction is $\frac{1}{2}$. Find the original fraction.

Solution

Step 1 The problem asks us to find the original fraction.

Step 2 Let n = the original numerator and d = the original denominator. Then $\frac{n}{d}$ = the original fraction.

Step 3 $\quad d = n + 2$

$$\underbrace{\frac{n-1}{d-1} = \frac{1}{2}}$$

Step 4 $\quad 2(n-1) = d - 1$

$2n - 2 = (n + 2) - 1$

$n = 3$

$d = n + 2$

$d = 3 + 2$

$d = 5$

Step 5 The check is left for you. $5 = 3 + 2; \frac{2}{4} = \frac{1}{2}\checkmark$

$\therefore$ the original fraction is $\frac{3}{5}$. **Answer**

Using two variables, find the original fraction.

A 1. The denominator is 10 more than the numerator. If each is increased by 3, the value of the resulting fraction is $\frac{9}{14}$. $\frac{15}{25}$

2. The denominator is 4 more than the numerator. If 2 is subtracted from each, the value of the resulting fraction is $\frac{1}{5}$. $\frac{3}{7}$

3. The denominator exceeds the numerator by 10. If 2 is subtracted from the numerator, and the denominator is unchanged, the resulting fraction has value $\frac{3}{5}$. $\frac{20}{30}$

4. The denominator exceeds the numerator by 7. If 3 is added to the denominator, a fraction is obtained whose value is $\frac{4}{9}$. $\frac{8}{15}$

5. If 6 is subtracted from the numerator of a certain fraction, the value of the fraction becomes $\frac{1}{8}$. If 4 is added to the denominator of the original fraction, its value becomes $\frac{2}{5}$. $\frac{8}{16}$

6. A certain fraction, if reduced, is equal to $\frac{5}{6}$. If 2 is added to the numerator, the fraction is equal to 1. $\frac{10}{12}$

7. The quotient of 2 numbers is equal to $\frac{7}{4}$. If the numerator and the denominator are each increased by 20, the quotient becomes equal to $\frac{11}{8}$. $\frac{35}{20}$

8. A fraction has a value of $\frac{2}{5}$. When 21 is subtracted from the denominator, the resulting fraction equals the reciprocal of the original fraction. $\frac{10}{25}$

9-7 Uniform-Motion Problems

> **OBJECTIVE** To learn how to use systems of equations to solve uniform-motion problems.

Recall (page 240) the basic formula for uniform-motion problems:

$$\text{Distance} = \text{Rate} \times \text{Time} \quad (D = RT)$$

Example A plane flew 600 kilometers downwind from Central City to Carlsbad in $1\frac{2}{3}$ hours and returned over the same route against the wind in 2 hours. Find the rate in kilometers per hour (km/h) of the plane in still air and the wind.

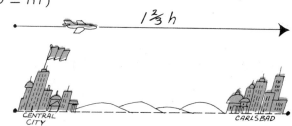

Solution

Step 1   The problem asks us to find the rate of the plane in still air and the rate of the wind.

Step 2   Let r = the rate in km/h of the plane and w = the rate in km/h of the wind.

Step 3

	R	T	D	
With the wind	$r + w$	$\frac{5}{3}$	600	$\rightarrow \frac{5}{3}(r + w) = 600$
Against the wind	$r - w$	2	600	$\rightarrow 2(r - w) = 600$

Step 4
$$\begin{array}{r} r + w = 360 \\ r - w = 300 \\ \hline 2r = 660 \\ r = 330 \\ w = 30 \end{array}$$

Steps 4 and 5 are left to you.
You should find that the rate of the plane in still air was 330 km/h, and the rate of the wind was 30 km/h. *Answer*

Step 5
$$\frac{5}{3}(330 + 30) = 600$$
$$2(330 - 30) = 600$$

Problems

Solve.

A   1. A boat can be rowed downstream at the rate of 14 kilometers per hour but only 4 kilometers an hour upstream. At what rate is the current flowing? What is the rate of rowing in still water?   current: 5 km/h
boat: 9 km/h

2. In 2 hours a canoeist can go 40 kilometers downstream but only 6 kilometers upstream. Find the rate of the current and that of the canoeist in still water.   current: $8\frac{1}{2}$ km/h
canoe: $11\frac{1}{2}$ km/h

4. boat: $16\frac{1}{2}$ km/h; current: $8\frac{1}{2}$ km/h
5. current: 5 km/h; boat: 15 km/h

3. It required 2 hours for a 560-kilometer plane trip and 4 hours for the return against the same wind. What would have been the rate of the plane without wind? What was the rate of the wind? plane: 210 km/h; wind: 70 km/h

4. A boat can go downstream at the rate of 25 kilometers per hour. It can return against the current at only 8 kilometers per hour. Find the rate of the boat and of the current. *(above)*

5. A motorboat can go 60 kilometers down a river in 3 hours. If it takes twice as long to return against the current, find the rate of the current and the rate of the boat in still water.*(above)*

6. An airplane flew 1800 kilometers in 5 hours with the wind. It would have taken 10 hours to have made the same trip against the wind. Find the rate of the plane and the rate of the wind. plane: 270 km/h; wind: 90 km/h

7. A certain plane has a 4-hour supply of gasoline. How far can it fly from an airport and return if the speed out with the wind is 200

kilometers per hour and the speed in against the wind is 130 kilometers per hour? 315.2 km

8. A crew that can row 20 kilometers an hour downstream finds that rowing 3 kilometers downstream takes the same amount of time as rowing 2 kilometers upstream. Find the rate of the current and of the rowers in still water. current: $3\frac{1}{3}$ km/h; boat: $16\frac{2}{3}$ km/h

9. Flying with the wind, an airplane can travel 1800 kilometers in 6 hours. It can travel only $\frac{2}{3}$ of this distance in the same time against the wind. What is the speed (rate) of the plane in still air and the speed of the wind? *(below)*

10. A plane flew 4000 kilometers in 4 hours from Vista to Ellwood City with a tailwind. Traveling in the opposite direction with a headwind, and over the same route, it took 4 hours and 48 minutes. Find the speed (rate) of the airplane in calm conditions and find the speed of the wind. plane: $916\frac{2}{3}$ km/h
wind: $83\frac{1}{3}$ km/h

B 11. A motorboat races a distance up the river in the time it races $1\frac{1}{2}$ times that distance downstream. If the speed of the boat is s and that of the current is c, find the relationship between s and c. $s = 5c$

12. A swimmer takes $1\frac{1}{2}$ hours on a 1-km round trip. On the return trip against the current, $\frac{1}{8}$ km took the same time as $\frac{1}{2}$ km did on the trip downstream. Find the swimmer's rate in still water and the rate of the current.
swimmer: $1\frac{1}{24}$ km/h; current: $\frac{5}{8}$ km/h

9. plane: 250 km/h; wind: 50 km/h

★ *Self-Test 2*

Solve.

1. The sum of the digits of a two-digit number is 10. The number is 16 times the units digit. Find the number.

Objective 9-6, p. 355

2. A father is twice as old as his daughter. Twelve years ago, he was 3 times as old. Find their ages.

3. The denominator of a fraction is 9 more than the numerator. If each is increased by 4, the value of the resulting fraction is $\frac{5}{8}$. Find the original fraction.

4. A boat can be rowed 6 kilometers per hour downstream but only half as fast on the return trip upstream. Find the rate of the current.

Objective 9-7, p. 358

Check your answers with those printed at the back of the book.

Systems of Linear Inequalities

9-8 Graphs of Linear Inequalities in Two Variables

> **OBJECTIVE** To learn how to graph the solution sets of systems of linear inequalities in two variables.

You can see in Figure 9-5 that the graph of

$$y = x + 1$$

separates the coordinate plane into two regions—one "above" the line and one "below" the line. Each region is called an open half-plane, and the line is the boundary of each.

If you start at any point on the line, say

$$(1, 2),$$

and move vertically *upward,* the *y*-coordinate *increases.* If you move vertically *downward* from this point, the *y*-coordinate *decreases.*

Thus, the upper half-plane is the graph of

$$y > x + 1,$$

and the lower half-plane is the graph of

$$y < x + 1.$$

The graphs of

$$y > x + 1$$
$$y = x + 1$$
$$y < x + 1$$

completely cover the coordinate plane. The equation "$y = x + 1$" is called the associated equation of "$y > x + 1$" or "$y < x + 1$."

Combining these ideas, you can see that the upper half-plane together with the boundary line is the graph of

$$y \geq x + 1$$

and the lower half-plane together with the boundary line is the graph of

$$y \leq x + 1.$$

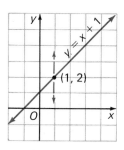

Figure 9-5

The graphs of the four inequalities are shown by shading in Figures 9-6, 9-7, 9-8, and 9-9. If the boundary line is part of the graph, it is drawn as a solid line. If the boundary line is not part of the graph, it is drawn as a dashed line.

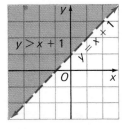
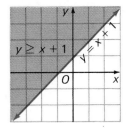
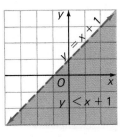
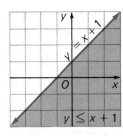

| Figure 9-6 | Figure 9-7 | Figure 9-8 | Figure 9-9 |

The union (page 271) of an open half-plane and its boundary is called a **closed half-plane.**

In general:

> The graph of a linear inequality in two variables is an open or a closed half-plane in the coordinate plane.

Example 1 Graph $3x - y \leq 6$.

Solution

1. Transform the given inequality into an equivalent inequality (page 263) having y as one member:

$$-y \leq 6 - 3x$$
$$y \geq 3x - 6$$

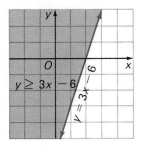

2. Graph the associated equation,

$$y = 3x - 6,$$

showing it as a solid line.

3. Shade the half-plane *above* the line, since $y \geq 3x - 6$.

Example 2 on page 362 shows how to graph a **system of inequalities.** The graph of the solution set of the system is the intersection (page 270) of the graphs of the inequalities.

Example 2 Graph the solution set of the system: $y > 3$

$$y \leq x + 1$$

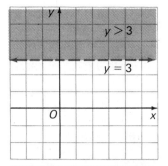

Solution

1. Graph $y > 3$ showing the boundary as a dashed line.

2. On the same coordinate plane, graph $y \leq x + 1$ showing the boundary as a solid line.

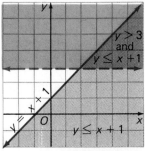

3. The graph of the solution set is the doubly-shaded region above the graph of $y = 3$ and below and on the graph of $y = x + 1$.

Example 3 Graph $x \geq -2$.

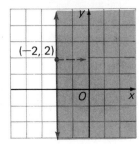

Solution

1. If you start at any point on the graph of "$x = -2$," say

$$(-2, 2),$$

and move horizontally *to the right,* the x-coordinate *increases.*

2. The graph of "$x \geq -2$" is the closed half-plane *to the right* of the graph of "$x = -2$."

Oral Exercises

Which of the given points belong to the graph of the given inequality?

1. $x - y < 0$; (5, 6), (1, −1) (5, 6) 2. $x + y \geq 0$; (3, 3), (4, −5) (3, 3) 3. $x < 3$; (2, 4), (−1, 2) bo
4. $2x + y \leq 5$; (0, 0), (2, 2) (0, 0) 5. $x - 2y > 3$; (0, −2), (1, 1)(0, −2) 6. $y \geq 4$; (2, 4), (−2, 5) bo

Transform each open sentence into an equivalent one having y alone as one member.

7. $x + y < 3$ $y < 3 - x$ 8. $-x + y > 2$ $y > x + 2$ 9. $5x + y \geq 6$ $y \geq 6 - 5x$ 10. $2x + y \leq -1$ $y \leq -1 -$
11. $3x + 4y > 0$ $y > -\frac{3}{4}x$ 12. $10x + 3y < 0$ $y < -\frac{10}{3}x$ 13. $2y < x$ $y < \frac{1}{2}x$ 14. $3x > 2y$ $y < \frac{3}{2}x$
15. $x - y \leq 2$ $y \geq x - 2$ 16. $8x - 4y \leq 0$ $y \geq 2x$ 17. $x - y > 5$ $y < x - 5$ 18. $2x - y < 7$ $y > 2x -$

Written Exercises

Graph each inequality.

A 1. $y \le 3$ 2. $y \ge -1$ 3. $x > 0$ 4. $y < 2$
  5. $y \le -x$ 6. $y \ge x$ 7. $y \le x + 1$ 8. $x + 3y < 6$

Graph each pair of inequalities and indicate their solution set with shading
or crosshatching.

9. $y \ge 0$ 10. $y \le 2$ 11. $y < x$ 12. $y > 2x$
   $x \ge 0$ $x \ge -2$ $x > 3$ $x < 5$

13. $y \le x + 1$ 14. $y > 2x - 3$ 15. $y > \frac{1}{2}x + 3$ 16. $y < 2x + 2$
    $y \ge x - 1$ $y < 2x + 4$ $x > 3$ $y > 2 - 2x$

B 17. $x + 1 > 0$ 18. $2x + y \ge 1$ 19. $3y - x \ge 2$ 20. $y \le 4x - 4$
    $x - 1 < 0$ $x - y \ge 2$ $x \le -4$ $y > 4 - 4x$

21. $x - 3y \le 2$ 22. $x - 2y \ge 4$ 23. $y > x - 3$ 24. $2y \ge x + 1$
    $x + 2y \ge -1$ $9y \ge 3x - 18$ $y > -x$ $2y + x \le 4$

Graph each inequality in the given system and indicate their solution set
as points in a three-way shaded region.

Sample $y \le -x$
  $y \ge x$
  $x \ge -6$

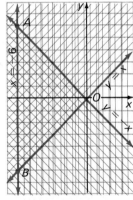

Solution

1. The graph of the solution set of "$y \le -x$" consists of points on the
   graph of "$y = -x$" and in the diagonally shaded region below it.

2. The graph of the solution set of "$y \ge x$" consists of points on the
   graph of "$y = x$" and in the diagonally shaded region above it.

3. The graph of the solution set of "$x \ge -6$" consists of points on the
   graph of "$x = -6$" and in the vertically shaded region to the right
   of it.

4. The intersection of these three sets is the three-way shaded region,
   triangle AOB, including points on its sides as well as in its interior.

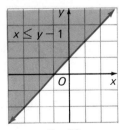

C 25. $x + y \le 1$ 26. $3x - y \le 3$ 27. $x + 3y < 6$
       $x \ge 0$ $x \ge 0$ $y \ge 0$
       $y \ge 0$ $y > 2$ $2x - y + 3 > 0$

28. Show by transforming the inequality $y \ge x + 1$ that the solution set can
    be graphed from $x \le y - 1$. $y - x \ge 1$; $-x \ge 1 - y$; $x \le y - 1$

Ex. 28

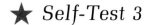 *Self-Test 3*

Be sure that you understand these terms:

open half-plane (p. 360)   boundary (p. 360)   associated equation (p. 360)
closed half-plane (p. 361)   system of inequalities (p. 361)

1. Graph "$y \leq -\dfrac{x}{2}$" in the coordinate plane.   Objective 9-8, p. 360

2. Transform "$3x - y \geq 4$" into an equivalent open sentence having y alone as one member.

3. Graph the solution set of the system: $x + y > 3$
                                                                                              $2x - y > 2$

Check your answers with those printed at the back of the book.

Chapter Summary

1. The solution set of a system of open sentences in two variables is the set of ordered pairs of numbers that satisfy all the sentences of the system.

2. The solutions of pairs of linear equations in two variables may be estimated by graphing, and computed by the substitution or the addition-or-subtraction method.

3. The graph of the solution set of a system of inequalities is the intersection of the graphs of the inequalities.

Chapter Test

9-1   1. Solve graphically: $x - y = 3$ (5, 2)
                                                    $x + y = 7$

Solve by substitution.

9-2   2. $a - 4b = 6(-\frac{2}{9}, -\frac{14}{9})$3. $3x + \ y = 4$ (2, −2)
                   $2a + \ b = -2$ $2x - 3y = 10$

9-3   4. Jane bought a used car and the cost of registering the car with the state was $20. The annual insurance cost twice as much as the car, and the cost of the car and registration together was $50 less than the cost of the insurance. Find the total cost of the car and the annual insurance. car: $70; insurance: $140

Solve each system by addition or subtraction.

9-4   5. $x + y = -6$ 6. $3r + s = 6$
            $-x + y = 4\,(-5, -1)$ $-3r + s = 10\,(-\frac{2}{3}, 8)$

9-5   7. $4a + 3b = -1$ 8. $2x + 5y = 9$
          $2a - 5b = 6\;(\frac{1}{2}, -1)$ $3x - 2y = 4\;(2, 1)$

9-6   9. The sum of the digits of a two-digit number is 7. If the order of
          the digits is reversed, the result names a number which is 27
          less than the original number. What is the original number?   52

9-7   10. Two airplanes leave 2 cities and fly toward each other. One plane
           is flying at the rate of 300 kilometers per hour and the other at
           the rate of 350 kilometers per hour. If the planes started at 7 A.M.,
           at what time will they meet if the 2 cities are 1300 kilometers
           apart?   9 A.M.

Graph.

9-8   11. $y - 2x \leq 4$ 12. $x + 3y > 9$ 13. $y \leq x + 1$
                                                             $x - y < 2$

Programmed Chapter Review

9-1   1. __?__ lines are lines that lie in the same plane, but have no point | Parallel
          in common.

       2. The graphs of "$y = -x + 1$" and "$y = -x + 3$" __?__ (inter- | have no
          sect, coincide, have no common point).   common point

9-2   3. In order to solve the system $\begin{aligned}3x + 2y &= -18\\x - 3y &= -6\end{aligned}$ by substitution, |

          transform the second equation to $x =$ __?__ . | $3y - 6$

       4. Substituting in the first equation in Exercise 3 gives __?__ = | $3(3y - 6) + 2y$
          __?__ . | -18

       5. A system equivalent to the one in Exercise 3 is:

                          $x =$ __?__ | -6
                          $y =$ __?__ | 0

       Translate each into a system of equations in two variables.

9-3   6. The sum of two numbers is 10 and their difference is 2. __?__ | $x + y = 10$
                                                                   __?__ | $x - y = 2$

       7. One number is 6 less than another, and their sum is 18. __?__ | $x = y - 6$
                                                                   __?__ | $x + y = 18$

Reduce each system of equations to an equation in one variable by addition or subtraction.

9-4

8. $4x + y = 12$
    $2x - y = 12$
    ___?___ = ___?___

6x, 24

9. $x - 3y = 7$
    $x + 2y = 12$
    ___?___ = ___?___

$-5y, -5$
(or $5y, 5$)

Begin the solution of each system by using the multiplication property of equality.

9-5

10. $3x + 2y = -18$
    $x - 3y = -6 \rightarrow$ ___?___ $(x - 3y) =$ ___?___ (-6)

3, 3

11. $7a - 3b = -1$ (Eliminate b) ___?___ $(7a - 3b) =$ ___?___ (-1)
    $-9a + 4b = 1$ ___?___ $(-9a + 4b) =$ ___?___ (1)

4, 4
3, 3

Solve.

9-6

12. The units digit of a two-digit number is 4 more than the tens digit. If the digits are reversed, the new number is 10 more than twice the original number. What is the original number?

26

13. The sum of the ages of 2 children is equal to $2\frac{1}{2}$ times the age of the younger child. In 6 years, the sum of their ages will be 37 years. Determine their ages now.

10 yr., 15 yr.

14. A fraction's value is $\frac{1}{3}$. When its numerator is increased by 48, the new fraction equals the reciprocal of the value of the original fraction. Find the original fraction.

$\frac{6}{18}$

9-7

15. An aviator is timed going in both directions over a 90-kilometer course. The time eastward, with the wind, is 24 minutes and westward, against the wind, is 30 minutes. Find the velocity of the wind in kilometers per hour.

22.5 km/h

9-8

16. Transform "$2x - y \le 4$" into "y ___?___."

$\ge 2x - 4$

17. Graph "$y < x$" and "$x > 2$" in the same coordinate plane and indicate their solution set with crosshatching.

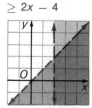

Cumulative Review, Chapters 1-9

If $x = 3$, $y = -2$, and $z = 0$, evaluate each expression.

1. $\dfrac{2x + 5y}{y}$ 2

2. $(x + y)(x - y)$ 5

3. $\dfrac{4x^2 - 2y^2}{x^2 + 2z}$ $\dfrac{28}{9}$

Simplify each expression.

4. $\dfrac{7 - 18}{11} + 1$ 0

5. $4(6 + 8) + 3(-10)$ 26

6. $(2x^2 - 3x + 2) + (x^2 - x - 5)$ $3x^2 - 4x - 3$

7. $(4t^2 - 3t - 5) - (3t^2 + t - 5)$ $t^2 - 4t$

8. $(2r - 3)(r + 3)$ $2r^2 + 3r - 9$

9. $(2r^2 + 9r - 5) \div (r + 5)$ $2r - 1$

If $f(x) = 2x^2 - 3x + 5$, find:

10. $f(-1)$ 10

11. $f(2)$ 7

12. $f(-10)$ 235

If $g(y) = 4 + 2y - 3y^2$, find:

13. $g(0)$ 4

14. $g(3)$ -17

15. $g(-3)$ -29

Factor completely.

16. $6a^3 - 9a^2 + 5a$ $a(6a^2 - 9a + 5)$

17. $2y^2 + 3y + 1$ $(2y + 1)(y + 1)$

18. $n^2 + 10n + 25$ $(n + 5)^2$

19. $4r^2 - s^2$ $(2r + s)(2r - s)$

20. $bx^3 - 6bx^2 + 5bx$ $bx(x - 5)(x - 1)$

21. $y^3 - y^2 + y - 1$ $(y - 1)(y^2 + 1)$

Simplify.

22. $\dfrac{-6rs}{5} \cdot \dfrac{10r}{3r^2s}$ -4

23. $\dfrac{81k^2}{28k} \div \dfrac{9k}{7k^3}$ $\dfrac{9k^3}{4}$

24. $\dfrac{p^2}{p^2 - q^2} \cdot \dfrac{p + q}{p - q} \div \dfrac{p}{(p - q)^2}$ p

25. $\dfrac{2 - x}{6} + \dfrac{3 + x}{2}$ $\dfrac{11 + 2x}{6}$

26. $\dfrac{2}{x + 2} - \dfrac{3}{x + 3}$ $\dfrac{-x}{x^2 + 5x + 6}$

27. $\dfrac{2}{y^2 - 4} + \dfrac{3}{2 - y} - \dfrac{5}{y + 2}$ $\dfrac{-8y + 6}{y^2 - 4}$

Solve each equation.

28. $3x + 1 - 2x = 3$ $\{2\}$

29. $2t - 3 + 5t = t + 15$ $\{3\}$

30. $(n - 3)(n + 5) = 0$ $\{3, -5\}$

31. $r^2 + 15 = -8r$ $\{-5, -3\}$

32. $6z^2 = 34z - 20$ $\left\{\dfrac{2}{3}, 5\right\}$

33. $4x^2 = 49$ $\left\{\dfrac{7}{2}, -\dfrac{7}{2}\right\}$

34. $\dfrac{x}{2} + \dfrac{x}{5} = 7$ $\{10\}$

35. $r^2 + \dfrac{2r}{12} - \dfrac{1}{6} = 0$ $\left\{\dfrac{1}{3}, -\dfrac{1}{2}\right\}$

36. $\dfrac{x}{4} + \dfrac{x}{2} = \dfrac{x}{8} + 1$ $\left\{\dfrac{8}{5}\right\}$

Solve each inequality. Graph the solution set.

37. $2z - 3 > 9$ $z > 6$

38. $-3x + 6 < x - 30$ $x > 9$

39. $16 - 8t \leq t - 20$ $t \geq 4$

40. $4(x - 2) > 5(x - 3)$ $x < 7$

41. $\dfrac{3y - 14}{6} \leq \dfrac{2y}{9} + \dfrac{y}{4}$ $y \leq 84$

42. $-5 \leq -2 + z \leq 0$ $-3 \leq z \leq 2$

Solve.

43. An apple has 29 more calories than a peach and 13 fewer calories than a banana. If 3 apples have 43 fewer calories than 2 bananas and 2 peaches, how many calories does a banana have? **88 calories**

44. The steamship Viking Explorer, sailing west at 32 knots, passed the freighter Santa Cruz, which was sailing due east at 24 knots. In how many hours after the meeting will the ships be 448 nautical miles apart? **8 hours**

45. Ed has an equal number of dimes and quarters. If he has $2.10 in all, how many coins of each type has he? **6 of each**

46. The length of a rectangle is 2 meters greater than twice its width, and its area is 60 square meters. Find its dimensions. **5 m by 12 m**

47. One pipe can fill a tank in 12 hours and another can fill the tank in 8 hours. How many hours will it take both pipes together to fill the tank? **$4\frac{4}{5}$ hours**

48. Amy's motorboat cruises at 20 kilometers per hour in still water. It takes her twice as long to go 90 kilometers upstream as it does to return 75 kilometers downstream. What is the speed of the current? **5 km/h**

Graph.

49. $x - 2y = 4$

50. $2x + 3y = 6$

51. $y = 6 - 2x$

52. $x = -5$

53. $3y = 12$

54. $3y - 2x = 7$

55. Find the slope and y-intercept of the graph of $x - 2y = 4$. **slope: $\frac{1}{2}$; y-intercept: -2**

56. Write an equation in standard form of the line containing the points $(-5, 1)$ and $(3, 7)$.
$3x - 4y = -19$

Solve.

57. $2x + y = 7$ **(5, −3)**
    $2x - y = 13$

58. $5a + 3b = 8$ **(1, 1)**
    $-7a - 3b = -10$

59. $4a - 3b = -1$ **(2,**
    $a - b = -1$

60. $2x + 3y = -1$ **(1, −1)**
    $3x + 5y = -2$

61. $x - 2y = 7$ **all real nos.**
    $3x - 6y = 21$

62. $2x - \dfrac{5y}{2} = 13$ **(4,**
    $\dfrac{x}{3} + \dfrac{y}{5} = \dfrac{14}{15}$

63. The denominator of a fraction is 2 greater than the numerator. If 1 is subtracted from each, the value of the resulting fraction is $\frac{1}{2}$. Find the original fraction. **$\frac{3}{5}$**

64. The sum of the digits of a two-digit numeral is 12. The value of the number is 13 times the tens digit. Find the number. **39**

Looking Ahead ▶

Up to now the problems that you have been solving involved primarily integers and fractions. (In some problems you used fractional approximations, $\frac{22}{7}$ or 3.14, for π, which cannot be expressed exactly as a fraction.) In the next two chapters you will learn how to use square roots of numbers in the solution of problems.

Maintaining Skills

Remember how?

$$\frac{2x + 14}{6x} \cdot \frac{9x^2}{x^2 + 7x} = 3$$

$$\frac{\overset{1}{\cancel{2}}(\cancel{x+7})}{\underset{3}{\cancel{6}x}} \cdot \frac{9x^2}{x(\cancel{x+7})}$$

$$\frac{1}{3x} \cdot \frac{9x^2}{x} = 3$$

Now practice:

1. $\dfrac{8x}{13y} \cdot \dfrac{26xy}{4x} = \underline{\ ?\ }$ $\quad 4x$

2. $\dfrac{-6ab}{5} \cdot \dfrac{10a}{3a^2b} = \underline{\ ?\ }$ $\quad -4$

3. $\dfrac{a^2 - ab}{ab} \cdot \dfrac{ab}{2a - 2b} = \underline{\ ?\ }$ $\quad \dfrac{a}{2}$

4. $\dfrac{2x - 2y}{xy} \cdot \dfrac{xy}{4x - 4y} = \underline{\ ?\ }$ $\quad \dfrac{1}{2}$

5. $\dfrac{3a + 15}{2a} \cdot \dfrac{4a}{4a + 40} = \underline{\ ?\ }$ $\quad \dfrac{3a + 15}{2a + 20}$

6. $\dfrac{2z + 14}{6z} \cdot \dfrac{9z^2}{z^2 + 7z} = \underline{\ ?\ }$ $\quad 3$

7. $\dfrac{x^2 - 4}{2x} \cdot \dfrac{1}{x + 2} = \underline{\ ?\ }$ $\quad \dfrac{x - 2}{2x}$

8. $\dfrac{y^2 + 2y}{2y + 1} \cdot \dfrac{y + 1}{y^3 + 2y^2} = \underline{\ ?\ }$ $\quad \dfrac{y + 1}{2y^2 + y}$

9. $\dfrac{x^2 - y^2}{x^2 - 16} \cdot \dfrac{x + 4}{x + y} = \underline{\ ?\ }$ $\quad \dfrac{x - y}{x - 4}$

10. $\dfrac{a^2 - 2a - 3}{3a^2} \cdot \dfrac{6a}{a + 1} = \underline{\ ?\ }$ $\quad \dfrac{2a - 6}{a}$

Remember how?

$$\frac{x^2 - 4}{x^3} \div \frac{x^2 - 4x + 4}{x^2} = \frac{x + 2}{x(x - 2)}$$

$$\frac{x^2 - 4}{x^3} \cdot \frac{x^2}{x^2 - 4x + 4}$$

$$\frac{(x - 2)(x + 2)}{x^3} \cdot \frac{x^2}{(x - 2)^2}$$

$$\frac{x + 2}{x^3} \cdot \frac{x^2}{x - 2} = \frac{x + 2}{x(x - 2)}$$

Now practice:

11. $\dfrac{x}{y^2} \div \dfrac{x^2}{y} = \underline{\ ?\ }$ $\quad \dfrac{1}{xy}$

12. $\dfrac{a^2}{b^2} \div \dfrac{a}{b^3} = \underline{\ ?\ }$ $\quad ab$

13. $\dfrac{3t}{8s^2} \div \dfrac{12t^2}{4s^3} = \underline{\ ?\ }$ $\quad \dfrac{s}{8t}$

14. $\dfrac{-24ab^2}{8a} \div \dfrac{14b}{21a^2b} = \underline{\ ?\ }$ $\quad -\dfrac{9a^2b^2}{2}$

15. $\dfrac{3x - 9}{5x - 15} \div \dfrac{8x - 4}{10x - 5} = \underline{\ ?\ }$ $\quad \dfrac{3}{4}$

16. $\dfrac{2a - 4b}{8a + 24b} \div \dfrac{4a - 8b}{2a + 6b} = \underline{\ ?\ }$ $\quad \dfrac{1}{8}$

17. $\dfrac{r + 2}{r^2 - 9} \div \dfrac{1}{r - 3} = \underline{\ ?\ }$ $\quad \dfrac{r + 2}{r + 3}$

18. $\dfrac{3c + 3d}{4c^2} \div \dfrac{c^2 - d^2}{2c^2} = \underline{\ ?\ }$ $\quad \dfrac{3}{2c - 2d}$

19. $\dfrac{x^2 - y^2}{x^2 - 3x - 4} \div \dfrac{x - y}{x^2 + x} = \underline{\ ?\ }$ $\quad \dfrac{x^2 + xy}{x - 4}$

20. $\dfrac{6a - 27}{5a} \div (4a - 18) = \underline{\ ?\ }$ $\quad \dfrac{3}{10a}$

Rational and Irrational Numbers

Social Science An Eskimo artist carved this chess set from walrus ivory and made the board from sealskin. Anthropologists study such crafts as an aspect of the cultural development of an ethnic group.

10

Rational Numbers

10-1 Properties of Rational Numbers

> **OBJECTIVE** To learn some properties of rational numbers and how to use them.

Up to now, you have been working with integers and positive and negative numbers represented by fractions. The union of these two sets of numbers is called the set of *rational numbers*. In general:

> A real number that can be expressed as a *ratio* of two integers (the second integer not zero) is called a **rational number.**

Thus, the following are examples of rational numbers:

$$0 = \frac{0}{1}, \quad 1 = \frac{1}{1}, \quad 3 = \frac{3}{1}, \quad 3\frac{1}{4} = \frac{13}{4}, \quad 0.7 = \frac{7}{10}, \quad -\frac{3}{4} = \frac{-3}{4} = \frac{3}{-4}$$

From your work with fractions, you can see that a rational number can be expressed as a quotient of integers in an unlimited number of ways:

$$1 = \frac{3}{3} = \frac{-5}{-5} = \frac{23}{23}, \cdots \qquad -\frac{6}{7} = \frac{-6}{7} = \frac{12}{-14} = \cdots \qquad 18\% = \frac{18}{100} = \frac{9}{50} = \cdots$$

You can always tell which of two rational numbers is the greater by writing them with the same positive denominator and comparing their numerators.

Example 1 Compare $-\frac{3}{4}$ and $-\frac{2}{3}$.

Solution The L.C.D. is 12.

Since $-\frac{3}{4} = \frac{-9}{12}$ and $-\frac{2}{3} = \frac{-8}{12}$, you compare $\frac{-9}{12}$ and $\frac{-8}{12}$.

Since $-9 < -8$, you can see that

$$-\frac{3}{4} < -\frac{2}{3}. \quad Answer$$

Example 2 Compare $\frac{7}{3}$ and $\frac{13}{6}$.

Solution Since $\frac{7}{3} = \frac{14}{6}$ and $14 > 13$, you can see that

$$\frac{7}{3} > \frac{13}{6}. \quad Answer$$

In general, let a and b be any integers and c and d be any positive integers. Then:

if $\frac{a}{c} > \frac{b}{d}$	if $ad > bc$
then $\frac{ad}{cd} > \frac{bc}{cd}$	then $\frac{ad}{cd} > \frac{bc}{cd}$ (since $cd > 0$)
and $ad > bc$;	and $\frac{a}{c} > \frac{b}{d}$.

Thus:

For all integers a and b and all positive integers c and d:

$$\frac{a}{c} > \frac{b}{d} \quad \text{if and only if} \quad ad > bc.$$

Similarly,

$$\frac{a}{c} < \frac{b}{d} \quad \text{if and only if} \quad ad < bc.$$

From this, you can see that

$$\frac{5}{6} > \frac{3}{4} \quad \text{because} \quad 5(4) > 3(6);$$

$$-\frac{1}{2} > -\frac{3}{2} \quad \text{because} \quad -1(2) > -3(2).$$

Integers and rational numbers have some distinctive properties.
For each integer, there is a next larger one. For example, -4 follows -5, 0 follows -1, and 4 follows 3.

There is no "next larger" rational number after a rational number.

For example, there is no next larger rational number after $\frac{2}{3}$. Instead,

the set of rational numbers has a property that the set of integers does not have, namely:

> **The Property of Density**
>
> Between every pair of different rational numbers there is another rational number.

Example 3 Find a rational number between $\frac{8}{5}$ and $\frac{16}{9}$.

Solution 1 One way to do this is to add half the difference to the smaller number:

$$\frac{8}{5} + \frac{1}{2}\left(\frac{16}{9} - \frac{8}{5}\right) = \frac{8}{5} + \frac{1}{2}\left(\frac{80}{45} - \frac{72}{45}\right)$$

$$= \frac{8}{5} + \frac{1}{2}\left(\frac{8}{45}\right) = \frac{72}{45} + \frac{4}{45} = \frac{76}{45}$$

Check: Is $\frac{8}{5} < \frac{76}{45} < \frac{16}{9}$?

$$\qquad\qquad ? \qquad\qquad\qquad ?$$

$$8(45) < 5(76) \quad 9(76) < 16(45)$$

$$360 < 380 \checkmark \quad 684 < 720 \checkmark$$

$\therefore$ a rational number between (exactly halfway between)

$\frac{8}{5}$ and $\frac{16}{9}$ is $\frac{76}{45}$. *Answer*

Solution 2 Find the average of the given numbers:

$$\frac{1}{2}\left(\frac{8}{5} + \frac{16}{9}\right) = \frac{1}{2}\left(\frac{72 + 80}{45}\right) = \frac{1}{2}\left(\frac{152}{45}\right) = \frac{76}{45}$$

This gives the same answer as Solution 1.

The method used in Solution 1 of Example 3 suggests a way of finding other rational numbers between $\frac{8}{5}$ and $\frac{16}{9}$. For example, you can add $\frac{1}{4}$ the difference to $\frac{8}{5}$:

$$\frac{8}{5} + \frac{1}{4}\left(\frac{8}{45}\right) = \frac{72}{45} + \frac{2}{45} = \frac{74}{45}$$

Check that $\frac{8}{5} < \frac{74}{45} < \frac{16}{9}$. You can also find that $\frac{78}{45}$ is $\frac{3}{4}$ of the way from $\frac{8}{5}$ to $\frac{16}{9}$ (see Figure 10-1).

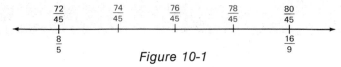

Figure 10-1

Do you see that the number of rational numbers between $\frac{8}{5}$ and $\frac{16}{9}$ is unlimited? The property of density implies that **between every pair of rational numbers there is an infinite set of rational numbers.**

Oral Exercises

Express each number as a quotient of integers.   Answers may vary.

Sample 1.8   *One Solution* $\frac{18}{10}$

1. 3.2 $\frac{32}{10}$ 2. 16.1 $\frac{161}{10}$ 3. $-3\frac{1}{3}$ $-\frac{10}{3}$ 4. $-5\frac{1}{4}$ $-\frac{21}{4}$ 5. 0.08 $\frac{8}{100}$ 6. 0.006 $\frac{6}{1000}$

7. 13% $\frac{13}{100}$ 8. 27% $\frac{27}{100}$ 9. -2 $-\frac{2}{1}$ 10. -3 $-\frac{3}{1}$ 11. 0 $\frac{0}{1}$ 12. $1 - 1$ $\frac{0}{1}$

13. $(-1)\left(-\frac{1}{3}\right)$ $\frac{1}{3}$ 14. $\frac{1}{4} \div \frac{1}{4}$ $\frac{1}{1}$ 15. $\frac{1}{4} + \left(-\frac{3}{4}\right)$ $-\frac{2}{4}$ 16. $\frac{5}{8} - \frac{3}{8}$ $\frac{2}{8}$

Determine which rational number is the greater.

17. $\frac{3}{7}, \frac{8}{7}$ $\frac{8}{7}$
18. $\frac{23}{3}, \frac{17}{3}$ $\frac{23}{3}$
19. $-2, \frac{1}{4}$ $\frac{1}{4}$
20. $\frac{3}{2}, -\frac{3}{2}$ $\frac{3}{2}$
21. $-\frac{1}{5}, -\frac{3}{5}$ $-\frac{1}{5}$
22. $-\frac{7}{6}, -\frac{5}{6}$ $-\frac{5}{6}$

23. $3, \frac{16}{3}$ $\frac{16}{3}$
24. $7, \frac{48}{7}$ 7
25. $\frac{5}{6}, \frac{4}{9}$ $\frac{5}{6}$
26. $\frac{11}{5}, \frac{7}{3}$ $\frac{7}{3}$
27. $-\frac{8}{5}, -\frac{9}{7}$ $-\frac{9}{7}$
28. $-\frac{11}{2}, -\frac{16}{3}$ $-\frac{16}{3}$

Written Exercises

Replace the ? with =, <, or > to make a true statement.

A 1. $\frac{1}{9}$? $\frac{4}{27}$ $<$
2. $\frac{3}{4}$? $\frac{5}{13}$ $>$
3. $-\frac{5}{16}$? $-\frac{13}{25}$ $>$
4. $\frac{23}{27}$? $\frac{41}{39}$ $<$

5. $\frac{137}{65}$? $\frac{122}{76}$ $>$
6. $-15\frac{1}{3}$? $-\frac{123}{11}$ $<$
7. $17\frac{2}{5}$? $\frac{131}{7}$ $<$
8. $\frac{317}{8}$? $39\frac{7}{9}$ $<$

Arrange the members of each set in increasing order.

9. $\left\{\frac{1}{3}, -\frac{3}{4}, \frac{7}{8}\right\}$ $-\frac{3}{4}, \frac{1}{3}, \frac{7}{8}$
10. $\left\{-\frac{5}{6}, -\frac{3}{7}, \frac{1}{21}\right\}$ as is
11. $\left\{-3.2, -\frac{24}{9}, -1.0\right\}$ as is

12. $\left\{-2.1, -\frac{43}{20}, -\frac{71}{35}\right\}$ $-\frac{43}{20}, -2.1, -\frac{71}{35}$
13. $\left\{\frac{2}{15}, \frac{3}{16}, \frac{5}{24}, \frac{1}{2}\right\}$ as is
14. $\left\{\frac{7}{24}, \frac{8}{9}, \frac{5}{16}, \frac{8}{7}\right\}$ $\frac{7}{24}, \frac{5}{16}, \frac{8}{9}, \frac{8}{7}$

Find the number halfway between the given numbers.

15. $\frac{3}{8}, \frac{1}{2}$ $\frac{29}{112}$
16. $\frac{3}{4}, \frac{1}{16}$ $\frac{13}{32}$
17. $-\frac{3}{50}, -\frac{7}{100}$ $-\frac{13}{200}$
18. $-\frac{5}{39}, -\frac{6}{117}$ $-\frac{21}{234}$
19. $-3\frac{1}{6}, 5\frac{1}{9}$ $\frac{35}{36}$
20. $1\frac{3}{5}, -2\frac{7}{8}$ $-\frac{51}{80}$

If $x \in \{0, 1, 2, 3\}$, taking each value in increasing order, state whether the given fraction increases or decreases in value. I = increases, D = decreases

21. $\frac{x}{3}$ I
22. $\frac{x+1}{2}$ I
23. $\frac{4}{x+3}$ D
24. $\frac{7}{x-4}$ D
25. $\frac{3x+1}{8}$ I
26. $\frac{6}{6-x}$ I

B 27. Find the number one fourth of the way from $\frac{3}{8}$ to $1\frac{1}{2}$. $\frac{21}{32}$

28. Find the number one third of the way from $-\frac{1}{6}$ to $-\frac{4}{5}$. $-\frac{17}{45}$

29. Find an expression for the number halfway between r and s. $\frac{r+s}{2}$

30. What number is one third of the way from x to y: a. if $x < y$? b. if $x > y$?
$x + \frac{1}{3}(y-x)$ $x - \frac{1}{3}(x-y)$

Explain why each statement is true.

31. -7 is the least integer greater than -8.

32. There is no least rational number greater than 0.

31. -7 is the next larger integer after -8, since $-8 + 1 = -7$. It is the least integer greater since there is no integer between -8 and -7.

32. For any rational number r we choose as least, there is another rational number between 0 and r, by the Property of Density.

Extra for Experts ExtraExtraExtraExtraExtraExt
Number Systems

> A set of numbers, together with the operations of addition and multiplication, is called a **number system.**

You have been working with several number systems:

the system of whole numbers
the system of integers
the system of rational numbers
the system of real numbers

Each system has certain special properties.

> A set of numbers is said to be **closed under an operation** performed on its members provided that each result of the operation is a member of the set.

1. The system of whole numbers is closed under addition and multiplication, but not under subtraction and division.
2. The system of integers is closed under addition, subtraction, and multiplication, but not under division.
3. The system of rational numbers is closed under addition, subtraction, multiplication, and division (except by zero), and so these operations are called the rational operations.
4. The system of real numbers is closed under the rational operations and is also closed under the operation of extracting a square root of a positive number (and other such operations).

In a logical development, the following are taken as axioms (page 88):

> Axioms of Closure for Addition and Multiplication
>
> For all real numbers a and b:
>
> $a + b$ is a unique real number.
> ab is a unique real number.

Since every real number has a unique opposite (Section 2-3), if you know b, then you know $-b$. Also, since $a + (-b)$ denotes a sum of real numbers, it represents a real number. Therefore, the rule for subtraction shows that the set of real numbers is *closed under subtraction*.

Since every nonzero real number has a unique reciprocal (Section 3-3), if you know a ($a \neq 0$), then you know $\dfrac{1}{a}$. Since $a \cdot \dfrac{1}{b}$ denotes a product of real numbers, it represents a real number. Therefore, the rule for division shows that the set of real numbers is *closed under division excluding division by zero*.

Show that the following sets are not closed under the stated operations by finding a result that is not a member of the set.

Sample   {the odd integers}; addition

Solution $7 + 5 = 12$, an even integer; not in the set.
  1. {the positive numbers}; subtraction $1 - 3 = -2$, a negative number
  2. {the natural numbers}; division $1 \div 2 = \frac{1}{2}$, a fraction
  3. {the negative numbers}; multiplication $(-1)(-2) = 2$, a positive number
  4. {the real numbers between 0 and 1}; addition $\frac{2}{4} + \frac{3}{4} = 1\frac{1}{4}$, a number greater than 1

Explain why you think each of the following sets is closed under the stated operation.   Answers on page A4 at the back of the book.

  5. {the real numbers between 0 and 1}; multiplication
  6. {the even integers}; addition and multiplication
  7. {the odd integers}; multiplication
  8. {the rational numbers}; division (except by zero)

Can a finite set be closed under an operation? Consider the set {0, 1} and make addition and multiplication tables for it:

+	0	1
0	0	1
1	1	2

×	0	1
0	0	0
1	0	1

You can see from the tables that {0, 1} is closed under multiplication but not closed under addition.

Make tables for each set and operation, and inspect the tables to determine closure.
  9. $\{-1, 0, 1\}$; addition and multiplication   not closed under add., closed under mult.
 10. $\{\frac{1}{2}, 1, 2\}$; multiplication and division   not closed under either
 11. $\{1\}$; multiplication   closed
 12. $\{0\}$; addition   closed

10-2 Decimal Forms for Rational Numbers

> **OBJECTIVE** To learn how to express rational numbers in fractional form or decimal form.

To change a common fraction to a decimal, you carry out the indicated division:

$$\frac{11}{16} = 11 \div 16 \qquad \frac{7}{12} = 7 \div 12 \qquad \frac{5}{11} = 5 \div 11 \qquad \frac{3}{7} = 3 \div 7$$

```
       0.6875              0.5833              0.4545                 0.4285714
16)11.0000          12)7.0000          11)5.0000             7)3.0000000
    9 6                  6 0                 4 4                   2 8
    ────                 ───                 ───                   ───
    1 40                 1 00                 60                    20
    1 28                  96                  55                    14
    ────                 ───                 ──                    ──
     120                  40                  50                    60
     112                  36                  44                    56
     ────                 ──                  ──                    ──
      80                  40                  60                    40
      80                  36                  55                    35
     ───                  ──                  ──                    ──
       0                   4                   5                    50
                                                                   49
                                                                   ──
                                                                   10
                                                                    7
                                                                   ──
                                                                   30
                                                                   28
                                                                   ──
                                                                    2
```

This decimal is terminating, end-ing, or finite.

$$\frac{11}{16} = 0.6875$$

These decimals are **nonterminating, unending,** or **infinite.** They are also called **repeating** or **periodic** because the same digit (or block of digits) repeats unendingly.

$$\frac{7}{12} = 0.5833\ldots \quad \text{or} \quad \frac{7}{12} = 0.58\overline{3}$$

$$\frac{5}{11} = 0.454545\ldots \quad \text{or} \quad \frac{5}{11} = 0.\overline{45}$$

$$\frac{3}{7} = 0.428571428\ldots \quad \text{or} \quad \frac{3}{7} = 0.\overline{428571}$$

The dots and bar mean "continue unendingly."

When you divide a positive integer n by a positive integer d, the remainder r at each step must be such that

$$0 \leq r \leq d - 1.$$

Within no more than $d - 1$ steps after only zeros are left to be brought down from the dividend, either the remainder is 0 and the division terminates, or a sequence of other remainders repeats unendingly. In general:

> For example, if $d = 7$, the remainders are:
> 0, 1, 2, 3, 4, 5, 6

> For every integer n and every positive integer d, the decimal numeral of the rational number $\dfrac{n}{d}$ either terminates or eventually repeats in a block of fewer than d digits.

To convert a terminating decimal to a common fraction, you simply express the decimal as a common fraction with a power of ten as denominator and then reduce to lowest terms. Thus:

$$0.6875 = \frac{\overset{\overset{11}{\cancel{275}}}{\cancel{6875}}}{\underset{\underset{16}{\cancel{400}}}{\cancel{10000}}} = \frac{11}{16}$$

To convert a repeating decimal to a common fraction, you may use the method shown in the following examples.

Example 1 Express $0.2\overline{34}$ as a common fraction.

Solution Let N = the number.
  Multiply the given number N by 10^n, where n is the number of digits in the block of repeating digits:
  $n = 2$; $10^2 = 100$. $100N = 23.4\overline{34}$
            Subtract: $N = 0.2\overline{34}$

$$99N = 23.200$$

$$N = \frac{23.2}{99} = \frac{232}{990} = \frac{116}{495} \quad \textit{Answer}$$

Example 2 Express $0.\overline{816}$ as a common fraction.

Solution Let N = the number.

$$1000N = 816.\overline{816}$$

Subtract: $N = \quad 0.\overline{816}$

$$999N = 816$$

$$N = \frac{816}{999} = \frac{272}{333} \quad \textit{Answer}$$

In general:

> All terminating decimals and all repeating decimals represent rational numbers which can be written in the form $\frac{n}{d}$ where n is an integer and d is a positive integer.

It is often convenient to break off a lengthy decimal, leaving an approximation of the number represented. You may write, for example,

$$\frac{1}{12} \doteq 0.08333 \quad \text{or} \quad \frac{1}{12} \doteq 0.083 \quad \text{or} \quad \frac{1}{12} \doteq 0.08.$$

In general (compare page 99):

> To **round a decimal,** add 1 to the value of the last digit kept if the first digit dropped is 5 or more; otherwise, leave unchanged the digits that are kept.

Thus,

$$\frac{2}{3} = 0.666\ldots \doteq 0.67 \text{ to the nearest hundredth}$$
$$\doteq 0.7 \text{ to the nearest tenth}$$

$$\frac{5}{9} = 0.555\ldots \doteq 0.56 \text{ to the nearest hundredth}$$
$$\doteq 0.6 \text{ to the nearest tenth}$$

$$\frac{161}{110} = 1.4\overline{63} \doteq 1.5 \text{ to the nearest tenth}$$
$$\doteq 1 \text{ to the nearest unit}$$

Oral Exercises

Round each number to the nearest tenth.

1. 2.17 2.2   2. 3.85 3.9   3. −6.23 −6.2 4. −7.554 −7.6 5. 0.31$\overline{7}$ 0.3   6. 0.5$\overline{3}$ 0.5

7. −18.6$\overline{5}$ −18.7 8. −41.66… −41.7 9. 0.03$\overline{9}$ 0.0   10. 0.09$\overline{4}$ 0.1   11. $\frac{1}{3}$ 0.3   12. $\frac{7}{6}$ 1.2

Give a second numeral naming the same number. Answers may vary.

13. $\frac{2}{3}$ 0.$\overline{6}$ 14. $\frac{1}{7}$ 0.$\overline{142857}$ 15. 8 $\frac{8}{1}$ 16. 0.1 $\frac{1}{10}$ 17. 8.2 8$\frac{2}{10}$ 18. −16.1 −16$\frac{1}{10}$

19. 0.$\overline{3}$ $\frac{1}{3}$ 20. 0.$\overline{6}$ $\frac{2}{3}$ 21. $-\frac{14}{2}$ −7   22. 0.875 $\frac{7}{8}$ 23. −0.0029 $-\frac{29}{10000}$ 24. −2.1$\overline{6}$ −2$\frac{1}{6}$

Written Exercises

Write each as a terminating or repeating decimal.

1. $\frac{2}{9}$ 0.$\overline{2}$ 2. $\frac{16}{3}$ 5.$\overline{3}$ 3. $\frac{3}{8}$ 0.375   4. $\frac{4}{5}$ 0.8   5. $-\frac{6}{25}$ −0.24   6. $-\frac{95}{2}$ −47.5

7. $\frac{-5}{18}$ −0.2$\overline{7}$ 8. $\frac{57}{100}$ 0.57   9. $\frac{-5}{8}$ −0.625   10. $\frac{3}{20}$ 0.15   11. $-\frac{19}{99}$ −0.$\overline{19}$ 12. $\frac{1}{13}$ 0.$\overline{076923}$

Write each as a common fraction reduced to lowest terms.

13. 0.21 $\frac{21}{100}$ 14. 0.4 $\frac{2}{5}$ 15. 0.$\overline{57}$ $\frac{19}{33}$ 16. 0.555… $\frac{5}{9}$ 17. −1.3$\overline{5}$ $-\frac{61}{45}$ 18. 2.$\overline{893}$ $\frac{2891}{999}$

Express each number in fractional form and find the product.

19. 0.5 and $\frac{1}{3}$
    $\frac{1}{2}, \frac{1}{3}; \frac{1}{6}$

20. 0.375 and $\frac{2}{5}$
    $\frac{3}{8}, \frac{2}{5}; \frac{3}{20}$

21. 2.$\overline{6}$ and −5.333…
    $\frac{8}{3}, -\frac{16}{3}; -14\frac{2}{9}$

22. 0.34$\overline{3}$ and −0.3
    $\frac{103}{300}, -\frac{3}{10}; -\frac{103}{1000}$

Find the difference of the given numbers, and name a number between them.

23. 0.33 and 0.$\overline{3}$
    0.003; 0.333

24. 0.17 and 0.$\overline{17}$
    0.001$\overline{7}$; 0.1717

25. 0.127 and $\frac{1}{8}$
    0.002; 0.126

26. 0.759 and $\frac{3}{4}$
    0.009; 0.752

Compare the decimal forms of the members of each set.

27. $\left\{\frac{1}{8}, \frac{2}{8}, \frac{3}{8}, \ldots, \frac{7}{8}\right\}$

28. $\left\{\frac{1}{7}, \frac{2}{7}, \frac{3}{7}, \ldots, \frac{6}{7}\right\}$

29. $\left\{\frac{1}{17}, \frac{2}{17}, \frac{3}{17}, \ldots, \frac{16}{17}\right\}$

30. Using the method shown in Examples 1 and 2, show that the value of any repeating decimal of the form $x.\overline{9}$, where x is a whole number, is $x + 1$.

27. $\frac{1}{8} = 0.125, \frac{2}{8} = 2(0.125)$, etc.

28. $\frac{1}{7} = 0.\overline{142857}, \frac{2}{7} = 2(0.\overline{142857})$, etc.

29. $\frac{1}{17} = 0.\overline{0588235294117647}, \frac{2}{17} = 2(0.\overline{0588235294117647})$, etc.

30. $10N = x9.9$
    $N = x.9$
    $9N = x9 - x$
    $= 10x + 9 - x$
    $= 9x + 9$
    $N = x + 1$

10-3 Rational Square Roots

> **OBJECTIVE** To learn how to find square roots of square numbers and quotients of square numbers.

You know that subtracting a number is the inverse of adding that number, and dividing by a (nonzero) number is the inverse of multiplying by that number. The inverse of *squaring a number* is *finding a square root:*

> If $a^2 = b$, then a is a **square root** of b.

Since $5^2 = 25$ and $(-5)^2 = 25$, both 5 and -5 are square roots of 25.

> The symbol $\sqrt{\ }$ is used to denote the **principal square root**. If $c > 0$, then $\sqrt{c} > 0$.

Thus:

$$\sqrt{25} = 5$$
$$-\sqrt{25} = -5$$

The symbol $\sqrt{\ }$ is called a radical sign, and $\sqrt{25}$ is an example of a radical (*rad*-i-kal). An expression beneath a radical sign, such as 25, is called the radicand (rad-i-*kand*). These words are derived from the Latin word *radix* meaning "root."

The preceding symbols can be combined:

$\pm\sqrt{25}$ is read "positive or negative square root of 25."

Zero has only one square root, zero:

$$\sqrt{0} = 0$$

Since the square of every real number is either positive or zero, *negative numbers do not have square roots in the set of real numbers.*

> Only *nonnegative* (positive or zero) numbers have square roots in the set of real numbers.

Factoring can be used to find square roots of square numbers. You may also use the rule of exponents for the power of a product (page 122): $(ab)^n = a^n b^n$.

Example 1 Find $\sqrt{256}$.

Solution Factor: $256 = 2 \cdot 128 = 2 \cdot 2 \cdot 64 = 2^2 \cdot 8^2 = (2 \cdot 8)^2 = 16^2$

$\sqrt{256} = \sqrt{16^2} = 16$

Check: $16 \cdot 16 = 256 \checkmark$ $\therefore \sqrt{256} = 16.$ **Answer**

Example 2 Find $\sqrt{2304}$.

Solution Factor: $2304 = 4 \cdot 576 = 4 \cdot 4 \cdot 144 = 4^2 \cdot 12^2$

$\sqrt{2304} = \sqrt{4^2 \cdot 12^2} = \sqrt{4^2} \cdot \sqrt{12^2} = 4 \cdot 12 = 48$

Check: $48 \cdot 48 = 2304 \checkmark$ $\therefore \sqrt{2304} = 48.$ **Answer**

The method of solution just shown is based on the following:

> **Product Property of Square Roots**
>
> For any nonnegative real numbers a and b:
> $$\sqrt{ab} = \sqrt{a} \cdot \sqrt{b}$$

The method of solution for Example 3 on page 384 is based on the following:

> **Quotient Property of Square Roots**
>
> For any nonnegative real number a and any positive real number b:
> $$\sqrt{\frac{a}{b}} = \frac{\sqrt{a}}{\sqrt{b}}$$

Example 3 Find $\sqrt{\dfrac{25}{441}}$.

Solution Factor: $25 = 5^5$; $441 = 9 \cdot 49 = 3^2 \cdot 7^2$

$$\sqrt{\frac{25}{441}} = \sqrt{\frac{5^2}{3^2 \cdot 7^2}} = \frac{\sqrt{5^2}}{\sqrt{3^2 \cdot 7^2}} = \frac{5}{3 \cdot 7} = \frac{5}{21}$$

Check: $\dfrac{5}{21} \cdot \dfrac{5}{21} = \dfrac{25}{441}$ ✓ $\therefore \sqrt{\dfrac{25}{441}} = \dfrac{5}{21}$. *Answer*

Oral Exercises

Find the principal square root.

1. 36 6   2. 81 9   3. 49 7   4. 100 10   5. $\dfrac{64}{9}$ $\dfrac{8}{3}$ 6. $\dfrac{16}{25}$ $\dfrac{4}{5}$

Simplify each expression.

7. $\sqrt{4}$ 2   8. $\sqrt{1}$ 1   9. $\sqrt{\dfrac{16}{25}}$ $\dfrac{4}{5}$ 10. $\sqrt{\dfrac{1}{9}}$ $\dfrac{1}{3}$ 11. $\sqrt{(32)^2}$ 32   12. $\sqrt{(63)^2}$ 63

13. $(\sqrt{5})^2$ 5   14. $(\sqrt{17})^2$ 17   15. $\sqrt{5^2 - 3^2}$ 4   16. $\sqrt{3^2 + 4^2}$ 5

Written Exercises

Simplify each expression.

A 1. $\sqrt{400}$ 20   2. $\sqrt{324}$ 18   3. $\sqrt{1024}$ 32   4. $\sqrt{1681}$ 41   5. $-\sqrt{2025}$ −45   6. $-\sqrt{1296}$ −36

7. $-\sqrt{\dfrac{196}{25}}$ $\dfrac{14}{5}$ 8. $-\sqrt{\dfrac{361}{49}}$ $-\dfrac{19}{7}$ 9. $\pm\sqrt{\dfrac{1}{256}}$ $\pm\dfrac{1}{16}$ 10. $\pm\sqrt{\dfrac{16}{484}}$ $\pm\dfrac{2}{11}$ 11. $\pm\sqrt{\dfrac{36}{169}}$ $\pm\dfrac{6}{13}$ 12. $\pm\sqrt{\dfrac{16}{729}}$ $\pm\dfrac{4}{27}$

13. $\sqrt{\dfrac{4}{100}}$ $\dfrac{1}{5}$ 14. $\sqrt{\dfrac{36}{100}}$ $\dfrac{3}{5}$ 15. $-\sqrt{\dfrac{144}{100}}$ $-\dfrac{6}{5}$ 16. $-\sqrt{\dfrac{256}{100}}$ $-\dfrac{8}{5}$ 17. $\pm\sqrt{\dfrac{81}{10000}}$ $\pm\dfrac{9}{100}$ 18. $\pm\sqrt{\dfrac{441}{10000}}$ $\pm\dfrac{2}{10}$

19. $\sqrt{0.09}$ 0.3   20. $\sqrt{0.25}$ 0.5   21. $-\sqrt{1.21}$ −1.1   22. $-\sqrt{2.25}$ −1.5   23. $\pm\sqrt{0.0324}$ $\pm\dfrac{4}{3}$ 24. $\pm\sqrt{0.0196}$ ±0.14

Sample $\sqrt{\dfrac{24}{150}} = \sqrt{\dfrac{4 \cdot 6}{6 \cdot 25}} = \sqrt{\dfrac{4}{25}} = \dfrac{2}{5}$

B 25. $\sqrt{\dfrac{28}{63}}$ $\dfrac{2}{3}$ 26. $\sqrt{\dfrac{48}{75}}$ $\dfrac{4}{5}$ 27. $-\sqrt{\dfrac{18}{32}}$ $-\dfrac{3}{4}$ 28. $-\sqrt{\dfrac{20}{45}}$ $-\dfrac{2}{3}$ 29. $\pm\sqrt{\dfrac{160}{90}}$ $\pm\dfrac{4}{3}$ 30. $\pm\sqrt{\dfrac{200}{32}}$ $\pm\dfrac{5}{2}$

Self-Test 1

Be sure that you understand these terms:

rational number (p. 371) property of density (p. 373) terminating decimal (p. 378)
nonterminating decimal (p. 378) repeating decimal (p. 378) rounding a decimal (p. 380)
square root (p. 382) principal square root (p. 382) radical sign (p. 382)
radical (p. 382) radicand (p. 382)

Determine which rational number is the greater.

1. $6, \dfrac{37}{8}$ 2. $\dfrac{3}{5}, \dfrac{1}{7}$ 3. $\dfrac{10}{21}, \dfrac{5}{6}$ 4. $10\dfrac{1}{3}, \dfrac{43}{7}$ Objective 10-1, p. 371

Find the number halfway between the given numbers.

5. $2, 7$ 6. $-\dfrac{1}{2}, -\dfrac{1}{8}$ 7. $-\dfrac{10}{3}, \dfrac{9}{5}$ 8. $1\dfrac{1}{2}, -2\dfrac{2}{3}$

Write each as a common fraction reduced to lowest terms.

9. 0.32 10. $0.\overline{6}$ 11. $1.\overline{25}$ 12. $0.\overline{69}$ Objective 10-2, p. 378

Simplify each expression.

13. $\sqrt{576}$ 14. $\pm\sqrt{5625}$ 15. $-\sqrt{\dfrac{36}{625}}$ 16. $\sqrt{\dfrac{225}{64}}$ Objective 10-3, p. 382

Check your answers with those printed at the back of the book.

Career Note
Livestock Production Technician

Livestock production technicians specialize in raising cattle, sheep, or hogs. They may be employed in livestock ranching, the feed industry, or veterinary medicine. Livestock production involves animal nutrition, disease control, and breeding. Most of the work of livestock production technicians is done outdoors.

Two-year programs leading to an associate degree in livestock production (sometimes called animal science or animal husbandry) are offered at colleges and technical institutes. The curriculum emphasizes courses in the sciences, including genetics and physiology, and applied agriculture. Laboratory and field work is also required.

Irrational Numbers

10-4 Irrational Square Roots

> **OBJECTIVE** To learn how to find decimal approximations to irrational square roots.

Do those integers which are not squares of integers have rational square roots? No, as we shall now see.

1. Consider some positive integer n.

2. Assume that

$$\sqrt{n} = \frac{a}{b},$$

where a, b, and n are positive integers, and a and b have no common integral factors.

3. If $\sqrt{n} = \frac{a}{b}$, then $n = \frac{a^2}{b^2}$. Since a^2 has the same prime factors as a, and b^2 has the same prime factors as b, if a and b have no factors in common, neither do a^2 and b^2, and $\frac{a^2}{b^2}$ is in lowest terms.

4. *If a fraction in lowest terms is equal to an integer, the denominator of the fraction must be 1.* Thus, since n is a positive integer, and $\frac{a^2}{b^2}$ is in lowest terms, $b^2 = 1$, and $b = 1$, which means that $\frac{a}{b} = \frac{a}{1} = a$.

5. Therefore, if the square root of a positive integer is a rational number, $\frac{a}{b}$, the root is in fact an integer, $\frac{a}{1}$. Thus, only integers which are squares of integers can have rational square roots.

Since integers such as 3, 5, and 7 are not the squares of integers, you must seek numbers like $\sqrt{3}$, $\sqrt{5}$, and $\sqrt{7}$ outside the set of rational numbers. You find such numbers in another major subset of the real numbers called the set of *irrational numbers*.

> **Irrational numbers** are real numbers which cannot be expressed in the form $\frac{r}{s}$, where r and s are integers, $s \neq 0$.

Thus, the set of real numbers is the union of the set of rational numbers and the set of irrational numbers.

The real numbers share with the set of rational numbers the property of density (page 373). In addition, the set of real numbers has the following property:

> **Property of Completeness**
>
> Every decimal represents a real number, and every real number has a decimal representation.

Terminating and repeating decimals represent rational numbers. Therefore, the decimals for irrational numbers neither terminate nor repeat.

One method of finding successive digits in the decimal approximations of irrational numbers which are square roots is based on the following.

> **Property of Pairs of Divisors of a Positive Real Number**
>
> If you divide a positive number by a positive divisor which is smaller than the square root of that number, the quotient will be larger than the square root.

Consider 100 and its square root, 10:

$$100 \div 10 = 10.$$

But if the divisor is less than 10, then the quotient is greater than 10:

$$100 \div 2 = 50, \quad 100 \div 4 = 25, \quad 100 \div 5 = 20.$$

Of course, if the divisor is greater than 10, then the quotient is less than 10:

$$100 \div 50 = 2, \quad 100 \div 25 = 4, \quad 100 \div 20 = 5.$$

One way of finding closer and closer decimal approximations to the square root of a number that is not a square is to keep averaging pairs of factors as shown in Example 1. This is sometimes called the divide-and-average method.

Example 1 Find a decimal approximation to $\sqrt{24}$ to 3 digits.

Solution

1. Select the integer whose square is nearest 24 as your first approximation.

   Let f be a number such that $f^2 \doteq 24$.
   First $f = 5$

2. Divide 24 by f. Carry the quotient to twice as many digits as are in the divisor.

   $24 \div 5 = 4.8$

3. From the property of pairs of divisors, you know that $\sqrt{24}$ is between f and $\dfrac{24}{f}$. Take their average to find a better approximation to $\sqrt{24}$.

   $\dfrac{1}{2}(5 + 4.8) = \dfrac{1}{2}(9.8)$

   $= 4.9$

4. Use this average as the new f. Repeat Steps 2, 3, 4 until you have as close an approximation as you wish.

   Second $f = 4.9$

   $24 \div 4.9 \doteq 4.897$ (2)

   $\dfrac{4.898}{2\overline{)9.797}}$ (3)

   Then $f = \quad 4.898$ (4)

   $24 \div 4.898 \doteq 4.8999591$ (2)

Your approximation is accurate to at least as many digits as match in f and $24 \div f$.

   Since $4.898 < \sqrt{24} < 4.8999$,
   and $4.898 \doteq 4.90 \doteq 4.8999$,
   $\sqrt{24} \doteq 4.90$ to 3 digits. *Answer*

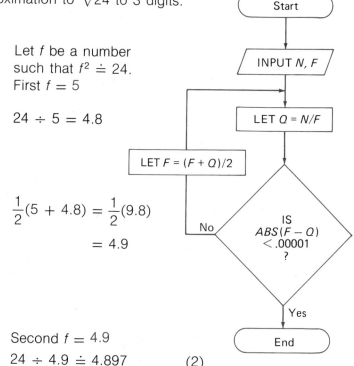

Start

INPUT *N, F*

LET *Q = N/F*

LET *F = (F + Q)/2*

IS
ABS(*F − Q*)
< .00001
?

No

Yes

End

Number = *N*
Factor = *F*

Check: $4.90 \times 4.90 = 24.01 \doteq 24$ ✓

Continuing one more sequence gives: $f = \dfrac{1}{2}(4.898 + 4.8999591) = 4.8989795$

$24 \div 4.8989795 \doteq 4.8989793 \qquad \therefore \sqrt{24} \doteq 4.898979. \quad Answer$

At the back of the book is a table that gives square roots of integers from 1 to 100.

Example 2 Find $\sqrt{85}$.

Solution From the table, $\sqrt{85} \doteq 9.220$. *Answer*

The next examples show how you can use the values in the table of square roots at the back of the book to solve some other square root problems.

Example 3 Find $\sqrt{450}$.

Solution Factor: $450 = 10 \cdot 45 = 2 \cdot 5 \cdot 5 \cdot 9$

$\sqrt{450} = 5 \cdot 3\sqrt{2} = 15\sqrt{2}$

From the table, $\sqrt{2} \doteq 1.414$.

$\therefore \sqrt{450} \doteq 15(1.414) = 21.21$. *Answer*

Example 4 Approximate to 4 digits: **a.** $\sqrt{510}$ **b.** $\sqrt{0.51}$

Solution Use the table at the back of the book.

a. $510 = 51(10)$

$\sqrt{51(10)} \doteq (7.141)(3.162)$

$\therefore \sqrt{510} \doteq 22.58$ *Answer*

b. $0.51 = \dfrac{51}{100}$; $\sqrt{\dfrac{51}{100}} \doteq \dfrac{7.141}{10}$

$\therefore \sqrt{0.51} \doteq 0.7141$. *Answer*

Oral Exercises

State whether the following represent rational or irrational numbers. If the number is rational, name it. R = rational, I = irrational

Sample $-\sqrt{29} + \sqrt{29}$ *Solution* Rational; 0

1. $\sqrt{7}$ I

2. $-\sqrt{25}$ R; -5

3. $\sqrt{\dfrac{4}{16}}$ R; $\dfrac{1}{2}$

4. $\sqrt{\dfrac{36}{3}}$ I

5. $3\sqrt{11}$ I

6. $\dfrac{\sqrt{7}}{\sqrt{7}}$ R; 1

7. $-3\sqrt{1}$ R; -3

8. $-\sqrt{0.16}$ R; -0.4

9. $\sqrt{0.81}$ R; 0.9

10. $\sqrt{9} - \sqrt{4}$ R; 1

11. $\sqrt{10} - \sqrt{10}$ R; 0

12. $\sqrt{81} - \sqrt{36}$ R; 3

Name the integer closest to the square root of the given number.

13. 5   2   14. 50   7   15. 7.2   3   16. 34.6   6   17. 63.91   8   18. 74.02   9

Express as the product of a number between 1 and 100 and a power of 100.

19. 800	20. 1200	21. 325.6	22. 898.7	23. 3826	24. 6274
8×100	12×100	3.256×100	8.987×100	38.26×100	62.74×100

Express as the quotient of a number between 1 and 100 divided by a power of 100.

25. $0.23 \frac{23}{100}$ 26. $0.76 \frac{76}{100}$ 27. $0.1515 \frac{15.15}{100}$ 28. $0.314 \frac{31.4}{100}$ 29. $0.1 \frac{10}{100}$ 30. $0.000823 \frac{8.2}{100}$

Written Exercises

Find the indicated square roots.

A 1. $\sqrt{3.24}$ 2. $\sqrt{21.16}$ 3. $\sqrt{1936}$ 4. $\sqrt{3969}$ 5. $-\sqrt{302.76}$ 6. $-\sqrt{420.25}$
  1.8   4.6   44   63 -17.4 -20.5

Find each square root to the nearest hundredth by averaging factors.

7. $\sqrt{41.3}$ 8. $\sqrt{18.6}$ 9. $-\sqrt{129}$ 10. $-\sqrt{376}$ 11. $\sqrt{223}$ 12. $\sqrt{167}$
  6.43   4.31 -11.36 -19.39 14.93   12.92

Find each square root to the nearest hundredth by using the table at the back of the book.

13. $\sqrt{21}$ 14. $\sqrt{97}$ 15. $-\sqrt{300}$ 16. $-\sqrt{1700}$ 17. $\sqrt{0.0062}$ 18. $\sqrt{0.88}$
  4.58   9.85 -17.32 -41.23 0.08   0.94

Computer Activity

If you have access to a computer that will accept BASIC, type in the program given below. It will print out successive stages of the divide-and-average method of computing a square root. You can try various values and see how rapidly the values approach a 5-digit value.

The last line prints the positive square root by using the built-in square root function, for comparison.

```
10   PRINT "INPUT A POSITIVE NUMBER";      [See the flowchart on page 388.]
20   INPUT N
30   IF N <= 0 THEN 10
40   PRINT "WHAT FACTOR WOULD YOU LIKE TO TRY";
50   INPUT F
60   IF F <= 0 THEN 40                     100   LET F=(F+Q)/2
70   LET Q=N/F                             110   GOTO 70
80   PRINT F,Q                             120   PRINT "CHECK:";SQR(N)
90   IF ABS(F-Q) < .00001 THEN 120         130   END
```

1. Find $\sqrt{11}$ by starting with the factor 3.   2. Find $\sqrt{11}$ by starting with the factor 1.
3. Find $\sqrt{1936}$.   Experiment with several numbers and factors.

10-5 Square Roots of Variable Expressions

> **OBJECTIVE** To learn how to find square roots of variable expressions and how to use them to solve equations and problems.

You know that $3^2 = 9$ and $(-3)^2 = 9$, but $\sqrt{9}$ is defined to be 3. Therefore, $\sqrt{y^2}$ must be positive or zero, and so

$$\sqrt{y^2} = |y|.$$

Example 1 What is the principal square root of $81y^2$ if y is a real number?

Solution Factor: $81 = 9^2$; $\therefore \sqrt{81y^2} = 9|y|$.

Check: For all real numbers y, $9|y| \geq 0$, and
$$(9|y|)^2 = 81|y|^2 = 81y^2. \checkmark$$
$\therefore \sqrt{81y^2} = 9|y|.$ *Answer*

Notice that in Example 1, "$9y$" would *not* be an acceptable answer unless you knew that $y \geq 0$.

Example 2 Find $\sqrt{x^2 + 4x + 4}$.

Solution $\sqrt{x^2 + 4x + 4} = \sqrt{(x + 2)^2} = |x + 2|$
Check: $(|x + 2|)^2 = x^2 + 4x + 4 \checkmark$
$\therefore \sqrt{x^2 + 4x + 4} = |x + 2|.$ *Answer*

Example 3 Find $\sqrt{16a^4}$.

Solution $\sqrt{16a^4} = \sqrt{(4)^2(a^2)^2} = 4a^2$, since $a^2 \geq 0$.

Check: $(4a^2)^2 = 16a^4 \checkmark$
$\therefore \sqrt{16a^4} = 4a^2.$ *Answer*

Example 4 Solve $x^2 = 36$.

Solution 1
$$x^2 = 36$$
$$x^2 - 36 = 0$$
$$(x - 6)(x + 6) = 0$$
$$x = 6 \text{ or } x = -6$$

Check: $6^2 = 36$ and $(-6)^2 = 36$ ✓
∴ the solution set is $\{6, -6\}$. *Answer*

Solution 2 $x^2 = 36$
$$x = \pm\sqrt{36} = \pm 6$$

The method of Solution 2 of Example 4 is based on the following:

> **Property of Square Roots of Equal Numbers**
>
> If r and s are any real numbers,
>
> $r^2 = s^2$ if and only if $r = s$ or $r = -s$.

Oral Exercises

Find.

1. $\sqrt{121a^2}$ $11|a|$
2. $\sqrt{144y^2}$ $12|y|$
3. $\sqrt{49x^4}$ $7x^2$
4. $\sqrt{100x^2y^2}$ $10|xy|$
5. $\sqrt{0.25s^8}$ $0.5s^4$
6. $\sqrt{0.09x^4}$ $0.3x^2$

7. $-\sqrt{36x^2}$ $-6|x|$
8. $-\sqrt{64t^8}$ $-8t^4$
9. $-\sqrt{81x^2y^2}$ $-9|xy|$
10. $-\sqrt{100r^8s^4}$ $-10r^4s^2$
11. $\pm\sqrt{\dfrac{a^2}{121}}$ $\pm\dfrac{|a|}{11}$
12. $\pm\sqrt{\dfrac{m^4}{9}}$ $\pm\dfrac{m^2}{3}$

Written Exercises

Solve.

A
1. $y^2 = 49$ $\{7, -7\}$
2. $s^2 = 81$ $\{9, -9\}$
3. $r^2 - 25 = 0$ $\{5, -5\}$
4. $t^2 - 64 = 0$ $\{8, -8\}$
5. $4x^2 - 9 = 0$ $\{\tfrac{3}{2}, -\tfrac{3}{2}\}$
6. $36y^2 - 81 = 0$ $\{\tfrac{3}{2}, -\tfrac{3}{2}\}$
7. $3a^2 - 12 = 0$ $\{2, -2\}$
8. $8b^2 - 72 = 0$ $\{3, -$

Find both roots to the nearest tenth.

B
9. $a^2 = 726$ ± 26.9
10. $x^2 = 288$ ± 17.0
11. $b^2 - 7.5 = 0$ ± 2.7
12. $y^2 - 12.8 = 0$ ± 3.6
13. $500 = 4x^2$ ± 11.2
14. $700 = 5x^2$ ± 11.8
15. $6r^2 - 0.16 = 0$ ± 0.2
16. $3s^2 - 0.99 = 0$ ± 0

C
17. $0.6x^2 = 3.72$ ± 2.5
18. $(y + 2)^2 + (y - 2)^2 = 76$ ± 5.8
19. $(x + 3)^2 + (x - 3)^2 = 120$ ± 7
20. $13x^2 = 100$ ± 2.8
21. $21y^2 = 1233$ ± 7.7
22. $17c^2 - 4 = 0$ ± 0.5

Problems

Solve. Find each answer to the nearest tenth, unless otherwise directed.
Use the approximation $\pi \doteq \frac{22}{7}$ when needed.

A 1. Find the side of a square whose area is 500 square centimeters. **22.4 cm**

2. The area of a square is 67 square centimeters. How long is one side? **8.2 cm**

3. A rectangle whose length is 3 times the width has an area of 123 square centimeters. Find the length and the width of the rectangle. (*below*)

4. Find the diameter of a circular plot that has the same area as a rectangular one that is 22 meters wide and 35 meters long. **31.3 cm**

5. What is the diameter of a circle having 3 times the area of one 6 centimeters in diameter? **10.4 cm**

3. length: 19.2 cm; width: 6.4 cm

6. A city is supplied with water by a pipe 30 centimeters in diameter. If twice as much water is needed, what must be the diameter of one pipe that will supply the required amount? **42.4 cm**

7. The search for a missing yacht covered a circular region with an area of 132 square kilometers. What was the radius of the search region? **6.5 km**

8. A television station claims clear reception in a circular area of 3300 square kilometers. Find, to the nearest kilometer, how far you could live from the station to get clear reception. **32.4 km**

Biographical Note
Sir Chandrasekhar Venkata Raman

Chandrasekhar Venkata Raman (1888–1970) was born and educated in the city of Madras, India. He received his master's degree in physics in 1907, but since at that time there was little opportunity for scientific research in India, he took a position as an accountant in the Finance Department. Raman continued his research in optics on his own until he received an appointment as professor of physics at Calcutta University in 1917.

Raman's research concentrated on the phenomena resulting from the scattering of light. An example of this scattering effect is the way a beam of light from a movie projector in a dark room behaves. Raman discovered that when a strong light passed through a liquid and was scattered by the molecules of the liquid, the spectrum of the scattered light showed lines that were not in the spectrum of the original light. This discovery was named the Raman effect. C. V. Raman received the 1930 Nobel Prize for his discovery. It had great influence on later work on molecular structure and radiation.

10-6 Geometric Interpretations of Square Roots

> **OBJECTIVE** To learn how to use the Pythagorean theorem and its converse to construct lengths measured by irrational numbers and to solve other geometric problems.

You know how to locate graphs of rational numbers on a number line. We shall now see that graphs of irrational square roots can be located on a number line by geometric constructions.

These constructions are based on the following theorem, named after the ancient Greek mathematician Pythagoras (pronounced Pith-*ag*-uh-ras). It is called the *Pythagorean* (Pith-*ag*-uh-*ree*-an) *theorem:*

> Pythagorean Theorem
> In any right triangle, the square of the length of the hypotenuse equals the sum of the squares of the lengths of the other two sides. 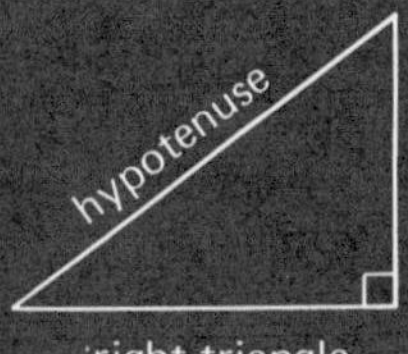
>
> hypotenuse
> right triangle

A geometric interpretation of this theorem is illustrated in Figure 10-2. A geometric proof is suggested in Figure 10-3.

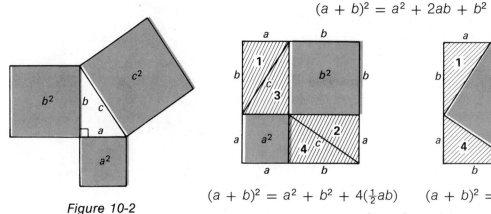

$$(a + b)^2 = a^2 + 2ab + b^2$$

Figure 10-2

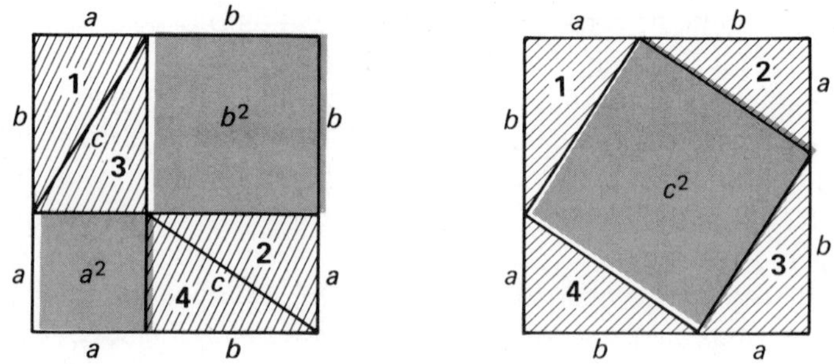

$$(a + b)^2 = a^2 + b^2 + 4(\tfrac{1}{2}ab) \qquad (a + b)^2 = c^2 + 4(\tfrac{1}{2}ab)$$
$$\therefore a^2 + b^2 = c^2.$$

Figure 10-3

To find a segment of length $\sqrt{2}$, draw a square whose sides are 1 unit long (Figure 10-4). The diagonal $\overline{OP}$ separates it into two right triangles in which $a = 1$ and $b = 1$. Then:

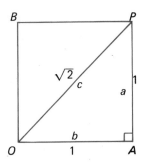

$$c^2 = a^2 + b^2$$
$$c^2 = 1^2 + 1^2$$
$$c^2 = 1 + 1$$
$$c^2 = 2$$

You can solve this equation by the method of Section 10-5. But since $c > 0$,

$$c = \sqrt{2}.$$

Figure 10-4

Figure 10-5

You can now use the length $\sqrt{2}$ to construct the length $\sqrt{3}$. Consider the rectangle in Figure 10-5, in which one side has been made $\sqrt{2}$. The diagonal $\overline{O'P'}$ separates it into two right triangles in which $a = 1$ and $b = \sqrt{2}$.

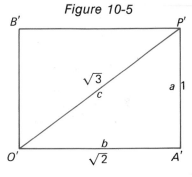

$$c^2 = a^2 + b^2$$
$$c^2 = 1^2 + (\sqrt{2})^2$$
$$c^2 = 1 + 2$$
$$c^2 = 3$$

Since $c > 0$, $c = \sqrt{3}$.

You can continue constructing rectangles that give $\sqrt{4} = 2$, $\sqrt{5}$, and so on. Each value is found by using the previous diagonal as a side of the next rectangle. The square and the rectangle are combined with the coordinate axes in Figure 10-6. The arcs are drawn to transfer the lengths from the diagonals to the x-axis. The semicircle has the origin as its center and $\sqrt{2}$ as its radius.

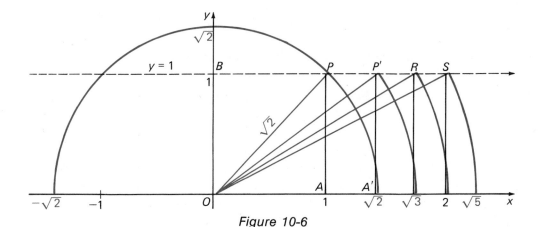

Figure 10-6

The converse (page 180) of the Pythagorean theorem can be used to test whether or not a triangle is a right triangle.

> ### Converse of the Pythagorean Theorem
>
> If the sum of the squares of the lengths of the two shorter sides of a triangle is equal to the square of the length of the longest side, then the triangle is a right triangle, with the right angle opposite the longest side.

Example Is a triangle whose sides measure 3, 4, and 5 units a right triangle?

Solution $c^2 = a^2 + b^2$
$5^2 \overset{?}{=} 3^2 + 4^2$
$25 = 25 \checkmark$ A 3-4-5 triangle is a right triangle. *Answer*

Written Exercises

Exercises 1–6 refer to the right triangle pictured at the right. Find the missing length correct to hundredths.

A 1. $a = 6, b = 8, c = $ _?_ 10 2. $a = 5, b = 7, c = $ _?_ 8.60

3. $b = 10, c = 11, a = $ _?_ 4.58 4. $b = 14, c = 17, a = $ _?_ 9.64

5. $a = 2, c = \sqrt{10}, b = $ _?_ 2.45 6. $a = \sqrt{2}, c = \sqrt{30}, b = $ _?_ 5.29

State whether or not each set of dimensions is a set of lengths of sides of a right triangle.

7. $\{12, 16, 20\}$ yes 8. $\{3, 9, 11\}$ no

9. $\{5, 12, 13\}$ yes 10. $\{9, 12, 14\}$ no

11. Verify that if the lengths of the two shorter sides of a right triangle are 1 and $\sqrt{3}$, the length of the hypotenuse is $\sqrt{4} = 2$. $c^2 = a^2 + b^2 = 1 + 3 = 4$, so $c = \sqrt{4} = 2$.

12. Verify that if the lengths of the two shorter sides of a right triangle are 2 and 1, the length of the hypotenuse is $\sqrt{5}$. $c^2 = a^2 + b^2 = 4 + 1 = 5$, so $c = \sqrt{5}$.

Problems

Make a sketch for each problem. Approximate each square root to the nearest hundredth.

A 1. Find the length of a diagonal of a rectangle whose dimensions are 5 by 7 centimeters. 8.60 cm

2. A rope 13 meters long from the top of a flagpole will just reach a point on the ground 9 meters from the foot of the pole. Find the height of the flagpole. 9.38 m

3. The base of an isosceles triangle is 16 cm and one of the equal sides is 18 centimeters. Find the altitude. 16.12 cm

4. In a "shed" roof, the height h is $\frac{1}{2}$ the width w of the building. Find the length of the rafter r if a building is 12 meters wide. 8.49 m

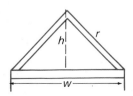

B 5. A right triangle has sides whose lengths in centimeters are expressed by consecutive even integers. Determine the length of each side. 6 cm, 8 cm, 10 cm

6. A rectangular doorway is 200 by 75 centimeters inside dimensions. Could a circular mirror measuring 220 cm in diameter be gotten through the doorway? no

7. Buzz wanted to keep a young tree from blowing over during a high wind. He decided that he should tie a rope around the tree at a height of 180 centimeters, then tie the rope to a stake 200 centimeters from the base. Allowing 30 centimeters of rope for doing the tying, would the 270-centimeter rope that he had be enough for the job? no

★ Self-Test 2

Be sure that you understand these terms:

irrational number (p. 387)
divide-and-average method (p. 388)

property of completeness (p. 387)
Pythagorean theorem (p. 394)

Find each square root to the nearest hundredth.

1. $\sqrt{10.4}$ 2. $\sqrt{189}$ Objective 10-4, p. 386

Simplify.

3. $-\sqrt{16x^2}$ 4. $\sqrt{10^2 - 8^2}$ Objective 10-5, p. 391

Solve.

5. $y^2 = 81$ 6. $r^2 = 400$ Objective 10-6, p. 394

7. Find the length of x in the right triangle at the right.

Check your answers with those printed at the back of the book.

Radical Expressions

10-7 Multiplication, Division, and Simplification of Radicals

> **OBJECTIVE** To learn how to simplify products and quotients of radicals.

The product and quotient properties of square roots (page 383) together with the commutative and associative axioms enable you to multiply, divide, and simplify square-root radicals.

> An expression having a square-root radical is in **simplest form** when
>
> **1.** no integral radicand has a square factor other than 1,
> **2.** no fractions are under a radical sign, and
> **3.** no radicals are in a denominator.

Examples

1 $\sqrt{28} = \sqrt{4} \cdot \sqrt{7} = 2\sqrt{7}$

2 $3\sqrt{20} = 3\sqrt{4 \cdot 5} = 3 \cdot 2\sqrt{5} = 6\sqrt{5}$

3 $\sqrt{\dfrac{5}{6}} = \dfrac{\sqrt{5}}{\sqrt{6}} = \dfrac{\sqrt{5} \cdot \sqrt{6}}{\sqrt{6} \cdot \sqrt{6}} = \dfrac{\sqrt{30}}{6}$

4 $\dfrac{4\sqrt{10}}{3\sqrt{27}} = \dfrac{4\sqrt{10} \cdot \sqrt{3}}{3\sqrt{27} \cdot \sqrt{3}} =$

$\dfrac{4\sqrt{30}}{3\sqrt{81}} = \dfrac{4\sqrt{30}}{3 \cdot 9} = \dfrac{4\sqrt{30}}{27}$

5 $\dfrac{2}{\sqrt{7}} = \dfrac{2 \cdot \sqrt{7}}{\sqrt{7} \cdot \sqrt{7}} = \dfrac{2\sqrt{7}}{7}$

The process of changing the form of a fraction with an irrational denominator such as $\dfrac{2}{\sqrt{7}}$ to an equal fraction with a rational denominator such as $\dfrac{2\sqrt{7}}{7}$ is called **rationalizing the denominator**. Rationalizing the denominator of a radical expression helps in approximating its value.

Example 6 Approximate $\dfrac{2}{\sqrt{7}}$ to three digits.

Solution $\quad\dfrac{2}{\sqrt{7}} = \dfrac{2 \cdot \sqrt{7}}{\sqrt{7} \cdot \sqrt{7}} = \dfrac{2\sqrt{7}}{7}$

From the table at the back of the book, $\sqrt{7} = 2.646$.

$\dfrac{2\sqrt{7}}{7} \doteq \dfrac{2(2.646)}{7} = \dfrac{5.292}{7} = 0.756$

$\therefore \dfrac{2}{\sqrt{7}} \doteq 0.756.$ *Answer*

Oral Exercises

Express in simplest form.

1. $\sqrt{2} \cdot \sqrt{11}$ $\sqrt{22}$ 2. $\sqrt{6} \cdot \sqrt{7}$ $\sqrt{42}$ 3. $\dfrac{\sqrt{15}}{\sqrt{5}}$ $\sqrt{3}$ 4. $\dfrac{\sqrt{32}}{\sqrt{2}}$ 4   5. $\sqrt{5} \cdot 2\sqrt{7}$ $2\sqrt{35}$

6. $3\sqrt{3} \cdot \sqrt{2}$ $3\sqrt{6}$ 7. $\sqrt{\dfrac{36}{6}}$ $\sqrt{6}$ 8. $\sqrt{\dfrac{108}{2}}$ $3\sqrt{6}$ 9. $3\sqrt{2} \cdot \sqrt{2}$ 6   10. $5 \cdot \sqrt{3} \cdot \sqrt{3}$ 15

11. $7\sqrt{2} \cdot 3\sqrt{8}$ 84   12. $3\sqrt{7} \cdot 4\sqrt{7}$ 84   13. $\sqrt{12}$ $2\sqrt{3}$ 14. $\sqrt{24}$ $2\sqrt{6}$ 15. $\sqrt{18}$ $3\sqrt{2}$

16. $\sqrt{32}$ $4\sqrt{2}$ 17. $\sqrt{40}$ $2\sqrt{10}$ 18. $\sqrt{300}$ $10\sqrt{3}$ 19. $\dfrac{1}{\sqrt{3}}$ $\dfrac{\sqrt{3}}{3}$ 20. $\dfrac{1}{\sqrt{7}}$ $\dfrac{\sqrt{7}}{7}$

21. $\sqrt{56}$ $2\sqrt{14}$ 22. $\sqrt{75}$ $5\sqrt{3}$ 23. $\sqrt{\dfrac{2}{5}}$ $\dfrac{\sqrt{10}}{5}$ 24. $\sqrt{\dfrac{3}{7}}$ $\dfrac{\sqrt{21}}{7}$ 25. $\sqrt{\dfrac{3}{4}}$ $\dfrac{\sqrt{3}}{2}$

Written Exercises

Express in simplest form. All radicands are nonnegative real numbers.

A 1. $\sqrt{5} \cdot 2\sqrt{5}$ 10   2. $3\sqrt{6} \cdot 4\sqrt{6}$ 72   3. $\sqrt{3} \cdot \sqrt{2} \cdot \sqrt{6}$ 6   4. $\sqrt{9} \cdot \sqrt{3} \cdot \sqrt{3}$ 9

5. $2\sqrt{5} \cdot \sqrt{2} \cdot \sqrt{3}$ $2\sqrt{30}$ 6. $3\sqrt{3} \cdot \sqrt{7} \cdot \sqrt{2}$ $3\sqrt{42}$ 7. $\sqrt{\dfrac{2}{3}} \cdot \sqrt{\dfrac{3}{2}}$ 1   8. $\sqrt{\dfrac{6}{5}} \cdot \sqrt{\dfrac{10}{6}}$ $\sqrt{2}$

9. $\sqrt{\dfrac{7}{9}} \cdot \sqrt{\dfrac{18}{14}}$ 1   10. $\sqrt{\dfrac{5}{3}} \cdot \sqrt{\dfrac{3}{20}}$ $\dfrac{1}{2}$ 11. $\sqrt{2\dfrac{1}{2}} \cdot \sqrt{3\dfrac{1}{3}}$ $\dfrac{5\sqrt{3}}{3}$ 12. $\dfrac{1}{6}\sqrt{\dfrac{9}{7}} \cdot \dfrac{1}{5}\sqrt{\dfrac{14}{18}}$ $\dfrac{1}{30}$

Express in simplest form. All radicands are nonnegative real numbers.

13. $\dfrac{15\sqrt{12}}{5\sqrt{3}}$ 2 14. $\dfrac{10\sqrt{7}}{2\sqrt{5}}$ $\sqrt{35}$ 15. $\sqrt{108}$ $6\sqrt{3}$ 16. $3\sqrt{18}$ $9\sqrt{2}$ 17. $7\sqrt{147}$ $49\sqrt{3}$ 18. $11\sqrt{75}$ $55\sqrt{3}$

19. $\dfrac{\sqrt{128}}{\sqrt{2}}$ 8 20. $\dfrac{\sqrt{11}}{\sqrt{44}}$ $\dfrac{1}{2}$ 21. $13\sqrt{\dfrac{32}{4}}$ $26\sqrt{2}$ 22. $5\sqrt{\dfrac{32}{9}}$ $\dfrac{20\sqrt{2}}{3}$ 23. $\dfrac{10\sqrt{2}}{2\sqrt{8}}$ $\dfrac{5}{2}$ 24. $\dfrac{\sqrt{72}}{3\sqrt{10}}$ $\dfrac{2\sqrt{5}}{5}$

B 25. $(-\sqrt{x^2y})(4\sqrt{y})$ $-4xy$ 26. $(-2\sqrt{rs^2})(-3\sqrt{r^2})$ $6rs\sqrt{r}$ 27. $\sqrt{b}(3+\sqrt{b})$ $3\sqrt{b}+b$

28. $\sqrt{c}(\sqrt{c}-2)$ $c-2\sqrt{c}$ 29. $(3\sqrt{2})(-\sqrt{4})(\sqrt{32})$ -48 30. $(2\sqrt{3})(\sqrt{18})(\sqrt{6})$ 36

31. $(\sqrt{13x})(\sqrt{2x})(3\sqrt{x^3})$ 32. $(\sqrt{2x})(\sqrt{3x})(\sqrt{6})$ $6x$ 33. $(2\sqrt{3x})^2$ $12x$

$3x^2\sqrt{26x}$

34. $(4y\sqrt{5y})^2$ $80y^3$ 35. $-7\sqrt{3\dfrac{1}{4}}$ $-\dfrac{7\sqrt{13}}{2}$ 36. $5\sqrt{1\dfrac{1}{2}}$ $\dfrac{5\sqrt{6}}{2}$

Consumer Note $$
Saving for Advanced Schooling

If you plan to go on to another school after high school, you should plan
ahead to save the money needed. Here is a formula that may help:

$$s = \frac{c \times n}{m + n - 1}$$

where: s = amount to save each year, beginning now
c = cost of each year of advanced schooling
n = number of years of advanced schooling
m = number of years from now until you start advanced schooling

Thus, suppose that four years from now you plan to enter a school for two
years costing $2000 a year. Then:

$$s = \frac{2000 \times 2}{4 + 2 - 1} = \frac{4000}{5} = 800$$

	1st yr.	2nd yr.	3rd yr.	4th yr.	5th yr.	6th yr.	Total
Save:	800	800	800	800	800		4000
Spend:					2000	2000	4000

Inflation makes it difficult to plan for several years in advance. However, if
you save the money in a bank at compound interest (see page 238), the
accumulated interest will help to make up the added cost due to inflation.
Try the formula for:

1. 3 years from now, 4-yr. school, $3000 per year $s = \$2000$
2. 4 years from now, 5-yr. school, $4000 per year $s = \$2500$

Problems

Solve by answering each to the nearest tenth, unless otherwise directed.

B 1. One number is 3 times another number, and the difference of their squares is 200. Find the numbers. **5 and 15, or −5 and −15**

2. Find two numbers in the ratio of 5 to 4 whose squares differ by 81. **15 and 12, or −15 and −12**

3. The base and the height of a parallelogram are in the ratio of $\frac{2}{3}$. If the area of the parallelogram is 216 square units, what are its dimensions? **base = 12, height = 18**

4. Find the length of a diagonal of a square with area 121 square centimeters. **15.6 cm**

5. Find the area of a triangle whose sides are 15, 17, and 20 centimeters long with the use of Hero's (ancient Greek) formula, $A = \sqrt{s(s-a)(s-b)(s-c)}$. In the formula, a, b, and c are the lengths of the sides and s is half the perimeter of the triangle. **124.3 cm²**

6. Find the radius r of the circle inscribed in the right triangle shown below. The radius of the circle is determined by the formula $r = \frac{1}{2}(a + b - c)$. The shorter sides of the triangle have lengths of 6 meters and 8 meters. **2 m**

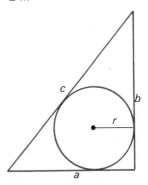

C 7. Using the figure and formula in Exercise 6, find r and c if the area of the circle is 28.26 square centimeters and the shorter sides of the right triangle are 9 and 12 centimeters. Use $\pi \doteq 3.14$. **$r = 3$ cm, $c = 15$ cm**

8. Find the length s of each side of a square if the diameter of the circle in which it is inscribed is 8.3 centimeters long. **5.9 cm**

10. Find the ratio between the length of h found in Exercise 9 and the length of h if s is tripled. **1:3**

11. A square is inscribed in a circle as shown in the diagram below. Find the radius of the circle if the area of the square is 64 square centimeters. **5.7 cm**

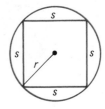

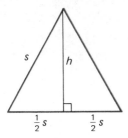

9. An altitude of an equilateral triangle separates the triangle into two triangles as pictured above. Find the length h of the altitude if the length s of a side is 2.5 meters. **2.2 m**

12. Show that an equilateral triangle with sides of length 10 centimeters is smaller in area than a square inscribed in a circle with a diameter of 10 centimeters.

12. triangle: $h = \sqrt{10^2 - 5^2} = 5\sqrt{3}$, so $A = \frac{1}{2} \cdot 10 \cdot 5\sqrt{3} = 25\sqrt{3} \doteq 43.3$ cm²
square: $s^2 + s^2 = 10^2$, so $A = s^2 = \frac{100}{2} = 50$ cm²

10-8 Addition and Subtraction of Radicals

> **OBJECTIVE** To learn how to simplify sums and differences of radicals.

Because $3\sqrt{7}$ and $2\sqrt{7}$ have the common factor $\sqrt{7}$, you can simplify the expression for their sum by using the distributive axiom:

$$3\sqrt{7} + 2\sqrt{7} = (3 + 2)\sqrt{7} = 5\sqrt{7}$$

On the other hand, the addition or subtraction of radicals having unlike radicands can only be indicated.

$$3\sqrt{5} - 5\sqrt{11} + 2\sqrt{5} + \sqrt{11} = 5\sqrt{5} - 4\sqrt{11}$$

By reducing each radical to simplest form, you sometimes can combine terms in a sum of radicals.

Example Simplify $5\sqrt{48} - 8\sqrt{27} + 3\sqrt{3}$.

Solution
$$
\begin{aligned}
5\sqrt{48} - 8\sqrt{27} + 3\sqrt{3} &= 5\sqrt{16\cdot3} - 8\sqrt{9\cdot3} + 3\sqrt{3} \\
&= 5(4\sqrt{3}) - 8(3\sqrt{3}) + 3\sqrt{3} \\
&= 20\sqrt{3} - 24\sqrt{3} + 3\sqrt{3} \\
&= -\sqrt{3} \quad \textit{Answer}
\end{aligned}
$$

> To simplify sums or differences of square-root radicals:
>
> 1. Express each radical in simplest form.
> 2. Use the distributive axiom to add or subtract radicals with like radicands.
> 3. Indicate the sum or difference of radicals with unlike radicands.

Oral Exercises

Select the radicals having the same radicand in each group.

1. $5\sqrt{7}, 7\sqrt{5}, \sqrt{7}$

2. $\sqrt{5}, 3\sqrt{5}, \sqrt{3}$

3. $6\sqrt{11}, 2\sqrt{10}, -2\sqrt{11}$

4. $-\sqrt{21}, \sqrt{13}, \frac{1}{2}\sqrt{13}$

5. $2\sqrt{8}, 7\sqrt{2}, \sqrt{11}, 6\sqrt{8}$

6. $3\sqrt{17}, \sqrt{17}, -\frac{1}{4}\sqrt{17}$ all

Simplify each radical expression.

7. $3\sqrt{3} + 2\sqrt{3}$ $5\sqrt{3}$

8. $5\sqrt{13} - \sqrt{13}$ $4\sqrt{13}$

9. $10\sqrt{2} - 5\sqrt{2}$ $5\sqrt{2}$

10. $8\sqrt{5} - 6\sqrt{5}$ $2\sqrt{5}$

11. $5\sqrt{7} - 3\sqrt{7} + \sqrt{7}$ $3\sqrt{7}$

12. $9\sqrt{10} + 2\sqrt{10} - 10\sqrt{10}$ $\sqrt{10}$

Written Exercises

Simplify each expression.

A

1. $3\sqrt{2} + 6\sqrt{2} - \sqrt{2}$ $8\sqrt{2}$

2. $8\sqrt{7} + \sqrt{7} + 3\sqrt{7}$ $12\sqrt{7}$

3. $\sqrt{3} - 2\sqrt{10} + 3\sqrt{10} - \sqrt{3}$ $\sqrt{10}$

4. $2\sqrt{11} + 7\sqrt{6} - \sqrt{11} + 3\sqrt{6}$ $\sqrt{11} + 10\sqrt{6}$

5. $\sqrt{8} + \sqrt{2}$ $3\sqrt{2}$

6. $\sqrt{3} + 2\sqrt{27}$ $7\sqrt{3}$

7. $\sqrt{16} - 2\sqrt{8}$ $4 - 4\sqrt{2}$

8. $\sqrt{50} + 5\sqrt{2}$ $10\sqrt{2}$

9. $3\sqrt{63} + \dfrac{1}{5}\sqrt{28}$ $\dfrac{47\sqrt{7}}{5}$

10. $2\sqrt{150} - \dfrac{1}{8}\sqrt{96}$ $\dfrac{19\sqrt{6}}{2}$

11. $\sqrt{2} - \sqrt{\dfrac{1}{2}}$ $\dfrac{\sqrt{2}}{2}$

12. $10\sqrt{\dfrac{3}{5}} - 30\sqrt{\dfrac{5}{3}}$ $-8\sqrt{15}$

13. $\dfrac{1}{4}\sqrt{48} + 3\sqrt{75}$ $16\sqrt{3}$

14. $\sqrt{192} + \dfrac{1}{3}\sqrt{50}$ $8\sqrt{3} + \dfrac{5\sqrt{2}}{3}$

15. $\sqrt{10} - \sqrt{\dfrac{2}{5}}$ $\dfrac{4\sqrt{10}}{5}$

16. $3\sqrt{27} - \sqrt{\dfrac{3}{9}}$ $\dfrac{26\sqrt{3}}{3}$

B 17. $3\sqrt{3} - 2\sqrt{12} + 4\sqrt{\dfrac{1}{3}}$ $\dfrac{\sqrt{3}}{3}$

18. $8\sqrt{10} - 3\sqrt{40} + 5\sqrt{\dfrac{1}{10}}$ $\dfrac{5\sqrt{10}}{2}$

19. $11\sqrt{\dfrac{2}{5}} + 5\sqrt{\dfrac{5}{2}} - \sqrt{160}$ $\dfrac{7\sqrt{10}}{10}$

20. $8\sqrt{\dfrac{2}{5}} + \sqrt{\dfrac{5}{2}} - \dfrac{1}{2}\sqrt{40}$ $\dfrac{11\sqrt{10}}{10}$

21. $\sqrt{\dfrac{3}{4}} + 7\sqrt{\dfrac{4}{3}} - \dfrac{1}{6}\sqrt{75}$ $\dfrac{13\sqrt{3}}{3}$

22. $3\sqrt{\dfrac{5}{12}} + \sqrt{\dfrac{12}{5}} - \dfrac{1}{3}\sqrt{60}$ $\dfrac{7\sqrt{15}}{30}$

23. $5\sqrt{3}(\sqrt{6} + 2\sqrt{8})$ $15\sqrt{2} + 20\sqrt{6}$

24. $3\sqrt{2}(2\sqrt{2} - 3\sqrt{5})$ $12 - 9\sqrt{10}$

Assume that all radicands are nonnegative real numbers, and simplify.

C 25. $x^6\sqrt{\dfrac{b}{x^3}} + 3\sqrt{bx^7}$
$(x^4 + 3x^3)\sqrt{bx}$

26. $5\sqrt{124} - \dfrac{2x^2}{5}\sqrt{\dfrac{108}{x}}$
$10\sqrt{31} - \dfrac{12x\sqrt{3x}}{5}$

27. $\sqrt{\dfrac{a^2}{64} + \dfrac{a^2}{36}}$
$\dfrac{5a}{24}$

28. $\sqrt{\dfrac{b^2}{9} + \dfrac{b^2}{25}}$
$\dfrac{b\sqrt{34}}{15}$

Solve each equation.

29. $b\sqrt{2} - \sqrt{6} = \sqrt{24} - b\sqrt{8}$ $b = \sqrt{3}$

30. $\sqrt{175} - a\sqrt{63} = a\sqrt{112} - \sqrt{448}$
$a = \dfrac{13}{7}$

10-9 Multiplication of Binomials Containing Radicals

> **OBJECTIVE** To learn how to multiply binomials containing square-root radicals.

You use the special methods of multiplying binomials that you learned in Chapter 5.

Example 1 Simplify $(5 + \sqrt{3})(5 - \sqrt{3})$.

Solution   The pattern is $(a + b)(a - b) = a^2 - b^2$.

$\therefore (5 + \sqrt{5})(5 - \sqrt{3}) = 5^2 - (\sqrt{3})^2 = 25 - 3 = 22.$ *Answer*

Example 2 Simplify $(2 + \sqrt{3})^2$.

Solution   The pattern is $(a + b)^2 = a^2 + 2ab + b^2$.

$\therefore (2 + \sqrt{3})^2 = 2^2 + 2(2)(\sqrt{3}) + (\sqrt{3})^2$

$\qquad\qquad = 4 + 4\sqrt{3} + 3 = 7 + 4\sqrt{3}.$ *Answer*

> Two binomials of the form $x + \sqrt{y}$ and $x - \sqrt{y}$ are called **conjugates** of each other.

Conjugates differ only in the sign before the radical.

Notice that as in Example 1, if x and y are rational numbers, then the product $(x + \sqrt{y})(x - \sqrt{y})$ is also a rational number.

You can use conjugates or their negatives to rationalize binomial denominators containing radicals.

Example 3 Rationalize the denominator in $\dfrac{2}{4 - 2\sqrt{5}}$.

Solution $\dfrac{2}{4 - 2\sqrt{5}} = \dfrac{2(4 + 2\sqrt{5})}{(4 - 2\sqrt{5})(4 + 2\sqrt{5})} = \dfrac{8 + 4\sqrt{5}}{4^2 - (2\sqrt{5})^2},$

$$\frac{8 + 4\sqrt{5}}{4^2 - (2\sqrt{5})^2} = \frac{8 + 4\sqrt{5}}{16 - 20} = \frac{8 + 4\sqrt{5}}{-4} = -2 - \sqrt{5} \quad \textit{Answer}$$

Written Exercises

Express in simplest form.

A 1. $(2 + \sqrt{3})(2 - \sqrt{3})$ 1

2. $(5 - \sqrt{11})(5 + \sqrt{11})$ 14

3. $(\sqrt{3} - \sqrt{2})(\sqrt{3} + \sqrt{2})$ 1

4. $(\sqrt{5} - \sqrt{7})(\sqrt{5} + \sqrt{7})$ −2

5. $(2\sqrt{7} + 1)(\sqrt{7} - 2)$ $12 - 3\sqrt{7}$

6. $(3\sqrt{5} - 1)(2\sqrt{5} + 2)$ $28 + 4\sqrt{5}$

7. $(1 + \sqrt{2})^2$ $3 + 2\sqrt{2}$

8. $(3 - \sqrt{7})^2$ $16 - 6\sqrt{7}$

9. $(2\sqrt{3} - 2)^2$ $16 - 8\sqrt{3}$

10. $(4\sqrt{10} + 3)^2$ $169 + 24\sqrt{10}$

11. $3\sqrt{5}(\sqrt{10} + \sqrt{5})$ $15\sqrt{2} + 15$

12. $4\sqrt{10}(2\sqrt{2} + 3\sqrt{5})$ $16\sqrt{5} + 60\sqrt{2}$

B 13. $(7\sqrt{7} + \sqrt{3})(2\sqrt{7} - \sqrt{3})$

14. $(5\sqrt{3} - 2\sqrt{7})(3\sqrt{3} + \sqrt{7})$ $31 - \sqrt{21}$

15. $(6\sqrt{2} + 4\sqrt{6})(\sqrt{2} - 2\sqrt{6})$

16. $(3\sqrt{5} + \sqrt{10})(2\sqrt{5} - 4\sqrt{10})$ $-10 - 50\sqrt{2}$

17. $(3\sqrt{2} + \sqrt{5})(\sqrt{2} + 2\sqrt{5})$

18. $(4\sqrt{3} + 2\sqrt{6})(5\sqrt{3} + 7\sqrt{6})$ $144 + 114\sqrt{2}$

13. $95 - 5\sqrt{21}$ **15.** $-36 - 16\sqrt{3}$ **17.** $16 + 7\sqrt{10}$

Rationalize the denominator of each fraction.

19. $\dfrac{1}{1 + \sqrt{5}}$ $\dfrac{1 - \sqrt{5}}{-4}$

20. $\dfrac{3}{\sqrt{7} - 1}$ $\dfrac{\sqrt{7} + 1}{2}$

21. $\dfrac{\sqrt{5}}{\sqrt{5} - 3}$ $\dfrac{5 + 3\sqrt{5}}{-4}$

22. $\dfrac{\sqrt{10}}{2 + \sqrt{10}}$ $\dfrac{\sqrt{10} - 5}{-3}$

23. $\dfrac{1 + \sqrt{7}}{2 - \sqrt{7}}$ $-3 - \sqrt{7}$

24. $\dfrac{5 + \sqrt{2}}{3 - \sqrt{2}}$ $\dfrac{17 + 8\sqrt{2}}{7}$

25. $\dfrac{7}{2\sqrt{5} + 1}$ $\dfrac{14\sqrt{5} - 7}{19}$

26. $\dfrac{4}{4\sqrt{7} - 3}$ $\dfrac{16\sqrt{7} + 12}{103}$

If $f(x) = x^2 - 3x + 1$, find:

27. $f(\sqrt{3})$ $4 - 3\sqrt{3}$

28. $f(\sqrt{2} + 1)$ $1 - \sqrt{2}$

29. $f(1 - \sqrt{5})$ $4 + \sqrt{5}$

30. $f(2 + \sqrt{7})$ $6 + \sqrt{7}$

31. Show that $(5 + \sqrt{2})$ and $(5 - \sqrt{2})$ are roots of the equation "$x^2 - 10x + 23 = 0$." *(below)*

32. Write an expression in simplest form for the area of a square whose perimeter is $6\sqrt{2} + 3$ centimeters. $\dfrac{81 + 36\sqrt{2}}{16}$

Simplify each, assuming that the value of each variable is nonnegative.

C 33. $(\sqrt{x} - y)(\sqrt{x} + y)$ $x - y^2$

34. $(x - 3\sqrt{2})^2$ $x^2 - 6x\sqrt{2} + 18$

35. $(3a\sqrt{b} - c)(5a\sqrt{b} + 3c)$ $15a^2b + 4ac\sqrt{b} - 3c^2$

36. $\sqrt{\dfrac{m}{n}} - 2\sqrt{\dfrac{n}{m}} + \sqrt{mn}$ $\dfrac{\sqrt{mn}(m - 2n + mn)}{mn}$

31. $(5 + \sqrt{2})^2 - 10(5 + \sqrt{2}) + 23 = 25 + 10\sqrt{2} + 2 - 50 - 10\sqrt{2} + 23 = 0$
$(5 - \sqrt{2})^2 - 10(5 - \sqrt{2}) + 23 = 25 - 10\sqrt{2} + 2 - 50 + 10\sqrt{2} + 23 = 0$

10-10 Simple Radical Equations

> **OBJECTIVE** To learn how to solve simple radical equations.

You can now learn how to solve still another kind of equation.

> An equation having a variable in a radicand is called a **radical equation.**

Example 1 Solve $\sqrt{x} = 7$.

Solution

$$\sqrt{x} = 7$$

Square both members: $(\sqrt{x})^2 = 49$

$$x = 49$$

Check: $\sqrt{49} \overset{?}{=} 7$; $7 = 7 \checkmark$

∴ the solution is 49. *Answer*

Example 2 Solve $\sqrt{2x + 1} = 3$.

Solution $2x + 1 = 9$

$$2x = 8$$
$$x = 4$$

Check: $\sqrt{2(4) + 1} \overset{?}{=} 3$; $\sqrt{9} \overset{?}{=} 3$; $3 = 3 \checkmark$

∴ the solution is 4. *Answer*

Solving radical equations is based on the property of square roots of equal numbers (page 392). But you must always remember that the radical sign means the *principal* root. (In solving more complicated radical equations, sometimes the squaring process will introduce roots that do not satisfy the original equation. *You must check every apparent root in the original equation to see if it is, in fact, a root.*)

Example 3 Solve $\sqrt{3x^2 - 8} = x$.

Solution $3x^2 - 8 = x^2$

$$2x^2 = 8$$
$$x^2 = 4$$
$$x = 2 \text{ or } x = -2$$

Check: $\sqrt{3(2)^2 - 8} \overset{?}{=} 2$ $\sqrt{3(-2)^2 - 8} \overset{?}{=} -2$

$\sqrt{4} \overset{?}{=} 2$ $\sqrt{4} \overset{?}{=} -2$

$2 = 2 \checkmark$ $2 \overset{?}{=} -2$ No

∴ the solution is 2. *Answer*

Written Exercises

Solve each equation.

A 1. $\sqrt{y} = 3$ 9

2. $\sqrt{2x} = 4$ 8

3. $\sqrt{10y} = \frac{1}{4}$ $\frac{1}{160}$

4. $\sqrt{5x} = \frac{4}{5}$ $\frac{16}{125}$

5. $\sqrt{r} - 3 = 1$ 16

6. $\sqrt{m} + 2 = 7$ 25

7. $\sqrt{y} - \frac{1}{2} = 2$ $\frac{25}{4}$

8. $\frac{2}{3} + \sqrt{b} = 1$ $\frac{1}{9}$

9. $\sqrt{\frac{r}{2}} = 3$ 18

10. $\sqrt{\frac{s}{5}} = 5$ 125

11. $\sqrt{x + 1} = 3$ 8

12. $\sqrt{z - 5} = 6$ 41

13. $2\sqrt{3x} = 5$ $\frac{25}{12}$

14. $5\sqrt{2x} = 20$ 8

15. $\sqrt{3x} + 4 = 7$ 3

16. $\sqrt{8b} + 7 = 3$ $\emptyset$

17. $\sqrt{4x + 1} - 1 = 2$ 2

18. $\sqrt{5m - 5} + 6 = 7$ $\frac{6}{5}$

19. $\sqrt{\frac{5a}{4}} - 2 = 8$ 80

20. $\sqrt{\frac{7u}{3}} + 2 = 14$ $\frac{432}{7}$

B 21. $\sqrt{\frac{2x + 1}{2}} = 3$ $\frac{17}{2}$

22. $\sqrt{\frac{5t - 3}{7}} = 4$ 23

23. $\sqrt{r} = 5\sqrt{2}$ 50

24. $5\sqrt{t} = 15\sqrt{2}$ 18

25. $5\sqrt{2n^2 - 20} = 10$ $\pm 2\sqrt{3}$

26. $3\sqrt{2m^2 - 10} = 12$ $\pm\sqrt{13}$

27. $\sqrt{x^2 + 1} = 1 - x$ 0

28. $\sqrt{y^2 - 3} = y + 1$ $\emptyset$

29. $\sqrt{2a^2 - 9} = a$ 3

30. $\sqrt{5b^2 - 7} = 2b\sqrt{7}$

Problems

Solve.

A 1. Twice the square root of a number is 24. Find the number. 144

2. One sixth of the square root of a number is 3. Find the number. 324

3. When 8 is subtracted from twice a certain number, the square root of the result is 2. Find the number. 6

4. Find the length of the hypotenuse of a right triangle whose sides are $(\sqrt{2} + 3)$ and $(\sqrt{2} - 3)$ centimeters. $\sqrt{22}$ cm

5. Find the edge of a cube if its surface area is 350 square meters. $\frac{5\sqrt{21}}{3}$ m

6. The formula for finding the area A of a circle with radius r is $A = \pi r^2$. Find r if $A = 154$ and $\pi \doteq \frac{22}{7}$. 7

7. The formula for finding the altitude h of an equilateral triangle with side s is $h = \frac{\sqrt{3}}{2}s$. Find s if h is $4\sqrt{3}$. 8

B 8. The current I (measured in amperes) which flows through an electrical appliance is expressed by $I = \sqrt{\frac{P}{R}}$, where P is power consumed (in watts) and R is the resistance of the appliance (in ohms). If an electric iron has a resistance of 25 ohms and draws 9 amperes of current, how much power does it consume? 2025 watts

9. The geometric average of two positive numbers is the positive square root of their product. Find a pair of consecutive positive integers whose geometric average is $2\sqrt{33}$. 11 and 12

10. Using the formula $a = \left(1 + \frac{r}{100}\right)^2$, the amount a to which $1 grows when invested for 2 years at r% per year can be found. At what rate will $1 become $1.44? 20%

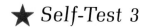 *Self-Test 3*

Be sure that you understand these terms:

simplest form of a radical (p. 398)   rationalizing a denominator (p. 398)
conjugate (p. 404)   radical equation (p. 406)

Express in simplest form.

1. $4 \cdot \sqrt{5} \cdot \sqrt{5}$ 2. $\sqrt{\dfrac{6}{x}},\ x > 0$ Objective 10-7, p. 398

3. $5\sqrt{2} + 6\sqrt{2} - 2\sqrt{2}$ 4. $2\sqrt{3} - 3\sqrt{5} - \sqrt{3}$ Objective 10-8, p. 402

5. $(1 + \sqrt{3})^2$ 6. $(2 + \sqrt{6})(2 - \sqrt{6})$ Objective 10-9, p. 404

Rationalize the denominator.

7. $\dfrac{5}{\sqrt{5} + 2}$ 8. $\dfrac{\sqrt{11}}{1 + \sqrt{11}}$

Solve.

9. $\sqrt{x} + 3 = 8$ 10. $6\sqrt{y} = 18\sqrt{2}$ Objective 10-10, p. 406

Check your answers with those printed at the back of the book.

Chapter Summary

1. A rational number can be represented in fractional form or as a terminating or repeating decimal.

2. An irrational number is represented by a nonterminating, non-repeating decimal. Such decimals are rounded to a convenient number of places for use in computation.

3. Approximate values of irrational square roots can be found by repeatedly averaging factors. Some values can be found in tables of square roots.

4. The property of square roots of equal numbers can be used to solve some kinds of equations: If r and s are any real numbers, then $r^2 = s^2$ if and only if $r = s$ or $r = -s$.

5. Many problems involving right triangles can be solved by using the Pythagorean theorem: $c^2 = a^2 + b^2$

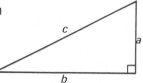

6. Radical expressions can be added, subtracted, and multiplied. The result of division is often simplified by rationalizing the denominator.

Chapter Test ▭

Arrange in order, from least to greatest.

10-1   1. $\dfrac{5}{11}, \dfrac{10}{33}, \dfrac{12}{25}$ $\dfrac{10}{33}, \dfrac{5}{11}, \dfrac{12}{25}$ 2. $\dfrac{3}{41}, \dfrac{5}{37}, \dfrac{7}{43}$ as is

Find the number halfway between the given numbers.

3. $\dfrac{5}{16}, \dfrac{1}{32}$ $\dfrac{11}{64}$ 4. $6\dfrac{1}{3}, 7\dfrac{1}{9}$ $6\dfrac{13}{18}$

Write as a terminating or repeating decimal.

10-2   5. $\dfrac{7}{40}$ 0.175   6. $\dfrac{5}{11}$ $0.\overline{45}$

Write as a common fraction.

7. 2.016 $\dfrac{252}{125}$ 8. $0.\overline{43}$ $\dfrac{43}{99}$

Simplify.

10-3   9. $-\sqrt{5625}$ -75 10. $\sqrt{\dfrac{121}{256}}$ $\dfrac{11}{16}$

Compute the given square root to the nearest hundredth.

10-4   11. $\sqrt{10.24}$ **3.20**   12. $-\sqrt{327}$ **−18.08**

Solve.

10-5   13. $y^2 = 400$ **±20**   14. $16x^2 - 256 = 0$ **±4**

10-6   15. Find the length, to the nearest tenth, of a diagonal of a rectangle whose dimensions are 4 by 7 centimeters. **8.1 cm**

       16. Find the length of the third side of a right triangle if its hypotenuse and one side have lengths 20 and 16, respectively. **12**

Simplify.

10-7   17. $\sqrt{25} \cdot 3\sqrt{10} \cdot 2\sqrt{2}$ $60\sqrt{5}$ 18. $\dfrac{14\sqrt{7}}{\sqrt{28}}$ **7**

10-8   19. $3\sqrt{3} + 2\sqrt{3} - \sqrt{3}$ $4\sqrt{3}$ 20. $4\sqrt{3} + \sqrt{12} - \sqrt{27}$ $3\sqrt{3}$

10-9   21. $(3\sqrt{2} - \sqrt{5})^2$ $23 - 6\sqrt{10}$ 22. $\dfrac{\sqrt{2} - 1}{\sqrt{2} + 1}$ $3 - 2\sqrt{2}$

Solve.

10-10   23. $\sqrt{5x} - 10 = 0$ **20**   24. $\sqrt{2r^2 - 10} = r$ $\sqrt{10}$

Programmed Chapter Review

10-1   1. "Between every pair of different rational numbers there is another rational number" describes the property of __?__ .   density

2. For all integers a and b and all positive integers c and d, $\frac{a}{c} > \frac{b}{d}$ if and only if __?__ . $ad > bc$

3. Of the two numbers $\frac{5}{9}$ and $-\frac{5}{9}$, the greater number is __?__ $\frac{5}{9}$

4. The number halfway between $\frac{1}{2}$ and $\frac{7}{8}$ is __?__ . $\frac{11}{16}$

10-2   5. The decimal numeral $0.\overline{6}$ is an example of a __?__ decimal numeral.   repeating (periodic)

6. Rounded to the nearest tenth, $0.32\overline{7}$ is __?__ .   0.3

7. The decimal form for $\frac{3}{40}$ is __?__ .   0.075

8. The decimal form for $\frac{5}{12}$ is __?__ . $0.41\overline{6}$

9. The fractional form for $0.1\overline{6}$ is __?__ . $\frac{1}{6}$

10-3   10. $\sqrt{3} \cdot \sqrt{3} = \sqrt{\;\underline{\;?\;}\;}$ 9

11. $\dfrac{\sqrt{25}}{\sqrt{144}} = \dfrac{\;?\;}{\;?\;}$ $\dfrac{5}{12}$

12. $\sqrt{2304} = \sqrt{4} \cdot \sqrt{\;\underline{\;?\;}\;} = \sqrt{4} \cdot \sqrt{4} \cdot \sqrt{\;\underline{\;?\;}\;}$ 576, 144

13. The principal square root of 0.36 is __?__ .   0.6

10-4   14. To find $\sqrt{7}$ by the divide-and-average method, let $a = 3$. Then $\dfrac{7}{a} \doteq \underline{\;?\;}$.   2.3

15. Then $\frac{1}{2}(3 + 2.3) \doteq \underline{\;?\;}$.   2.6

16. The integer closest to the square root of 123 is __?__ .   11

17. Correct to hundredths, $\sqrt{19} = \underline{\;?\;}$.   4.36

18. Correct to tenths, $\sqrt{157} = \underline{\;?\;}$.   12.5

10-5   19. $-\sqrt{100r^2s^2}$ when simplified is __?__ . $-10|rs|$

20. If $t^2 = 169$, then $t = \pm \underline{\;?\;}$.   13

10-6   21. The longest side of a right triangle is called the __?__ .   hypotenuse

22. A set of lengths of sides of a right triangle is $\{5, 12, \underline{\;?\;}\}$.   13

23. If c denotes the length of the hypotenuse, and a and b denote the lengths of the other two sides of a right triangle, then __?__ = __?__ + __?__ .

$c^2 = a^2 + b^2$

10-7 24. In simplified form, $\dfrac{1}{\sqrt{6}} = \underline{\ ?\ }$.

$\dfrac{\sqrt{6}}{6}$

25. In simplified form, $\sqrt{a}(\sqrt{a} - 1) = \underline{\ ?\ }$.

$a - \sqrt{a}$

26. If one number is twice another number, and the difference of their squares is 300, then the numbers are __?__ and __?__ .

20, 10

10-8 27. In simplified form, $3\sqrt{6} + 5\sqrt{24} = \underline{\ ?\ }$.

$13\sqrt{6}$

28. In simplified form, $6\sqrt{\dfrac{3}{2}} + \sqrt{\dfrac{2}{3}} - \dfrac{1}{2}\sqrt{6} = \underline{\ ?\ }$.

$\dfrac{17}{6}\sqrt{6}$

10-9 29. Two binomials of the form $x + \sqrt{y}$ and $x - \sqrt{y}$ are called __?__ .

conjugates

30. In simplified form, $(6\sqrt{5} - 1)(\sqrt{5} + 3) = \underline{\ ?\ }$.

$27 + 17\sqrt{5}$

31. If $f(x) = x^2 - x + 1$, then $f(\sqrt{2}) = \underline{\ ?\ }$.

$3 - \sqrt{2}$

10-10 32. If $\sqrt{\dfrac{a}{6}} = 8$, then $a = \underline{\ ?\ }$.

384

33. If $\sqrt{5x + 1} - 6 = 8$, then $x = \underline{\ ?\ }$.

39

Extra for Experts ExtraExtraExtraExtraExtraExt
The Distance Formula

The distance between two points on the x-axis or on a line parallel to that axis is the absolute value of the difference between their abscissas:

$$A'B' = |3 - 8| = |8 - 3| = 5$$
$$AB = |3 - 8| = |8 - 3| = 5$$

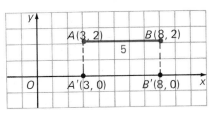

The distance between two points on the y-axis or on a line parallel to that axis is the absolute value of the difference between their ordinates:

$$A''C'' = |2 - 5| = |5 - 2| = 3$$
$$AC = |2 - 5| = |5 - 2| = 3$$

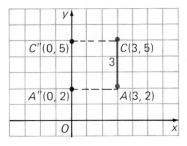

To find the distance between two points not on an axis or a line parallel to an axis, use the Pythagorean theorem (page 394):

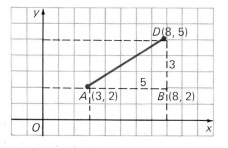

$$AD = \sqrt{(AB)^2 + (BD)^2} = \sqrt{(8-3)^2 + (5-2)^2}$$
$$= \sqrt{5^2 + 3^2} = \sqrt{25 + 9} = \sqrt{34}$$

In general:

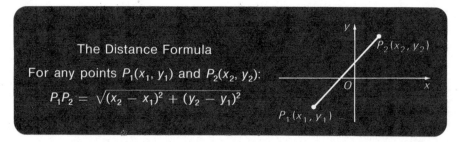

The Distance Formula

For any points $P_1(x_1, y_1)$ and $P_2(x_2, y_2)$:

$$P_1P_2 = \sqrt{(x_2 - x_1)^2 + (y_2 - y_1)^2}$$

Example Find the distance between points $M(-3, 8)$ and $N(5, 2)$.

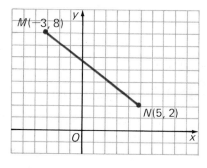

Solution 1 $MN = \sqrt{(-3-5)^2 + (8-2)^2}$

$\qquad = \sqrt{(-8)^2 + 6^2} = \sqrt{64 + 36}$

$\qquad = \sqrt{100} = 10$ *Answer*

Solution 2 $MN = \sqrt{(5-(-3))^2 + (2-8)^2}$

$\qquad = \sqrt{8^2 + (-6)^2} = \sqrt{64 + 36}$

$\qquad = \sqrt{100} = 10$ *Answer*

Use the distance formula to find the distance to the nearest tenth between the points.

1. $(-2, 0)$, $(7, 0)$ **9**
2. $(0, -4)$, $(0, 12)$ **16**
3. $(1, 1)$, $(7, 9)$ **10**
4. $(-1, 2)$, $(-8, 6)$ **8.1**
5. $(-1, -3)$, $(-6, -9)$ **7.8**
6. $(2, -7)$, $(5, -2)$ **5.8**
7. $(3, 1)$, $(-3, 7)$ **8.5**
8. $(-2, 1)$, $(-8, -5)$ **8.5**
9. $(-7, -2)$, $(2, -2)$ **9**
10. $(4, -3)$, $(9, -8)$ **7.1**
11. $(2, 3)$, $(-7, -8)$ **14.2**
12. $(-8, 5)$, $(7, -2)$ **16.6**

13. Show that points $(0, 3)$, $(3, 9)$, $(6, 0)$, $(9, 6)$ are the vertices of an equal-sided quadrilateral.

14. Show that point $(-2, 2)$ is the midpoint of the segment joining $(-7, 0)$ and $(3, 4)$. $\sqrt{(-2+7)^2 + (2-0)^2} = \sqrt{29}$; $\sqrt{(-2-3)^2 + (2-4)^2} = \sqrt{29}$

13. Let $A = (0, 3)$, $B = (3, 9)$, $C = (6, 0)$, $D = (9, 6)$; $AB = \sqrt{(3-0)^2 + (9-3)^2} = \sqrt{45}$, and, similarly, $BD = DC = AC = \sqrt{45}$.

Maintaining Skills

Remember how?

$$\underbrace{\frac{a^2}{a-b} - \frac{b^2}{a-b}}_{\displaystyle \frac{a^2-b^2}{a-b}} = a+b$$

$$\frac{(a+b)\overset{1}{\cancel{(a-b)}}}{\underset{1}{\cancel{(a-b)}}} = a+b$$

Now practice:

1. $\dfrac{x-y}{2y} + \dfrac{x}{2y} = \underline{\ ?\ } \dfrac{2x-y}{2y}$

2. $\dfrac{z+1}{a} + \dfrac{z-1}{a} = \underline{\ ?\ } \dfrac{\frac{2z}{a}}{\frac{1}{3a}}$

3. $\dfrac{7}{10z} + \dfrac{9}{10z} - \dfrac{19}{10z} = \underline{\ ?\ } \dfrac{-3}{10z}$

4. $\dfrac{4}{3a} - \dfrac{5}{3a} + \dfrac{2}{3a} = \underline{\ ?\ }$

5. $\dfrac{4a}{a+b} + \dfrac{4b}{a+b} = \underline{\ ?\ } \ 4$

6. $\dfrac{t}{t-7} - \dfrac{7}{t-7} = \underline{\ ?\ } \ 1$

Remember how? $\dfrac{2x-1}{4} + \dfrac{x+3}{6} = \dfrac{8x+3}{12}$

$$\frac{3(2x-1)}{3\cdot 4} + \frac{(x+3)2}{6\cdot 2}$$

$$\frac{(6x-3)+(2x+6)}{12} = \frac{8x+3}{12}$$

Now practice:

7. $\dfrac{2}{az} - \dfrac{2}{z} = \underline{\ ?\ } \dfrac{2-2a}{az}$

8. $\dfrac{b-3}{6} - \dfrac{b}{3} = \underline{\ ?\ } \dfrac{-b-3}{6}$

9. $\dfrac{5}{3a} + \dfrac{2}{a} = \underline{\ ?\ } \dfrac{11}{3a}$

10. $\dfrac{x+3}{4} + \dfrac{3}{8} = \underline{\ ?\ } \dfrac{2x+9}{8}$

Remember how?

$$x + \frac{2}{x+3} = \frac{x^2+3x+2}{x+3}$$

$$\frac{x(x+3)}{1(x+3)} + \frac{2}{x+3}$$

$$\frac{x^2+3x}{x+3} + \frac{2}{x+3} = \frac{x^2+3x+2}{x+3}$$

Now practice:

11. $a + \dfrac{3}{a-1} = \underline{\ ?\ } \dfrac{a^2-a+3}{a-1}$

12. $2b - \dfrac{5}{b+2} = \underline{\ ?\ } \dfrac{2b^2+4b-5}{b+2}$

13. $c + \dfrac{2c}{c-1} = \underline{\ ?\ } \dfrac{c^2+c}{c-1}$

14. $2 + \dfrac{x+2}{x-1} = \underline{\ ?\ } \dfrac{3x}{x-1}$

Remember how?

$$\frac{t^2-3t+2}{t+3} = t-6+\frac{20}{t+3}$$

$$\begin{array}{r} t-6 \\ t+3 \overline{)\, t^2-3t+2} \\ \underline{t^2+3t} \\ -6t+2 \\ \underline{-6t-18} \\ 20 \end{array}$$

Now practice:

15. $\dfrac{x^2-3x+1}{x+2} = \underline{\ ?\ } \ x-5+\dfrac{11}{x+2}$

16. $\dfrac{y^2+2y+3}{y-1} = \underline{\ ?\ } \ y+3+\dfrac{6}{y-1}$

17. $\dfrac{a^2+3}{a-1} = \underline{\ ?\ } \ a+1+\dfrac{4}{a-1}$

18. $\dfrac{r^2+5r}{r+2} = \underline{\ ?\ } \ r+3-\dfrac{6}{r+2}$

Quadratic Functions and Equations

Social Science Political scientists rely on computers and mathematical methods in collecting and analyzing data about voting patterns.

11

Quadratic Functions

11-1 Quadratic Direct Variation

OBJECTIVE To learn how to use quadratic direct variation to solve problems.

In Chapter 8, you studied linear functions and linear direct variation. We shall now go on to study *quadratic functions* and *quadratic direct variation*.

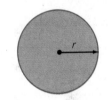

Sometimes a statement such as this is made: "The area of a circle *varies directly as the square* of its radius." This is an example of a *quadratic direct variation,* since $A = \pi r^2$.

In general:

> A **quadratic direct variation** is a function defined by an equation of the form
>
> $$y = kx^2, \text{ where } k \text{ is a nonzero constant.}$$
>
> $$\frac{y}{x^2} = k \text{ for all ordered pairs other than } (0, 0).$$

You say that

y varies directly as x^2

or

y is directly proportional to x^2.

The graph of a quadratic direct variation when the domain is the set of real numbers has the shape of Figure 11-1 or Figure 11-2. Notice that if $k > 0$, the graph opens upward. If $k < 0$, the graph opens downward.

In practical applications, the domain is usually the set of nonnegative real numbers, and k is usually positive.

x	x^2	y
-3	$(-3)^2$	9
-2	$(-2)^2$	4
-1	$(-1)^2$	1
0	0^2	0
1	1^2	1
2	2^2	4
3	3^2	9

$f: x \rightarrow x^2$

or

$y = x^2$

Figure 11-1

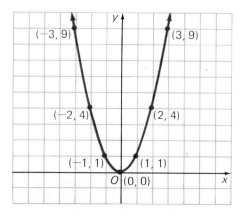

x	$-1.5x^2$	y
-2.5	$-1.5(-2.5)^2$	-9.375
-2	$-1.5(-2)^2$	-6
-1	$-1.5(-1)^2$	-1.5
0	$-1.5(0)^2$	0
1	$-1.5(1)^2$	-1.5
2	$-1.5(2)^2$	-6
2.5	$-1.5(2.5)^2$	-9.375

$g: x \rightarrow -1.5x^2$

or

$y = -1.5x^2$

Figure 11-2

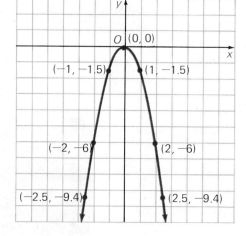

If (x_1, y_1) and (x_2, y_2) are ordered pairs of a quadratic direct variation, then:

$$\frac{y_1}{x_1{}^2} = \frac{y_2}{x_2{}^2}.$$

Multiplying both members of $\dfrac{y_1}{x_1{}^2} = \dfrac{y_2}{x_2{}^2}$ by $\dfrac{x_1{}^2}{y_2}$ $(x_1 \neq 0, y_2 \neq 0)$, you have another useful form:

$$\frac{y_1}{y_2} = \frac{x_1{}^2}{x_2{}^2}.$$

Example The distance required for an automobile to come to a stop varies directly as the square of its speed. If the stopping distance for a car traveling at 16 kilometers per hour is 7 meters, what is the distance for a car traveling at 80 kilometers per hour?

Solution Let d = distance required to stop in meters, and s = speed in kilometers per hour.

Method I	Method II
Use $d = ks^2$.	Use $\dfrac{d_1}{s_1{}^2} = \dfrac{d_2}{s_2{}^2}$.
$7 = k(16)^2$; $k = \dfrac{7}{256}$	$\dfrac{7}{(16)^2} = \dfrac{d_2}{(80)^2}$
$d = \dfrac{7}{256}s^2$	$\dfrac{7}{256} = \dfrac{d_2}{6400}$
$= \dfrac{7}{256}(80)^2$	
$= \dfrac{7}{\underset{1}{\cancel{256}}} \cdot \overset{25}{\cancel{6400}} = 175$	$d_2 = \dfrac{7 \cdot \overset{25}{\cancel{6400}}}{\underset{1}{\cancel{256}}} = 175$

$\therefore$ it takes the car 175 meters to stop from a speed of 80 kilometers per hour. *Answer*

Oral Exercises

Which of these quadratic functions with domain the set of real numbers have graphs opening upward and which have graphs opening downward?

1. $F: x \to 2x^2$ **up**

2. $f: x \to 0.2x^2$ **up**

3. $g: x \to -3x^2$ **down**

4. $G: x \to -0.4x^2$ **down**

5. $H: x \to -\dfrac{1}{2}x^2$ **down**

6. $h: x \to \dfrac{2}{3}x^2$ **up**

7. $f: x \to \dfrac{5}{4}x^2$ **up**

8. $g: x \to -\dfrac{4}{3}x^2$ **down**

Written Exercises

Graph.

A 1. $y = 3x^2$ 2. $y = 5x^2$ 3. $y = \dfrac{1}{4}x^2$ 4. $y = \dfrac{1}{2}x^2$

5. $y = -\dfrac{1}{2}x^2$ 6. $y = -4x^2$ 7. $y = -0.2x^2$ 8. $y = -\dfrac{3}{2}x^2$

9. $y = 1.4x^2$ 10. $y = \dfrac{3}{5}x^2$ 11. $y = -3.6x^2$ 12. $y = -\dfrac{7}{8}x^2$

Problems

Solve.

A 1. The radii of two circles are 3 and 6, respectively. Find the ratio of their areas. **1:4**

2. What is the ratio of the areas of two squares if one is 2 centimeters on a side and the other is 5 centimeters on a side? **4:25**

3. The distance a body falls varies directly as the square of the time. If a body falls 78 meters in 4 seconds, what distance will it fall in 8 seconds? **312 m**

4. The price of a diamond varies directly as the square of its weight. If one weighing $\frac{7}{8}$ carat is worth $625, find the cost of a similar diamond of $1\frac{1}{2}$ carats. **about $1836.73**

5. The surface area of a sphere varies directly as the square of its diameter. If the surface area of a sphere 10 meters in diameter is 314.16 square meters, find the surface area of a sphere 15 meters in diameter. **706.86 m**

6. If the pressure is constant, the amount of water delivered through a pipe in a given time varies directly as the square of the diameter of the pipe. When a pipe 1 centimeter in diameter will deliver 0.5 kiloliter in a certain time, what will a 2.5 centimeter pipe deliver in the same time? **3.125 kl**

7. A basketball has a radius 4 times that of a tennis ball. If the surface area of a sphere varies directly as the square of the radius, find the surface area of the tennis ball if the surface area of the basketball is 144π square centimeters. **9π cm²**

B 8. Find the ratio of the areas of two circular table tops if the circumference of the larger is 132 centimeters and that of the other is 88 centimeters. (The area of a circle varies directly as the square of its circumference.) **9:4**

9. Two spheres have a surface area of 1256 square centimeters and 113.04 square centimeters, respectively. If the radius of the larger sphere is 10 centimeters, find the radius of the smaller sphere (see Problem 7). **3 cm**

10. The pressure from a 33-kilometer-per-hour wind registered 0.028 gram per square centimeter on a very sensitive gauge. Find the rate of the wind which registered a 0.035-gram increase on the gauge. (Pressure varies directly as the square of the rate of wind.)
$$\frac{33\sqrt{5}}{2} \text{ km/h}$$

11-2 Inverse Variation

OBJECTIVE To learn how to use inverse variation to solve problems.

Three rectangles whose lengths and widths are

(12, 1), (6, 2), (4, 3)

have the same area:

$12 \cdot 1 = 12, \quad 6 \cdot 2 = 12, \quad 4 \cdot 3 = 12, \quad lw = 12$

The statement is sometimes made that in rectangles having the same area, the length *varies inversely* as the width. In general:

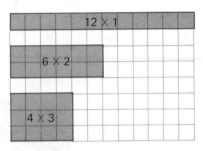

An **inverse variation** is a function defined by an equation of the form

$$xy = k, \text{ where } k \text{ is a nonzero constant.}$$

$$y = \frac{k}{x} \text{ for all ordered pairs other than (0, 0).}$$

You say that

y varies inversely as x

or

y is inversely proportional to x.

Because $y = k\left(\dfrac{1}{x}\right)$, *y* varies *directly* as the *multiplicative inverse* of *x*.

You would not expect the graph of an inverse variation to be a straight line because its equation,

$xy = k$,

is not linear; one term, *xy*, is of the second degree. The graph of $xy = 1$ is shown in Figure 11-3 on the next page.

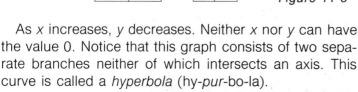

x	y
-4	$-\frac{1}{4}$
-2	$-\frac{1}{2}$
-1	-1
$-\frac{1}{2}$	-2
$-\frac{1}{4}$	-4

x	y
$\frac{1}{4}$	4
$\frac{1}{2}$	2
1	1
2	$\frac{1}{2}$
4	$\frac{1}{4}$

$xy = 1$

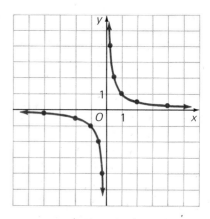

Figure 11-3

As x increases, y decreases. Neither x nor y can have the value 0. Notice that this graph consists of two separate branches neither of which intersects an axis. This curve is called a *hyperbola* (hy-*pur*-bo-la).

In general:

> The graph of every equation of the form
>
> $$xy = k, \ k \neq 0 \ (x \neq 0, y \neq 0)$$
>
> is a **hyperbola.**

The curve is in the first and third quadrants if k is positive and in the second and fourth quadrants if k is negative. If k were 0, what would be the range and domain of the function defined by $xy = k$? the axes

When negative answers are meaningless, as they often are in practical problems, the range and domain are limited to positive numbers. The graph of such an inverse variation has only one branch—the one in the first quadrant.

If (x_1, y_1) and (x_2, y_2) are ordered pairs of an inverse variation, then

$$x_1 y_1 = k \quad \text{and} \quad x_2 y_2 = k.$$

Therefore,

$$x_1 y_1 = x_2 y_2.$$

Since neither x_1 nor x_2 is 0, you can divide both members by $x_1 x_2$, obtaining

$$\frac{y_1}{x_2} = \frac{y_2}{x_1}$$

Multiplying this by $\dfrac{x_2}{y_2}$ $(x_2 \neq 0, y_2 \neq 0)$ gives another useful form,

$$\frac{y_1}{y_2} = \frac{x_2}{x_1}$$

Compare:

Direct Variation	Inverse Variation
$x_1 y_2 = x_2 y_1$	$x_1 y_1 = x_2 y_2$
$\dfrac{y_1}{x_1} = \dfrac{y_2}{x_2}$ or $\dfrac{y_1}{y_2} = \dfrac{x_1}{x_2}$	$\dfrac{y_1}{x_2} = \dfrac{y_2}{x_1}$ or $\dfrac{y_1}{y_2} = \dfrac{x_2}{x_1}$

One instance of inverse variation is the law of the lever (*lee*-ver), a bar pivoted at a point called the fulcrum (*ful*-krum) (Figure 11-4). If weights w_1 and w_2 are placed at distances d_1 and d_2 from the fulcrum, and the lever is in balance, then

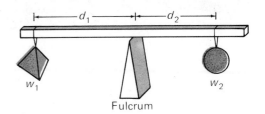

$$\frac{d_1}{d_2} = \frac{w_2}{w_1} \quad \text{or} \quad d_1 w_1 = d_2 w_2.$$

Figure 11-4

Example A 15-kilogram weight located 66 centimeters from the fulcrum of a lever is balanced by a second weight located 45 centimeters from the fulcrum. What is the second weight?

Solution Let $w_1 = 15$, $d_1 = 66$, $d_2 = 45$.

$$\frac{d_1}{d_2} = \frac{w_2}{w_1}$$

$$\frac{66}{45} = \frac{w_2}{15}$$

$$\frac{w_2}{15} = \frac{22}{15} \quad \text{or} \quad w_2 = 22$$

Check: $\dfrac{66}{45} \overset{?}{=} \dfrac{22}{15}$ $\left[\text{or} \quad (66)(15) \overset{?}{=} (45)(22) \right.$

$\dfrac{22}{15} = \dfrac{22}{15}$ ✓ $\left. \quad\quad 990 = 990 \; ✓ \right]$

∴ the second weight is 22 kilograms. *Answer*

Oral Exercises

Tell whether each formula expresses inverse or direct variation (k constant).

1. $xy = k$ inverse   2. $s = \dfrac{1}{r}$ inverse   3. $b = \dfrac{k}{s}$ inverse   4. $y = \dfrac{k}{x}$ inverse

5. $\dfrac{u}{v} = k$ direct   6. $t = \dfrac{40}{r}$ inverse   7. $\dfrac{x_1}{x_2} = \dfrac{y_1}{y_2}$ direct   8. $\dfrac{a_1}{a_2} = \dfrac{b_2}{b_1}$ inverse

9. $\dfrac{c}{d} = 10$ direct   10. $\dfrac{m_2}{m_1} = \dfrac{n_2}{n_1}$ direct   11. $\dfrac{b}{g} = \dfrac{1}{k}$ direct   12. $kxy = 1$ inverse

Translate each statement into a formula expressing inverse variation.

Sample The base of a rectangle of constant area varies inversely as its height.

Solution Let b = base and h = height.

$$\therefore bh = k, \text{ or } b = \frac{k}{h}, \text{ or } \frac{b_1}{b_2} = \frac{h_2}{h_1}, \text{ or } b_1 h_1 = b_2 h_2. \quad \textit{Answer}$$

13. The number n of shirts that can be bought for $30.00 varies inversely as the cost c of each shirt. $nc = 30$, or $n = \dfrac{30}{c}$, or $\dfrac{n_1}{n_2} = \dfrac{c_2}{c_1}$

14. The time t required to go a distance varies inversely as the rate, r. $tr = k$, or $t = \dfrac{k}{r}$, or $\dfrac{t_1}{t_2} = \dfrac{r_2}{r_1}$

Written Exercises

Graph each of the following equations if the domain and range elements are limited to the set of positive numbers.

A 1. $xy = 6$ 2. $3xy = 1$ 3. $x = \dfrac{2}{y}$ 4. $\dfrac{x}{4} = \dfrac{3}{y}$

In these inverse variations, find the value of the indicated variable.

5. $x_1 = 20$, $x_2 = 5$, $y_2 = 2$, $y_1 = $ __?__ $\dfrac{1}{2}$ 6. $s_1 = 0.9$, $s_2 = 0.03$, $r_1 = 0.6$, $r_2 = $ __?__ 18

7. $x_1 = \dfrac{1}{2}$, $x_2 = \dfrac{1}{4}$, $y_1 = 4$, $y_2 = $ __?__ 8   8. $x_2 = \dfrac{7}{20}$, $x_1 = \dfrac{2}{5}$, $t_2 = \dfrac{1}{3}$, $t_1 = $ __?__ $\dfrac{7}{24}$

B 9. If $a = bt$ and b is doubled while a remains constant, how does t change? t is halved.

10. If $xy = k$ and y is doubled when k remains constant, how does x change? x is halved.

Problems

Solve.

A 1. At 100 kilometers per hour, how long does a journey take if it takes 8 hours at 75 kilometers per hour? **6 hours**

2. If 4 men do a job in 10 days, how long do 16 men take, working at the same rate? **2½ days**

3. If Joe weighs 40 kilograms and Sam weighs 60 kilograms, how far from the seesaw support must Joe sit to balance Sam who is 2 meters from it? **3 m**

4. Jill, sitting 1.5 meters from the seesaw support, balances a friend who weighs 50 kilograms and sits 2 meters from the support. How much does Jill weigh? **66⅔ kg**

5. The number of plants that are needed to fill a row of given length varies inversely as the distance between the plants. If 90 plants are needed when they are planted 20 centimeters apart, how many are needed if planted 15 centimeters apart? **120 plants**

6. How much will each of 5 girls pay to rent an apartment for which 3 girls are each paying $60? **$36**

7. A weight of 200 grams is 40 centimeters from the center support of a meter stick. Where would a weight of 300 grams balance the stick? $26\frac{2}{3}$ cm

8. A rectangle has a base of 42 centimeters and a height of 12 centimeters. Find the base of another rectangle of equal area whose height is 14 centimeters. 36 cm

For the wave motion of sound, the following formula holds:

$$fl = v,$$

where f is the frequency (number of waves per second), l is the wavelength (in meters), and v is the speed of sound (about 335 meters per second in air). Use this information in the following problems.

B 9. The frequency of a note an octave above a given note is twice that of the given note. How does the wavelength of the higher note compare with that of the lower note? It is halved.

10. If the wavelength of a note is $\frac{3}{2}$ that of a given note, how do the frequencies compare?

11. An open organ pipe produces a sound wave that has a length that is twice the length of

the pipe. Find the length of an open pipe that will produce the note A with the frequency 440. about 0.4 m

12. A stopped organ pipe produces a sound wave that has a length that is four times the length of the pipe. What is the frequency of the sound produced by a stopped organ pipe 2 meters long? 41.875 waves/second

10. If $l_1 = \frac{3}{2}l$, then $f_1 = \frac{2}{3}f$.

Career Note
Airline Dispatcher

Each airline company hires dispatchers to coordinate flight schedules and to enforce federal and company regulations. They examine weather maps and other meteorological data to determine whether or not flights can take off on schedule. Before each flight, the dispatcher and the pilot discuss the quantity of fuel needed, the best route and altitude, and alternative plans in case of bad weather.

Another part of the job is maintaining company records. These records contain information about the availability of equipment, the distance flown by each plane, and the flying time acquired by each crew member.

Employees who have worked for an airline for at least five years are eligible to become dispatchers. To obtain certification, one must complete either a dispatcher course or a year's training under supervision.

The educational requirements for an assistant dispatcher are as follows: either experience in air transportation or two years of college with emphasis on mathematics, physics, and related subjects. An interest in flying, meteorology, or business administration is also helpful.

11-3 Variation Inversely as the Square

> **OBJECTIVE** To learn how to use inverse variation as the square to solve problems.

Several physical quantities vary inversely as the square of another quantity. For example, the brightness of the illumination of an object varies inversely as the square of the distance of the object from the source of illumination.

In general:

> An **inverse variation as the square** is a function defined by an equation of the form
>
> $x^2 y = k$, where k is a nonzero constant.
>
> $y = \dfrac{k}{x^2}$, for all ordered pairs other than $(0, 0)$.

You say that

$$y \text{ varies inversely as } x^2$$

or

$$y \text{ is inversely proportional to } x^2.$$

If $x_1{}^2 y_1 = k$ and $x_2{}^2 y_2 = k$, then $x_1{}^2 y_1 = x_2{}^2 y_2$.

Verify that

$$\frac{y_1}{x_2{}^2} = \frac{y_2}{x_1{}^2} \quad \text{and} \quad \frac{y_1}{y_2} = \frac{x_2{}^2}{x_1{}^2}, \text{ for nonzero values.}$$

$$x_1{}^2 y_1 = x_2{}^2 y_2, \text{ or } \frac{y_1}{x_2{}^2} = \frac{y_2}{x_1{}^2}$$

$$\frac{x_2{}^2}{y_2}\left(\frac{y_1}{x_2{}^2}\right) = \frac{x_2{}^2}{y_2}\left(\frac{y_2}{x_1{}^2}\right), \text{ or } \frac{y_1}{y_2} = \frac{x_2{}^2}{x_1{}^2}$$

Example If y varies inversely as x^2, and $y = 256$ when $x = 50$, find y when $x = 80$.

Solution Let $y_1 = 256$, $x_1 = 50$, and $x_2 = 80$.

$$\frac{y_1}{x_2{}^2} = \frac{y_2}{x_1{}^2}$$

Check: $\quad\dfrac{256}{6400} \overset{?}{=} \dfrac{100}{2500}$

$$\frac{256}{(80)^2} = \frac{y_2}{(50)^2}$$

$$\frac{1}{25} = \frac{1}{25} \; \checkmark$$

$$\frac{256}{64} = \frac{y_2}{25}$$

$$\left[\text{or} \quad \begin{array}{c} (256)(2500) \overset{?}{=} (6400)(100) \\ 640{,}000 = 640{,}000 \; \checkmark \end{array} \right]$$

$$y_2 = 25 \cdot 4 = 100$$

$\therefore$ the required value of y is 100. *Answer*

Written Exercises

B 1. If x varies inversely as y^2, and $x = 25$ when $y = 2$, find x when $y = 5$. **4**

2. If y varies inversely as x^2, and $x = 2$ when $y = 36$, find x when $y = 16$. **3**

3. If r varies inversely as s^2, and $r = 15$ when $s = 9$, find r when $s = 6$. $\frac{135}{4}$

4. If s varies inversely as r^2, and $r = 8$ when $s = 3$, find r when $s = 12$. **4**

5. If W varies inversely as Z^2, what value of Z causes W to become one sixteenth as much as it is when $Z = 10$? **40**

6. If p varies inversely as q^2, what happens to the value of p if the value of q is doubled? **The value is divided by 4.**

Problems

Solve.

The brightness of the illumination of an object varies inversely as the square of the distance of the object from the source of illumination.

B 1. How far from a lamp does a book receive 9 times as much illumination as a book 2 meters from the lamp? $\frac{2}{3}$ m

2. If you move a newspaper from a position 25 centimeters from the lamp to a position 100 centimeters from it, what part of the original illumination will you get? $\frac{1}{16}$

3. What is the effect on the brightness of a projected picture of moving the projector from 4 meters away from the screen to 6 meters away? $b_2 = \frac{4}{9}b_1$

4. If you want to double the illumination on a picture, how should you move the light source? d_2 **must be** $\dfrac{\sqrt{2}}{2}d_1$.

11-4 Quadratic Functions

OBJECTIVE To learn about quadratic functions.

A quadratic direct variation (page 415) is a special kind of *quadratic function*.

A **quadratic function** is a function defined by an equation of the form

$$y = ax^2 + bx + c, \quad a \neq 0.$$

Consider the function

$$f: x \longrightarrow x^2 - 4x + 3,$$

which is defined by the equation "$y = x^2 - 4x + 3$." You graph this function by finding the coordinates of selected points as shown in Figure 11-5.

x	$x^2 - 4x + 3$	y
-1	$1 + 4 + 3$	8
0	$0 - 0 + 3$	3
1	$1 - 4 + 3$	0
2	$4 - 8 + 3$	-1
3	$9 - 12 + 3$	0
4	$16 - 16 + 3$	3
5	$25 - 20 + 3$	8

$$y = x^2 - 4x + 3$$

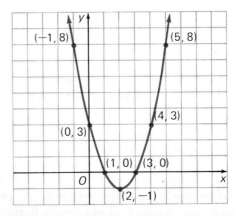

Figure 11-5

The graph of every quadratic function defined by an equation of the form

$$y = ax^2 + bx + c, \quad a \neq 0$$

is called a **parabola** (pa-*rab*-oh-la).

The graphs in Figure 11-1 (page 416), Figure 11-2 (page 416), and Figure 11-5 are all parabolas.

Notice that the graphs of

$$y = x^2 \text{ (Figure 11-1, page 416)}$$

and

$$y = x^2 - 4x + 3 \text{ (Figure 11-5)}$$

open upward so that each has a *lowest point*. The *y*-coordinate of this point is the least value that the function can have, and this point is also called the **minimum point.**
On the other hand, the graph of

$$y = -1.5x^2 \text{ (Figure 11-2, page 416)}$$

opens downward so that it has a *highest point*. The *y*-coordinate of this point is the greatest value that the function can have, and this point is also called the **maximum point.**
The lowest or highest point of each of these parabolas is called the **vertex.**

Notice also that in these examples the points, except the lowest or highest point, occur in *pairs that have the same ordinate.* For example:

In Figure 11-1		In Figure 11-2		In Figure 11-5	
$(-3, 9)$	$(3, 9)$	$(-1, -1.5)$	$(1, -1.5)$	$(-1, 8)$	$(5, 8)$
$(-2, 4)$	$(2, 4)$	$(-2, -6)$	$(2, -6)$	$(0, 3)$	$(4, 3)$
$(-1, 1)$	$(1, 1)$	$(-2.5, -9.4)$	$(2.5, -9.4)$	$(1, 0)$	$(3, 0)$

Moreover, *the average of the abscissas of any pair of points having the same ordinate is the abscissa of the lowest or highest point (vertex):*

In Figure 11-1, $\frac{1}{2}(-3 + 3) = 0$, and so on.

In Figure 11-2, $\frac{1}{2}(-1 + 1) = 0$, and so on.

In Figure 11-5, $\frac{1}{2}(-1 + 5) = 2$, and so on.

When you graph an equation of the form $y = ax^2 + bx + c$ $(a \neq 0)$, it is useful to find the abscissa of the vertex, and then to choose values of x on both sides of that value.

Figure 11-6 shows that the abscissa of the vertex is the same for equations that differ only in the constant term (the y-intercept). Thus, a formula for the abscissa of the vertex can be found by making the y-intercept zero:

Find the points of intersection of $y = ax^2 + bx$ with the x-axis $y = 0$:

$$ax^2 + bx = 0$$
$$x(ax + b) = 0$$
$$x = 0 \quad \text{or} \quad x = -\frac{b}{a}$$

The average of these abscissas is $\frac{1}{2}\left(0 + \left(-\frac{b}{a}\right)\right) = -\frac{b}{2a}$.

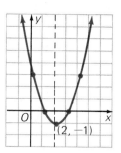
$$y = x^2 - 4x + 3$$
$$-\frac{b}{2a} = -\frac{-4}{2} = 2$$

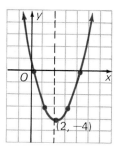
$$y = x^2 - 4x$$

Figure 11-6

In general:

> The graph of $y = ax^2 + bx + c$, $a \neq 0$:
>
> opens upward if $a > 0$; opens downward if $a < 0$.
>
> The abscissa of the vertex is $-\dfrac{b}{2a}$.

Oral Exercises

Which of these quadratic functions have a graph opening downward and which have a graph opening upward?

1. $T: x \rightarrow x^2 - 1$ up   2. $S: x \rightarrow -x^2 + 4$ down   3. $r: x \rightarrow 6 - x^2$ down   4. $p: x \rightarrow \frac{2}{3}x^2$ up

Written Exercises

Find the coordinates of the vertex of the graph of each of the following equations. Use the vertex and 6 more points to graph the equation.

A 1. $y = x^2 - 1$ $(0, -1)$ 2. $y = -x^2 + 1$ $(0, 1)$ 3. $y = x^2 - 4$ $(0, -4)$ 4. $y = 2x^2 + 3$ $(0, 3)$
  5. $y = 3 - 2x^2$ $(0, 3)$ 6. $y = 2x^2 - 1$ $(0, -1)$ 7. $y = x^2 - x$ $\left(\frac{1}{2}, -\frac{1}{4}\right)$ 8. $y = x^2 + 2x$ $(-1, $
  9. $y = x^2 - 3x - 4$ $\left(1\frac{1}{2}, -6\frac{1}{4}\right)$ 10. $y = x^2 - 2x - 8$ $(1, -9)$ 11. $y = \frac{1}{2}x^2 - 2x + 2$ $(2, 0)$ 12. $y = -\frac{1}{4}x^2 + 4$ $(0, $

Find the greatest value of *y*.

13. $y = -3x^2 + 4$ 4

14. $y = -2x^2 - 7$ -7

15. $y = -x^2 + 2x$ 1

16. $y = -x^2 - 3x$ $2\frac{1}{4}$

17. $y = -3x^2 - 6x + 4$ 7

18. $y = -5x^2 - 10x - 6$ -1

Find the least value of *y*.

19. $y = 2x^2 - 3$ -3

20. $y = 4x^2 - 6$ -6

21. $y = x^2 - 4x$ -4

22. $y = x^2 + 5x$ $-6\frac{1}{4}$

23. $y = 3x^2 - 6x - 2$ -5

24. $y = 7x^2 + 14x + 8$ 1

Computer Activity

If you have access to a computer that will accept BASIC, you can use it to compute coordinates for use in graphing quadratic functions. The program below will compute the coordinates of the vertex and 5 points on each side of it. When you use this program, you input the values *A*, *B*, *C* of

$$y = Ax^2 + Bx + C.$$

```
10  PRINT "INPUT A (NOT ZERO), B, C";
20  INPUT A,B,C
30  IF A=0 THEN 10
40  LET X1=-B/(2*A)
50  LET Y1=A*X1*X1+B*X1+C
60  PRINT "VERTEX AT (";X1;",";Y1;")"
70  LET X1=INT(X1)
80  PRINT "X", "Y"
90  FOR X=X1-5 TO X1+5
100  PRINT X,A*X*X+B*X+C
110  NEXT X
120  END
```

★ *Self-Test 1*

Be sure that you understand these terms:

quadratic direct variation (p. 415)
inverse variation as the square (p. 424)
minimum point (p. 427)

inverse variation (p. 419)
quadratic function (p. 426)
maximum point (p. 427)

hyperbola (p. 420)
parabola (p. 426)
vertex (p. 427)

1. Write an equation to describe "*y* varies directly as x^2." — Objective 11-1, p. 415

2. If *m* varies inversely as *n*, and *m* = 12 when *n* = 4, find *m* when *n* = 24. — Objective 11-2, p. 419

3. If *y* is inversely proportional to the square of *x*, and *y* = 5 when *x* = 5, what is *y* when $x = \frac{1}{2}$? — Objective 11-3, p. 424

4. Find the coordinates of the vertex of the graph of $y = 2x^2 + 4x - 5$. — Objective 11-4, p. 426

5. Is the *y*-coordinate of the vertex of the graph of $y = 2x^2 + 4x - 5$ the greatest or least value of *y*?

Check your answers with those printed at the back of the book.

Quadratic Equations

11-5 Quadratic Functions and Quadratic Equations

> **OBJECTIVE** To learn how quadratic equations are related to quadratic functions.

When the function

$$f: x \longrightarrow x^2$$

was graphed on page 416, x was given certain values, and corresponding values of y were computed.

What happens if we give values to y in $y = x^2$ and solve for x?

For example, let $y = 4$. Then: $4 = x^2$

By the method of Section 10-5 $x = \pm 2$.

Thus, $(-2, 4)$ and $(2, 4)$

are coordinates of the points in which the line with equation "$y = 4$" intersects the parabola (see Figure 11-7).

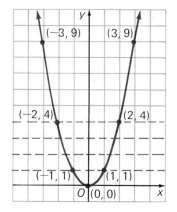

$$y = x^2$$

Figure 11-7

Other examples are:

$x^2 = 0$	$x^2 = 1$	$x^2 = 2$	$x^2 = 3$
$x = 0$	$x = \pm 1$	$x = \pm\sqrt{2}$	$x = \pm\sqrt{3}$
$(0, 0)$	$(-1, 1)(1, 1)$	$(-\sqrt{2}, 2)(\sqrt{2}, 2)$	$(-\sqrt{3}, 3)(\sqrt{3}, 3)$

In Section 11-4, we found the abscissa of the vertex of a parabola by finding the abscissas of the points in which the line with equation "$y = 0$" intersected a parabola with y-intercept equal to 0.

Now consider the function $f: x \longrightarrow x^2 - 4x + 3$ (page 426).

Let us give values to y in the equation $y = x^2 - 4x + 3$.

Let $y = 0$. Then we have the quadratic equation in one variable

$$x^2 - 4x + 3 = 0.$$

This equation can be solved by the factoring method given in Section 5-13:

$$x^2 - 4x + 3 = 0$$
$$(x - 1)(x - 3) = 0$$
$$x = 1 \text{ or } x = 3$$

Thus,
$$\textbf{(1, 0) and (3, 0)}$$

are the coordinates of the points where the parabola intersects the x-axis ($y = 0$).

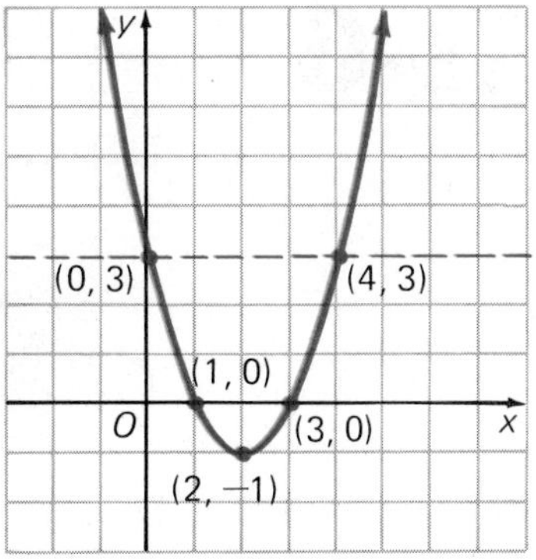

If we let $y = 3$, we obtain the equation

$$x^2 - 4x + 3 = 3$$

or

$$x^2 - 4x = 0$$

This can be solved by factoring:

$$x(x - 4) = 0$$
$$x = 0 \text{ or } x = 4$$

Thus,
$$\textbf{(0, 3) and (4, 3)}$$

are the coordinates of the points where the parabola intersects the line with equation "$y = 3$" (see Figure 11-8).

However, if we let $y = 2$, we obtain

$$x^2 - 4x + 3 = 2$$

or

$$x^2 - 4x + 1 = 0.$$

This equation cannot be solved by factoring using rational numbers. In the next few sections we shall learn how to solve such equations.

$$y = x^2 - 4x + 3$$

Figure 11-8

Written Exercises

Show the relationship between the quadratic function and the quadratic equation by graphing the quadratic function and marking the roots of the quadratic equation on the x-axis.

A 1. $y = 2x^2 - 6x$; $2x^2 - 6x = 0$

2. $y = x^2 - 3x$; $x^2 - 3x = 0$

3. $y = x^2 - 25$; $x^2 - 25 = 0$

4. $y = 4x^2 - 81$; $4x^2 - 81 = 0$

5. $y = x^2 + 3x - 4$; $x^2 + 3x - 4 = 0$

6. $y = x^2 - 2x - 15$; $x^2 - 2x - 15 = 0$

1. (0, 0) and (3, 0)

2. (0, 0) and (3, 0)

3. (5, 0) and (−5, 0)

4. $(\frac{9}{2}, 0)$ and $(-\frac{9}{2}, 0)$

5. (1, 0) and (−4, 0)

6. (5, 0) and (−3, 0)

11-6 More about Quadratic Equations

> **OBJECTIVE**   To learn how to solve quadratic equations that are in the form perfect square = constant.

In Chapter 5, certain quadratic equations were solved by factoring. But as was shown in Section 11-5, not all quadratic equations can be factored.

In Chapter 10, you learned how to solve quadratic equations of the form

$$x^2 = k.$$

In general:

> If $k > 0$, $x^2 = k$ has two real-number solutions: $x = \pm\sqrt{k}$
>
> If $k = 0$, $x^2 = k$ has one real-number solution: $x = 0$
>
> If $k < 0$, $x^2 = k$ has no real-number solutions.

The basic strategy in solving more general quadratic equations is to put them into the form

perfect square = constant

where by "perfect square" we mean the square of an expression, such as x^2, $(x - 2)^2$, $(3x + 4)^2$.

Example 1   Solve $x^2 - 18 = 0$.

Solution $x^2 - 18 = 0$

$$x^2 = 18 \quad \longleftarrow \text{ perfect square = constant}$$

$$x = \pm\sqrt{18}$$

$$x = \pm 3\sqrt{2} \quad \textit{Answer}$$

Example 2   Solve $3y^2 - 25 = 0$.

Solution $3y^2 = 25$

$$\longrightarrow \quad y^2 = \frac{25}{3}$$

$$y = \pm\sqrt{\frac{25}{3}} = \pm\frac{5}{\sqrt{3}}$$

$$y = \frac{\pm 5\sqrt{3}}{3} \quad \textit{Answer}$$

The perfect squares occurring in Examples 1 and 2 are x^2 and y^2.

In Examples 3 and 4, which follow, the perfect squares are $(x + 3)^2$ and $(y - 1)^2$.

Example 3 Solve $2(x + 3)^2 = 14$.

Solution $2(x + 3)^2 = 14$

$(x + 3)^2 = 7 \leftarrow$ perfect square = constant

$x + 3 = \pm\sqrt{7}$

$x = -3 \pm \sqrt{7}$ *Answer*

Example 4 Solve $y^2 - 2y + 1 = 16$.

Solution $y^2 - 2y + 1 = 16$

$\longrightarrow (y - 1)^2 = 16$

$y - 1 = \pm\sqrt{16}$

$y = 1 \pm 4$

$y = 5, -3$ *Answer*

Example 5 Solve $8s^2 + 1 = 0$.

Solution $8s^2 + 1 = 0$

$8s^2 = -1$

$s^2 = \dfrac{-1}{8} \leftarrow$ perfect square = negative constant

$\therefore$ there is no real-number solution.   *Answer*

Oral Exercises

Give the roots of each equation.

1. $x^2 = 1$ ± 1
2. $x^2 = 100$ ± 10
3. $x^2 = 7$ $\pm\sqrt{7}$
4. $x^2 = 8$ $\pm 2\sqrt{2}$
5. $x^2 = \dfrac{1}{9}$ $\pm\dfrac{1}{3}$
6. $4y^2 = 100$ ± 5
7. $5y^2 = 45$ ± 3
8. $r^2 - 4 = 0$ ± 2
9. $s^2 - 5 = 0$ $\pm\sqrt{5}$
10. $2t^2 - 6 = 0$ $\pm\sqrt{3}$
11. $49z^2 - 4 = 0$ $\pm\dfrac{2}{7}$
12. $49z^2 + 4 = 0$ $\emptyset$
13. $49z^2 = 0$ 0
14. $12y^2 - \dfrac{1}{3} = 0$ $\pm\dfrac{1}{6}$
15. $(x - 3)^2 = 1$ $2, 4$
16. $(x - 3)^2 = 0$ 3
17. $(x - 3)^2 = -1$ $\emptyset$
18. $(x - 2)^2 = 7$ $2 \pm \sqrt{7}$
19. $(x - 5)^2 = 6$ $5 \pm \sqrt{6}$
20. $(x + 3)^2 = 100$ $7, -13$
21. Challenge: Can you solve $x^2 - 2x + 1 = 7$? $(x - 1)^2 = 7; x = 1 \pm \sqrt{7}$

Written Exercises

Give the roots of each equation.

A
1. $x^2 = 4$ ± 2
2. $x^2 = 144$ ± 12
3. $4x^2 = 36$ ± 3
4. $5x^2 = 20$ ± 2
5. $\frac{1}{4}x^2 = 9$ ± 6
6. $x^2 = 11$ $\pm\sqrt{11}$
7. $3x^2 = 21$ $\pm\sqrt{7}$
8. $5y^2 = 40$ $\pm 2\sqrt{2}$

Give the roots of each equation.

9. $2y^2 = \frac{1}{8}$ $\pm\frac{1}{4}$
10. $3z^2 = 3.63$ ±1.1
11. $y^2 - 9 = 0$ ±3
12. $y^2 - 10 = 0$ $\pm\sqrt{10}$

13. $y^2 + 10 = 0$ $\emptyset$
14. $2r^2 - 50 = 0$ ±5
15. $3s^2 - 12 = 0$ ±2
16. $4t^2 - 24 = 0$ $\pm\sqrt{6}$

17. $7y^2 - 8 = 6$ $\pm\sqrt{2}$
18. $8x^2 + 7 = 23$ $\pm\sqrt{2}$
19. $3z^2 + 11 = 8$ $\emptyset$
20. $\frac{4}{9}z^2 - 1 = 0$ $\pm\frac{3}{2}$

21. $(x - 4)^2 = 34$ $\pm\sqrt{3}$
22. $(x - 5)^2 = 7$ $5 \pm \sqrt{7}$
23. $(r + 1)^2 = 2$ $-1 \pm \sqrt{2}$
24. $(s + 3)^2 = 6$ $-3 \pm$

25. $(t - 7)^2 = 16$ 11, 3
26. $2(x - 1)^2 = 34$ $1 \pm \sqrt{17}$
27. $3(z - 2)^2 = 27$ 5, -1
28. $5(y + 3)^2 = 80$ 1, $-$

B 29. $x^2 + 2x + 1 = 25$ 4, -6
30. $m^2 - 10m + 25 = 49$ 12, -2
31. $s^2 - 14s + 49 = 1$ 8, 6

32. $t^2 - 6t + 9 = 100$ 13, -7
33. $\frac{1}{2}y^2 - \frac{8}{9} = 0$ $\pm\frac{4}{3}$
34. $\frac{1}{2}z^2 - 4 = \frac{1}{2}$ ±3

35. $1.44y^2 + 2 = 2.81$ $\pm\frac{3}{4}$
36. $0.36z^2 - 1 = 0.44$ ±2
37. $7(x - 2)^2 = \frac{1}{7}$ $2\frac{1}{7}, 1\frac{6}{7}$

38. $2(x + 5)^2 = \frac{1}{8}$ $-4\frac{3}{4}, -5\frac{1}{4}$
39. $(x + \frac{1}{2})^2 = \frac{1}{2}$ $\frac{-1 \pm \sqrt{2}}{2}$
40. $(x - \frac{2}{3})^2 = \frac{1}{3}$ $\frac{2 \pm \sqrt{3}}{3}$

Solve each equation by factoring.

41. $5x^3 - 20x = 0$ $\{0, 2, -2\}$
42. $2x^3 - 18x = 0$ $\{0, 3, -3\}$
43. $7y - \frac{1}{7}y^3 = 0$ $\{0, 7, -7\}$

44. $\frac{1}{3}s^3 - 3s = 0$ $\{0, 3, -3\}$
45. $3z^3 = 27z$ $\{0, 3, -3\}$
46. $2t^3 = 8t$ $\{0, 2, -2\}$

Solve.

C 47. $3(2x - 5)^2 = 12$ $\{\frac{7}{2}, \frac{3}{2}\}$
48. $4(7x + 3)^2 + 9 = 1$ $\emptyset$
49. $x^2 - 2\sqrt{6}x + 6 = 0$ $\{\sqrt{ }$

50. How many real number solutions are there to the equation
$$a(x - b)^2 = c \text{ if}$$

a. $a > 0$ and $c > 0$? 2
b. $a > 0$ and $c = 0$? 1
c. $a > 0$ and $c < 0$? 0
d. $a < 0$ and $c < 0$? 2

Just for Fun ₒₒ OOOOO

You can see parabolas if you know where to look. The path of a projectile moving in a vacuum is a parabola, but drops of water in a fountain follow paths that are nearly parabolas (look at the picture of the Alhambra on page 19). The cables of a suspension bridge usually hang in the form of parabolas. (If you just hang a rope freely from two supports, it does not form a parabola—but another curve called a *catenary*.) The cross sections of the reflectors of some search lights are parabolas.

11-7 Completing the Square

> **OBJECTIVE** To learn how to "complete the square" and how to use the result to solve quadratic equations.

You have seen that it is always possible to solve a quadratic equation which has the form:

$$\text{perfect square} = \text{nonnegative constant}$$

If a quadratic equation does not have this form, it may be possible to transform it into one which does by a method called **completing the square**.

The main idea behind completing the square can be seen by analyzing the following perfect squares.

$$(x + 6)^2 = x^2 + 12x + 36 \qquad (x - 5)^2 = x^2 - 10x + 25 \qquad (x + a)^2 = x^2 + 2ax + a^2$$

$$\left(\frac{12}{2}\right)^2 = 36 \qquad\qquad \left(\frac{-10}{2}\right)^2 = 25 \qquad\qquad \left(\frac{2a}{2}\right)^2 = a^2$$

Notice that in each case the constant term is the square of half the coefficient of x. This observation gives us the following:

> ### Method of Completing the Square
>
> For $x^2 + bx + \underline{\ ?\ }$:
> 1. Find half the coefficient of x.
> 2. Square the result of Step 1.
> 3. Add the result of Step 2 to $x^2 + bx$.

Example 1 Complete the square:

$$x^2 - 14x + \underline{\ ?\ }$$

Solution $x^2 - 14x + 49 = (x - 7)^2$

$$\left(\frac{-14}{2}\right)^2 = 49$$

Example 2 Complete the square:

$$x^2 + 3x + \underline{\ ?\ }$$

Solution $x^2 + 3x + \dfrac{9}{4} = \left(x + \dfrac{3}{2}\right)^2$

$$\left(\frac{3}{2}\right)^2 = \frac{9}{4}$$

Example 3   Solve $x^2 + 12x + 32 = 0$ by completing the square.

Solution $\qquad\qquad\qquad\qquad\qquad x^2 + 12x + 32 = 0$

1. Subtract 32 from both members: $\qquad x^2 + 12x \qquad = -32$

2. Complete the square by adding ($\frac{1}{2}$ coefficient of x)^2 to *both* members:
$$x^2 + 12x + \left(\frac{12}{2}\right)^2 = -32 + \left(\frac{12}{2}\right)^2$$

3. Proceed as in Section 11-6:
$$x^2 + 12x + 36 = -32 + 36$$
$$(x + 6)^2 = 4$$
$$x + 6 = \pm\sqrt{4} = \pm 2$$
$$x = -6 \pm 2$$

4. The check is left for you. $\qquad\qquad\qquad x = -4 \text{ or } -8$

$\therefore$ the solution set is $\{-4, -8\}$. **Answer**

$(-4)^2 + 12(-4) + 32 = 16 - 48 + 32 = 0;\ (-8)^2 + 12(-8) + 32 = 64 - 96 + 32 = 0\ \checkmark$

Example 4   Solve $2x^2 + 3x - 4 = 0$ by completing the square.

Solution   In order to complete the square, it is first necessary to divide both members by 2 so the coefficient of x^2 will be 1. This gives

$$x^2 + \frac{3}{2}x - 2 = 0$$

Now proceed as in Example 3.

$$x^2 + \frac{3}{2}x \qquad = 2 \qquad\qquad\qquad \left(x + \frac{3}{4}\right)^2 = \frac{41}{16}$$

$$x^2 + \frac{3}{2}x + \left(\frac{3}{4}\right)^2 = 2 + \left(\frac{3}{4}\right)^2 \qquad x + \frac{3}{4} = \pm\sqrt{\frac{41}{16}} = \frac{\pm\sqrt{41}}{4}$$

$$x^2 + \frac{3}{2}x + \frac{9}{16} = 2 + \frac{9}{16} \qquad\quad x = \frac{-3}{4} \pm \frac{\sqrt{41}}{4} = \frac{-3 \pm \sqrt{41}}{4}$$

For computational purposes, you may need decimal approximations of these roots. To approximate them to the nearest tenth, use a two-place approximation of $\sqrt{41}$ from the table at the back of the book.

$$x = \frac{-3 + \sqrt{41}}{4} \doteq \frac{-3 + 6.40}{4} = \frac{3.40}{4} = 0.85 \doteq 0.9$$

$$x = \frac{-3 - \sqrt{41}}{4} \doteq \frac{-3 - 6.40}{4} = \frac{-9.40}{4} = -2.35 \doteq -2.4$$

$\therefore$ the roots to the nearest tenth are 0.9 and -2.4. **Answer**

Oral Exercises

Complete the square.

1. $x^2 + 6x +$ _?_ $= (x +$ _?_ $)^2$ 9; 3

2. $x^2 + 4x +$ _?_ $= (x +$ _?_ $)^2$ 4; 2

3. $x^2 - 18x +$ _?_ $= (x -$ _?_ $)^2$ 81; 9

4. $y^2 - 8y +$ _?_ $= (y -$ _?_ $)^2$ 16; 4

5. $y^2 + 5y +$ _?_ $= (y +$ _?_ $)^2$ $\frac{25}{4}$; $\frac{5}{2}$

6. $z^2 - 3z +$ _?_ $= (z -$ _?_ $)^2$ $\frac{9}{4}$; $\frac{3}{2}$

7. $x^2 + 1.4x +$ _?_ $= (x +$ _?_ $)^2$ 0.49; 0.7

8. $t^2 - 2.2t +$ _?_ $= (t -$ _?_ $)^2$ 1.21; 1.1

9. $y^2 + \frac{2}{3}y +$ _?_ $= (y +$ _?_ $)^2$ $\frac{1}{9}$; $\frac{1}{3}$

10. $x^2 - x +$ _?_ $= (x -$ _?_ $)^2$ $\frac{1}{4}$; $\frac{1}{2}$

What is the *first* step that you would use to solve the following equations by the method of completing the square?

11. $x^2 + 10x - 3 = 0$ Add 3 to both sides.

12. $3x^2 - 12x = -1$ Divide both sides by 3.

Written Exercises

Answers on page A4 at the back of the book.

Solve by completing the square. Give irrational roots in simplest radical form and also approximate them to the nearest tenth.

A 1. $x^2 - 2x = 35$

2. $x^2 + 6x = 91$

3. $x^2 - 4x = 45$

4. $x^2 - 12x = 1$

5. $y^2 - 8y = 14$

6. $y^2 + 10y - 7 = 0$

7. $z^2 + 2z - 143 = 0$

8. $z^2 + 6z - 836 = 0$

9. $x^2 + x = 3$

10. $y^2 + 5y = 1$

11. $2x^2 - 8x = 5$

12. $3x^2 + 12x = 7$

13. $2x^2 - 10x - 1 = 0$

14. $3y^2 - 9y - 2 = 0$

15. $2r^2 = r + 2$

16. $4s^2 = 1 + 2s$

Solve the equations in Exercises 17–22 by two methods:
a. factoring; and b. completing the square.

17. $x^2 - 12x + 35 = 0$ {7, 5}

18. $x^2 + 4x - 77 = 0$ {−11, 7}

19. $x^2 - 6x - 16 = 0$ {8, −2}

20. $2x^2 + x - 1 = 0$ {$\frac{1}{2}$, −1}

21. $3x^2 + x - 10 = 0$ {$\frac{5}{3}$, −2}

22. $5x^2 = 10x + 495$ {11, −9}

Solve by factoring or by completing the square. Give irrational roots in simplest radical form.

B 23. $\frac{1}{4}s^2 = s + 3$ {6, −2}

24. $x^2 - 1 = \frac{4}{3}x$ $\left\{ \frac{2 \pm \sqrt{13}}{3} \right\}$

25. $\frac{1}{3}r^2 + \frac{2}{3}r = 3$ $\left\{ \frac{3}{2}, -6 \right\}$

26. $x - 2 = \frac{5 + x}{6x}$ $\left\{ -\frac{1}{3}, \frac{5}{2} \right\}$

27. $5x = \frac{1 - 3x}{x - 1}$ $\left\{ \frac{1 \pm \sqrt{6}}{5} \right\}$

28. $x - \frac{1}{2} = \frac{3}{x}$ $\left\{ 2, -\frac{3}{2} \right\}$

29. $y + \frac{2y}{y + 1} = 1$ {−1 ± $\sqrt{2}$}

30. $3r = \frac{r + 2}{r - \frac{1}{2}}$ $\left\{ \frac{2 \pm \sqrt{10}}{3} \right\}$

Solve for x in terms of a, b, and c.

C 31. $x^2 - 2x + c = 0$ $x = 1 \pm \sqrt{1 - c}$

32. $x^2 - bx + 1 = 0$ $x = \frac{b \pm \sqrt{b^2 - 4}}{2}$

33. $x^2 + bx + c = 0$ $x = \frac{-b \pm \sqrt{b^2 - 4c}}{2}$

34. $ax^2 + bx + c = 0$ $x = \frac{-b \pm \sqrt{b^2 - 4ac}}{2a}$

11-8 The Quadratic Formula

OBJECTIVE To learn the quadratic formula and how to use it to solve quadratic equations.

In the preceding section you learned how to solve an equation like

$$3x^2 - 7x + 1 = 0$$

by completing the square. The very same method can be used to solve the standard quadratic equation

$$ax^2 + bx + c = 0.$$

$$3x^2 - 7x + 1 = 0 \qquad\qquad ax^2 + bx + c = 0$$

$$x^2 - \frac{7}{3}x + \frac{1}{3} = 0 \qquad\qquad x^2 + \frac{b}{a}x + \frac{c}{a} = 0 \quad (a \neq 0)$$

$$x^2 - \frac{7}{3}x = -\frac{1}{3} \qquad\qquad x^2 + \frac{b}{a}x = -\frac{c}{a}$$

$$x^2 - \frac{7}{3}x + \left(\frac{7}{6}\right)^2 = -\frac{1}{3} + \left(\frac{7}{6}\right)^2 \qquad x^2 + \frac{b}{a}x + \left(\frac{b}{2a}\right)^2 = -\frac{c}{a} + \left(\frac{b}{2a}\right)^2$$

$$\left(x - \frac{7}{6}\right)^2 = -\frac{1}{3} + \frac{49}{36} \qquad\qquad \left(x + \frac{b}{2a}\right)^2 = -\frac{c}{a} + \frac{b^2}{4a^2}$$

$$\left(x - \frac{7}{6}\right)^2 = \frac{37}{36} \qquad\qquad \left(x + \frac{b}{2a}\right)^2 = \frac{b^2 - 4ac}{4a^2}$$

$$x - \frac{7}{6} = \pm\sqrt{\frac{37}{36}} \qquad\qquad x + \frac{b}{2a} = \pm\sqrt{\frac{b^2 - 4ac}{4a^2}} \quad \text{(If } b^2 - 4ac \geq 0)$$

$$x = \frac{7}{6} \pm \sqrt{\frac{37}{36}} \qquad\qquad x = -\frac{b}{2a} \pm \sqrt{\frac{b^2 - 4ac}{4a^2}}$$

$$x = \frac{7}{6} \pm \frac{\sqrt{37}}{6} \qquad\qquad x = -\frac{b}{2a} \pm \frac{\sqrt{b^2 - 4ac}}{2a}$$

$$x = \frac{7 \pm \sqrt{37}}{6} \qquad\qquad x = \frac{-b \pm \sqrt{b^2 - 4ac}}{2a}$$

The last equation in the preceding proof is called the *quadratic formula*. It gives the roots of $ax^2 + bx + c = 0$ in terms of the coefficients a, b, and c. In developing the quadratic formula, notice the assumptions that $a \neq 0$ and that $b^2 - 4ac \geq 0$.

> ### The Quadratic Formula
>
> If $ax^2 + bx + c = 0,$ $a \neq 0,$ and $b^2 - 4ac \geq 0,$
>
> then $x = \dfrac{-b \pm \sqrt{b^2 - 4ac}}{2a}.$

Example Solve $3x^2 - 7x + 1 = 0$ by using the quadratic formula.

Solution $3x^2 - 7x + 1 = 0$

$$x = \frac{-b \pm \sqrt{b^2 - 4ac}}{2a} \quad \text{where } a = 3, b = -7, c = 1$$

$$x = \frac{-(-7) \pm \sqrt{(-7)^2 - 4(3)(1)}}{2(3)} = \frac{7 \pm \sqrt{49 - 12}}{6} = \frac{7 \pm \sqrt{37}}{6}$$

$\therefore$ the solution set is $\left\{ \dfrac{7 + \sqrt{37}}{6}, \dfrac{7 - \sqrt{37}}{6} \right\}.$ *Answer*

Notice that this answer obtained by using the formula agrees with the one on the previous page obtained by completing the square. This, of course, is what you would expect since the quadratic formula was derived by completing the square.

Oral Exercises

State the values of a, b, and c for each equation.

1. $2x^2 + 9x + 4 = 0$ 2, 9, 4
2. $3x^2 - 7x + 5 = 0$ 3, −7, 5
3. $5x^2 + x - 3 = 0$ 5, 1, −3
4. $7x^2 - 3x = 1$ 7, −3, −1
5. $3y^2 - 8y = 1$ 3, −8, −1
6. $2y^2 = 5 + y$ 2, −1, −5
7. $3z^2 = 8 - z$ 3, 1, −8
8. $5 - y^2 = 2y$ −1, −2, 5
9. $x^2 = 5x$ 1, −5, 0
10. $3x^2 - 7 = 0$ 3, 0, −7
11. $0 = y - 6y^2$ 6, −1, 0
12. $7x^2 = 0$ 7, 0, 0

Written Exercises

Answers on page A4 at the back of the book.

Use the quadratic formula to solve each equation. Give irrational roots in simplest radical form and also approximate them to the nearest tenth.

A
1. $x^2 + 3x + 1 = 0$
2. $x^2 + 2x - 1 = 0$
3. $x^2 + 6x + 7 = 0$
4. $2x^2 - 3x - 2 = 0$
5. $3y^2 - 7y - 3 = 0$
6. $5y^2 - 8y - 2 = 0$
7. $4y^2 = 3 - 5y$
8. $t^2 = 3t + 6$
9. $5 = 9s - 3s^2$
10. $5r^2 = 1 + 6r$
11. $2 = 11z - 5z^2$
12. $12x^2 = 5 - 6x$

Solve each of the following equations   **a.** by inspection; and   **b.** by the quadratic formula.

13. $(x + 3)^2 = 0$ $\{-3\}$ 14. $(2x - 5)^2 = 0$ $\{2.5\}$ 15. $y^2 - y = 0$ $\{0, 1\}$

16. $3y^2 = 12$ $\{\pm 2\}$ 17. $(z - 7)^2 = 3$ $\{7 \pm \sqrt{3}\}$ 18. $(z - 2)^2 = 5$ $\{2 \pm \sqrt{5}\}$

Solve by using the quadratic formula. Leave irrational
roots in simplest radical form.

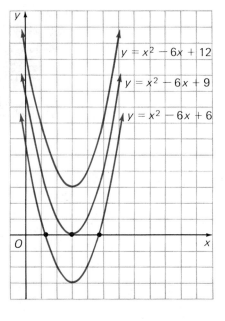

$y = x^2 - 6x + 12$

$y = x^2 - 6x + 9$

$y = x^2 - 6x + 6$

B 19. $\dfrac{2}{x} - \dfrac{1}{3x + 4} = \dfrac{1}{4}$ $\left\{\dfrac{8 \pm 4\sqrt{10}}{3}\right\}$

20. $\dfrac{2x}{x + 1} - \dfrac{x + 1}{x} = 0$ $\{1 \pm \sqrt{2}\}$

21. $4x = \dfrac{2.75}{x + 1}$ $\left\{\dfrac{-2 \pm \sqrt{15}}{4}\right\}$

22. $\dfrac{3}{x - 1} - \dfrac{x - 4}{x - 3} = 1$ $\{4, 2\}$

The diagram at the right shows the graphs of three quadratic functions whose equations are:

(1) $y = x^2 - 6x + 6$
(2) $y = x^2 - 6x + 9$
(3) $y = x^2 - 6x + 12$

The abscissas of the points of intersection with the x-axis (x-intercepts) are
found by setting $y = 0$ and solving the resulting equations:

Case 1	Case 2	Case 3
$0 = x^2 - 6x + 6$	$0 = x^2 - 6x + 9$	$0 = x^2 - 6x + 12$
$x = \dfrac{6 \pm \sqrt{36 - 24}}{2}$	$x = \dfrac{6 \pm \sqrt{36 - 36}}{2}$	$x = \dfrac{6 \pm \sqrt{36 - 48}}{2}$
$x = \dfrac{6 \pm \sqrt{12}}{2}$	$x = \dfrac{6 \pm \sqrt{0}}{2}$	Since $36 - 48 = -12$ and $-12 < 0$, there is no solution.
$x \doteq 4.7$ and 1.2	$x = 3$	
two x-intercepts	*one x-intercept*	$\therefore$ *no x-intercept.*
$b^2 - 4ac > 0$	$b^2 - 4ac = 0$	$b^2 - 4ac < 0$

In general:

	Value of $b^2 - 4ac$	Number of different real roots of $ax^2 + bx + c = 0$	Number of x-intercepts of the graph of $y = ax^2 + bx + c$
Case 1	positive	2	2
Case 2	zero	1 (a double root)	1
Case 3	negative	0	0

Because the value of $b^2 - 4ac$ distinguishes (or discriminates) between these
three cases, it is called the **discriminant** of the quadratic equation.

Give the value of the discriminant of each equation. Then tell how many
real roots the equation has.

23. $x^2 + 3x - 5 = 0$ 29; 2
24. $x^2 - x + 3 = 0$ -11; none
25. $3x^2 - 5x - 1 = 0$

26. $2x^2 - 8x + 8 = 0$ 0; 1
27. $x^2 - 5x + 2 = 0$ 17; 2
28. $x^2 + 4x + 9 = 0$

29. $2x^2 - 3x - 2 = 0$ 25; 2
30. $\frac{1}{2}x^2 - 2x + 2 = 0$ 0; 1
31. $3y^2 - y + 1 = 0$

32. $-4y^2 - 5y + 4 = 0$ 89; 2
33. $2t^2 - 12t + 18 = 0$ 0; 1
34. $\frac{1}{3}t^2 + 2t + 3 = 0$

35. Suppose that a, b, and c are integers such that $b^2 - 4ac$ is the square
of a rational number. Explain why the roots of the quadratic equation
$ax^2 + bx + c = 0$ must be rational numbers.

25. 37; 2
28. -20; none
31. -11; none
34. 0; 1

36. Suppose that a, b, and c are integers such that $b^2 - 4ac$ is not the square
of a rational number. Explain why the roots of $ax^2 + bx + c = 0$ must
be irrational numbers.

Answers to Exs. 35 and 36 on page A4 at the back of the book.

Computer Activity

You can use the computer to determine the real
roots of any equation of the form $ax^2 + bx + c = 0$
($a \neq 0$). Depending on the value of the discriminant,
a quadratic equation has either two different real
roots, one double real root, or no real roots.

The flow chart at the right illustrates the steps
followed by the computer. If you have access
to a computer that will accept BASIC, study the
flow chart and then try this program:

```
10   PRINT "INPUT A (NOT ZERO), B, C";
20   INPUT A,B,C
30   IF A=0 THEN 10
40   LET D=B*B-4*A*C
50   IF D<0 THEN 130
60   LET E=-B/(2*A)
70   IF D=0 THEN 110
80   LET D1=SQR(D)/(2*A)
90   PRINT "THE ROOTS ARE ";E-D1;", ";E+D1
100  STOP
110  PRINT "THE ROOT IS ";E
120  STOP
130  PRINT "NO REAL ROOTS"
140  END
```

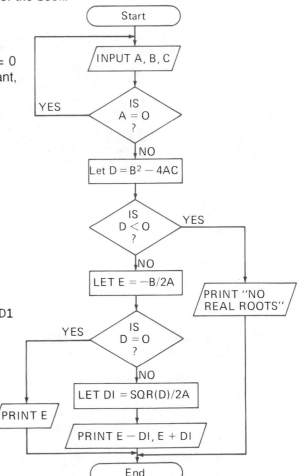

11-9 Using Quadratic Equations to Solve Problems

OBJECTIVE To learn how to use quadratic equations to solve problems.

In the Example and Exercises of this section you will have a chance to solve a variety of problems leading to quadratic equations. For each equation, you have a choice of using one of the methods listed below.

> Methods for Solving a Quadratic Equation
>
> 1. Factoring.
> 2. Using the property of square roots of equal numbers (p. 392).
> 3. Completing the square.
> 4. Using the quadratic formula.

Here are some general rules to guide you in selecting a method for solving a quadratic equation

$$ax^2 + bx + c = 0.$$

1. The quadratic formula can *always* be used, but sometimes another method may be easier.

2. The completing-the-square method can *always* be used, but it probably should be avoided unless the equation has the form

$$x^2 + (\text{even number})x + \text{constant} = 0.$$

3. If $b = 0$ (as in $2x^2 - 9 = 0$), use the property of square roots of equal numbers.

4. If $c = 0$ (as in $5x^2 + 3x = 0$) or if factors are easily seen, use factoring.

Example A rectangular picture is 5 centimeters longer than it is wide, and the picture has a 2-centimeter frame as shown in the diagram. If the area of the picture is half of the total area, what are the dimensions of the frame?

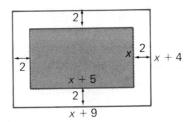

Solution

Step 1 The problem asks for the dimensions of the frame.

Step 2 Let x = the width of the picture. Then the remaining dimensions are as shown in the diagram.

Step 3 The area of the picture is half of the total area.

$$x(x + 5) \doteq \frac{1}{2} \cdot (x + 4)(x + 9)$$

Step 4
$$x^2 + 5x = \frac{1}{2}(x^2 + 13x + 36)$$
$$2x^2 + 10x = x^2 + 13x + 36$$
$$x^2 - 3x - 36 = 0$$

Using the quadratic formula:

$$x = \frac{-(-3) \pm \sqrt{(-3)^2 - 4 \cdot 1(-36)}}{2 \cdot 1} = \frac{3 \pm \sqrt{153}}{2} \doteq \frac{3 \pm 12.4}{2}$$

$x \doteq 7.7$ or -4.7

Step 5 *Check:* $x \doteq -4.7$ clearly does not satisfy the original problem.

If $x \doteq 7.7$, then the dimensions of the picture are approximately 7.7 and 12.7, and the dimensions of the frame are approximately 11.7 and 16.7.

The area of the picture = $\frac{1}{2}$ (total area).

$$(7.7)(12.7) \overset{?}{=} \frac{1}{2}(11.7)(16.7)$$

$$97.8 \overset{?}{=} \frac{1}{2}(195.39)$$

$$97.8 \doteq 97.7 \checkmark$$

The check is approximate since the solution is approximate.

∴ the dimensions of the frame to the nearest tenth are 11.7 cm and 16.7 cm. *Answer*

Oral Exercises

For each of the following equations, tell which method seems to you the easiest method of solving.

1. $x^2 - 12x + 35 = 0$ factoring
2. $x^2 - 6x = 91$ factoring
3. $2x^2 - 5x - 9 = 0$ quadr formu

4. $x^2 - 10x - 4 = 0$ completing the square
5. $3x^2 - 7x - 6 = 0$ quadratic formula
6. $x^2 - 2x - 1599 = 0$ completi the squa

Written Exercises

A 1-6. Solve the quadratic equations given in Oral Exercises 1-6. Give irrational answers to the nearest tenth.
1. $\{5, 7\}$ 2. $\{13, -7\}$ 3. $\{3.7, -1.2\}$
4. $\{10.4, -0.4\}$ 5. $\{3, -\frac{2}{3}\}$ 6. $\{41, -39\}$

Solve by the most efficient method. Leave your answers in simplest radical form.

7. $2(x - 5)^2 = 12$ $\{5 \pm \sqrt{6}\}$
8. $x^2 - 12x = 30$ $\{6 \pm \sqrt{66}\}$
9. $2x^2 - x - 1 = 0$ $\{-\frac{1}{2}, 1\}$

10. $3x^2 - 11x = 7$ $\left\{\dfrac{11 \pm \sqrt{205}}{6}\right\}$
11. $5x^2 - 50x - 500 = 0$ $\{5 \pm 5\sqrt{5}\}$
12. $ax^2 + bx = 0$ $\left\{0, -\dfrac{b}{a}\right\}$

B 13. Show that the equation $4x^4 - 13x^2 + 9 = 0$ has four real roots. (Hint: Substitute y for x^2 so that the equation becomes $4y^2 - 13y + 9 = 0$.)

14. Show that the equation $x^4 - 8x^2 - 9 = 0$ has only two real roots. (See hint for Exercise 13.)

13. $4y^2 - 13y + 9 = 0$; $(4y - 9)(y - 1) = 0$; $y = \frac{9}{4}$ or 1, so $x = \pm\frac{3}{2}$ or ± 1.
14. If $y = x^2$, $y^2 - 8y - 9 = 0$; $(y - 9)(y + 1) = 0$; $y = 9$ or -1, so $x^2 = 9$ or -1, and the only real roots are ± 3.

Problems

Give irrational answers to the nearest tenth, and reject inappropriate roots.

A 1. Find two integers whose sum is 11 and whose squares differ by 55. **8 and 3**

2. Find two integers which differ by 8 and whose product is -15. **5 and -3, or 3 and -5**

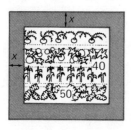

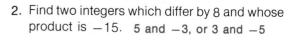

3 m

4 m

3. A rectangular garden measures 50 meters by 40 meters. How wide must a concrete walk of uniform width around the garden be if the walk is to cover an area of 784 square meters? **4 m**

4. A billboard measures 3 meters by 4 meters. A border of uniform width is painted around the outer edges of the board in black paint. How wide is the border if it covers half the area of the billboard? **$\frac{1}{2}$ m**

5. Alice and Bobby Jo live 15 kilometers apart. The diagram shows that Alice lives north of the school and Bobby Jo lives east of the school. If Bobby Jo is 3 kilometers further from the school than Alice, how far is each from the school? **Alice: 9 km; Bobby Jo: 12 km**

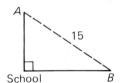

6. Suzanne sailed her boat 6 kilometers across Lake Frazar and then sailed back. If her rate returning was 2 kilometers per hour less than her rate going, and if the entire trip took $2\frac{1}{2}$ hours, what was her rate each way? (Hint: time = distance ÷ rate.) **6 km/h, 4 km/h**

7. Jack rode a bicycle 16 kilometers and then walked for 4 kilometers. If his rate riding was 6 kilometers per hour greater than his rate walking, and if the entire trip took 4 hours, what was his rate walking? **2 km/h**

Extra for Experts ExtraExtraExtraExtraExtraEx
Quadratic Inequalities

The graph of $y = x^2 - 3x - 4$ can be used to illustrate the solutions of:

(1) $x^2 - 3x - 4 < 0$
(2) $x^2 - 3x - 4 = 0$
(3) $x^2 - 3x - 4 > 0$

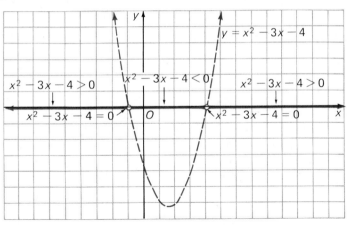

The solution set of the quadratic equation (2) is $\{-1, 4\}$. These two values of x are called the *zeros* of the quadratic function.

To solve inequality (3), we reason as follows:

a. If (x, y) is on the graph, then $y = x^2 - 3x - 4$.
b. If (x, y) is *above* the x-axis, then $y > 0$.
c. ∴ if (x, y) is on the graph *and* above the x-axis, then $y = x^2 - 3x - 4 > 0$.
d. ∴ the solution set for (3) is

$$\{\text{all real numbers less than } -1 \text{ or greater than } 4\}$$

because these values of x give points that are on the graph and above the x-axis.

Similar reasoning shows that the solution set for (1) is

$$\{\text{all real numbers between } -1 \text{ and } 4\}$$

because these values of x give points on the graph and *below* the x-axis.

Example Use the graph of

$$y = x^2 + 4x + 4$$

to solve the inequalities

(1) $x^2 + 4x + 4 > 0$

and

(2) $x^2 + 4x + 4 < 0$.

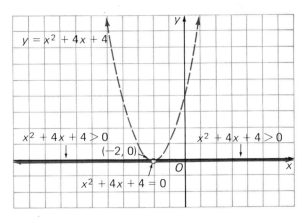

Solution Since the graph lies above the x-axis for all x except -2, we have $x^2 + 4x + 4 > 0$ for all $x \neq -2$. Do you see that there are no values of x for which $x^2 + 4x + 4 < 0$, since the graph does not go below the x-axis?

Graph each equation and mark the sections of the x-axis which correspond to $y = 0$, $y > 0$, and $y < 0$.

1. $y = x^2 - 4$
2. $y = 4 - x^2$
3. $y = x^2 + 3x$
4. $y = x^2 - 6x + 8$
5. $y = x^2 - 3x - 10$
6. $y = 2x^2 + x - 3$

Find the values of x for which each expression represents a real number.

7. $\sqrt{x^2 + 6x}$ $x \leq -6$ or $x \geq 0$
8. $\sqrt{x^2 - 5x + 6}$ $x \geq -2$ or $x \leq -3$

★ *Self-Test 2*

Be sure that you understand these terms:

completing the square (p. 435)   quadratic formula (p. 439)
x-intercept (p. 440)   discriminant (p. 440)

1. Graph $y = 2x^2 - 3x - 9$ and solve $2x^2 - 3x - 9 = 0$ by factoring.   Objective 11-5, p. 430

Give the roots of each equation.

2. $3x^2 - 15 = 0$ 3. $3(x - 15)^2 = 0$ Objective 11-6, p. 432

Complete the square.

4. $x^2 + 6x + \underline{} = (x + \underline{})^2$ 5. $x^2 - 9x + \underline{} = (x - \underline{})^2$ Objective 11-7, p. 435

6. Solve $x^2 - 12x - 9 = 0$ by completing the square. Leave your answer in simplest radical form.

7. State the quadratic formula.   Objective 11-8, p. 438

8. Use the quadratic formula to find the roots of $3x^2 - 2x = 7$ to the nearest tenth.

For each equation give its discriminant and tell how many real roots the equation has.

9. $x^2 - 5x - 7 = 0$

10. $3x^2 - 5x = 0$

11. $2x^2 - 3x + 5 = 0$

12. $x^2 - 3x + \frac{9}{4} = 0$

13. A rectangle is 4 centimeters longer than it is wide. If its area is 20 square centimeters, find its width to the nearest tenth of a centimeter. **Objective 11-9, p. 442**

Check your answers with those printed at the back of the book.

Chapter Summary

1. Several functions have been defined in this chapter, each having the set of real numbers as domain, except as noted.
   a. A quadratic function is defined by an equation of the form

   $$y = ax^2 + bx + c, a \neq 0.$$

   b. A quadratic direct variation is a special kind of quadratic function defined by an equation of the form

   $$y = kx^2, k \neq 0.$$

   c. An inverse variation is a function defined by an equation of the form

   $$y = \frac{k}{x}, k \neq 0, x \neq 0.$$

   d. An inverse variation as the square is a function defined by an equation of the form

   $$y = \frac{k}{x^2}, k \neq 0, x \neq 0.$$

2. When y is given a value in $y = ax^2 + bx + c, a \neq 0$, a quadratic equation in x is formed.

3. a. A quadratic equation can always be solved by completing the square or by using the quadratic formula.
   b. Some quadratic equations can be solved more easily by factoring or by using the property of square roots of equal numbers.
   c. The discriminant, $b^2 - 4ac$, gives information about the roots:
   If $b^2 - 4ac > 0$, there are two real roots.
   If $b^2 - 4ac = 0$, there is one (double) real root.
   If $b^2 - 4ac < 0$, there are no real roots.

Chapter Test

11-1   1. Graph $y = 2x^2$.

2. Complete the following sentence to describe $A = \pi r^2$ in the language of variation: A varies __?__   **directly as the square of r**

11-2   3. For every nonzero value of k, the graph of "$xy = k$" is called a __?__.   **hyperbola**

4. If a varies inversely as b, and $a = \frac{1}{2}$ when $b = 12$, find a when $b = 18$. $a = \frac{1}{3}$

11-3   5. Write an equation to describe "y varies inversely as the square of x." $y = \frac{k}{x^2}$

11-4   6. Find the coordinates of the vertex of the graph of "$y = 3x^2 + 7$."   **(0, 7)**

7. When $y = -4x^2 + 2x - 3$, does y have a greatest or a least value?   **greatest**

11-5   8. Graph "$y = x^2 - 4$" and solve "$x^2 - 4 = 0$."   **{±2}**

Solve, using the property of square roots of equal numbers.

11-6   9. $2x^2 = 162$ **{±9}**   10. $3y^2 - 36 = 0$ **{±2√3}**

11. $(x + 3)^2 = 49$ **{4, −10}**   12. $4(z - 5)^2 = 100$ **{10, 0}**

11-7   13. Complete the square: $x^2 - 12x + $ __?__ $= (x - $ __?__ $)^2$ **36; 6**

14. Solve by completing the square: $x^2 + 14x - 851 = 0$ **{23, −37}**

Solve by using the quadratic formula. Express irrational answers in simplest radical form and also to the nearest tenth.

11-8   15. $3y^2 - 6y + 2 = 0$ $\left\{\dfrac{3 \pm \sqrt{3}}{3}\right\}$ or **{1.6, 0.4}** 16. $10t^2 = 3 + t$ $\{\frac{3}{5}, -\frac{1}{2}\}$

For each equation give its discriminant and tell how many real roots the equation has.

17. $4x^2 - 20x + 25 = 0$ **0; 1**   18. $3x^2 - 7x + 5 = 0$ **−11; none**

11-9   19. Art and Bill hike away from camp at the same time, Art traveling north and Bill traveling west. Bill hikes 1 km/h faster than Art and at the end of 5 hours they are 25 kilometers apart. How fast does Bill hike?   **4 km/h**

Programmed Chapter Review

11-1　　1. An equation that describes "y varies directly as the square of x" is "$y = $ _?_."

kx^2

2. If a varies directly as the square of b and $a = 32$ when $b = 4$, find b when $a = 18$. (Assume that $b > 0$.)

3

11-2　　3. If y varies inversely as x, and $y = 3$ when $x = 21$, then when $x = 14$, $y = $ _?_.

$\dfrac{9}{2}$ or 4.5

4. In giving a party, Suzanne found that if she invited 12 persons, she could spend \$4 per person on refreshments. If she invited 4 additional persons, then for the same total cost she could only spend _?_ per person.

\$3

11-3　　5. The equation "$y = \dfrac{k}{x^2}$" means that "y varies _?_ as x^2."

inversely

6. In "$y = \dfrac{k}{x^2}$" if x is doubled, then y _?_.

is multiplied by $\dfrac{1}{4}$

11-4　　7. The graph of "$y = 3x^2 - 2x$" opens _?_ (upward/downward).

upward

8. When a parabola opens downward, the corresponding function has a _?_ value.

maximum

11-5　　9. "$y = 2x^2 - 3x + 4$" defines a quadratic _?_.

function

10. "$2x^2 - 3x + 4 = 0$" is a quadratic _?_.

equation

11-6　　11. How many real-number solutions are there for the equation $x^2 = k$ if

　　　　a. $k > 0$?　　　　b. $k = 0$?　　　　c. $k < 0$?

2, 1, none

Solve.

12. $2x^2 - 16 = 0$

$\{2\sqrt{2}, -2\sqrt{2}\}$

13. $(t - 7)^2 = 36$

$\{1, 13\}$

Complete the square:

11-7　　14. $x^2 + 8x + $ _?_ $= (x + $ _?_ $)^2$

16, 4

15. $x^2 - 5x + $ _?_ $= (x + $ _?_ $)^2$

$\dfrac{25}{4}, -\dfrac{5}{2}$

Solve by completing the square. Express irrational answers in simplest radical form and also to the nearest tenth.

16. $x^2 - 10x - 20 = 0$

$\{5 + 3\sqrt{5}, 5 - 3\sqrt{5}\}$
$\{11.7, -1.7\}$

17. $y^2 + 3y + 1 = 0$

$\left\{\dfrac{-3 + \sqrt{5}}{2}, \dfrac{-3 - \sqrt{5}}{2}\right\}$
$\{-0.4, -2.6\}$

11-8   18. State the quadratic formula.

$x = \dfrac{-b \pm \sqrt{b^2 - 4ac}}{2a}$

19. The quadratic formula is derived by using the __?__ method on the equation __?__ $= 0$.

completing the square
$ax^2 + bx + c$

Solve by using the quadratic formula. Express irrational answers in simplest radical form and also to the nearest tenth.

20. $2x^2 + 4x - 1 = 0$

$\left\{\dfrac{-2 + \sqrt{6}}{2}, \dfrac{-2 - \sqrt{6}}{2}\right\}$
$\{0.2, -2.2\}$

21. $3x^2 - 7x + 4 = 0$

$\left\{\dfrac{4}{3}, 1\right\}, \{1.3, 1\}$

Give the discriminant of each equation. Then tell how many real roots the equation has.

22. $5x^2 - 6x + 2 = 0$

-4, no real roots

23. $3x^2 - 5x - 1 = 0$

37, two real roots

24. The graph of $y = ax^2 + bx + c$ is shown at the right. What is the value of $b^2 - 4ac$?

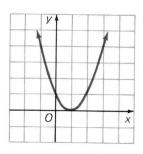

0

11-9   25. The area of a rectangle is 28 square centimeters. If it is 3 centimeters longer than it is wide, what are its dimensions?

4 cm, 7 cm

26. A rectangular picture 12 centimeters by 9 centimeters is mounted so that there is a border of uniform width all around the outside of the picture. Find the width of this border if its area is $\frac{2}{3}$ the area of the picture.

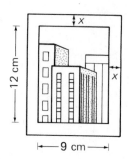

1.5 cm

Maintaining Skills

Remember how?

If $4t - 3 = 6t + 1$, then $t = -2$.

$4t + (-3 + 3) = 6t + \underbrace{1 + 3}$

$\underbrace{4t - 6t} = (6t - 6t) + 4$

$-2t = 4$

$t = \dfrac{4}{-2} = -2$

Now practice:

1. If $2x + 3 = x - 1$, then $x = $ __?__ . -4

2. If $3y - 2 = 2y + 5$, then $y = $ __?__ . 7

3. If $3 - 2n = 7 - n$, then $n = $ __?__ . -4

4. If $6 - 5t = 3t - 2$, then $t = $ __?__ . 1

5. If $2 + 3g = g - 8$, then $g = $ __?__ . -5

6. If $3a + 2 - a = 4 + a$, then $a = $ __?__ . 2

7. If $2x + 3 - 5x = 2x - 2$, then $x = $ __?__ . 1 　8. If $2 - 3n + 5 = 2n - 8$, then $n = $ __?__ . 3

9. If $4r + 6 = r - 4 - 2r$, then $r = $ __?__ . -2 　10. If $6t + 2t - t = t + 18$, then $t = $ __?__ . 3

Remember how?

If $3(2 - x) + 2x = 3x - 6$, then $x = 3$.

$6 \underbrace{- 3x + 2x} = 3x - 6$

$6 \underbrace{- x - 3x} = (3x - 3x) - 6$

$(-6 + 6) - 4x = \underbrace{-6 - 6}$

$-4x = -12$

$x = \dfrac{-12}{-4} = 3$

Now practice:

11. If $5(t + 1) = 4(t + 2)$, then $t = $ __?__ . 3

12. If $3(8y - 2) = 3(4 + 2y)$, then $y = $ __?__ . 1

13. If $2[x - (2x + 1)] = 6$, then $x = $ __?__ . -4

14. If $-5[2r - 2(r + 1)] = 6 - r$, then $r = $ __?__ . -4

15. If $4(z - 2) = 3(z + 5)$, then $z = $ __?__ . 23

16. If $-3x + 2(2x + 1) = 9 + 2x$, then $x = $ __?__ . -7

Remember how?

If $\dfrac{2z}{5} + \dfrac{z}{6} = \dfrac{1}{3}$, then $z = \dfrac{10}{17}$.

$30\left(\dfrac{2z}{5}\right) + 30\left(\dfrac{z}{6}\right) = 30\left(\dfrac{1}{3}\right)$

$12z + 5z = 10$

$17z = 10$

$z = \dfrac{10}{17}$

Now practice:

17. If $\dfrac{5x}{2} - 1 = x + \dfrac{1}{2}$, then $x = $ __?__ . 1

18. If $t - \dfrac{3}{10} = \dfrac{1}{2} + \dfrac{3t}{5}$, then $t = $ __?__ . 2

19. If $\dfrac{5n}{6} - \dfrac{1}{6} = \dfrac{2n}{3} + \dfrac{5}{6}$, then $n = $ __?__ . 6

20. If $\dfrac{m}{2} + 1 = \dfrac{m}{3} - m$, then $m = $ __?__ . $-\dfrac{6}{7}$

21. If $4 + \dfrac{r}{5} = \dfrac{5}{3}$, then $r = $ __?__ . $-11\dfrac{2}{3}$ 　22. If $\dfrac{z}{5} - \dfrac{z}{2} = 9$, then $z = $ __?__ . -30

23. If $\dfrac{k}{4} - \dfrac{7k}{12} = 2$, then $k = $ __?__ . -6 　24. If $2t - \dfrac{5t}{6} - 1 = \dfrac{t}{2} + \dfrac{1}{3}$, then $t = $ __?__ . 2

Geometry and Trigonometry

Social Science This French market scene symbolizes the basic economic principle of supply and demand. It applies to a family's food shopping as well as to trade among nations.

12

Geometry

12-1 Lines and Angles

> **OBJECTIVE** To learn about lines and angles, how to label them and their parts, and how to measure angles.

Earlier in this book, we used the concept of a *line* as a set of **points** to help us visualize number relationships on a number line. Then, in Chapter 8, we used the concept of a *plane* as a set of points to help us visualize relationships between ordered pairs of numbers. The concepts of a *line* and a *plane* as certain kinds of sets of points come from a branch of mathematics called *geometry*.

Like numbers, geometric **points** and sets of points are abstract concepts, not concrete objects. To help us visualize these concepts, however, we represent them as dots and other marks on paper.

Any subset of a line consisting of two points and the part of the line between these points is called a **line segment** or a **segment**.

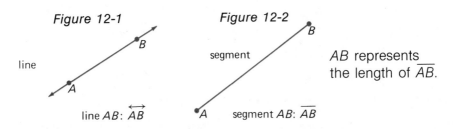

Figure 12-1

line

line *AB*: $\overleftrightarrow{AB}$

Figure 12-2

segment

segment *AB*: $\overline{AB}$

AB represents the length of $\overline{AB}$.

453

A subset of a line that consists of a point *A* and all points of the line on one side of *A* is called a ray. You name a ray by using the symbol for its single endpoint (initial point) and that for one other point in the ray. Thus, $\overrightarrow{AB}$ names the ray with endpoint *A* and which contains point *B* (Figure 12-3).

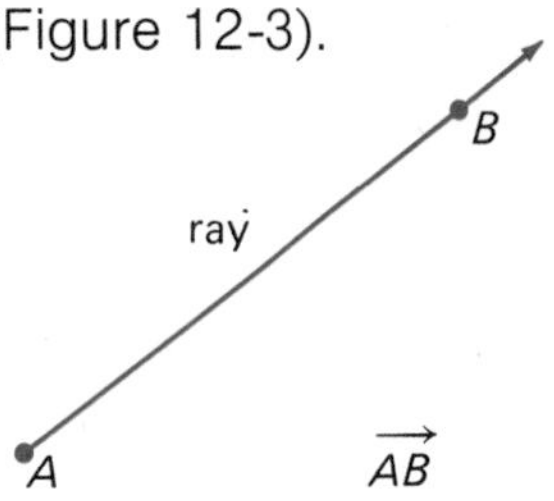

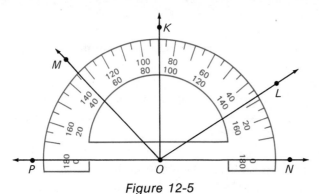

Figure 12-3 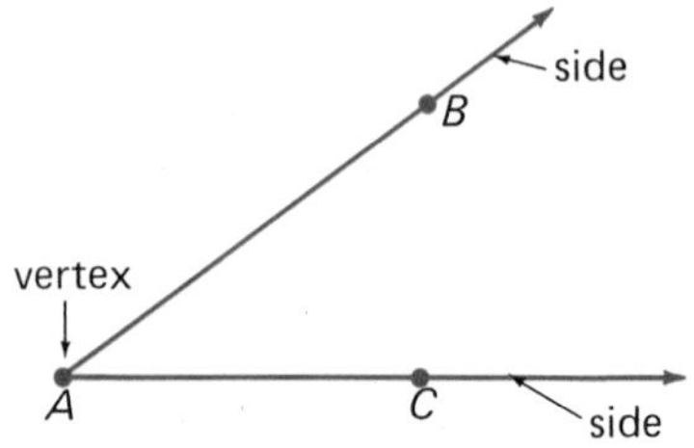   *Figure 12-4*

Angle *A*:
∠*A* or ∠*BAC*
or ∠*CAB*
(Vertex: letter
in the middle)

The figure shown in Figure 12-4 is formed by two rays starting from the same point and is called an **angle**. The point *A* is called the **vertex** of the angle, and the two rays $\overrightarrow{AB}$ and $\overrightarrow{AC}$ are called its **sides**.

To find the **degree measure** of an angle, you use a *protractor* as pictured in Figure 12-5. You can see that ∠*NOL* measures 32° (32 degrees), ∠*NOK* measures 90°, and ∠*NOM* measures 135°.

Figure 12-5

Angles measuring between 0° and 90° are called **acute angles**, angles measuring 90° are called **right angles**, and angles measuring between 90° and 180° are called **obtuse angles**.

To represent the measure of an angle *ABC*, you use the symbol m∠*ABC*. For example, by subtracting 32° from 90°, you can see in Figure 12-5 that m∠*LOK* = 58°. Angle *LOK* is said to be an angle of 58° or a 58° angle.

Do you see that ∠*NOK* is a right angle because m∠*NOK* = 90° and that ∠*KOP* is a right angle because m∠*KOP* = 90°?

Some protractors have a second scale reading from left to right.

Oral Exercises

Exercises 1–6 refer to the figure shown.

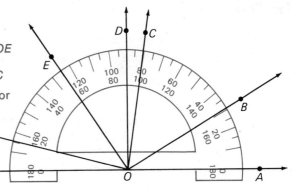

1. Name the angle that measures 125°. ∠AOE

2. Name the angle that measures 80°. ∠AOC

3. Name an angle that measures 90°. ∠AOD or
   ∠DOG

4. What is the measure of ∠AOF? 165°

5. What is the measure of ∠BOE? 95°

6. What is the measure of ∠FOB? 135°

Written Exercises

In Exercises 1–4, name 5 different line segments in each figure.

A 1.

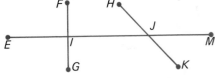

any 5 of: $\overline{AB}, \overline{AC}, \overline{AD}, \overline{BC}, \overline{BD}, \overline{CD}$

2. R•

any 5 of: $\overline{SY}, \overline{SL}, \overline{SK}, \overline{YL},$
$\overline{YK}, \overline{LK}, \overline{RY}$

3.

any 5 of: $\overline{EI}, \overline{EJ}, \overline{EM}, \overline{IJ}, \overline{IM}, \overline{JM},$
$\overline{FI}, \overline{IG}, \overline{FG}, \overline{HJ}, \overline{JK}, \overline{HK}$

4.

any 5 of: $\overline{IO}, \overline{OV}, \overline{IV},$
$\overline{UO}, \overline{OQ}, \overline{UQ}$

Decide whether the following angles are acute, obtuse,
or right angles.

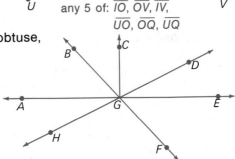

5. ∠CGA right

6. ∠DGE acute

7. ∠CGF obtuse

8. ∠BGA acute

9. ∠AGH acute

10. ∠AGD obtuse

Graph the solution set of each sentence on a number line, and identify
the graph as a point, a line segment, a ray, or a line.

B 11. $x = 2$ point

12. $x \geq 7$ ray

13. $2 \leq x \leq 3$ segment

14. $x \leq 0$ ray

12-2 Pairs of Angles

OBJECTIVE To learn the names and properties of some special pairs of angles.

Some pairs of angles whose measures are related are given special names. Figure 12-6 shows two lines intersecting at point *O* and forming ∠*AOB*, ∠*BOC*, ∠*COD*, and ∠*DOA*. Two angles such as ∠*BOA* and ∠*DOC*, whose sides are rays in the same line but in opposite directions are called **vertical angles**. ∠*DOA* and ∠*BOC* are also vertical angles.

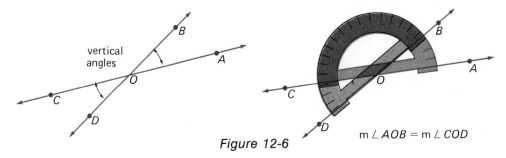

Figure 12-6

You can see by placing a protractor in two positions as shown above that vertical angles have the same measure.

Any pair of angles with a common vertex and which share a common side between them are called **adjacent angles**. Thus, ∠*AOB* and ∠*BOC* in Figure 12-6 are adjacent angles.

Any pair of angles the sum of whose measures is 90° are called **complementary angles**. Thus, in Figure 12-7, ∠*EGF* and ∠*HJI* are complementary angles, and ∠*MOP* and ∠*PON* are complementary angles. Each of the pair is a **complement** of the other.

∠*MOP* and ∠*PON* are *adjacent* complementary angles.

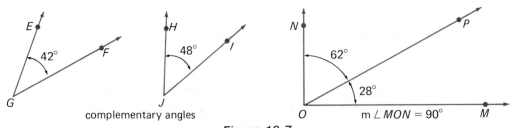

Figure 12-7

Two angles are **supplementary angles** if the sum of their measures is 180°. Each is a **supplement** of the other. If an angle measures $n°$, then its supplement measures $(180 - n)°$. Figure 12-8 pictures two pairs of supplementary angles. $\angle XOY$ and $\angle YOZ$ are adjacent supplementary angles.

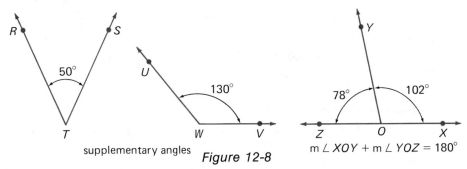

supplementary angles   *Figure 12-8* $m \angle XOY + m \angle YOZ = 180°$

Example   Find the measure of an angle for which the sum of the measures of its complement and its supplement is 104°.

Solution   Let n represent the measure of the angle.
Then $90 - n$ represents the measure of its complement, and $180 - n$ represents the measure of its supplement.

$$90 - n + 180 - n = 104$$
$$270 - 2n = 104$$
$$-2n = -166$$
$$n = 83$$

The measure of the complement is $(90 - 83)°$, or $7°$, and the measure of the supplement is $(180 - 83)°$, or $97°$.
Does $97 + 7 = 104$? Yes.
Therefore, the measure of the angle is 83°.   *Answer*

Oral Exercises

State the measure of the complement of the angle with the given measure.

1. 80°	2. 7°	3. 65°	4. 12°	5. x degrees	6. $5x$ degrees
10°	83°	25°	78°	$(90 - x)°$	$(90 - 5x)°$

State the measure of the supplement of the angle with the given measure.

7. 120°	8. 10°	9. 90°	10. 34°	11. r degrees	12. $6s$ degrees
60°	170°	90°	146°	$(180 - r)°$	$(180 - 6s)°$

Written Exercises

In Exercises 1–4, use the diagram at the right, assuming that m∠ACB = m∠EGF.

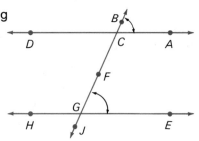

A 1. List all the angles with measures equal to m∠ACB.

2. List all the angles that are supplementary to ∠ACB

3. If m∠ACB = 40°, find m∠BCD. 140°

4. If m∠FGH = 140°, find m∠FGE. 40°

1. ∠DCF, ∠FGE, ∠HGJ   2. ∠BCD, ∠ACF, ∠FGH, ∠EGJ

Problems

A 1. What are the measures of two supplementary angles, the larger of which measures three times the smaller? 45° and 135°

2. The measure of an angle is 35° more than the measure of its supplement. Find the measures of both angles. 72.5° and 107.5°

3. Find the measure of the angle which measures 10° more than its complement. 50°

4. Two angles are supplementary and one measures 60° less than the other. Find the measure of the larger angle. 120°

★ Self-Test 1

Be sure that you understand these terms:

point (p. 453)	line (p. 453)	line segment (p. 453)
ray (p. 454)	angle (p. 454)	vertex of an angle (p. 454)
sides of an angle (p. 454)	protractor (p. 454)	degree (p. 454)
right angle (p. 454)	obtuse angle (p. 454)	acute angle (p. 454)
vertical angles (p. 456)	adjacent angles (p. 456)	complementary angles (p. 456)
supplementary angles (p. 457)		

Be sure that you understand these symbols:

$\overleftrightarrow{AB}$ (p. 453) $\overline{AB}$ (p. 453) AB (p. 453) $\overrightarrow{AB}$ (p. 454)   ∠ (p. 454)

° (p. 454)   m∠A (p. 454)

1. When an angle is named ∠PQR, the vertex is __?__ .   Objective 12-1, p. 453

2. The measure of an acute angle is between __?__ and __?__ .

3. Angles measuring between 90° and 180° are called __?__ angles.

4. The complement of an angle of 43° measures __?__ .   Objective 12-2, p. 456

5. The supplement of an angle of 110° measures __?__ .

6. If the measure of one of a pair of vertical angles is 52°, what is the measure of the other angle?

Check your answers with those printed at the back of the book.

12-3 Triangles

OBJECTIVE To learn some properties of triangles in general and some facts about some special triangles.

A **triangle** is the figure formed by connecting three points not on a line by segments. Figure 12-9 pictures a triangle ABC for which the segments $\overline{AB}$, $\overline{BC}$, and $\overline{CA}$ are the **sides.** You use the symbol $\triangle ABC$ to name the triangle.

Figure 12-9

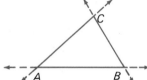

The points A, B, and C, which are the vertices of the **angles** of the triangle ($\angle BAC$, $\angle ACB$, and $\angle CBA$), are called the **vertices** of the triangle.

In any triangle, the sum of the measures of the angles is equal to 180°. You can see this by tearing off the corners of any paper triangle and fitting them together as shown in Figure 12-10.

Some triangles are given special names.

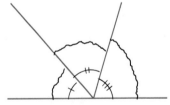

Figure 12-10

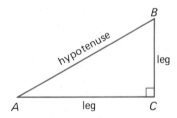

Figure 12-11

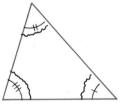

Figure 12-12

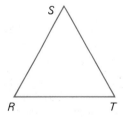

Figure 12-13

Right triangle

$AC^2 + BC^2 = AB^2$
[Pythagorean
theorem, p. 394
converse, p. 396]

Isosceles triangle

$MN = NP$; $m\angle M = m\angle P$
Base: $\overline{MP}$
Base angles: $\angle M$ and $\angle P$

Equilateral triangle

$RS = ST = TR$
$m\angle R = m\angle S$
$= m\angle T = 60°$

Written Exercises

In Exercises 1–6, use the converse of the Pythagorean theorem to determine which of the given triangles are right triangles.

A 1. $\triangle ABC$: $AB = 4$, $BC = 5$, $CA = 6$ no   2. $\triangle SRO$: $SR = 3$, $RO = 4$, $OS = 5$ yes

3. $\triangle XYZ$: $XY = 8$, $YZ = 15$, $ZX = 17$ yes   4. $\triangle MNP$: $MN = 6$, $NP = 8$, $PM = 10$ yes

5. $\triangle DEF$: $DE = 9$, $EF = 12$, $FD = 16$ no   6. $\triangle DEF$: $DE = 2$, $EF = 3$, $FD = 4$ no

7. Given: $\triangle FGH$ is a right triangle with m $\angle G = 90°$, $FG = 8$, and
$FH = 10$. Find GH. 6

8. Given: $\triangle IJK$ is a right triangle with m $\angle J = 90°$, $IJ = 7$, and $JK = 24$.
Find IK. 25

9. If $\triangle ABC$ is equilateral, find the measure of each angle. 60°

10. In $\triangle EFG$, $\angle E$ measures 80° and $\angle F$ measures 60°. What is the measure
of $\angle G$? 40°

11. Given: $\triangle LMN$ is isosceles with $LM = MN$. If $\angle M$ measures 80°, what
is the measure of $\angle L$ and $\angle N$? 50°

12. Given: $\triangle PQR$ is an isosceles right triangle with m$\angle Q = 90°$ and
$PQ = QR$. If the length of the hypotenuse is $\sqrt{2}$, find the length of each
leg. 1

Problems

A 1. In a right triangle the measure of one of the
acute angles is 8 times the measure of the
other. Find the measure of each angle. 10°, 80°

2. Find the number of degrees in each angle of
an isosceles triangle if the measure of the third
angle is 4 times the measure of either of the
two base angles. 30°, 30°, 120°

3. How many degrees are there in each angle of
a triangle if the measure of the second of the
angles is twice that of the first, and the measure of the third is 5° more than 4 times that
of the first? 25°, 50°, 105°

4. The number of degrees in each angle of a
triangle are in the ratio of 1 to 2 to 3. Find
the measure of each. 30°, 60°, 90°

5. The measure of the second angle of a triangle
is $\frac{1}{2}$ of that of the first, and the measure of the
third is 3 times that of the second. Find the
measure of the smallest angle. 30°

6. The measures of two of the angles of a triangle
are equal and that of the third is $\frac{4}{7}$ of their sum.
Find the measures. 70°, 70°, 40°

7. The sum of four angles about a point is 360°.
The measure of the third is 4 times that of the
first, the measure of the fourth is twice that of
the second, and the measure of the second
is 40° more than that of the first. What is the
measure of each angle? 30°, 70°, 120°, 140°

8. Find the number of degrees in each angle of
a triangle if the number of degrees in the first
angle is 2 less than twice the number of
degrees in the second angle, and the number
of degrees in the third angle is 35 more than
half the number of degrees in the first.
37°, 72°, 71°

12-4 Similar Triangles

> **OBJECTIVE** To learn about similar triangles and how to use them in solving practical problems.

In $\triangle ABC$ and $\triangle DEF$ in Figure 12-14, the measures of two angles of one are equal to the measures of two angles of the other ($m\angle A = m\angle D$ and $m\angle B = m\angle E$). The third angles also have equal measures ($m\angle C = m\angle F$) because the sum of the angles in each triangle must equal 180°. Such triangles are called **similar triangles**.

Figure 12-14

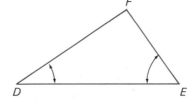

Similar triangles have the same shape.

You can denote that triangles ABC and DEF are similar by writing

$$\triangle ABC \sim \triangle DEF.$$

Here angles with equal measures are listed in corresponding positions. They are called **corresponding angles**. The sides opposite corresponding angles are called **corresponding sides**. Thus, AC corresponds to DF, and so on. **It is a geometric fact that the lengths of corresponding sides of similar triangles are proportional (p. 328).** Thus

$$\frac{AB}{DE} = \frac{BC}{EF} = \frac{CA}{FD}.$$

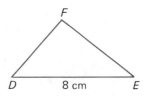

Example 1 If $\triangle ABC \sim \triangle DEF$ with dimensions as shown, find EF and FD.

Solution Substituting known values in the proportion, you have:

$$\frac{12}{8} = \frac{8}{EF} \quad \text{and} \quad \frac{12}{8} = \frac{6}{FD}$$

You can complete the solution. $12EF = 64$, $EF = 5\frac{1}{3}$

$12FD = 48$, $FD = 4$

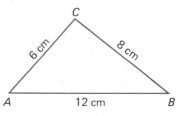

Example 2 The figure shows a means of measuring the width x of a river at a given point. If the measurements are taken as shown, how wide is the river at point T; that is, what is TS?

Solution   Since $\angle PNR$, $\angle NRS$, $\angle RSP$, and $\angle P$ are shown as right angles, the figure $NRSP$ is a rectangle. Since opposite sides of a rectangle have equal lengths,

$$SP = RN = 27 \text{ m.} \qquad \begin{matrix} m \angle M = m \angle M \\ m \angle N = m \angle P \end{matrix}$$

Then $x = TP - 27$. $\triangle MNR \sim \triangle MPT$ (Why?) From

$\dfrac{TP}{RN} = \dfrac{MP}{MN}$ you have $\dfrac{TP}{27} = \dfrac{80}{30}$. You can complete the solution.

$$30TP = 2160$$
$$TP = 72$$
Thus, $x = 72 - 27 = 45$ m.

Written Exercises

A 1. Triangles DEF and XYZ are similar. Write three equal ratios. $\dfrac{DE}{XY} = \dfrac{EF}{YZ} = \dfrac{DF}{XZ}$

2. Triangles ABC and DEF are similar. Name the corresponding angles. $\angle A$ and $\angle D$
$\angle B$ and $\angle E$
$\angle C$ and $\angle F$

Solve.

3. A vertical stick 2 meters long casts a shadow 3 meters long at the same time that a tower casts a shadow 30 meters long. Find the height of the tower.   20 m

(Not drawn to scale)

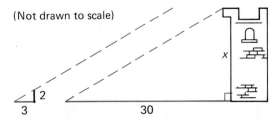

4. A man 2 meters tall casts a shadow 1 meter long at the same time a tree casts a shadow 5 meters long. Find the height of the tree. 10 m

5. A contact print and an enlarged print of a negative are made. In the contact print an object has a width of 5 cm and a height of 6 cm. In the enlargement the same object has a width of 20 cm. What is its height in the enlargement?   24 cm

6. A triangle has sides with lengths 9, 15, and 18. If the longest side of a similar triangle is 22, find its shortest side.   11

7. To find the length of a pond, similar triangles were drawn. The measurements are shown on the figure below. How long is the pond?   600 m

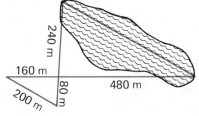

8. The corresponding sides of two similar triangles measure 12 cm and 15 cm. What is the ratio of their perimeters?   4:5

9. An isosceles triangle has sides with lengths 12 cm, 12 cm, and 15 cm. The base of a similar triangle is 20 cm. Find the perimeter of the larger triangle.   52 cm

★ *Self-Test 2*

Be sure that you understand these terms:

triangle (p. 459)
vertices of a triangle (p. 459)
leg (p. 459)
base angles (p. 459)
corresponding angles (p. 461)

sides of a triangle (p. 459)
right triangle (p. 459)
isosceles triangle (p. 459)
equilateral triangle (p. 459)
corresponding sides (p. 461)

angles of a triangle (p. 459)
hypotenuse (p. 459)
base (p. 459)
similar triangles (p. 461)

Be sure that you understand these symbols:

$\triangle$ (p. 459) $\sim$ (p. 461)

1. What is the degree measure of each of the base angles of an isosceles triangle whose remaining angle measures 70°?   Objective 12-3, p. 459

2. Find the hypotenuse of a right triangle whose legs have lengths 3 and 4.

3. Can an isosceles triangle be a right triangle?

4. Corresponding sides of similar triangles are __?__.   Objective 12-4, p. 461

5. If $\triangle ABC \sim \triangle DEF$, and $AB = 6$, $BC = 8$, $CA = 10$, and $DE = 12$, find EF and FD.

Check your answers with those printed at the back of the book.

Historical Note
Thales

Thales (pronounced *thay-leez*) (about 640–550 B.C.) was a Greek merchant who lived in Miletus on the coast of Asia Minor but traveled around the Mediterranean sea in conducting his business. He became much interested in mathematics and made a great impression on the people in Egypt by using the shadow method with similar triangles to find the height of a pyramid.

We don't know how Thales did it. Since point C is inaccessible, one method would be to choose a time when the shadow is symmetrical. Then the horizontal leg of the right triangle ABC can be determined.

$$\frac{h}{d} = \frac{m}{n}$$

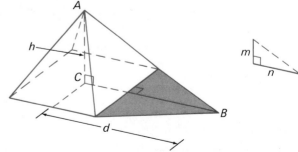

Trigonometry

12-5 Trigonometric Ratios and Functions

> **OBJECTIVE** To learn how to find the cosine, sine, and tangent of an acute angle.

Notice that any acute angle, like $\angle A$ in Figure 12-15, can be made an angle of a right triangle ABC. Ratios of the lengths of the sides of $\triangle ABC$ are called **trigonometric ratios** associated with $\angle A$. They have been given special names and symbols.

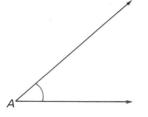
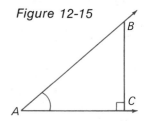

Figure 12-15

$\cos A$ (read "**cosine** of A") $= \dfrac{\text{length of leg adjacent to } \angle A}{\text{length of hypotenuse}} = \dfrac{AC}{AB}$

$\sin A$ (read "**sine** of A") $= \dfrac{\text{length of leg opposite } \angle A}{\text{length of hypotenuse}} = \dfrac{BC}{AB}$

$\tan A$ (read "**tangent** of A") $= \dfrac{\text{length of leg opposite } \angle A}{\text{length of leg adjacent to } \angle A} = \dfrac{BC}{AC}$

The values of these trigonometric ratios depend only on the *measure* of $\angle A$ and not on the particular right triangle which contains $\angle A$. In Figure 12-16, if $m\angle A = m\angle A'$, $\triangle ABC \sim \triangle A'B'C'$. (Why?) Then:

$$\frac{AC}{A'C'} = \frac{AB}{A'B'}$$

Multiply both members of this proportion by $\dfrac{A'C'}{AB}$:

$$\frac{AC}{A'C'} \cdot \frac{A'C'}{AB} = \frac{AB}{A'B'} \cdot \frac{A'C'}{AB}$$

Since $m\angle C = m\angle C' = 90°$.

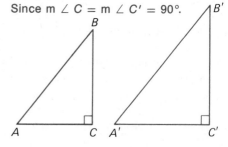

Figure 12-16

Therefore

$$\frac{AC}{AB} = \frac{A'C'}{A'B'}, \text{ or } \cos A = \cos A'.$$

You can show similarly that $\sin A = \sin A'$ and $\tan A = \tan A'$.

You can find the trigonometric ratios of two complementary acute angles using just one triangle:

$$\cos A = \frac{b}{c} \quad \cos B = \frac{a}{c}$$

$$\sin A = \frac{a}{c} \quad \sin B = \frac{b}{c}$$

$$\tan A = \frac{a}{b} \quad \tan B = \frac{b}{a}$$

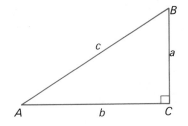

$BC = a$
$AC = b$
$AB = c$
a is opposite
$\angle A$, and so on.

Example Find the cosine, sine, and tangent of $\angle A$ in the right triangle shown below.

Solution You first determine the value of c by using the Pythagorean theorem. Then, using the definitions given above,

$$c^2 = 3^2 + 5^2$$
$$c^2 = 9 + 25 = 34$$
$$c = \sqrt{34}$$

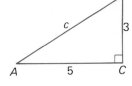

$$\cos A = \frac{5}{\sqrt{34}} \qquad \sin A = \frac{3}{\sqrt{34}}$$

$$= \frac{5\sqrt{34}}{34}, \qquad = \frac{3\sqrt{34}}{34}, \qquad \tan A = \frac{3}{5}. \quad \textit{Answer}$$

We often regard

$$\cos A, \sin A, \text{ and } \tan A; \qquad A \in \{\text{acute angles}\}$$

as the values of three functions each having the set of acute angles as its domain. These functions are called trigonometric functions.

Oral Exercises

State the value of each expression.

1. $\cos A \frac{21}{29}$

2. $\sin A \frac{20}{29}$

3. $\tan A \frac{20}{21}$

4. $\cos B \frac{20}{29}$

5. $\sin B \frac{21}{29}$

6. $\tan B \frac{21}{20}$

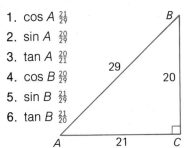

7. $\sin E \frac{12}{13}$

8. $\cos D \frac{12}{13}$

9. $\cos E \frac{5}{13}$

10. $\sin D \frac{5}{13}$

11. $\tan E \frac{12}{5}$

12. $\tan D \frac{5}{12}$

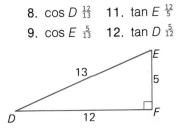

13. $\tan R \frac{24}{7}$

14. $\cos T \frac{24}{25}$

15. $\sin R \frac{24}{25}$

16. $\tan T \frac{7}{24}$

17. $\cos R \frac{7}{25}$

18. $\sin T \frac{7}{25}$

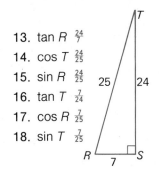

Written Exercises

For each right triangle shown, find cos A, sin A, tan A, cos B, sin B, and tan B.

A 1.

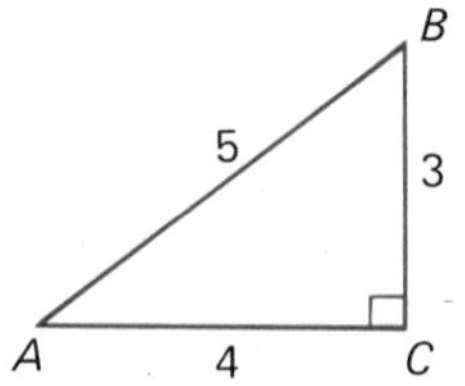

2.

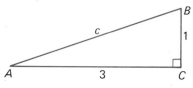

3.

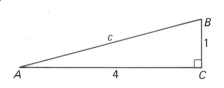

4.

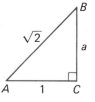

5.

6.

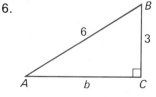

B 7. Show that for all right triangles ABC, where $\angle C$ is a right angle, $\sin A = \cos B$. $\sin A = \dfrac{BC}{AB} = \cos B$

8. Show that for all right triangles ABC, where $\angle C$ is a right angle, $\cos A = \sin B$. $\cos A = \dfrac{AC}{AB} = \sin B$

9. Show that $(\sin A)^2 + (\cos A)^2 = 1$ for all angles A. $(\sin A)^2 + (\cos A)^2 = \left(\dfrac{BC}{AB}\right)^2 + \left(\dfrac{AC}{AB}\right)^2 = \dfrac{BC^2 + A}{AB^2}$

10. Show that $\tan A = \dfrac{\sin A}{\cos A}$ for all angles A for which $\cos A \neq 0$. $\dfrac{\sin A}{\cos A} = \dfrac{BC}{AB} \div \dfrac{AC}{AB} = \dfrac{BC}{AC} = \tan A$ $= \dfrac{AB^2}{AB^2} = 1$

Answers (right margin):

1. $\dfrac{4}{5}, \dfrac{3}{5}, \dfrac{3}{4}$; $\dfrac{3}{5}, \dfrac{4}{5}, \dfrac{4}{3}$

2. $\dfrac{3\sqrt{10}}{10}, \dfrac{\sqrt{10}}{10}$, $\dfrac{\sqrt{10}}{10}, \dfrac{3\sqrt{10}}{10}$,

3. $\dfrac{4\sqrt{17}}{17}, \dfrac{\sqrt{17}}{17}$, $\dfrac{\sqrt{17}}{17}, \dfrac{4\sqrt{17}}{17}$,

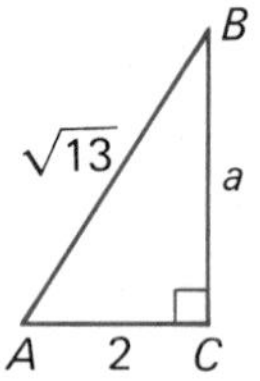

4. $\dfrac{2\sqrt{13}}{13}, \dfrac{3\sqrt{13}}{13}$, $\dfrac{3\sqrt{13}}{13}, \dfrac{2\sqrt{13}}{13}$,

5. $\dfrac{\sqrt{2}}{2}, \dfrac{\sqrt{2}}{2}, 1$; $\dfrac{\sqrt{2}}{2}, \dfrac{\sqrt{2}}{2}, 1$

6. $\dfrac{\sqrt{3}}{2}, \dfrac{1}{2}, \dfrac{\sqrt{3}}{3}$; $\dfrac{1}{2}, \dfrac{\sqrt{3}}{2}, \sqrt{3}$

Puzzle Time

Suppose a semicircle with radius 1 is drawn with its center at the vertex, B, of $\angle ABC$. Suppose also that $\angle DEB$ and $\angle FGB$ are right angles. Then:

$$\cos \angle ABC = \dfrac{BE}{1} = BE$$

$$\sin \angle ABC = \dfrac{DE}{1} = DE$$

Find the segment whose length is $\tan \angle ABC$. $\overline{FG}$

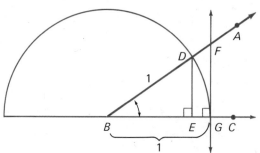

12-6 Using Trigonometric Tables

> **OBJECTIVE** To learn how to find values for trigonometric functions for given angles and how to find measures of angles for given values of trigonometric functions.

In order to solve practical problems, you will need to be able to find values of trigonometric functions for degree measures of angles. A few values can be computed easily by using the properties of special triangles (Section 12-3) and the Pythagorean theorem.

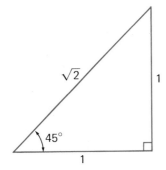

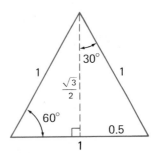

Isosceles right triangle:

$$\sin 45° = \frac{1}{\sqrt{2}} = \frac{\sqrt{2}}{2}$$
$$\doteq 0.707$$

$$\cos 45° = \frac{1}{\sqrt{2}} = \frac{\sqrt{2}}{2}$$
$$\doteq 0.707$$

$$\tan 45° = \frac{1}{1} = 1$$

Half an equilateral triangle:

$$\sin 60° = \frac{\sqrt{3}}{2} \qquad \sin 30° = \frac{1}{2}$$
$$\doteq 0.866 \qquad\qquad = 0.5$$

$$\cos 60° = \frac{1}{2} \qquad \cos 30° = \frac{\sqrt{3}}{2}$$
$$= 0.5 \qquad\qquad \doteq 0.866$$

$$\tan 60° = \frac{\sqrt{3}}{1} \qquad \tan 30° = \frac{1}{\sqrt{3}}$$
$$\doteq 1.732 \qquad\qquad \doteq 0.577$$

Most values of trigonometric functions have to be computed by advanced methods. Approximate values are listed in tables such as the table of trigonometric functions at the back of the book. On the next page we shall see how to use that table.

How do you find the value of sin 32° from the table? By locating 32 in the left-hand column and then reading across to the right you find:

$m \angle A$	sin A	cos A	tan A
1	0.0175	0.9998	0.0175
31	0.5150	0.8572	0.6009
32	0.5299	0.8480	0.6249
33	0.5446	0 8387	0.6494
34	0.5592	0 8290	0.6745
35	0.5736	0 8192	0.7002

$$\sin 32° \doteq 0.5299$$
$$\cos 32° \doteq 0.8480$$
$$\tan 32° \doteq 0.6249$$

For ordinary computation we write $=$ instead of $\doteq$ in such equations as these.

You can use the table in this way to find the sin A, cos A, and tan A for any angle with whole-number measure from 1° to 90°. The values listed for sin 90° and cos 90° are

$$\sin 90° = 1, \quad \cos 90° = 0.$$

The tangent of 90° is not defined.

If the value of one of its trigonometric ratios is given, the measure of the angle having that ratio can be estimated. For example, the table indicates that an angle whose sine is approximately 0.5736 has a measure of 35°.

Suppose that tan A = 0.6500, a number not listed in the table. To find the approximate measure of $\angle A$, locate in the tangent column the entries between which 0.6500 lies:

$$\tan 33° = 0.6494 \quad \text{and} \quad \tan 34° = 0.6745$$

Thus, $$33° < m\angle A < 34°.$$

Since 0.6500 is much closer to 0.6494 than it is to 0.6745,

$$m\angle A = 33°, \text{ to the nearest degree.}$$

Written Exercises

Use the table at the back of the book to find (a) sin A, (b) cos A, and (c) tan A, for the $\angle A$ with the given measure.

A   1. 15° (*below*)   2. 23°   3. 38°   4. 46° 1.0355   5. 51° 1.2349   6. 63° 1.96
     7. 71°   8. 81°   9. 3°   10. 88° 0.9994   11. 32° 0.5299   12. 77° 0.97

0.7193   0.7771   0.89
0.6947   0.6293   0.45
0.0349   0.8480   0.22
28.6363   0.6249   4.33

Find the measure of $\angle A$ to the nearest degree.

13. sin A = 0.6691   42°   14. cos A = 0.8572   31°   15. cos A = 0.4384   64°   16. sin A = 0.9613   74°
17. tan A = 0.1944   11°   18. tan A = 4.7046   78°   19. sin A = 0.1450   8°   20. cos A = 0.5300   58°

1. 0.2588, 0.9659, 0.2679   2. 0.3907, 0.9205, 0.4245   3. 0.6157, 0.7880, 0.7813
7. 0.9455, 0.3256, 2.9042   8. 0.9877, 0.1564, 6.3138   9. 0.0523, 0.9986, 0.0524

12-7 Numerical Trigonometry

> **OBJECTIVE** To learn how to use trigonometric ratios in solving problems.

Many practical problems involve right triangles and can be solved easily by use of trigonometric ratios.

Example 1 The entrance concourse leading to the lobby floor of the Central City Civic Auditorium starts at a point 50 meters from the building and makes an angle with the level ground measuring 5°. How far off of the ground, to the nearest meter, is the floor of the lobby?

Solution Draw a triangle showing the known values:

You wish to find x, the height of the lobby floor above the ground. Since $\triangle ABC$ is a right triangle, you can see that

$$\tan 5° = \frac{x}{50} \quad \text{or} \quad x = 50 \tan 5°.$$

From the table, $\tan 5° = 0.0875$. Then

$$x = 50(0.0875) = 4.375.$$

∴ to the nearest meter, the floor of the auditorium is 4 meters above the ground. *Answer*

Example 2 A swimming pool is 12 meters long. To the nearest degree, what should be the measure of the angle that the bottom of the pool makes with the horizontal if the depth of the pool is to vary from 1 meter to 3 meters?

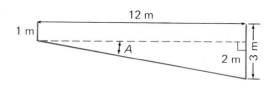

Solution You have a right triangle in which one leg is 12 m long and the other is 3 − 1, or 2, m long. Using the tangent ratio,

$$\tan A = \frac{2}{12} = \frac{1}{6} \doteq 0.1667.$$

From the table, to the nearest degree, the measure of $\angle A$ is 9°. ∴ the bottom should form an angle with the horizontal measuring 9° to the nearest degree. *Answer*

Written Exercises

Find *x* for each figure using the table in the back of the book as needed and rounding answers to the nearest unit of length.

A 1. 23

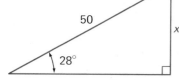

2. 63

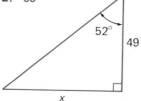

3. 13

4. 9

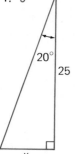

5. 33

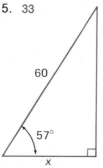

6. 75

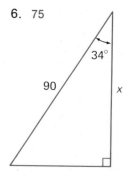

Problems

Solve each problem drawing a sketch for each. Express distances to the
nearest unit. Use the table in the back of the book as needed.

A 1. To the nearest meter, how far is it across the
river? **141 m**

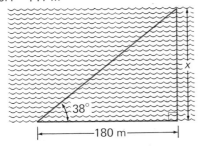

2. To the nearest centimeter, how high is the
tree? **858 cm**

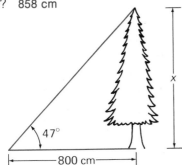

3. A cantilever home extends 4 meters from
the side of a hill. The floor makes an angle
measuring 48° with the hill. How far is the
outer edge of the floor vertically from the side
of the hill? **4 m**

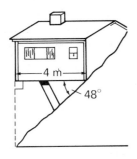

4. A ramp 300 cm long is dropped from the rear
of a furniture truck to the ground. If the ramp
makes an angle measuring 12° with the
ground, to the nearest centimeter, how high
is the bed of the truck from the ground? **62 cm**

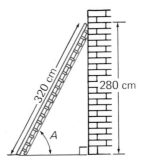

5. To the nearest degree what is the measure
of the angle formed with the ground by a
ladder 320 cm long if the ladder is leaning
against a wall at a height of 280 cm? **61°**

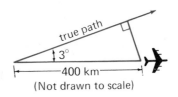

6. If an airplane flies 3° off course for 400 kilometers, to the nearest kilometer, how far
away from the correct path will the airplane
then be? **21 km**

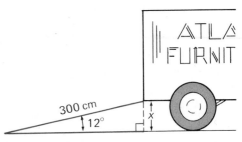

(Not drawn to scale)

In Problems 7–10, the term *angle of elevation,* and a related term, *angle of depression,* will be used. The exact meaning of these terms is illustrated in the accompanying diagram. $\angle CAB$ is an angle of elevation, the point B is *elevated* with respect to the observer at A and the horizontal line AC through A. $\angle SRQ$ is an angle of depression; the point Q is *depressed* with respect to the observer at R and the horizontal line SR through R.

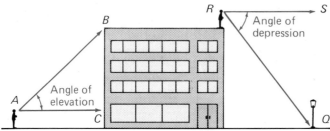

Give each answer to the nearest tenth unless otherwise specified. Use the table as needed.

7. A surveyor finds that the angle of elevation from a point on level ground to the top of a building 110 meters high measures 18°. How far is the point on the ground from the base of the building? 338.6 m

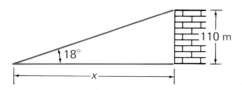

8. An oil well is drilled on a slant line having an angle of depression with the level ground measuring 58°. How far below the surface is the drill bit when 1800 meters of drill rod is in the ground? 1526.4 m

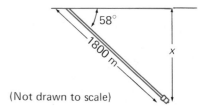

(Not drawn to scale)

B 9. A diving submarine travels through the water at a steady rate of 280 meters per minute on a diving path that forms an angle of depression measuring 5° with the surface of the water. How far beneath the surface is the submarine after 6 minutes? 146.5 m

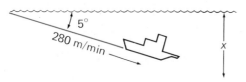

(Not drawn to scale)

10. The Capps Building is 98 meters in height, and is located 120 meters from the Sullivan Building. If the angle of elevation from the top of the Capps Building to the top of the Sullivan Building measures 31°, how tall is the Sullivan Building? 170.1 m

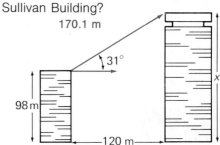

★ *Self-Test 3*

Be sure that you understand these terms.

trigonometric ratios (p. 464) cosine (p. 464) sine (p. 464)
tangent (p. 464) trigonometric functions (p. 465) angle of elevation (p. 472)
angle of depression (p. 472)

Be sure that you understand these symbols.

cos (p. 464) sin (p. 464) tan (p. 464)

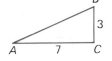

1. Find cos A, sin A, and tan A for the triangle shown. Objective 12-5, page 464

2. Use the table to find Objective 12-6, page 467
   a. sin 32° b. cos 27° c. tan 89°

3. Use the table to find the measure of ∠A to the nearest degree if sin A = 0.8100.

4. Find the height of the flagpole to the nearest meter. Objective 12-7, page 469

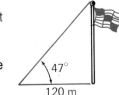

Check your answers with those printed at the back of the book.

Chapter Summary

1. Geometry deals with the properties of sets of points such as lines, rays, angles, triangles, rectangles, and circles.

2. Two angles whose sides are rays in the same line but in opposite directions are called **vertical angles**. Any pair of angles the sum of whose measures is 90° are called **complementary angles**. Any pair of angles which share a vertex and a common side between them are called **adjacent angles**. Two angles are **supplementary** if the sum of their measures is 180°.

3. The sum of the measures of the angles of a triangle is 180°.

4. Some special triangles are right triangles, isosceles triangles, and equilateral triangles.

5. **Similar triangles** have the same shape; that is, corresponding angles respectively have the same measure. Sides of similar triangles are proportional.

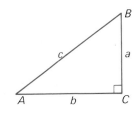

6. Trigonometric ratios: $\cos A = \dfrac{b}{c}$, $\sin A = \dfrac{a}{c}$, $\tan A = \dfrac{a}{b}$

Chapter Test

12-1 1. Determine whether the following measures indicate an acute, obtuse, or right angle. A = acute, O = obtuse, R = right
   a. 10° A   b. 129° O   c. 90° R   d. 78° A   e. 93° O

12-2 2. State the number of degrees contained in the supplement and complement of the angle with the given measure.
   a. 50°   b. $x°$ c. 72° **a.** 130°; 40°   **b.** $(180 - x)°$; $(90 - x)°$ **c.** 108°; 18°

12-3 3. Find the hypotenuse of a right triangle whose legs have lengths 9 meters and 12 meters. 15 m

12-4 4. Given: $\triangle ABC \sim \triangle DEF$. If $\dfrac{AB}{DE} = \dfrac{7}{2}$, and $CA = 10$, find FD. $\dfrac{20}{7}$

12-5 5. Find:
   a. sin A   b. cos B
   $\dfrac{3}{5}$ $\dfrac{3}{5}$

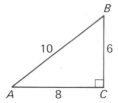

12-6 6. Using the table, find 1.6 sin 35° to the nearest tenth. 0.9

12-7 7. The top of a stairway is 2 meters higher than the bottom. The angle of elevation from the bottom of the stairs to the top is 25°. What is the horizontal length of the staircase? about 4.3 m

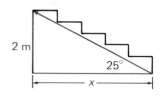

Programmed Chapter Review

12-1 1. You read $\overline{AB}$ as __?__ .   segment AB

   2. A subset of a line that consists of a point A and all points of the line on one side of A is called a __?__ .   ray

   3. Two rays starting from the same point form a figure called an __?__ .   angle

   4. An angle of 91° is called an __?__ angle.   obtuse

12-2 5. Angles *ABC* and *DBE* are called __?__ angles.   vertical

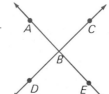

6. What is the measure of the complement of a 60° angle?   30°

7. Any pair of angles which share a common side between them are called __?__ angles.   adjacent

8. True or false: In order for two angles to be supplementary, they must be adjacent.   false

12-3   9. A triangle that has two sides of equal length is called an __?__ triangle.   isosceles

10. The sum of the measures of the three angles of a triangle is __?__ .   180°

11. In this right triangle, $DF^2 + FE^2 = $ __?__ . DE^2 (or ED^2)

12-4   12. What is the replacement for each variable so the result is a true statement?

a. $\dfrac{10}{18} = \dfrac{5}{b}$ b. $\dfrac{m}{6} = \dfrac{4}{8}$ c. $\dfrac{3}{a} = \dfrac{10}{20}$

a. 9
b. 3
c. 6

13. $\triangle XYZ$ and $\triangle BTR$ are similar. What are the measures of $\overline{YZ}$ and $\overline{BR}$?   8 cm; 17.5 cm

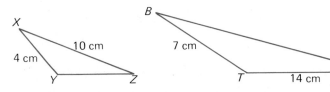

12-5   14. The ratio of the length of the side opposite $\angle A$ to the length of the hypotenuse is called __?__ .   sin A

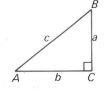

15. The formula for cosine of $\angle A$ is
$\cos A = $ __?__ . $\dfrac{b}{c}$

12-6   16. Use the table to find the following:
a. sin 25°   b. cos 81°   c. tan 56°

a. 0.4226
b. 0.1564
c. 1.4826

17. Use the table to find the measure of $\angle A$ to the nearest degree.
a. $\sin A = 0.7660$ b. $\cos A = \frac{1}{3}$ a. 50° b. 71°

18. Using the table, compute each of the following to the nearest tenth.
a. $\frac{2}{5} \sin 30°$ b. $8.9 \tan 19°$ a. 0.2 b. 3.1

12-7 **19.** A guy wire is used to brace a telephone pole (see figure). If the angle formed by the wire and the ground has a measure of 35°, and the height of the wire attachment on the pole is 9 meters, what is the length of the guy wire to the nearest meter?

6 m

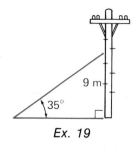

Ex. 19

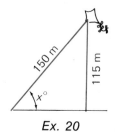

Ex. 20

20. A flying kite is 115 meters above the ground. If the length of the string to the kite is 150 meters, measured from the ground, what is the angle of elevation to the nearest whole degree from the position of the kite flyer?

50°

Cumulative Review, Chapters 1–12

Simplify each expression.

1. $\dfrac{2(10 - 3)}{6 - 4} + 2(8 - 12)$ −1

2. $6(y - 1) - 3(2y + 1)$ −9

3. $(3t^2 - 2t + 5) + 2(t^2 - t + 2)$ $5t^2 - 4t + 9$

4. $(4b^2 - 3b + 1) - 3(b^2 + 2b)$ $b^2 - 9b + 1$

5. $(x - 2)(5x - 1)$ $5x^2 - 11x + 2$

6. $(a^2 + 2ab + b^2)(a - b)$ $a^3 + a^2b - ab^2 - b^3$

7. $(1 - 2r)^2$ $1 - 4r + 4r^2$

8. $(n^3 + 27) \div (n + 3)$ $n^2 - 3n + 9$

9. $(21ax^3 - 18a^2x^2 + 3a^3x) \div (-3ax)$ $-7x^2 + 6ax - a^2$

10. $4(x - 2) + 2[(x + y) - 6(y - 1)]$ $6x - 10y$

11. $[5(2a - 1) + (a - 4)] - 2[12a - (-a + 1)]$ $-15a - 7$

12. $(2x - y)(x + y)$ $2x^2 + xy - y^2$

Factor completely.

13. $24a^3 - 3a^2$ $3a^2(8a - 1)$

14. $9t^2 - 1$ $(3t + 1)(3t - 1)$

15. $4ar^2 - 2arh$ $2ar(2r - h)$

16. $t^2 - t - 6$ $(t - 3)(t + 2)$

17. $b^2 - 12b + 36$ $(b - 6)^2$

18. $x - xyz$ $x(1 - yz)$

19. $36a^2 - 5a - 1$

20. $3x^2 - 27$

21. $y^4 - 25y^2 + 144$ $(y + 4)(y - 4)(y + 3)(y - 3)$

22. $2a^6 - 18$ $2(a^3 + 3)(a^3 - 3)$

23. $18t^3 + 39t^2 - 15t$ $3t(3t - 1)(2t + 5)$

24. $80r^5 - 5r$ $5r(4r^2 + 1)(2r + 1)(2r$

19. $(9a + 1)(4a - 1)$

20. $3(x + 3)(x - 3)$

Simplify.

25. $\dfrac{2x + 12}{x^2 + 10x + 24} \cdot \dfrac{2}{x + 4}$

26. $\dfrac{3a^2y^4}{12x^4} \div \dfrac{9ay^3}{3x^4y} \quad \dfrac{ay^2}{12}$

27. $\dfrac{3c^2 - 27}{15} \cdot \dfrac{5}{c^2 - 3c}$

28. $\dfrac{9y^2 - 1}{3y + 1} \div \dfrac{6y^2 + 2y}{6y - 2} \cdot \dfrac{9y^2 - 6y + 1}{3y^2 + y}$ 29. $\dfrac{1}{x + y} - \dfrac{1}{x - y} \cdot \dfrac{-2y}{x^2 - y^2}$ 30. $\dfrac{\dfrac{b^2}{b^2 - 1} - \dfrac{1}{b + 1}}{\dfrac{b^2 - b + 1}{b^2 - 1}}$

Solve.

31. $2z - 1 = 3z + 4$ $\{-5\}$

32. $4t = 3(4t - 3)$ $\left\{\dfrac{9}{8}\right\}$

33. $\dfrac{2a}{5} + \dfrac{3a}{5} + \dfrac{17}{10} = 0$ $\left\{-\dfrac{17}{10}\right\}$

34. $\dfrac{w}{3} - \dfrac{w + 1}{2} = 1$ $\{-9\}$

35. $\dfrac{1}{2m} - \dfrac{1}{5m} = \dfrac{1}{10}$ $\{3\}$

36. $\dfrac{2}{2x + 5} + 1 = \dfrac{5}{3}$ $\{-1\}$

37. $\dfrac{16}{3x - 1} - \dfrac{4}{1 - 3x} = 1$ $\{7\}$

38. $\dfrac{3}{x^2 - 1} + \dfrac{1}{x - 1} = 0$ $\{-4\}$

39. $t^2 = 19t - 84$ $\{12, 7\}$

40. $2m^2 + 5m + 3 = 0$ $\left\{-\dfrac{3}{2}, -1\right\}$

Simplify.

41. $\sqrt{32}$ $4\sqrt{2}$ 42. $\dfrac{1}{4}\sqrt{16b^4}$ b^2 43. $2\sqrt{\dfrac{1}{2}}$ $\sqrt{2}$ 44. $\dfrac{1}{\sqrt{5}}$ $\dfrac{\sqrt{5}}{5}$

45. $\dfrac{\sqrt{5}}{2\sqrt{7}}$ $\dfrac{\sqrt{35}}{14}$ 46. $\sqrt{8} - \sqrt{64}$ $2\sqrt{2} - 8$ 47. $4\sqrt{72} - 3\sqrt{36}$ $24\sqrt{2} - 18$ 48. $(2\sqrt{5} + 3)(2\sqrt{5} - 3)$ 11

Graph each equation.

49. $3x + y = -1$

50. $y = -\dfrac{1}{2}x + 4$

51. $2x + y = 6$

52. $3x - 5y = 15$

53. $x + 4y = -8$

54. $5x = 20$

Solve each system.

55. $\begin{aligned} x - y &= 0 \\ 3x - 2y &= 1 \end{aligned}$ (1, 1)

56. $\begin{aligned} x - 2y &= 16 \\ x + y &= 10 \end{aligned}$ (12, −2)

57. $\begin{aligned} 3x - 2y &= 4 \\ 2x + 3y &= 7 \end{aligned}$ (2, 1)

58. Find the slope and y-intercept of the graph of $6x - 12y = 5$. slope: $\frac{1}{2}$; y-intercept: $-\frac{5}{12}$

59. Find the value of a for which the graph of $4x - ay = 5$ contains the point $(3, 1)$. 7

Find an equation in standard form of the line meeting the given conditions.

60. Slope 2; containing the point $(-1, -1)$. $2x - y = -1$

61. Slope $-\frac{3}{4}$; containing the point $(0, 5)$. $3x + 4y = 20$

62. If $f(x) = 2t^2 - 3t + 1$, find (a) $f(-2)$, (b) $f(0)$, (c) $f(5)$. 15; 1; 36

64. If y varies directly as x, and $y = 2$ when $x = 6$, find y when $x = -6$. −2

63. If $g(t) = t^3 - 4t$, find (a) $g(10)$, (b) $g(-1)$, (c) $g(-3)$. 960; 3; −15

65. If y varies inversely as x^2, and $y = 2$ when $x = 9$, for what value of x will $y = 5$? $\pm\dfrac{9\sqrt{10}}{5}$

Graph the solution set.

66. $3 - 2y > 16$

67. $4x + 1 \geq 9$

68. $3x - y < 5$

69. Rita has 4 times as much money as Amy. If Rita gives Amy 39 cents, they would then have equal amounts. What is that new amount? 65¢

70. The Shop-Smart Market made a blend of two grades of coffee, one worth $2.00 per kilogram and the other worth $2.80 per kilogram. If 80 kilograms of the blend is to sell for $2.20 per kilogram, how many kilograms of each coffee did the market use? (*below*)

71. Given a triangle with area of 42 square centimeters, find its base and altitude if together they measure 19 centimeters. $b = 12, a = 7$ or $b = 7, a = 12$

72. A plane left St. Louis at 12 noon flying west at 250 kilometers per hour. At 2 P.M. another plane left the same airport, flying west at 350 kilometers per hour. At what time did the second plane overtake the first? 7 P.M.

73. A tank can be filled in 9 minutes when both of two intake pipes are open. When one of the pipes is open it takes 15 minutes. How long would the second pipe alone take to fill the tank? $22\frac{1}{2}$ minutes

74. The sum of the digits in a 2-digit numeral is 12. The units digit is twice the tens digit. Find the numeral. 48

70. 60 kg of $2.00 coffee, 20 kg of $2.80 coffee

Just for Fun

On page 16, some tessellations were suggested. Other interesting patterns can be made by using equilateral triangles. Notice that if you put six equilateral triangles together, you can make a six-sided figure called a **hexagon**. You can use a protractor to make equilateral triangles (each angle measures 60°).

You can combine equilateral triangles and hexagons with the figures you used earlier.

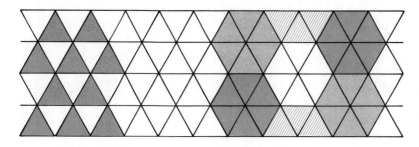

Make up some patterns of your own.

Extra Practice in Problem Solving

Section 6–13

A 1. The Colsoms borrowed $5250 to buy an avocado grove. Part of the loan was at 6% interest, and the remainder at 4½%. If the yearly interest on each sum was the same, find the amount of each portion of the loan. $2250 at 6%, $3000 at 4½%

B 3. Sue Lovine invested some money at 7% per year. If she adds $1000 to what she has, the new total would return the same amount each year at 6% as the original investment does at 7%. Find the initial investment. $6000

4. After investing $2800 in bonds paying 4% annually, Paul Elwood deposited a second sum in a bank paying 5½% annually. His yearly return on the two investments was the same as if both sums had been invested at 5%. Find the amount deposited at the bank. $5600

C 7. The Satos loaned a specific amount at 6% and twice as much at 4%. They receive ⅓ more interest from the sum loaned at 4% than from that loaned at 6%. Their total yearly interest is $490. Find how much they have loaned at each rate. $3500 at 6%, $7000 at 4%

2. A man loaned $1000, part at 4% and part at 5%. He gets $14 more annually from the amount loaned at 5% than from the amount loaned at 4%. Find the amount loaned at each rate. $400 at 4%, $600 at 5%

5. Tina Olson has $1200 less invested at 6% than at 5%. Her income from the smaller is only $16 less than the income from the larger investment. How much has she invested at each rate? $5600 at 5%, $4400 at 6%

6. Calvin Cook loaned $9800, part at 5% and the remainder at 6%. If each rate of interest had been interchanged, his annual interest would have been only $2 less. Find the amount loaned at each rate. $4800 at 5%, $5000 at 6%

8. A woman has $6000 to invest, and intends to obtain an income of at least $300. What is the largest amount she can invest at 4%, if she invests the balance in a riskier investment at 6%? $3000

Section 6–14

Use this information in Problems 1 and 2: Skydivers fall at 54 meters per second before their chutes open. They fall at 6 meters per second after their chutes open.

B 1. If a skydiver jumped from a plane 1400 meters high and reached the ground in 100 seconds, how high was she when she opened her chute? 500 m

2. If a skydiver opened his chute when halfway from the plane to the ground, and the total time for the descent was 5 minutes, how high was the plane? 3240 m

3. The train from Boston to Erehwon travels at 100 km/h, while the bus travels at 80 km/h. The train makes a round trip in 3 hours more time than it takes the bus to travel one way. How long does it take the train to make the round trip? 8 hours

4. A private plane leaves Edmonton, Alberta for Winnipeg, Manitoba, flying at 200 km/h. Two and a half hours later a jet leaves Winnipeg for Edmonton, flying at 800 km/h. The planes pass each other midway between the two cities. How far apart are the cities? 1333⅓ km

479

Sample   Karen's airplane cruises at 120 kilometers per hour in still air. If she flies downwind 420 km in the same length of time it takes her to fly 300 km against the wind, what is the speed of the wind?

Solution

Step 1 The problem asks for the speed of the wind.

Step 2 Let r = the speed of the wind.
   Since the plane's speed in still air is 120 km per hour:

$$120 + r = \text{speed downwind} \quad \text{Distance downwind} = 420 \text{ km}$$
$$120 - r = \text{speed upwind} \quad \text{Distance upwind} \quad = 300 \text{ km}$$

Step 3

	R	D	T
Down-wind	$120 + r$	420	$\dfrac{420}{120 + r}$
Up-wind	$120 - r$	300	$\dfrac{300}{120 - r}$

$$\underbrace{\text{Time}}_{\text{downwind}} = \underbrace{\text{Time}}_{\text{upwind}}$$

$$\frac{420}{120 + r} = \frac{300}{120 - r}$$

$$\text{L.C.D.} = (120 + r)(120 - r)$$

Step 4 $(120 + r)(120 - r)\dfrac{420}{120 + r} = (120 + r)(120 - r)\dfrac{300}{120 - r}$

$$420(120 - r) = 300(120 + r)$$
$$21(120 - r) = 15(120 + r)$$
$$2520 - 21r = 1800 + 15r$$
$$720 = 36r$$
$$20 = r$$

Step 5 The check is left for you. $\dfrac{420}{120 + 20} = \dfrac{420}{140} = 3; \quad \dfrac{300}{120 - 20} = \dfrac{300}{100} = 3 \checkmark$

∴ the speed of the wind is 20 km per hour.   *Answer*

A 5. One car can travel 20 kilometers per hour faster than another. The faster can go 360 kilometers in the same time that the slower can go 300 kilometers. Find the rate of each.   100 km/h and 120 km/h

6. Jack can ride 25 kilometers on his bicycle in the same time it takes him to walk 12 kilometers. If his rate riding is 8 kilometers per hour faster than his rate walking, find how fast he can walk. $7\frac{5}{13}$ km/h

7. Water flows down the Fallbrook River at the rate of 5 kilometers per hour. A barge can travel 60 kilometers down the river in the same time that it takes to travel 40 kilometers back up. What is the rate of the barge in still water?   25 km/h

8. A girl rows 15 kilometers downstream and then back. Her time returning was 3 times that going downstream. If the stream flows at 5 kilometers per hour, find the rate at which the girl rows in still water.   10 km/h

9. The Jenkins family drove 210 kilometers from New Castle to Wampum. If they had increased their speed by 35 kilometers per hour, they could have completed the trip in $\frac{2}{3}$ of the time. What was their average speed?   70 km/h

B 10. George Kratz found that his small airplane cruised at 5 times the rate of the wind. If he flew 220 kilometers against the wind in one-half hour less time than he flew 660 kilometers with the wind, what was the speed of the wind? 110 km/h

11. If the average speed of a car is increased by 35 kilometers per hour, the number of hours to take a trip of 250 kilometers is $\frac{3}{5}$ of the time at the slower speed. What are the two rates of speed? $52\frac{1}{2}$ km/h and $87\frac{1}{2}$ km/h

C 14. A plane has a 6-hour supply of gasoline. What is the greatest distance it can reach from the airport if the speed going is 240 kilometers per hour and the speed on the return trip is 260 kilometers per hour? $748\frac{4}{5}$ km

15. Lon and Connie live in cities which are 350 kilometers apart. If they drive toward each other, they will meet in 2 hours. If they drive in the same direction, it will take Lon 10 hours

12. A boat takes 1 hour and 20 minutes longer to sail 50 kilometers up a river than to return. If the river flows at 5 kilometers per hour, find the speed of the boat in still water. 20 km/h

13. A man had to row 1 kilometer up the Azusa River in order to board a motorboat to take him 20 kilometers down the river. In still water he rows 6 kilometers per hour, and the motorboat travels 22 kilometers per hour. Find the speed of the current if the trip takes 1 hour and 5 minutes. 5   2 km/h

to overtake Connie. Find the rate at which each can travel.   Lon: 105 km/h; Connie: 70 km/h

16. A plane, carrying mail, leaves port at 8 A.M. to overtake a ship traveling 30 kilometers per hour which left port at midnight. If the plane has a ground speed of 350 kilometers per hour going and 200 kilometers per hour returning, when will it overtake the ship and at what time will it return to port?
8:45 A.M., 10:03 A.M.

Section 6–15

C 1. Professor Alvarez can grade a set of examination papers in 2 hours, but her assistant requires $2\frac{1}{2}$ hours. After working together for an hour, Professor Alvarez left to attend a meeting and her assistant completed the grading. How long did it take the assistant? $\frac{1}{4}$ hour

2. If 10 skilled laborers and 15 unskilled laborers work together, they can complete a construction job in 12 days. The same job can be done in 6 days by 25 skilled laborers. How

long should it take one unskilled laborer, working alone, to complete the job? 900 days

3. Anthony began to paint the garage of his home. After $1\frac{1}{4}$ hours, he was joined by his older brother and they finished in $2\frac{1}{2}$ hours more. If Anthony had worked 2 hours before he received help, it would have taken them $2\frac{1}{3}$ hours to complete the job. How long would it take each boy to paint the garage alone?   Anthony: $12\frac{1}{2}$ hours
brother: $3\frac{4}{7}$ hours

Section 9–6

Digit Problems

A 1. The tens digit exceeds the units digit by 1. The number with the digits reversed is 45 more than the sum of the digits. Find the original number. 65

2. The units digit is 3 more than the tens digit. If the digits are reversed, the new number is one less than three times the original number. What is the original number? 14

B 3. Two numbers are represented with the same digits, interchanged. In the larger number, the tens digit exceeds the units digit by 3. The sum of the two numbers is 67 more than twice their difference. Find the numbers. **74, 47**

4. The tens digit is 1 more than the units digit. If the number with the digits reversed is subtracted from the original number, the remainder is 3 times the sum of the digits. Find the original number.   **21**

C 5. Show that the sum of a number and the number with the digits reversed is divisible by 11.
$10t + u + (10u + t) = 11t + 11u = 11(t + u)$

6. Show that the difference between a number and the number with the digits reversed is divisible by 9.
$10t + u - (10u + t) = 9t - 9u = 9(t - u)$

Age Problems

A 1. Ramona said that the sum of her age, in years, and the number of the street on which she lives is 105. She also found that the street number, decreased by 5 times her age, is 15. How old is Ramona? What is her street number?   **15 years old; 90**

2. Michael says that 3 times his age is 12 years more than 3 times his brother's age. He also says that 4 times his age is 4 years more than 5 times his brother's age. How old are Michael and his brother?   **Michael: 16
brother: 12**

B 3. A father's age is 8 years more than 3 times his son's age. The mother's age is 18 years more than 2 times the son's age. What are the ages of the father, mother, and son, if the mother is 4 years younger than the father?
father: 50; mother: 46; son: 14

4. The sum of the ages of 2 children is 26 years. In three years, the older child will be 2 years older than the younger one will then be. Determine their present ages.   **12 and 14**

C 5. Colette is twice as old as Bonnie will be when Colette is 5 times as old as Bonnie is now. Find the relationship between Colette's present age (c) and Bonnie's present age (b). $c = 4b$

6. Ann is twice as old as Judy was at the time when Ann was as old as Judy is now. The sum of the present ages of Ann and Judy is 28 years. What is the present age of each person?   **Ann: 16; Judy: 12**

7. A man is 3 times as old as his son was at the time when the father was twice as old as his son will be 2 years from now. Find the present age of each person if the sum of their ages is 55 years.   **father: 39
son: 16**

Fraction Problems

B 1. The value of the fraction is $\frac{1}{2}$. When both numerator and denominator are increased by 3, the resulting fraction has the value $\frac{4}{7}$. $\frac{9}{18}$

2. If 5 is added to the numerator and subtracted from the denominator, the value of the resulting fraction is $\frac{3}{2}$. If 5 is subtracted from the numerator and added to the denominator of the fraction, the value of the resulting fraction is $\frac{4}{11}$. $\frac{13}{17}$

List all possible members of each solution set.

C 3. The numerator of a fraction whose value is $\frac{334}{667}$ is a four-digit number whose hundreds and tens digits are 0. The denominator contains the same digits in reverse order. $\left\{\frac{1002}{2001}, \frac{2004}{4002}, \frac{3006}{6003}, \frac{4008}{8004}\right\}$

4. The numerator is a two-digit number and the denominator is that number with the digits reversed. The value of the fraction is $\frac{17}{5}$. $\left\{\frac{51}{15}\right\}$

Section 10–6

Make a sketch for each problem. Approximate each square root to the nearest hundredth.

A 1. The length of the hypotenuse of an isosceles right triangle is H. Show that the length of each leg equals $\dfrac{H}{\sqrt{2}}$. $\quad \begin{aligned} l^2 + l^2 &= H^2 \\ l^2 &= \dfrac{H^2}{2}, \text{ so } l = \dfrac{H}{\sqrt{2}} \end{aligned}$

2. Several young students wanted to help their community in its new beautification program. They decided to plant flowers in a rectangular lot which measured 20 meters by 50 meters, and place stepping stones on a diagonal path. Find the length of the path. 53.85 m

B 3. A new housing development extends 8 kilometers in one direction, makes a right turn, then continues for 6 kilometers. A new road runs between the beginning and ending points of the development. What is the perimeter of the triangle formed by the homes and the road? 24 km

C 4. A rhombus has four equal sides, but its angles may not be right angles. Its diagonals are perpendicular to and bisect each other. Show that $S = \frac{1}{2}\sqrt{D^2 + d^2}$, where D and d represent the lengths of the diagonals.

$$
\begin{aligned}
S^2 &= \left(\frac{D}{2}\right)^2 + \left(\frac{d}{2}\right)^2 \\
&= \frac{D^2 + d^2}{4} \\
S &= \sqrt{\frac{D^2 + d^2}{4}} \\
&= \frac{1}{2}\sqrt{D^2 + d^2}
\end{aligned}
$$

5. Find the length of a diagonal of a cube if one of the edges is z. $d = z\sqrt{3}$

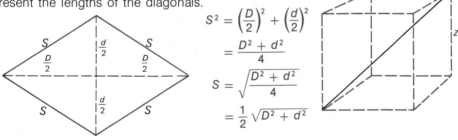

Section 11–9

Give irrational answers to the nearest tenth, and reject inappropriate roots.

A 1. The base of a triangle is 3 cm longer than its altitude. Find the altitude if the area of the triangle is 44 square centimeters. (Hint: The area of a triangle $= \frac{1}{2} \cdot$ base $\cdot$ altitude.) 8 cm

2. The altitude of a triangle is 4 cm shorter than its base. Find the altitude if the area of the triangle is 90 square centimeters. 11.6 cm

B 3. A packing case is 4 meters long and has square ends x meters on a side.

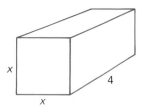

a. Show that the total surface area of the outside of the case is $A = 2x^2 + 16x$. $\quad A = 2 \cdot x^2 + 4 \cdot 4x$
$= 2x^2 + 16x$

b. Find x if $A = 48$ square meters. 2.3 m

C 5. The motion of a freely falling body is described approximately by $h = vt - 4.9t^2$, where h represents the height above the ground, v the initial velocity of the body (positive if the body is propelled away from the earth and negative if propelled toward the earth), and t the elapsed time of fall. In how many seconds will an object thrown upward from the ground with an initial velocity of 24.5 meters per second first reach a height of 19.6 meters? When will it again be 19.6 meters above the ground? When will it strike the ground? after 1 sec; after 4 sec; after 5 sec

6. At Hillsdale High School 1000 students buy lunch every day for 25 cents each. If the cafeteria raises the price, for each increase

4. A box without a top is to be made by cutting squares measuring 4 cm on a side from each corner of a square piece of cardboard and folding up the sides. If the box is to hold 121 cubic cm, what should be the length of a side of the cardboard? 13.5 cm

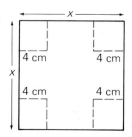

of 1 cent, 10 students will bring their own lunches. After a price increase, 35 dollars more than usual was taken in by the cafeteria. How many students had stopped buying lunch? 5 or 70 students

7. A ski club is going to charter a bus for a ski weekend. They promise the bus company there will be 30 persons making the trip at 15 dollars per person. The company agrees to reduce the price for everyone by $1.00 for every 4 additional people who are signed up. (Hence if 8 additional people go, all persons pay $13 instead of $15.) If the bus company receives $504, how many persons went on the trip? 42 or 48 persons

Section 12-4

A 1. To determine the width of a stream, right triangles can be laid out and distances measured as shown on the figure at the right. How wide is the stream? $13\frac{1}{3}$ m

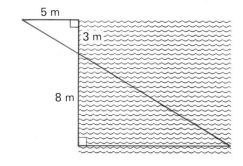

B 2. A boy whose eye level is 1.5 meters above the ground wants to find the height of a tree *ED*. He places a plane mirror horizontally on the ground 15 meters from the tree. If he stands at a point *B* which is 2 meters from the mirror *C*, he can see the reflection of the top of the tree. Find the height of the tree. 20 m

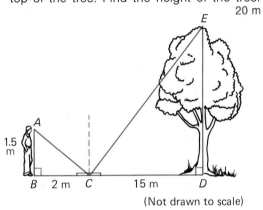

(Not drawn to scale)

3. A flagpole on top of a building casts a shadow 6 meters long beginning at a point 30 meters from the foot of the building. If a meter stick standing vertically casts a shadow 2 meters long, what is the length of the flagpole? 18 m

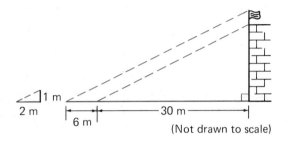

(Not drawn to scale)

Section 12–7

Give each answer to the nearest degree. Use the trigonometric table as needed.

B 1. Two support cables to a TV antenna are anchored to the same spot on the ground 1000 cm from the base of the tower. If one cable is fastened to the tower 1000 cm above the ground and the other is fastened to the tower 1400 cm above the ground, what is the measure of the angle between the cables? 9°

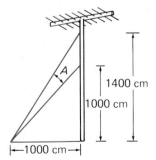

2. A light-house that is 80 meters tall sits atop a cliff that rises vertically 140 meters from the sea. What is the measure of the angle of elevation to the top of the light-house from a point directly opposite the light-house and 2800 meters out to sea? 4°

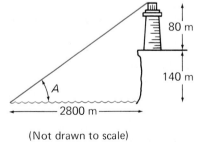

(Not drawn to scale)

Table of Squares of Integers from 1 to 100

Number	Square	Number	Square	Number	Square	Number	Square
1	1	26	676	51	2601	76	5776
2	4	27	729	52	2704	77	5929
3	9	28	784	53	2809	78	6084
4	16	29	841	54	2916	79	6241
5	25	30	900	55	3025	80	6400
6	36	31	961	56	3136	81	6561
7	49	32	1024	57	3249	82	6724
8	64	33	1089	58	3364	83	6889
9	81	34	1156	59	3481	84	7056
10	100	35	1225	60	3600	85	7225
11	121	36	1296	61	3721	86	7396
12	144	37	1369	62	3844	87	7569
13	169	38	1444	63	3969	88	7744
14	196	39	1521	64	4096	89	7921
15	225	40	1600	65	4225	90	8100
16	256	41	1681	66	4356	91	8281
17	289	42	1764	67	4489	92	8464
18	324	43	1849	68	4624	93	8649
19	361	44	1936	69	4761	94	8836
20	400	45	2025	70	4900	95	9025
21	441	46	2116	71	5041	96	9216
22	484	47	2209	72	5184	97	9409
23	529	48	2304	73	5329	98	9604
24	576	49	2401	74	5476	99	9801
25	625	50	2500	75	5625	100	10,000

Table of Square Roots of Integers from 1 to 100

Exact square roots are shown in red. For the others, rational approximations are given correct to three decimal places.

Number	Positive Square Root	Number	Positive Square Root	Number	Positive Square Root	Number	Positive Square Root
N	$\sqrt{N}$	N	$\sqrt{N}$	N	$\sqrt{N}$	N	$\sqrt{N}$
1	1	26	5.099	51	7.141	76	8.718
2	1.414	27	5.196	52	7.211	77	8.775
3	1.732	28	5.292	53	7.280	78	8.832
4	2	29	5.385	54	7.348	79	8.888
5	2.236	30	5.477	55	7.416	80	8.944
6	2.449	31	5.568	56	7.483	81	9
7	2.646	32	5.657	57	7.550	82	9.055
8	2.828	33	5.745	58	7.616	83	9.110
9	3	34	5.831	59	7.681	84	9.165
10	3.162	35	5.916	60	7.746	85	9.220
11	3.317	36	6	61	7.810	86	9.274
12	3.464	37	6.083	62	7.874	87	9.327
13	3.606	38	6.164	63	7.937	88	9.381
14	3.742	39	6.245	64	8	89	9.434
15	3.873	40	6.325	65	8.062	90	9.487
16	4	41	6.403	66	8.124	91	9.539
17	4.123	42	6.481	67	8.185	92	9.592
18	4.243	43	6.557	68	8.246	93	9.644
19	4.359	44	6.633	69	8.307	94	9.695
20	4.472	45	6.708	70	8.367	95	9.747
21	4.583	46	6.782	71	8.426	96	9.798
22	4.690	47	6.856	72	8.485	97	9.849
23	4.796	48	6.928	73	8.544	98	9.899
24	4.899	49	7	74	8.602	99	9.950
25	5	50	7.071	75	8.660	100	10

Table of Values of Sine, Cosine, and Tangent
For angles A such that $1° \leq m\angle A \leq 90°$

$m\angle A$	sin A	cos A	tan A	$m\angle A$	sin A	cos A	tan A
1	0.0175	0.9998	0.0175	46	0.7193	0.6947	1.0355
2	0.0349	0.9994	0.0349	47	0.7314	0.6820	1.0724
3	0.0523	0.9986	0.0524	48	0.7431	0.6691	1.1106
4	0.0698	0.9976	0.0699	49	0.7547	0.6561	1.1504
5	0.0872	0.9962	0.0875	50	0.7660	0.6428	1.1918
6	0.1045	0.9945	0.1051	51	0.7771	0.6293	1.2349
7	0.1219	0.9925	0.1228	52	0.7880	0.6157	1.2799
8	0.1392	0.9903	0.1405	53	0.7986	0.6018	1.3270
9	0.1564	0.9877	0.1584	54	0.8090	0.5878	1.3764
10	0.1736	0.9848	0.1763	55	0.8192	0.5736	1.4281
11	0.1908	0.9816	0.1944	56	0.8290	0.5592	1.4826
12	0.2079	0.9781	0.2126	57	0.8387	0.5446	1.5399
13	0.2250	0.9744	0.2309	58	0.8480	0.5299	1.6003
14	0.2419	0.9703	0.2493	59	0.8572	0.5150	1.6643
15	0.2588	0.9659	0.2679	60	0.8660	0.50	1.7321
16	0.2756	0.9613	0.2867	61	0.8746	0.4848	1.8040
17	0.2924	0.9563	0.3057	62	0.8829	0.4695	1.8807
18	0.3090	0.9511	0.3249	63	0.8910	0.4540	1.9626
19	0.3256	0.9455	0.3443	64	0.8988	0.4384	2.0503
20	0.3420	0.9397	0.3640	65	0.9063	0.4226	2.1445
21	0.3584	0.9336	0.3839	66	0.9135	0.4067	2.2460
22	0.3746	0.9272	0.4040	67	0.9205	0.3907	2.3559
23	0.3907	0.9205	0.4245	68	0.9272	0.3746	2.4751
24	0.4067	0.9135	0.4452	69	0.9336	0.3584	2.6051
25	0.4226	0.9063	0.4663	70	0.9397	0.3420	2.7475
26	0.4384	0.8988	0.4877	71	0.9455	0.3256	2.9042
27	0.4540	0.8910	0.5095	72	0.9511	0.3090	3.0777
28	0.4695	0.8829	0.5317	73	0.9563	0.2924	3.2709
29	0.4848	0.8746	0.5543	74	0.9613	0.2756	3.4874
30	0.50	0.8660	0.5774	75	0.9659	0.2588	3.7321
31	0.5150	0.8572	0.6009	76	0.9703	0.2419	4.0108
32	0.5299	0.8480	0.6249	77	0.9744	0.2250	4.3315
33	0.5446	0.8387	0.6494	78	0.9781	0.2079	4.7046
34	0.5592	0.8290	0.6745	79	0.9816	0.1908	5.1446
35	0.5736	0.8192	0.7002	80	0.9848	0.1736	5.6713
36	0.5878	0.8090	0.7265	81	0.9877	0.1564	6.3138
37	0.6018	0.7986	0.7536	82	0.9903	0.1392	7.1154
38	0.6157	0.7880	0.7813	83	0.9925	0.1219	8.1443
39	0.6293	0.7771	0.8098	84	0.9945	0.1045	9.5144
40	0.6428	0.7660	0.8391	85	0.9962	0.0872	11.4301
41	0.6561	0.7547	0.8693	86	0.9976	0.0698	14.3007
42	0.6691	0.7431	0.9004	87	0.9986	0.0523	19.0811
43	0.6820	0.7314	0.9325	88	0.9994	0.0349	28.6363
44	0.6947	0.7193	0.9657	89	0.9998	0.0175	57.2900
45	0.7071	0.7071	1	90	1	0	Undefined

Acknowledgments

Illustrations by Bill Morrison. Photos were provided by the following sources:

American Geographical Society, 349
Peter Arnold, Manfred Kage, 138
The Bettmann Archive, 59, 300 (top)
Ernest D. Courant, 319
Donald Dietz, Dietz/Hamlin, 385
Editorial Photocolor Archives, 100; Alva Ramphal, 155
Elizabeth Hamlin, Dietz/Hamlin, 41, 69, 278
Historical Pictures Service, 106, 300 (bottom)
Honeywell, Inc., 84, 196
IBM Corporation, 25
Information Canada Phototheque, xvi, 370
Information Service of India, 393
Michigan Tourist Council, 434
Maria Mitchell Association, 15 (top)
Mitchell's Book Corner, 15 (bottom)
Monkmeyer Press Photo Service, Michal Heron, 232; Fujihira, 254; Mimi Forsyth, 310
NASA, 235
New York Daily News, 423
Photoworld (FPG), 336
Santa Fe Railway, 30
James R. Smith, 126
Spanish National Tourist Office, 19
Star Markets, 73
The State Historical Society of Colorado Library, 265
Stock, Boston, Franklin Wing, 452
Tufts New England Medical Center, 286
U. S. Energy Research and Development Administration, 58
U. S. Geological Survey, 343
University of California at San Diego, 194
Wide World Photos, 354
Frank Willett, 62

Answers to Self-Tests

Chapter 1, Self-Test 1, Page 6
1. 21   2. 12   3. 3   4. 1

Chapter 1, Self-Test 2, Page 16
1. 2^2a^3 2. 11   3. 2   4. $P = 32$ cm; $A = 64$ cm²

Chapter 1, Self-Test 3, Page 25
1. $\{1, 2, 10\}$ 2. $\{5\}$ 3. $n - 3 = 7$ 4. 8 points

Chapter 2, Self-Test 1, Page 46
1.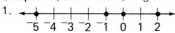
 $^{-}5$ $^{-}4$ $^{-}3$ $^{-}2$ $^{-}1$ 0 1 2
2.
 $^{-}6$ $^{-}5$ $^{-}4$ $^{-}3$ $^{-}2$ $^{-}1$ 0 1 2 3 4 5 6
3. 5   4. 5   5. 3   6. commutative   7. -4 8. 3
9. -11 10. 11

Chapter 2, Self-Test 2, Page 58
1. $x = 1$ 2. $q = 5$ 3. -11 4. -9 5. 14
6. -12 7. $y = 9$ 8. $w = -5$ 9. 17 baskets

Chapter 3, Self-Test 1, Page 72
1. 48   2. 48   3. -48 4. -48 5. -8 6. 1
7. -77 8. -30 9. 300   10. 237   11. x
12. $-2y$ 13. $2a + 3$ 14. $2 - 3b$

Chapter 3, Self-Test 2, Page 94
1. $x = 26$ 2. $x = 50$ 3. -3 4. -5 5. 4
6. -125 7. $x = -3$ 8. $x = -6$ 9. $x = -1$
10. $x = 3$ 11. 100 centimeters   12. Additive property of equality (Sample 2, page 91); Example 1, page 89; Multiplicative property of equality (Exercise 9, page 92); Exercise 7, page 91

Chapter 4, Self-Test 1, Pages 111–112
1. $7x$ 2. $4a - b$ 3. $y = 3$ 4. $c = 9$ 5. length: 9 centimeters;   width: 7   centimeters   6. $x = 6$
7. $t = 5$ 8. Tom's age: 12; Ann's age: 6

Chapter 4, Self-Test 2, Page 119
1. 5 and 7   2. 3; 6   3. 1; 3   4. 2 and 3; 5   5. $2y^2 + 1$; 2   6. $4u + 2$ 7. $x + 3y + a$ 8. $3z^2 + z + 3$
9. $s^2 - 3st + 2t^2$

Chapter 4, Self-Test 3, Page 133
1. z^4 2. $6x^6$ 3. $8a^6b^6$ 4. $27c^6d^3k^2$ 5. $2ax^2 + 2a^3$ 6. $y^2 + 5y$ 7. $9u^4 - 1$ 8. $t^3 - 1$ 9. length: 5 decimeters; width: 3 decimeters

Chapter 5, Self-Test 1, Page 155
1. $2^2 \cdot 3 \cdot 5$ 2. $1 \cdot 42, 2 \cdot 21, 3 \cdot 14, 6 \cdot 7, (-1)(-42),$ $(-2)(-21), (-3)(-14), (-6)(-7)$ 3. 6   4. $-6a^2$
5. 12   6. $8a^2b^3$ 7. $5t^2 + 4t - 3$
8. $3xy^2(x^2 - 2x + 2)$

Chapter 5, Self-Test 2, Page 164
1. $4x^2 - 9$ 2. $ax^5 - a^5x$ 3. $(7z^2 + 9)(7z^2 - 9)$
4. $ab^2(b + a)(b - a)$ 5. $x^2 + 12x + 36$ 6. $4c^2 - 12c + 9$ 7. $y^3z - 6y^2z^2 + 9yz^3$ 8. $x^5 + 4x^4 + 4x^3$ 9. $(n - 2)^2$ 10. $(3x - 1)^2$ 11. $(a^2 + b^3)^2$
12. $x^2y(2x - 3y)^2$

Chapter 5, Self-Test 3, Page 174
1. $x^2 + x - 6$ 2. $2u^2 + 5u + 2$ 3. $(x - 5)(x - 6)$
4. $(6 + t)(8 + t)$ 5. $(c + 9)(c - 5)$
6. $(d - 12)(d + 3)$ 7. $(6y - 1)(y + 1)$
8. $(4x - 3y)(2x - 3y)$

Chapter 5, Self-Test 4, Page 179
1. $(t - 4)(t^2 + 4)$ 2. $(z + w)(x + 2y)$
3. $z(5z + 2)(z - 3)$ 4. $2a^2x(x + a)(x - 4a)$

Chapter 5, Self-Test 5, Page 190
1. $\{2, 7\}$ 2. $\{0, -1, 1\}$ 3. $\{1, 2\}$ 4. $\{-2, 4\}$
5. $\{-3, \frac{1}{2}\}$ 6. $\{0, 2\}$ 7. 7 and 9   8. 7 meters by 7 meters

Chapter 6, Self-Test 1, Page 204
1. $-(x + 4)$, $x \neq 4$ 2. $\dfrac{x}{x - 2}$, $x \neq 2$, $x \neq 3$
3. $1 : (c + d)$ 4. $12 : 1$ 5. 12 centimeters

Chapter 6, Self-Test 2, Pages 212–213
1. $\dfrac{2 + 3x}{4x - 4}$ 2. $\dfrac{y + 4}{y - 3}$ 3. $y - 4$ 4. $\dfrac{x^2 - 1}{x^2 - 6x + 9}$
5. $\dfrac{1}{2}$ 6. $\dfrac{a - b}{b^4}$ 7. $\dfrac{xy^2 - 2y^2}{y - 1}$ 8. $\dfrac{1}{x + 1}$

Chapter 6, Self-Test 3, Page 223

1. $\dfrac{x + 11}{7x}$ 2. $\dfrac{x - 2y}{x - y}$ 3. $\dfrac{3x + 11}{x^2 - 4}$

4. $\dfrac{3(5x - 1)}{(x - 2)(x + 1)(x + 1)}$ 5. $\dfrac{10a + b}{a + b}$

6. $\dfrac{50 - 13y}{y - 3}$ 7. $2x + 5$

Chapter 6, Self-Test 4, Page 232

1. $r = 8$ 2. $x = 1$ 3. $x = -\frac{12}{17}$ 4. $x = 1$ 5. $y = -7\frac{1}{2}$ 6. $s = \frac{1}{3}$ 7. $a = -\frac{1}{6}, a = -\frac{2}{3}$ 8. $0.33\frac{1}{3}\%$ or $\frac{1}{3}\%$ 9. $4.05

Chapter 6, Self-Test 5, Page 245

1. $\frac{4}{5}$ kilogram 2. $104 3. $1300 at 4%, $5700 at 5% 4. first driver: 50 km/h; second driver: 70 km/h 5. $1\frac{5}{7}$ hours

Chapter 7, Self-Test 1, Page 260

1. $>$ 2. $<$ 3. -3 is less than 4. 4. 0 is greater than -7. 5. 0 is between -2 and 3, or -2 is less than 0 and 0 is less than 3 6. 3 is between 7 and -1, or 7 is greater than 3 and 3 is greater than -1 7. $\subset$ 8. $\in$ 9. finite 10. infinite

Chapter 7, Self-Test 2, Page 282

1. {all real numbers less than 3}

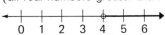

2. {all real numbers greater than 4}

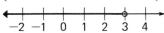

3. {2, 4, 6}, {4, 6, 8}, {6, 8, 10}, {8, 10, 12}, {10, 12, 14} 4. {4, 5} 5. {4, 5, 6, 7, 8} 6. ∅ 7. {5 and all real numbers between 0 and 5}

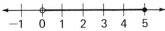

8. {all real numbers greater than 3 or less than 1}

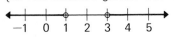

Chapter 8, Self-Test 1, Page 295

1. {1, 5} 2. 10

3.

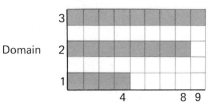

4. (1, 4), (2, 8), (3, 9) 5. (1, 3), (2, 5), (3, 7), (4, 9)

Chapter 8, Self-Test 2, Pages 309–310

1. fourth quadrant 2. horizontal axis 3. origin 4. domain; range 5. A relation is a function if each member of the domain is paired with one and only one member of the range. 6. $y = -\frac{1}{4}x + 2$ 7. {(0, −1), (1, 1), (2, 3)}

Chapter 8, Self-Test 3, Page 331

1. a and b 2.

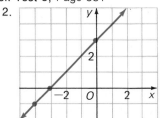

3. $\frac{3}{2}$

4. slope: $-\frac{2}{3}$; y-intercept: 1 5. $x - y = -1$
6. $x - y = -5$ 7. $x = 9$

Chapter 9, Self-Test 1, Page 354

1.

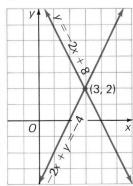

2. (1, 6) 3. length: 20 m; width: 10 m 4. (−2, −6) 5. (2, −1)

Chapter 9, Self-Test 2, Page 359

1. 64   2. father: 48; son: 24   3. $\frac{11}{20}$ 4. 1.5 km/h

Chapter 9, Self-Test 3, Page 364

1.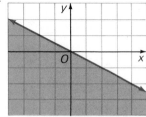

2. $y \le 3x - 4$

3.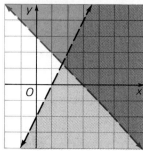

Chapter 11, Self-Test 1, Page 429

1. $y = kx^2$ 2. $m = 2$ 3. $y = 500$ 4. $(-1, -7)$

5. least

Chapter 11, Self-Test 2, Pages 446–447

1. $x = -\frac{3}{2}$ or $x = 3$ 2. $\pm \sqrt{5}$ 3. 15

4. 9; 3   5. $\frac{81}{4}$; $\frac{9}{2}$

6. $x = \pm 3\sqrt{5} + 6$

7. If $ax^2 + bx + c = 0$, and $b^2 - 4ac > 0$, then

$$x = \frac{-b \pm \sqrt{b^2 - 4ac}}{2a}$$

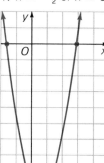

$(\frac{3}{4}, -10\frac{1}{8})$

8. 1.9 and -1.2 9. 53; 2 real roots   10. 25; 2 real roots   11. -31; no real roots   12. 0; one real root

13. 2.9 cm

Chapter 10, Self-Test 1, Page 385

1. 6   2. $\frac{3}{5}$ 3. $\frac{5}{6}$ 4. $10\frac{1}{3}$ 5. $4\frac{1}{2}$ 6. $-\frac{5}{16}$ 7. $-\frac{23}{30}$
8. $-\frac{7}{12}$ 9. $\frac{8}{25}$ 10. $\frac{2}{3}$ 11. $\frac{124}{99}$ 12. $\frac{23}{33}$ 13. 24
14. ± 75 15. $-\frac{6}{25}$ 16. $\frac{15}{8}$

Chapter 10, Self-Test 2, Page 397

1. 3.22   2. 13.75   3. $-4|x|$ 4. 6   5. $x = \pm 9$
6. $x = \pm 20$ 7. 15

Chapter 10, Self-Test 3, Page 408

1. 20   2. $\frac{\sqrt{6x}}{x}$ 3. $9\sqrt{2}$ 4. $\sqrt{3} - 3\sqrt{5}$

5. $4 + 2\sqrt{3}$ 6. -2 7. $5\sqrt{5} - 10$ 8. $\frac{\sqrt{11} - 11}{-10}$

9. $x = 25$ 10. $y = 18$

Chapter 12, Self-Test 1, Page 458

1. Q   2. 0° and 90°   3. obtuse   4. 47°   5. 70°
6. 52°

Chapter 12, Self-Test 2, Page 463

1. 55°   2. 5   3. yes   4. proportional   5. $EF = 16$, $FD = 20$

Chapter 12, Self-Test 3, Page 473

1. $\cos A = \frac{7\sqrt{58}}{58}$, $\sin A = \frac{3\sqrt{58}}{58}$, $\tan A = \frac{3}{7}$

2.a. 0.5299 b. 0.8910 c. 57.2900   3. 54°
4. 129 m

Glossary

abscissa (p. 297). The coordinate of the point on the horizontal axis where a vertical line from a given point meets the horizontal axis.

absolute value (p. 39). The positive number of any pair of opposite real numbers is called the absolute value of each of the numbers. The absolute value of 0 is 0.

acute angle (p. 454). An angle measuring between 0° and 90°.

addition axiom of order (p. 262). For all real numbers a, b, and c:

1. If $a < b$, then $a + c < b + c$;

2. If $a > b$, then $a + c > b + c$.

addition property of equality (p. 48). For all real numbers a, b, and c, if $a = b$ then $a + c = b + c$ and $c + a = c + b$.

additive inverse (p. 38). The additive inverse of the real number a is the real number $-a$ such that $a + (-a) = 0$ and $-a + a = 0$. Also called *opposite of a, negative of a*.

adjacent angles (p. 456). A pair of angles with a common vertex which share a common side between them.

angle (p. 454). A figure formed by two rays starting from the same point. The point is called the *vertex* of the angle, and the rays are called the *sides*.

angles of a triangle (p. 459). *See under* triangle.

area (p. 12). The area of a region is the number of unit squares it contains.

associated equation (p. 360). The equation which results when you replace an inequality symbol in an inequality with the symbol $=$.

associative axioms (p. 88). For all real numbers a, b, and c:
(Addition) $(a + b) + c = a + (b + c)$
(Multiplication) $(ab)c = a(bc)$.

axes (pp. 296–8). *See under* coordinate axes.

average (p. 81). The average of n numbers is the sum of the numbers divided by n.

axiom (p. 88). A statement that is assumed to be true.

axiom of comparison (p. 261). For all real numbers a and b, one and only one of the following statements is true: $a < b$, $a = b$, $b < a$.

axiom of inverses for addition (p. 88). For every real number a, there is a real number $-a$ such that $a + (-a) = 0$ and $(-a) + a = 0$.

axiom of inverses for multiplication (p. 88). For every nonzero real number a, there is a real number $\frac{1}{a}$ such that $a \cdot \frac{1}{a} = 1$ and $\frac{1}{a} \cdot a = 1$.

axioms of closure (p. 88). For all real numbers a and b:
(Addition) $a + b$ is a real number.
(Multiplication) ab is a real number.

base (in percent problems) (p. 229). *See under* percentage.

base (in a power) (p. 7). One of the equal factors.

base angles of an isosceles triangle (p. 459). *See under* isosceles triangle.

base of an isosceles triangle (p. 459). *See under* isosceles triangle.

between (p. 256). b is between a and c if $a < b < c$ or $c > b > a$.

binary system of numeration (p. 266). A numeration system with base two, using digits "0" and "1".

binomial (p. 116). A polynomial of two terms.

boundary line (p. 360). A line which separates the plane into two half-planes.

circumference (p. 12). The perimeter of a circle.

closed half-plane (p. 361). The union of an open half-plane and its boundary.

commutative axioms (p. 88). For all real numbers a and b:

(Addition)	$a + b = b + a$
(Multiplication)	$ab = ba$.

complementary angles (p. 456). A pair of angles the sum of whose measures is 90°.

completing the square (p. 435). Adding a term to an expression in the form "$x^2 + bx$" to produce a trinomial square.

complex fraction (p. 210). A fraction whose numerator or denominator contains one or more fractions.

conjugates (p. 404). Two binomials of the form $x + \sqrt{y}$ and $x - \sqrt{y}$.

conjunction (p. 274). A sentence formed by joining two sentences by the word *and*.

consecutive even integers (p. 114). Obtained by counting by two's from any even integer.

consecutive integers (p. 113). Obtained by counting by one's from any given integer.

consecutive odd integers (p. 114). Obtained by counting by two's from any odd integer.

consistent equations (pp. 337–8). Simultaneous equations having at least one solution in common.

constant of variation (p. 327). In a direct variation expressed by $y = kx$, k is the constant of variation. Also called *constant of proportionality*.

constant term (p. 116). A numerical term with no variable expression.

converse (p. 180). The converse of a theorem is obtained by interchanging the "if" and "then" portions.

coordinate (p. 32). The number assigned to a point on the number line.

coordinate axes (p. 298). The axes (horizontal and vertical) of a coordinate system set up in a plane.

coordinate plane (p. 298). A plane in which a coordinate system has been set up.

coordinate system (pp. 296–8). A system of graphing ordered pairs of numbers in relation to two *axes* (*horizontal* and *vertical*) which in-tersect at right angles at their zero point (the *origin*). *See also under* plane rectangular coordinate system.

coordinates of a point (p. 297). The abscissa and ordinate of the point, written as an ordered pair of numbers.

correspondence (p. 287). A matching between the members of two sets.

corresponding angles (p. 461). *See under* similar triangles.

corresponding sides (p. 461). *See under* similar triangles.

cosine (p. 464). The cosine of $\angle A$ of a right triangle $= \dfrac{\text{length of leg adjacent to } \angle A}{\text{length of hypotenuse}}$.

counting numbers (p. 32). *See under* natural numbers.

cubic equation (p. 183). A polynomial equation of degree three.

degree (measure of an angle) (p. 454). $\frac{1}{180}$ of the rotation of a ray from one direction to its opposite.

degree of a monomial (p. 116). The number of times that a variable occurs as a factor in a monomial is the degree of the monomial in that variable. The sum of the degrees in each of the variables is the degree of the monomial. A nonzero constant has degree 0. 0 has no degree.

degree of a polynomial (p. 117). The greatest of the degrees of its terms after it has been simplified.

denominator (p. 197). In the fraction $\dfrac{a}{b}$, b is the denominator.

dependent equations (p. 338). If the equations of a system of simultaneous equations are equivalent, they are sometimes called dependent.

difference (p. 52). For any two real numbers a and b, the difference $a - b$ is the number whose sum with b is a.

directly proportional (p. 328). y is directly proportional to x if (x_1, y_1) and (x_2, y_2) are ordered pairs of a function, neither of which is $(0, 0)$, and this statement is true: $\dfrac{y_1}{x_1} = \dfrac{y_2}{x_2}$.

direct variation (p. 327). A function defined by an equation of the form $y = kx$, where k is a nonzero constant.

discriminant (p. 440). The value of $b^2 - 4ac$ is called the discriminant of the quadratic equation $ax^2 + bx + c = 0$.

disjoint sets (p. 270). Sets that have no members in common.

disjunction (p. 275). A sentence formed by joining two sentences by the word *or*.

distance formula (p. 412). For any points $P_1(x_1, y_1)$ and $P_2(x_2, y_2)$:
$$P_1P_2 = \sqrt{(x_2 - x_1)^2 + (y_2 - y_1)^2}.$$

distributive axiom of multiplication with respect to addition (p. 88). For all real numbers a, b, and c, $a(b + c) = ab + ac$ and $(b + c)a = ba + ca$.

divide-and-average method (p. 388). A way to find closer and closer approximations to the square root of a number that is not a perfect square by continuing to average pairs of factors.

domain of a function (p. 287). *See under* function.

domain of a relation (p. 301). *See under* relation.

domain of a variable (p. 4). The set of numbers that the variable may represent. Also called *replacement set*.

empty set (p. 107). The set with no members.

equal expressions (p. 1). Expressions that name the same number.

equal sets (p. 258). Sets that have the same members.

equation (p. 17). A statement formed by placing an equality symbol between two numerical or variable expressions.

equilateral triangle (p. 459). A triangle with all sides of equal length.

equivalent equations (inequalities) (pp. 49, 263). Equations (inequalities) having the same solution set over a given domain.

equivalent expressions (p. 102). Expressions which represent the same number for all values of the variables that they contain.

equivalent systems (p. 340). Systems of equations having the same solution set.

evaluate an expression (p. 5). Replace each variable in the expression by the numeral for a given value of the variable, and simplify the result.

exponent (p. 7). In a power, the number of times the base occurs as a factor.

exponential form (p. 8). The expression "x^3" is the exponential form of the third power of x.

extremes (p. 328). In the proportion $\dfrac{y_1}{x_1} = \dfrac{y_2}{x_2}$, y_1 and x_2 are the extremes.

factor (p. 7). When two or more numbers are multiplied, each of the numbers is a factor of the product.

factored form (p. 8). The expression "$x \cdot x \cdot x$" is the factored form of the third power of x, that is, x^3.

factoring (pp. 139, 151). Finding the factors of a number or an expression over a specified factor set.

factor set (p. 139). The set from which factors of a number may be selected.

finite set (p. 258). A set whose members can be counted.

first component (p. 293). The first number in an ordered pair.

formula (p. 12). An expression of numerical relationships between quantities such as physical or other measurements.

fraction (p. 197). An expression in the form $\dfrac{a}{b}$, $b \neq 0$.

fractional equation (p. 226). An equation which has a variable in the denominator of one or more terms.

function (p. 287). A function consists of two sets, the domain and the range, together with a rule which assigns to each member of the domain exactly one member of the range. Each member of the range must be assigned to at least one member of the domain.

graph of an equation (p. 312). All points, and only those points, whose coordinates satisfy the equation.

graph of an ordered pair of numbers (p. 297). The point in the plane paired with an ordered pair of real numbers.

graph of a number (p. 32). The point on the number line paired with the number.

graph of a function (relation) (p. 302). The graphs in the coordinate plane of all the ordered pairs that form the function (relation).

greatest common factor (p. 142). The greatest integer which is a factor of each of two or more integers.

greatest monomial factor of a polynomial (p. 152). The monomial factor having the greatest numerical coefficient and the greatest degree.

grouping symbol (p. 2). A device used to enclose a numerical expression. Examples include parentheses, brackets, and fraction bars.

half-plane (pp. 360–1). *See under* closed half-plane and open half-plane.

horizontal axis (p. 296). Horizontal number line in a plane.

hyperbola (p. 420). The graph of an equation of the form
$$xy = k, \; k \neq 0 \; (x \neq 0, y \neq 0).$$

hypotenuse (p. 459). The side of a right triangle opposite the right angle.

identity (p. 108). An equation which is true for every numerical replacement of the variable(s).

identity axioms (p. 88). For any real number a:
(Addition) $\qquad a + 0 = 0 + a = a$
(Multiplication) $\qquad a \cdot 1 = 1 \cdot a = a.$

identity elements (p. 88). 0 is the identity element for addition. 1 is the identity element for multiplication.

inconsistent equations (p. 338). Simultaneous equations having no solution in common.

independent equations (pp. 337–8). Simultaneous equations that are not equivalent.

inequality (p. 18). A statement formed by placing an inequality symbol between two numerical or variable expressions.

infinite set (p. 258). A set for which the counting of members would never end.

integers (p. 32). The numbers in the set
$$\{ \ldots, -3, -2, -1, 0, 1, 2, 3, \ldots \}.$$

integral factors (p. 139). Factors taken from the set of integers.

intersection of sets (p. 270). For any two sets A and B, the set consisting of all members belonging to both A and B is the intersection of A and B.

inverse operations (p. 85). Operations that "undo" each other; for example, addition and subtraction.

inverse variation (p. 419). A function defined by an equation of the form $xy = k$, where k is a nonzero constant.

inverse variation as the square (p. 424). A function defined by an equation of the form $x^2 y = k$, where k is a nonzero constant.

irrational number (p. 387). A real number which cannot be expressed in the form $\dfrac{r}{s}$, where r and s are integers, $s \neq 0$.

irreducible polynomial (p. 168). A polynomial which is not the product of polynomials of lower positive degree belonging to a specified set.

isosceles triangle (p. 459). A triangle with two sides of equal length. If $MN = NP$ in $\triangle MNP$, MP is the *base* of the triangle and $\angle M$ and $\angle P$ are the *base angles*.

least common denominator (L.C.D.) (p. 215). The least positive common multiple of the denominators of two or more fractions.

leg of a right triangle (p. 459). One of the two sides which form the right angle.

linear direct variation (p. 327). *See under* direct variation.

linear equation in one variable (p. 183). A polynomial equation of degree one.

linear equation in two variables (p. 312). Any equation equivalent to one of the form $Ax + By + C$, where A, B, and C are real numbers with A and B not both zero.

linear function (p. 313). A function whose ordered pairs satisfy a linear equation.

linear term (p. 165). A term of degree one in the variable.

line segment (p. 453). A subset of a line consisting of two points and the part of the line between them.

lowest terms (p. 197). The fraction $\frac{a}{b}$ is in lowest terms when c is the greatest common factor of ac and bc in $\frac{ac}{bc}$.

maximum point of a quadratic function (p. 427). The point whose y-coordinate is the greatest value the function can have.

means (p. 328). In the proportion $\frac{y_1}{x_1} = \frac{y_2}{x_2}$, x_1 and y_2 are the means.

member of a set (p. 17). Any object in the set.

members of an equation (p. 17). The expressions joined by the symbol of equality.

members of an inequality (pp. 255, 262). The expressions joined by an inequality symbol.

minimum point of a quadratic function (p. 427). A point whose y-coordinate is the least value the function can have.

mixed expression (p. 218). The sum or difference of a polynomial and a fraction.

mixed numeral (p. 218). A numeral, like $3\frac{2}{5}$, which denotes the sum of an integer and a fraction.

monomial (p. 116). A term which is either a numeral, a variable, or a product of a numeral and one or more variables.

monomial factor (p. 152). A monomial which is a factor of each of the terms of a polynomial.

multiple (p. 114). The product of any real number and an integer is a multiple of the real number.

multiplication axiom of order (p. 263). For all real numbers a, b, and c:

1. If $a < b$ and $c > 0$, then $ac < bc$;
   if $a > b$ and $c > 0$, then $ac > bc$.

2. If $a < b$ and $c < 0$, then $ac > bc$;
   if $a > b$ and $c < 0$, then $ac < bc$.

multiplication property of equality (p. 74). If $a = b$, then $ac = bc$ and $ca = cb$.

multiplicative inverse (p. 70). For a nonzero real number b, the real number $\frac{1}{b}$, for which $b \cdot \frac{1}{b} = 1$ and $\frac{1}{b} \cdot b = 1$. Also called *reciprocal*.

multiplicative property of -1 (p. 63). For all real numbers a, $a(-1) = -a$ and $(-1)a = -a$.

multiplicative property of zero (p. 92). $a \cdot 0 = 0$ and $0 \cdot a = 0$.

natural numbers (p. 32). The numbers in the set $\{1, 2, 3, 4, \ldots\}$.

negative direction (p. 31). The direction from "0" to "-1" on a number line.

negative numbers (pp. 31–2). The numbers whose graphs are in the negative direction on a number line.

negative of a number (p. 38). *See under* additive inverse.

nonterminating decimal (p. 378). A decimal for which the division process is unending.

number system (p. 376). A set of numbers together with the operations of addition and multiplication.

numeral (p. 1). A name for a number. Also called *numerical expression*.

numerator (p. 197). In the fraction $\frac{a}{b}$, a is the numerator.

numerical coefficient (p. 101). In a term, the factor which is not a variable; for example, 5 in $5xy$.

obtuse angle (p. 454). An angle measuring between 90° and 180°.

one-to-one correspondence (p. 33). A pairing of the members of two sets such that each member of one set is paired with one and only one member of the other set, and each member of the second set is paired with one and only one member of the first set.

open expression (p. 4). *See under* variable expression.

open half-plane (p. 360). One of the two regions into which a line separates the plane. The boundary line is not a member of either open half-plane.

open sentence (p. 18). An equation or inequality which contains a variable.

open sentence in two variables (p. 306). An equation or inequality which contains two variables.

opposite of a number (p. 38). *See under* additive inverse.

ordered pair (p. 291). A pair of elements in which the order is specified.

ordinate (p. 297). The coordinate of the point on the vertical axis where a horizontal line from a given point meets the vertical axis.

origin (pp. 31, 296). The starting point, labeled "0", on a number line; the zero point of both of two number lines that intersect at right angles.

parabola (p. 426). The graph of a quadratic function.

parallel lines (p. 338). Lines that lie in the same plane but have no point in common.

percent (p. 228). A notation for a ratio with the denominator 100; $\frac{3}{100} = 3\%$.

percentage (p. 229). A number equal to the product of a *rate* (percent) and another number, called the *base*.

perimeter (p. 12). The perimeter of a geometric figure is the distance around it.

plane rectangular coordinate system (p. 298). One-to-one correspondence between ordered pairs of real numbers and points of a coordinate plane.

plotting a point (p. 297). Locating the graph of an ordered pair of real numbers on the coordinate plane.

polynomial (p. 116). A sum of monomials.

polynomial equation (p. 183). An equation in which both members are polynomials in one variable.

positive direction (p. 31). The direction from "0" to "1" on a number line.

positive numbers (pp. 31–2). The numbers whose graphs are in the positive direction on a number line.

power (p. 7). A product in which all the factors, except 1, are the same. For example, the fourth power of 5 is defined by $5^4 = 5 \cdot 5 \cdot 5 \cdot 5$.

prime factorization (p. 140). The expression of a positive integer as a product of prime factors is the prime factorization of the integer.

prime factors (p. 140). Factors which are prime numbers or prime polynomials.

prime number (p. 140). An integer, greater than one, which has no positive integral factor other than itself and one.

prime polynomial (p. 168). An irreducible polynomial whose greatest monomial factor is 1.

principal square root (p. 382). The positive square root, denoted by $\sqrt{}$.

proof (p. 89). Logical reasoning from known facts and axioms to a theorem.

property of completeness (p. 387). Every decimal represents a real number, and every real number has a decimal representation.

property of density (p. 373). Between every pair of different rational numbers there is another rational number.

property of the opposite of a sum (p. 91). $-(a + b) = (-a) + (-b)$.

property of square roots of equal numbers (p. 392). If r and s are any real numbers, then $r^2 = s^2$ if and only if $r = s$ or $r = -s$.

proportion (p. 228). An equation made up of two equal ratios.

protractor (p. 454). An instrument used to find the degree measure of an angle.

Pythagorean theorem (p. 394). In any right triangle, the square of the length of the hypotenuse equals the sum of the squares of the lengths of the other two sides.

quadrant (p. 298). One of the four regions into which the coordinate axes separate the plane.

quadratic direct variation (p. 415). A function defined by an equation of the form $y = kx^2$, where k is a nonzero constant.

quadratic equation (p. 183). A polynomial equation of degree two.

quadratic formula (p. 439). If $ax^2 + bx + c = 0$, $a \neq 0$, and $b^2 - 4ac \geq 0$, then

$$x = \frac{-b \pm \sqrt{b^2 - 4ac}}{2a}.$$

quadratic function (p. 426). A function defined by an equation of the form
$$y = ax^2 + bx + c, \; a \neq 0.$$

quadratic polynomial (p. 165). A polynomial of degree two that contains a single variable.

quadratic term (p. 165). A term of degree two in the variable.

quotient (p. 78). The quotient $a \div b$, $b \neq 0$, is the number whose product with b is a.

radical (p. 382). An expression of the form $\sqrt{a}$.

radical equation (p. 406). An equation having a variable in a radicand.

radical sign (p. 382). The symbol $\sqrt{}$.

radicand (p. 382). An expression beneath a radical sign.

range of a function (p. 287). *See under* function.

range of a relation (p. 301). *See under* relation.

ratio (p. 201). The ratio of one number to another (not zero) is the quotient of the first number divided by the second.

rational expression (pp. 197, 371). A fraction; an expression for a rational number.

rationalizing a denominator (p. 398). The process of changing the form of a fraction with an irrational denominator to an equal fraction with a rational denominator.

rational number (p. 371). A real number that can be expressed as a ratio of two integers (the second integer not zero).

ray (p. 454). A subset of a line that consists of a point A and all points of the line on one side of A.

real number (p. 32). Any number paired with a point on the number line.

reciprocal (p. 70). *See under* multiplicative inverse.

reducing to lowest terms (p. 197). Dividing the numerator and the denominator of a fraction by their greatest common denominator.

reflexive property of equality (p. 88). $a = a$.

relation (p. 301). Any set of ordered pairs. The set of first components is the *domain* and the set of second components is called the *range*.

repeating decimal (p. 378). A nonterminating decimal in which the same digit or block of digits repeats unendingly. Also called *periodic decimal*.

replacement set (p. 4). *See under*, domain of a variable.

right angle (p. 454). An angle measuring $90°$.

right triangle (p. 459). A triangle with a right angle.

root of an open sentence (p. 18). A solution of the sentence.

rounding a decimal (p. 380). Breaking off a decimal to achieve an approximation, by adding 1 to the value of the last digit kept if the first digit dropped is 5 or more, or, otherwise, by leaving unchanged the digits that are kept.

satisfy (p. 18). Each member of the solution set of an open sentence satisfies that sentence.

second component (p. 293). The second number in an ordered pair.

set (p. 4). Collection of objects.

sides of an angle (p. 454). *See under* angle.

sides of a triangle (p. 459). *See under* triangle.

significant digits (p. 66). The following numbers are expressed with 6 significant digits: 123,475; 2.00027; 235.650; 0.0123456; 243,724,000 or 2.43724×10^8.

similar terms (p. 102). Terms that are exactly alike or that differ only in their numerical coefficients.

similar triangles (p. 461). $\triangle ABC$ and $\triangle DEF$ are similar triangles if $m\angle A = m\angle D$, $m\angle B = m\angle E$, and $m\angle C = m\angle F$. $\angle A$ and $\angle D$ are corresponding angles (as are $\angle B$ and $\angle E$, $\angle C$ and $\angle F$). The sides opposite corresponding angles are corresponding sides.

simple form of a polynomial (p. 117). A polynomial is in simple form if no two of its terms are similar.

simple interest (p. 236). Simple interest I on an investment of P dollars at the interest rate R for T years is given by the formula $I = PRT$.

simplest form of a radical (p. 398). A radical expression in which no integral radicand has a square factor other than 1, no fractions are under a radical sign, and no radicals are in a denominator.

simplify (p. 1). Replace a numerical expression by the simplest, or most common, name of its value.

simultaneous equations (p. 337). *See under* system of simultaneous equations.

sine (p. 464). The sine of $\angle A$ of a right triangle =
$$\frac{\text{length of leg opposite } \angle A}{\text{length of hypotenuse}}.$$

slope of a line (p. 315). The steepness of a non-vertical line as defined by the quotient
$$\frac{\text{difference of ordinates}}{\text{difference of abscissas}}.$$
A horizontal line has slope 0; a vertical line has no slope.

slope-intercept form of a linear equation (p. 321). $y = mx + b$, where m is the slope of the line represented by the equation and b is its y-intercept.

solution (p. 18). A value of a variable that converts an open sentence into a true statement.

solution of an open sentence in two variables (p. 306). An ordered pair of values for which the sentence becomes a true sentence.

solution of a system of two equations in two variables (p. 337). An ordered pair of numbers that satisfies both equations.

solution set of an open sentence (p. 18). The set that consists of the members of the domain of the variable for which the sentence is true is called the solution set of the sentence over that domain.

solve (p. 18). Find the solution set of an open sentence over a given domain.

square root (p. 382). The number a is a square root of the number b if $a^2 = b$.

subset (p. 258). If every member of a set B is also a member of a set A, then B is a subset of A.

substitution method (p. 341). A method for finding the solution of a pair of linear equations in two variables by: (1) solving one equation for one of the variables, (2) substituting the resulting expression in the other equation, (3) solving this derived equation, (4) finding the corresponding value of the other variable.

substitution principle (p. 2). Changing the numeral by which a number is named in an expression does not change the value of the expression.

supplementary angles (p. 457). Two angles the sum of whose measures is $180°$.

symmetric property of equality (p. 88). If $a = b$, then $b = a$.

system of simultaneous equations (p. 337). A set of equations in the same variables.

tangent (p. 464). The tangent of $\angle A$ of a right triangle $= \dfrac{\text{length of leg opposite } \angle A}{\text{length of leg adjacent to } \angle A}$.

term (p. 101). A mathematical expression using numerals or variables or both to indicate a product or a quotient.

terminating decimal (p. 378). A decimal for which the division process stops because a remainder of 0 is reached.

theorem (p. 88). A statement that is shown to be true using axioms, definitions, and other theorems in a logical development.

transformation Each of the following always produces an equation equivalent to the original equation:

by addition (p. 49). Adding the same number to each member.

by division (p. 82). Dividing each member by the same nonzero number.

by multiplication (p. 74). Multiplying each member by the same nonzero number.

by substitution (p. 49). Replacing either member by an expression equivalent to it.

by subtraction (p. 56). Subtracting the same number from each member.

transitive axiom of order (p. 261). For all real numbers a, b, and c:

1. If $a < b$ and $b < c$, then $a < c$.

2. If $c > b$ and $b > a$, then $c > a$.

transitive property of equality (p. 88). If $a = b$ and $b = c$, then $a = c$.

triangle (p. 459). A figure formed by connecting three points not on a line by segments. In $\triangle ABC$: $\overline{AB}$, $\overline{BC}$, and $\overline{CA}$ are the *sides* of the triangle; A, B, and C are the *vertices* of the triangle; and $\angle BAC$, $\angle ACB$, and $\angle CBA$ are the *angles* of the triangle.

trigonometric functions (p. 465). Functions having the values $\cos A$, $\sin A$, and $\tan A$, where A is a member of the set of acute angles.

trigonometric ratios (p. 464). In a right triangle, the ratios (sine, cosine, tangent) of the sides associated with an acute angle of the triangle.

trinomial (p. 116). A polynomial of three terms.

trinomial square (p. 160). A trinomial obtained by squaring a binomial. The pattern of the terms is $a^2 + 2ab + b^2$ or $a^2 - 2ab + b^2$.

uniform motion (p. 240). An object which moves without changing its speed, or rate, is said to be in uniform motion.

union of sets (p. 271). For any two sets A and B, the set consisting of all members belonging to at least one of the sets A and B is the union of A and B.

unit distance (p. 31). The distance between "0" and "1" on a number line.

values of a function (p. 288). Members of the range of the function.

values of a variable (p. 4). Numbers in the domain of the variable.

variable (p. 4). A symbol used to represent one or more numbers.

variable expression (p. 4). An expression containing a variable. Also called *open expression*.

Venn diagram (p. 270). A representation of the relationships among some sets.

vertex of an angle (p. 454). *See under* angle.

vertex of a parabola (p. 427). The maximum or minimum point of the graph of
$$y = ax^2 + bx + c, a \neq 0.$$

vertical angles (p. 456). Two angles whose sides are rays in the same line but in opposite directions.

vertical axis (p. 296). A vertical number line at right angles to a horizontal number line such that both lines have the same zero point.

vertices of a triangle (p. 459). *See under* triangle.

volume (p. 12). The volume of a solid is the number of unit cubes it contains.

whole numbers (p. 32). The numbers in the set $\{0, 1, 2, 3, \ldots\}$.

x-intercept (p. 440). The abscissa of the point of intersection of a graph with the x-axis.

y-intercept (p. 321). The ordinate of the point where a line crosses the y-axis.

zero of a function (p. 445). A zero of a function f is a solution of the equation $f(x) = 0$.

zero-product property (p. 180). For all real numbers a and b, $ab = 0$ if and only if $a = 0$ or $b = 0$.

Index

Answers to Odd-Numbered Exercises

CHAPTER 1   INTRODUCTION TO ALGEBRA

Written Exercises, page 3   1. 12   3. 42   5. 3
   7. 30   9. 6   11. 7   13. 7   15. 12   17. equal
   19. not equal   21. not equal   23. equal

Written Exercises, page 6   1. 0   3. 4   5. 16
   7. 10   9. 6   11. 6   13. 60   15. 63   17. 4
   19. 1   21. 16   23. 10   25. 3

Written Exercises, page 9   1. a^3 3. b^2 5. $5a^2$
   7. $8a^2b$ 9. $12c^3d^2$ 11. $(a + b)^3$ 13. $(y - 1)^2$
   15. $\dfrac{32}{(c + d)^3}$ 17. $(x + y)^4$ 19. 49   21. 5   23. 18
   25. 36   27. 512   29. 72   31. 75   33. 45   35. 10
   37. 5   39. 3   41. 1   43. 2

Written Exercises, page 11   1. 8   3. 5   5. 9
   7. 3   9. 1   11. 3   13. 25   15. 3   17. 2   19. 9
   21. 4   23. 1   25. 2   27. 17   29. 1   31. 5
   33. 5   35. 6

Written Exercises, pages 12–15   1. 12   3. 11
   5. 14   7. 10   9. 6   11. 66   13. 44   15. 30
   17. 28   19. 64   21. 12   23. 44   25. 60
   27. 55   29. 154   31. 27   33. 15   35. 30
   37. 100   39. 1694   41. 8624   43. 40 cm
   45. 40 m   47. 24 cm²   49. 160 cm³
   51. $P = 2a + \frac{1}{2}\pi b$

Written Exercises, page 19   1. {6}   3. {3}
   5. {5}   7. {2}   9. {2, 3, 4, 5, 6}   11. {2}
   13. {4}   15. {1, 3, 4, 5, 6}

Written Exercises, page 21   1. a. s b. $4s = 20$
   3. a. r b. $2\pi r = 35$ 5. a. c b. $6c = 1.20$
   7. a. p b. $1.50 = p - 1.00$ 9. a. f
   b. $2f + 2 = 10 - 4$

Written Exercises, page 24   1. 14 points
   3. 15 minutes   5. 60 kilograms

Maintaining Skills, page 29   1. 2108   3. 5092
   5. 7377   7. 1011   9. 3108   11. 759   13. 2772
   15. 165,678   17. 2,469,392   19. 28   21. 54
   23. 243

CHAPTER 2   ADDITION AND SUBTRACTION

Written Exercises, page 34   1. {0, 1, 2}
   3. {⁻1, 1, 3}   5. {⁻3, ⁻2, 0}   7. {⁻3, ⁻1, 1}
   9. {1, 2, 4, 6}   11. {⁻6, ⁻4, ⁻2, 0}   13. W, Y, Z
   15. V, T, R 17. P, Q, R 19. U, W, Y
   21.
   23.

Written Exercises, pages 36–37   1. 0   3. ⁻5
   5. 52   7. ⁻28   9. ⁻58   11. ⁻14   13. $a = 3$
   15. $x = ⁻4$ 17. $r = ⁻8$ 19. $t = ⁻7$ 21. $d = 9$
   23. $n = 0$

Problems, page 37   1. 7600 meters   3. $121
   5. 2:00 P.M.

Written Exercises, page 40   1. 12   3. −8
   5. −11   7. 10   9. −8   11. 4   13. 10   15. 18
   17. 6   19. −2   21. 6   23. −20

Just for Fun, page 41

			1	4	2	8	5	7		
				2	8	5	7	1	4	
					4	2	8	5	7	1
		5	7	1	4	2	8			
			7	1	4	2	8	5		
8	5	7	1	4	2					

Written Exercises, page 44   1. 14   3. 56   5. 71
   7. 7   9. 0   11. −31   13. −37   15. 123
   17. −18

Problems, page 45   1. $167   3. net gain of
   $29,000   5. $272.10   7. 216 meters

Consumer Note, page 47   Outstanding checks:
   $20.38; Corrected balance: $241.39

Written Exercises, pages 50–51 1. $y = 25$
3. $t = 18$ 5. $x = 30$ 7. $z = -16$
9. $x = -37$ 11. $k = -18$ 13. $x = -21$
15. $p = -21$ 17. $t = 38$ 19. $z = -3$
21. $r = 12$ 23. $v = 0$ 25. $t = 6$ 27. $z = -6$
29. $v = 3$ 31. $y = -3$ 33. $x = -9$ 35. $x = 9$

Problems, page 51 1. 5 3. -6 5. $2.00
7. 24 bottles 9. 3

Written Exercises, page 55 1. -180 3. 31
5. -12 7. -70 9. -120 11. 275 13. 107
15. 255 17. 0 19. -8 21. 1350 23. -1
25. 22 27. -33 29. 45

Problems, page 55 1. 7 blocks 3. 10 °C
5. 4504 meters

Written Exercises, page 57 1. $u = 24$
3. $w = -22$ 5. $s = 0$ 7. $x = 17$ 9. $r = 10$
11. $s = 16$ 13. $x = 14$ 15. $s = -8$
17. $u = 9$ 19. $w = 8$ 21. $p = -9$ 23. $x = 7$

Problems, page 57 1. 30 3. -5 5. 1 7. $4
9. 23 seconds

Maintaining Skills, page 61 1. 22.073 3. 41.109
5. 419.66 7. 610.00 9. 6.09 11. 2.746
13. 97.83 15. 11.2179 17. 21.735
19. 56.862 21. 2.9848 23. 88.4802
25. 22.7115

CHAPTER 3 MULTIPLICATION AND DIVISION
Written Exercises, page 65 1. 960 3. -480
5. -90 7. 0 9. 2,000,000 11. -8000
13. 20 15. 120 17. 240 19. 10,000
21. -400 23. 280 25. -9 27. 350

Problems, page 65 1. $240 3. $12.50

Just for Fun, page 66 The sum of each row,
column, and diagonal is 0.

Written Exercises, pages 68–69 1. -60
3. -26 5. 0 7. -28 9. 64 11. 0
13. -399 15. -12 17. -90 19. 0 21. 76
23. -15 25. 0 27. 3600 29. 4251
31. 553,553 33. 390,000 35. -3600
37. 518 39. 15

Written Exercises, pages 71–72 1. 2 3. -10
5. 1 7. $-\frac{13}{2}$ 9. $-ab$ 11. $6b$ 13. $7a^2$
15. $-4c^4$ 17. $3x + 5$ 19. $7a - 12b$
21. $5x + y$ 23. $-b^2 + c^2$

Consumer Note, page 73 1. $.48 per pound
2. one 24-ounce can

Puzzle Time, page 73 Three possible numbers are
11, 23, and 35.

Written Exercises, page 76 1. $u = 126$
3. $x = -738$ 5. $t = 13$ 7. $y = -150$
9. $x = 105$ 11. $r = -5$ 13. $w = 3$ 15. $s = -7$
17. $t = 6$ 19. $y = -\frac{1}{5}$ 21. $t = \frac{4}{5}$ 23. $s = -\frac{1}{10}$

Problems, page 77 1. 21 meters
3. 48 years old 5. 16¢ 7. 12 kilometers

Written Exercises, page 81 1. -4 3. -81
5. 64 7. -30 9. $-5x$ 11. -35 13. -3
15. -3 17. -1 19. 3 21. 8 23. -3
25. -3 27. -3 29. 5 31. -16

Written Exercises, page 83 1. $t = 30$
3. $z = -9$ 5. $w = -17$ 7. $z = 14$
9. $a = 12$ 11. $s = -31$ 13. $d = 37$
15. $g = -17$ 17. $j = 420$ 19. $r = 710$
21. $h = -24$ 23. $c = 13$

Problems, page 83 1. -15 3. $1.08 5. 15¢
7. $.15

Written Exercises, pages 86–87 1. $t = 4$
3. $x = -1$ 5. $z = 14$ 7. $t = -60$
9. $x = -7$ 11. $x = -4$ 13. $z = -4$
15. $t = 8$ 17. $x = -1$ 19. $r = 5$ 21. $s = 5$
23. $a = -3$ 25. $x = -2$ 27. $w = 0$
29. $a = -3$ 31. $x = 3$ 33. $t = 3$ 35. $r = 1$

Problems, page 87 1. 31 3. 7 5. -9 7. 4
9. 20 points 11. 8 13. -3

Written Exercises, page 90 1. $a = 11, b = 4$
3. $a = -4, b = 3$ 5. $a = -12, b = -4$

Cumulative Review, page 98 1. 90 3. 19 5. 1
7. 10 9. 7 11. -1 13. -30 15. 32
17. $3a + 6b$ 19. $-4\frac{2}{9}$ 21. 40 23. 3 25. {4}
27.

29. $t = 4$ 31. $y = 2$ 33. $m = -2$ 35. $t = 0$
37. $y = 18$ 39. $y = -\frac{2}{3}$ 41. $x = 4$
43. $b = -5$ 45. 3 47. 26

Maintaining Skills, page 99 1. 5.3 3. 13.2
5. 62.4 7. 0.0314 9. 5 11. 13 13. 62
15. 0 17. 0.25 19. 0.01 21. 25% 23. 60%
25. 5% 27. 110% 29. 71 31. 198

CHAPTER 4   WORKING WITH POLYNOMIALS

Written Exercises, page 103 1. $2y$ 3. $2a - b$
5. $5s - 17$ 7. $47x - 2y$ 9. $-6p + q$ 11. -2
13. $a + 5b$ 15. $-3h - 9m$ 17. $-a^2 - 25d$
19. $-12x^2 + x - 2$ 21. $-148rp + 68$

Just for Fun, page 103 20 problems

Written Exercises, page 105 1. $v = 6$ 3. $w = 5$
5. $y = -1$ 7. $m = -8$ 9. $t = -5$ 11. $x = 3$
13. $k = 1$ 15. $z = -8$ 17. $x = -8$
19. $t = 2$ 21. $r = 4$ 23. $x = 5$ 25. $t = -3$
27. $y = 3$ 29. $z = -2$

Problems, pages 105–106 1. 48 kg 3. 54 points
5. 18 cm and 9 cm 7. 45 9. Joe: 68 kg;
sister: 32 kg 11. 9 years old 13. 750 m
15. $130 in July, $260 in August, $235 in
September 17. 44 m wide, 59 m long

Written Exercises, pages 108–109 1. $u = 4$
3. $x = 20$ 5. $h = 5$ 7. $u = -8$ 9. $x = 12$
11. $z = -5$ 13. $x = -11$ 15. $v = -3$
17. no root 19. $u = -4$ 21. $x = 3$
23. $n = 13$ 25. $x = -6$ 27. $t = 5$ 29. $k = 9$
31. $y = 0$ 33. no root 35. identity
37. $x = -2$ 39. $v = 2$

Problems, page 109 1. 9 3. 8 5. Jim: $3;
Joan: $9 7. quarters 9. 11 and -3
11. Steve: 8 baskets; Mike: 24 baskets
13. 51 mg

Problems, page 111 1. 12 years old
3. Roger: 12; sister: 5 5. 16 years
7. 33 years old

Applications, page 112 1. $40; $10; $\frac{10}{40} = 25\%$
3. $20; $4; $\frac{4}{20} = 20\%$ 5. $30; $3; $\frac{3}{30} = 10\%$

Problems, page 115 1. 16 and 17 3. 18, 20,
and 22 5. $-3, -1, 1,$ and 3 7. 25
9. -9 and -8 11. 7, 9, and 11 13. always
15. always 17. never

Written Exercises, pages 118–119 1. $5x + 1$
3. $4a + b$ 5. $7a - b + 6$ 7. $2x^2 + 3x + 3$
9. a^2 11. $2a^2 + 2b^2$ 13. $3x + 3$ 15. $2a + 3b$
17. $3a - 3b + 2$ 19. $-7x + 3$

21. $2x^2y - 3a^2$ 23. $-4ab$ 25. $x = 6$
27. $u = 6$ 29. $x = 8$ 31. $x = 3$ 33. $z = -7$
35. $x = 5$

Puzzle Time, page 119 David is now 24.

Written Exercises, page 121 1. $8a^3b^3$
3. $-4h^4k^3$ 5. $6m^2n^2$ 7. $2x^2y^3$ 9. $-6p^5q^5$
11. $-a^2b^2$ 13. $u^3v^3w^3$ 15. $k^3l^3m^3$
17. $-6x^3y^2z$ 19. x^{n+1} 21. a^{3r} 23. b^n 25. $8a^4$
27. $11x^4$ 29. $5a^4b^4$ 31. $16x^3y^4z^3$

Written Exercises, page 123 1. $25c^2$ 3. $-8x^6$
5. $8a^7$ 7. a^4b^4 9. $-24s^4t^3$ 11. $32w^7$
13. $-4x^7y^8$ 15. a^9b^7 17. $2x^6y^4z^4$ 19. $27c^7d^2$
21. a^nb^n 23. $x^{2n}y^{2n}$ 25. $2a^4b^6$ 27. $8x^3y^4$
29. $7h^{10}k^5$

Written Exercises, pages 125–126
1. $2x^2 - 2xy + 6y^2$ 3. $-6 + 3x + 3x^2$
5. $2a^3 - 2ab^2$ 7. $c^4d^4 + 2c^3d^3 + c^2d^2$
9. $-2a^3b + 6a^2b^2 + 4ab^3$
11. $-w^2z^3 + 2wz^3 - z^3$
13. $3x^2y^2 - 6x^3y^3 + 9x^4y^4 - 12x^5y^5$
15. $-12k^3m^2 + 18k^2m^3 - 24k^3m^3 + 6k^4m^4$
17. $x = 5$ 19. $t = 3$ 21. $z = 2$ 23. $x = 3$
25. $x = 7$ 27. $n = -18$ (Answers to Exs.
29–36 may vary.) 29. $2w^2$, where w = width
31. $\frac{1}{2}b^2 - \frac{3}{2}b$, where b = length of base
33. $12r + 360$, where r = rate/month the first
3 months 35. $60w - 2w^2$, where w = width
37. $s = -10$ 39. $x = 1$ 41. $t = -14$
43. $t = 3$

Extra for Experts, page 127 1. 200 3. 4 5. 2

Written Exercises, page 130 1. $c^2 + 3c + 2$
3. $t^2 + t - 2$ 5. $a^2 - 4$ 7. $z^2 - 6z + 9$
9. $2x^2 + 5x + 2$ 11. $3r^2 + 10r - 8$
13. $2z^2 - 5z + 2$ 15. $6u^2 + 7u + 2$
17. $9x^2 - 1$ 19. $6a^2 - 17a + 12$
21. $a^2 + 3ab + 2b^2$ 23. $4c^2 - 20cd + 25d^2$
25. $a^4 - 1$ 27. $u^4 - 4u^2v^2 + 4v^4$
29. $a^3 + 3a^2 - a - 3$ 31. $r^3 + r^2 - 7r - 3$
33. $2x^3 + x^2 + 5x - 3$ 35. $s^3 + s^2t - st^2 + 2t^3$
37. $3x^2 + 5x - 5$ 39. $x^4 + x^3 - x^2 - 7x - 6$
41. $a^3 - b^3$ 43. $s^4 - t^4$
45. $x^4 + 3x^3y + x^2y^2 - 2xy^3 - y^4$

Just for Fun, page 130

When $x = 1$:

⑮

7	0	8	15
6	5	4	15
2	10	3	15
15	15	15	⑮

When $x = -1$:

⑨

5	4	6	15
10	3	2	15
0	8	7	15
15	15	15	⑮

When $x = 2$:

⑨

14	-5	6	15
1	3	11	15
0	17	-2	15
15	15	15	⑮

Problems, pages 132–133 1. 40.8 cm by 50.8 cm 3. 15 m by 22 m 5. Ace: 3 m; Goliath: 4 m 7. 5 m 9. 40 cm by 120 cm

Just for Fun, page 133 25, 30, 35; 30, 35, 40; 35, 40, 45

Consumer Note, page 134 1. 14.75 3. 13.93 5. 23.94

Maintaining Skills, page 137 1. $\frac{1}{2}$ 3. $\frac{1}{3}$ 5. $\frac{5}{7}$ 7. $\frac{4}{9}$ 9. $\frac{7}{11}$ 11. $\frac{2}{3}$ 13. $\frac{3}{4}$ 15. $\frac{9}{10}$ 17. $\frac{2}{15}$ 19. $\frac{5}{4}$ 21. $\frac{6}{35}$ 23. $\frac{5}{12}$ 25. $\frac{11}{15}$ 27. $\frac{21}{10}$ 29. $\frac{3}{10}$ 31. 6

CHAPTER 5 FACTORING

Written Exercises, pages 141–142 1. $3 \cdot 17$ 3. $2^4 \cdot 3^2$ 5. $2^5 \cdot 5$ 7. $2^3 \cdot 3 \cdot 5^2$ 9. $2^3 \cdot 31$ 11. $5 \cdot 7 \cdot 13$ 13. 1, 3, 7, 21 15. 1, 2, 5, 7, 10, 14, 35, 70 17. 1, 2, 3, 4, 6, 8, 9, 12, 18, 24, 36, 72 19. 1, 2, 3, 4, 6, 8, 12, 16, 24, 48 21. 1, 2, 4, 8, 11, 22, 44, 88 23. 1, 3, 5, 9, 15, 45 25. $1 \cdot 21$, $3 \cdot 7$, $(-1)(-21)$, $(-3)(-7)$ 27. $1 \cdot 70$, $2 \cdot 35$, $5 \cdot 14$, $7 \cdot 10$, $(-1)(-70)$, $(-2)(-35)$, $(-5)(-14)$, $(-7)(-10)$ 29. $1 \cdot 72$, $2 \cdot 36$, $3 \cdot 24$, $4 \cdot 18$, $6 \cdot 12$, $8 \cdot 9$, $(-1)(-72)$,

$(-2)(-36)$, $(-3)(-24)$, $(-4)(-18)$, $(-6)(-12)$, $(-8)(-9)$ 31. $1 \cdot 48$, $2 \cdot 24$, $3 \cdot 16$, $4 \cdot 12$, $6 \cdot 8$, $(-1)(-48)$, $(-2)(-24)$, $(-3)(-16)$, $(-4)(-12)$, $(-6)(-8)$ 33. $1 \cdot 88$, $2 \cdot 44$, $4 \cdot 22$, $8 \cdot 11$, $(-1)(-88)$, $(-2)(-44)$, $(-4)(-22)$, $(-8)(-11)$ 35. $1 \cdot 45$, $3 \cdot 15$, $5 \cdot 9$, $(-1)(-45)$, $(-3)(-15)$, $(-5)(-9)$ 37. $(-1)(21)$, $(1)(-21)$, $(-3)(7)$, $(3)(-7)$ 39. $(-1)(70)$, $(1)(-70)$, $(-2)(35)$, $(2)(-35)$, $(-5)(14)$, $(5)(-14)$, $(-7)(10)$, $(7)(-10)$ 41. $(-1)(72)$, $(1)(-72)$, $(-2)(36)$, $(2)(-36)$, $(-3)(24)$, $(3)(-24)$, $(-4)(18)$, $(4)(-18)$, $(-6)(12)$, $(6)(-12)$, $(-8)(9)$, $(8)(-9)$ 43. $(-1)(48)$, $(1)(-48)$, $(-2)(24)$, $(2)(-24)$, $(-3)(16)$, $(3)(-16)$, $(-4)(12)$, $(4)(-12)$, $(-6)(8)$, $(6)(-8)$ 45. $(-1)(88)$, $(1)(-88)$, $(-2)(44)$, $(2)(-44)$, $(-4)(22)$, $(4)(-22)$, $(-8)(11)$, $(8)(-11)$ 47. $(-1)(45)$, $(1)(-45)$, $(-3)(15)$, $(3)(-15)$, $(-5)(9)$, $(5)(-9)$ 49. 13 51. 42 53. 28 55. 84

Extra for Experts, page 144
1. $a_3(1000) + a_2(100) + a_1(10)$ is divisible by 2; hence, if a_0 is divisible by 2, the whole number is also. 3. $a_3(1000) + a_2(100) + a_1(10)$ is divisible by 10; hence, if a_0 is divisible by 10 (i.e., $a_0 = 0$), the whole number is also. 5. Yes 7. Yes 9. $a_3(1000) + a_4(10,000) + a_5(100,000) + \cdots$ is divisible by 8; thus, the whole number is divisible if $a_2(100) + a_1(10) + a_0$ is divisible. If $4a_2 + 2a_1 + a_0$ is divisible by 8, then
$4a_2 + 2a_1 + a_0 = 8n$;
$25(4a_2 + 2a_1 + a_0) = 25 \cdot 8n$;
$100a_2 + 50a_1 + 25a_0 = 8 \cdot 25n$;
$100a_2 + 10a_1 + a_0 = 8 \cdot 25n - 40a_1 - 24a_0 = 8(25n - 5a_1 - 3a_0)$. Since $8(25n - 5a_1 - 3a_0)$ is divisible by 8, so is $100a_2 + 10a_1 + a_0$, and the number.

Written Exercises, page 147 1. m^5 3. $2k^4$ 5. $\frac{x}{2}$ 7. $3s^5t^2$ 9. $\frac{2b}{a}$ 11. $-\frac{3}{2u^2v^2}$ 13. $3ab^2$ 15. $-4x^2z$ 17. $-25r^2st$ 19. $7x^5y^{10}$ 21. $8x^2y^2$ 23. $24a^3bc$ 25. $5ab$ 27. $(2x)^3$ 29. $(u^3)^3$ 31. $(2ab)^2$ 33. $(5x^2y)^3$

Applications, pages 149–150
1. $60 \cdot 60 \cdot 24 \cdot 365 = 31{,}536{,}000 \doteq 3.2 \times 10^7$ 3. 65,000 5. 500 m 7. 1.992×10^{-23} grams 9. 1.793×10^{-22} grams

Written Exercises, page 153 1. $2x - 3$
3. $3 - 2u$ 5. $2a + 3$ 7. $2r - 3r^2$ 9. $y + x$
11. $a + \dfrac{2}{a}$ 13. $-5u^2 + 3u + 1$

15. $4a^2 - 2a + 1$ 17. $x^2 - 2xy + y^2$ 19. $4x$
21. $-t + 6$ 23. $5xy$ 25. $5; 5(u^2 - 2)$
27. $a; a(4a + 9)$ 29. $2r^2; 2r^2(3r^2 - 1)$
31. $2x; 2x(x - 5y)$ 33. $3ab; 3ab(4a^2 + 5b^2)$
35. $2; 2(2x^2 - 2x - 3)$
37. $3y^2; 3y^2(2y^2 - 3y + 4)$
39. $ax; ax(a^2x^2 - ax + 2)$
41. $6xy^2; 6xy^2(3y^2 - 2y + 4)$ 43. $x = 7$
45. $y = -5$

Problems, page 154 1. $r^2(4 + \pi)$ 3. $r^2(4 - \pi)$
5. $r(2s + \pi r)$ 7. $2x(y + \pi x)$

Written Exercises, pages 158–159 1. $9z^2 - 25$
3. $4x^2 - y^4$ 5. $100a^2b^2 - 9c^4$ 7. $x^6 - 25x^2y^2$
9. $r^2s^3t - 36st^3$ 11. $m^5n^2 - mn^4$ 13. 91
15. 896 17. 3575 19. 39,936
21. $(z + 4)(z - 4)$ 23. $(5r + 1)(5r - 1)$
25. $(4u + v)(4u - v)$ 27. $(s + 11t)(s - 11t)$
29. $(a^2 + c^3)(a^2 - c^3)$
31. $(14s^3 + 25t)(14s^3 - 25t)$
33. $x(x + 4)(x - 4)$ 35. $2z(5z + 1)(5z - 1)$
37. $xy(y + x)(y - x)$
39. $2a(15a^2 + 2)(15a^2 - 2)$
41. $(a^n + b^n)(a^n - b^n)$
43. $(2u^n + 13)(2u^n - 13)$
45. $(x^{2n} + 2y^n)(x^{2n} - 2y^n)$
47. $x(x^n + y^2)(x^n - y^2)$
49. 0, 1, 4, 6, and 9 51. $(x + 1)^2 - x^2 =$
$x^2 + 2x + 1 - x^2 = 2x + 1 = x + (x + 1)$

Written Exercises, pages 162–164
1. $x^2 - 16x + 64$ 3. $4a^2 + 12ab + 9b^2$
5. $c^2d^2 + 14cd + 49$ 7. $4a^4 - 12a^2b + 9b^2$
9. $r^2s^2 - 20rst^2 + 100t^4$
11. $u^4 + 12u^2vw + 36v^2w^2$ 13. $(h + 2)^2$
15. $(a - 4)^2$ 17. $(6 - u)^2$ 19. $(2v + 5)^2$
21. $(a - 3b)^2$ 23. $(5t + 1)^2$ 25. $4a(a + 1)^2$
27. $4a(2x - 5)^2$ 29. $ab(a + b)^2$
31. $2cd(2cd - 3)^2$ 33. $uv(3u - 2v)^2$
35. $t^2(7s^3 + t^2)^2$ 37. $(a + c + 1)(a - c + 1)$
39. $(4s - 2t - 1)(4s + 2t + 1)$
41. $(x - 3y + z)(x - 3y - z)$ 43. $k = 4$
45. $k = 16$ 47. $k = 4$ 49. $k = 6$
51. $A = \pi(R + r)(R - r)$

53. $A = (b + a)(b - a)$ 55. $A = 4w(b - w)$
57. $A = (R - w)[2s + \pi(R - w)]$
59. $T = w[2s + \pi(2r + w)]$ 61. $T = r^2(8 + 3\pi)$
63.

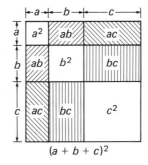

65. $(a + b + c)^2 = a^2 + b^2 + c^2 +$
$2ab + 2bc + 2ac$

$(a + b + c)^2$

Written Exercises, page 166 1. $n^2 - 9n + 14$
3. $x^2 - 3x - 10$ 5. $18 + 3t - t^2$
7. $2y^2 + 5y + 3$ 9. $3r^2 - 10r - 8$
11. $12u^2 - u - 6$ 13. $x^2 + 3xy + 2y^2$
15. $4s^2 - 8st + 3t^2$ 17. $3h^2 - 7hk - 6k^2$
19. $8z^2 + 2zw - 15w^2$ 21. $2a^2b^2 - abyz - y^2z^2$
23. $x^4 - x^2y - 2y^2$ 25. $x = 1$ 27. $x = 1$
29. $x = 1$ 31. $x = -9$

Written Exercises, page 169 1. $(z + 1)(z + 6)$
3. $(c + 1)(c + 5)$ 5. $(r - 1)(r - 7)$
7. $(x + 3)(x + 4)$ 9. $(k - 4)(k - 5)$
11. $(7 + s)(3 + s)$ 13. $(x + y)(x + 4y)$
15. $(r - s)(r - 19s)$ 17. $(m - 13n)(m - 2n)$
19. $(x + 5a)(x + 8a)$ 21. $(z + 5w)(z + 20w)$
23. $(b - 4c)(b - 13c)$ 25. 7, 5, -7, -5
27. 13, 8, 7, -13, -8, -7 29. 3, 4
31. 6, 10, 12 33. $(u + v - 2)(u + v - 3)$
35. $(x - 2)(x + 2)$ 37. $1 = 1 \cdot 1$ or $(-1)(-1)$,
but $1 + 1 \neq 3$ and $(-1) + (-1) \neq 3$.
39. $6 = 1 \cdot 6, 2 \cdot 3, (-1)(-6)$, or $(-2)(-3)$, but
$1 + 6 \neq 4, 2 + 3 \neq 4, (-1) + (-6) \neq 4$, and
$(-2) + (-3) \neq 4$.

Written Exercises, page 171 1. $(x + 4)(x - 2)$
3. $(h + 9)(h - 1)$ 5. $(u - 11)(u + 1)$
7. $(r + 5)(r - 4)$ 9. $(k - 5)(k + 4)$
11. $(t - 10)(t + 2)$ 13. $(z + 6)(z - 5)$
15. $(y - 10)(y + 3)$ 17. $(c - 6)(c + 4)$
19. $(x + 8y)(x - y)$ 21. $(u - 6v)(u + 4v)$
23. $(a + 9b)(a - 5b)$ 25. 7, 2, -7, -2
27. 19, 8, 1, -19, -8, -1
29. Answers may vary; -2 and -6.
31. Answers may vary; -4 and -10.
33. $(u + v - 3)(u + v + 2)$ 35. $(t - 7)(t + 7)$

Written Exercises, page 174 1. $(3x + 1)(x + 1)$
3. $(2k + 1)(k + 3)$ 5. $(5z + 2)(z + 1)$
7. $(3y - 1)(y - 2)$ 9. $(2x + 3)(x + 2)$
11. $(3z - 2)(z + 1)$ 13. $(2t + 3)(t - 2)$
15. $(5h - 7)(h + 1)$ 17. $(5h - 7k)(h + k)$
19. $(3u - 2v)(2u + v)$ 21. $(3x - 7y)(x - 2y)$
23. $(5r - 4s)(r + 2s)$ 25. $(3x + 5)(2x + 3)$
27. $(4t + 3)(2t - 3)$ 29. $(9c - 8)(4c + 3)$
31. $(4a + 3b)(3a - 2b)$ 33. $(9a + 4)(2a - 3)$
35. $(6y + 7z)(y - 9z)$
37. $(7u + 7v + 2)(2u + 2v + 3)$
39. $(5r + 5s - 3t)(2r + 2s - t)$

Written Exercises, page 176 1. $(a + 1)(a + 3)$
3. $(x^2 + 4)(2x - 1)$ 5. $(t^2 + 1)(1 + t)$
7. $(a + b)(a - 2b)$ 9. $(r^2 - 2s^2)(r^2 + s^2)$
11. $(x - 1)(x + 2y)$ 13. $(x + 2)(x + y)$
15. $(t + 3)(t - 2)$ 17. $(2u + v)(2u + 1)$
19. $(t^2 + 1)(t - 1)$ 21. $(r - s)(r + s)^2$
23. $(d^2 - c)(d - 1)$

Written Exercises, page 178 1. $3(t + 1)(t - 1)$
3. $(2 + r)^2$ 5. $2(y - 1)^2$ 7. $v(u^2 + u + 1)$
9. $2x(1 + y)(1 - y)$ 11. $ax(x^2 + 3x + 4)$
13. $k^2(5k - 2)(k + 2)$ 15. $2y(-3 + x)(2 + x)$
17. $(11 + t)(1 + 10t)$ 19. $(8a + 7b^2)(8a - 7b^2)$
21. $5t(t - 3)(t + 1)$ 23. $(a + 4b)(a + b)$
25. $2(c - d)^2$ 27. $(x^2 + y)(x^2 - y)$
29. $u^2v^2(1 + 2uv)(1 - 2uv)$
31. $2hk(k + 2h)(k - 2h)$ 33. $2y(3 + 4y)(2 - y)$
35. $ax(2x^2 + 3ax + 4a^2)$
37. $(x + 2)(x - 2)(x^2 + 1)$
39. $(z^2 + 1)(z + 1)(z - 1)$
41. $x^2(y^2 + x^2)(y + x)(y - x)$
43. $(r + 2s)(r - 2s)(r + 3s)(r - 3s)$
45. $x^2(x + 2)^2(x - 2)^2$ 47. $x^2(xy - 5)^2$
49. $(s - 1)(s + 10)(s + 1)$
51. $(h + 3)(2h - 1)(h + 3)$ 53. $(x - 2)(x + 2)^3$

55. $(t - 1)(t + 1)^2$ 57. $(u + v - 1)(u - v - 1)$
59. $(x - y + z)(x - y - z)$

Written Exercises, pages 181–182 1. $\{0, 2\}$
3. $\{3, 5\}$ 5. $\{-2, 5\}$ 7. $\{-7, 1\}$
9. $\{-1, -3, 5\}$ 11. $\{0, 2, 4\}$ 13. $\{-3, \frac{1}{3}\}$
15. $\{5, -\frac{1}{5}\}$ 17. $\{\frac{7}{2}, -\frac{9}{2}\}$ 19. Multiplication
property of equality; Multiplicative property of zero;
Associative axiom of multiplication; Axiom of
inverses for multiplication; Identity axiom for
multiplication

Written Exercises, page 185 1. $\{1, 3\}$
3. $\{3, -2\}$ 5. $\{-7, 7\}$ 7. $\{0, 9\}$
9. $\{0, -2, 2\}$ 11. $\{1, 9\}$ 13. $\{-8, 3\}$
15. $\{-\frac{1}{2}, 1\}$ 17. $\{\frac{1}{2}, 2\}$ 19. $\{-\frac{1}{5}, 4\}$
21. $\{0, -2, 2\}$ 23. $\{-1, 1\}$ 25. $\{0, 2, 4\}$
27. $\{0, 3\}$ 29. $\{0, -5, 2\}$ 31. $\{-3, 3, -1, 1\}$
33. $\{-2, 2\}$ 35. $\{-1, 1\}$ 37. $\{-1, -\frac{1}{2}, \frac{1}{2}\}$
39. $\{0, -1, 1\}$ 41. $\{-4, 3\}$ 43. $\{3, 7\}$
45. $\{3, \frac{10}{3}\}$ 47. $\{\frac{1}{2}, 5, 6\}$ 49. $x^2 - 4x + 3 = 0$
51. $x^3 + 2x^2 - 3x = 0$
53. $x^3 - 6x^2 + 11x - 6 = 0$

Puzzle Time, page 185 We can divide by $r - t$
only if $r - t \neq 0$, or $r \neq t$; hence r cannot
equal t.

Problems, pages 188–189 1. 8 and 9
3. -11 and -9 5. width: 2 cm; length: 5 cm
7. 1 km by 3 km 9. 4 cm by 7 cm
11. after 2 seconds and 3 seconds
13. 30 seconds 15. **a.** after 3 seconds **b.** Since
the ball reaches a height of 44.1 m once, 44.1 m
is the greatest height attained. 17. 9 m by 12 m
19. 2 cm or 13 cm
21. 5 m by 40 m, or 20 m by 10 m
23. $2 \times 2 \times 2$ 25. $\frac{2}{3}$

Puzzle Time, page 189 The Zero-Product Property
does not apply to nonzero products.
$2^2 - 3 \cdot 2 - 4 = 6 \neq 0$ and
$5^2 - 3 \cdot 5 - 4 = 6 \neq 0$; $x^2 - 3x - 4 = 0$,
$(x - 4)(x + 1) = 0$, $x = 4$ or $x = -1$.

Maintaining Skills, page 195 1. $\frac{17}{3}$ 3. $\frac{23}{5}$ 5. $\frac{57}{23}$
7. $\frac{127}{3}$ 9. $1\frac{7}{10}$ 11. $5\frac{6}{11}$ 13. $2\frac{14}{17}$ 15. $12\frac{2}{3}$
17. $4\frac{1}{12}$ 19. $1\frac{1}{15}$ 21. $20\frac{1}{6}$ 23. $10\frac{1}{2}$ 25. $3\frac{1}{2}$
27. 9 29. 2 31. $\frac{15}{22}$ 33. $\frac{27}{91}$

CHAPTER 6   WORKING WITH FRACTIONS

Written Exercises, pages 199–200 1. $b \neq 3$
3. $x \neq -7, 2$ 5. $3a^2$ 7. $\frac{2}{3}$, $y \neq -2$
9. $\frac{x - y}{x + y}$, $x \neq -y$ 11. $d + 2$, $d \neq 2$
13. $-(4 + y)$, $y \neq 4$ 15. $-\frac{a + 4}{4}$, $a \neq 3$
17. $\frac{2}{2a - 1}$, $a \neq 0, \frac{1}{2}$
19. $\frac{b^2 + 1}{b + 1}$, $a \neq 0$, $b \neq -1$
21. $\frac{x + 7}{x + 1}$, $x \neq 1, -1$ 23. $\frac{r + 4s}{r + 3s}$, $r \neq 3s, -3s$
25. $\frac{b + 1}{b + 2}$, $b \neq 6, -2$ 27. $\frac{x - 2}{x - 5}$, $x \neq -3, 5$
29. $\frac{s + 5}{s + 9}$, $s \neq -9, 2$ 31. $\frac{p + 4}{p + 15}$, $p \neq -15, 2$
33. $\frac{y + 6}{y - 1}$, $y \neq 0, 1, 2$
35. $\frac{2(r - 3)}{5(r - 2)}$, $r \neq 0, -8, 2$
37. $\frac{x + 7}{5(x - 1)}$, $x \neq 0, 1, -5$
39. $\frac{x - 5}{x + b}$, $x \neq -b, -1$
41. $\frac{m + 2n}{m + n}$, $m \neq 3n, -n$
43. $x^2 + 2$, $x \neq -6$, $\sqrt{2}, -\sqrt{2}$

Written Exercises, pages 202–203 1. $\frac{1}{2}$ 3. $\frac{1}{2}$
5. $\frac{1}{2}$ 7. $\frac{15}{17}$ 9. $\frac{15}{16}$ 11. $\frac{15}{2}$ 13. 3:2 15. 1:2
17. 7:3 19. -5:3 21. -1:6 23. 9:4
25. 1:1

Problems, page 204 1. 45 3. 12 boys
5. 36 cm 7. 80 trees 9. 22 cm, 44 cm, 88 cm

Written Exercises, page 207 1. $\frac{70}{39}$ 3. $\frac{1}{5}$ 5. $\frac{5}{39}$
7. $\frac{15}{4}$ 9. $12a$ 11. a^2 13. $-11c^3d$
15. $\frac{18x + 54}{5x + 10}$ 17. $\frac{5}{24}$ 19. $a + b$ 21. $\frac{1}{6xy + 2xy^2}$
23. $\frac{a^2 + b^2}{a^2 + 2ab + b^2}$ 25. $\frac{2x + 4}{x - 2}$ 27. $\frac{a + 1}{a}$
29. $\frac{a^2 + a}{2a - 3}$ 31. $\frac{c^2 - 13c + 40}{c^2 + 14c + 49}$ 33. $\frac{h + 2}{h - 1}$

35. $\frac{x - 2y}{x + 2y}$ 37. $\frac{y^2 - 4y}{y^2 - 8y + 15}$ 39. -1

Written Exercises, pages 209–210 1. $\frac{5}{6}$ 3. $\frac{2}{3b}$
5. $\frac{lm}{27n}$ 7. $\frac{1}{ut}$ 9. $-12a$ 11. $\frac{1}{3}$ 13. $\frac{a - 2}{3a}$
15. $\frac{b + 2}{b + 3}$ 17. $\frac{1}{a^2 + a - 6}$ 19. $\frac{x - 2}{6x}$ 21. $\frac{y^2}{5}$
23. $\frac{a^2 + 2ab + b^2}{a^2 + 2ab}$ 25. $\frac{a + 6}{a - 2}$ 27. $\frac{3a - 2}{3a + 2}$
29. $\frac{n^2 + 2n - 35}{4n^2 + 26n - 48}$ 31. -1
33. $ab - 6a + 3b - 18$ 35. $\frac{(a - b)(2x - y)}{4ax(2x + y)}$
37. $\frac{2}{5}$ 39. 1 41. $\frac{2a^2b}{7}$ 43. $\frac{d}{c}$ 45. $\frac{2}{3}$ 47. $\frac{x + 4}{x}$
49. $\frac{ay}{ay + b}$ 51. $\frac{x}{m - n}$

Written Exercises, page 212 1. $\frac{1}{10}$ 3. cd^2 5. b
7. s 9. c 11. $\frac{6a}{a - 3}$ 13. $\frac{x - 1}{x + 3}$ 15. $2y - d$
17. $\frac{x^2 + x - 2}{x^2 - 3x}$

Written Exercises, page 217 1. $\frac{8}{19}$ 3. $\frac{2}{5}$ 5. 0
7. $\frac{3x + 2}{3}$ 9. 4 11. $b + c$ 13. $7\frac{2}{3}$ 15. $\frac{6 + a}{2a}$
17. $\frac{a + 3}{6}$ 19. $\frac{3x + 3}{8}$ 21. $\frac{6a^2 + 3ab - 2b^2}{6ab}$
23. $\frac{x^2 + 2x - 1}{x^3}$ 25. $\frac{-1}{x^2 + 5x + 6}$
27. $\frac{5x - 9}{x^2 - 5x + 6}$ 29. $\frac{3a^3 + 6a^2 - 16a - 1}{12a^2}$
31. $\frac{2a - 1}{(a - 2)(a + 1)^2}$ 33. $\frac{9x + 6}{(x + 2)^2(x + 1)}$
35. $\frac{a^3 - 3}{a^2 - 1}$

Written Exercises, page 219 1. $\frac{b^2 - b + 6}{b - 1}$
3. $\frac{4a - b}{a - b}$ 5. $\frac{x^2 - y^2 + 1}{x + y}$ 7. $\frac{x + 7}{x + 2}$
9. $\frac{7ab + 3b + 6a}{ab}$ 11. $\frac{d^2 + 3d - 7}{d - 2}$ 13. $5\frac{2}{3}$
15. $3 + 2a^2$ 17. $2a - \frac{3}{5a^2}$ 19. $cd + \frac{3}{4}$

Just for Fun, page 219

1.

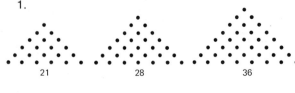

21   28   36

45   55

2. $n = 1: \dfrac{1(1 + 1)}{2} = 1$; $n = 2: \dfrac{2(2 + 1)}{2} = 3$;

$n = 3: \dfrac{3(3 + 1)}{2} = 6$; $n = 4: \dfrac{4(4 + 1)}{2} = 10$;

$n = 5: \dfrac{5(5 + 1)}{2} = 15$; $n = 6: \dfrac{6(6 + 1)}{2} = 21$;

$n = 7: \dfrac{7(7 + 1)}{2} = 28$; $n = 8: \dfrac{8(8 + 1)}{2} = 36$;

$n = 9: \dfrac{9(9 + 1)}{2} = 45$; $n = 10: \dfrac{10(10 + 1)}{2} = 55$

Written Exercises, pages 221–222   1. $x + 3$

3. $u - 4$ 5. $s - 1$ 7. $a - 1 + \dfrac{6}{a + 3}$

9. $x - 1 + \dfrac{4}{x - 3}$ 11. $t - 4$ 13. $x + 2 + \dfrac{8}{x - 2}$

15. $x - 3 + \dfrac{1}{2x + 1}$ 17. $3r + 5 + \dfrac{10}{2r - 3}$

19. $3t - 2 + \dfrac{5}{3t + 2}$ 21. $3x - a - \dfrac{a^2}{2x + a}$

23. $3s - 4t + \dfrac{2t^2}{s + 2t}$ 25. $x^2 + ax + a^2$

27. $z^2 - 2z + 3$ 29. $3x^2 - 2x + 3$ 31. $2y + 3$

33. $t^2 - 2t + 3 + \dfrac{18}{t^2 - 3}$ 35. $a^4 + a^2 + 1$

37. $c = -6$

Just for Fun, page 222   1. $4 = 1 + 3$; $9 = 3 + 6$;
$16 = 6 + 10$; $25 = 10 + 15$; $36 = 15 + 21$;
$49 = 21 + 28$; $64 = 28 + 36$; $81 = 36 + 45$;
$100 = 45 + 55$

2.

25 = 10 + 15

Written Exercises, pages 224–225   1. $x = 4$

3. $b = -4$ 5. $y = 14$ 7. $b = 10$ 9. $x = -\frac{1}{7}$

11. $b = 4$ 13. $d = \frac{15}{7}$ 15. $y = 6$ 17. $x = -7$

19. $x = -\frac{90}{19}$ 21. $x = \frac{10}{3}$ 23. $x = 6000$

25. $x = \frac{5}{7}$ 27. $t = \frac{14}{17}$ 29. $x = 2$

Puzzle Time, page 225   If $x =$ his age at death,
then $\frac{1}{6}x + \frac{1}{12}x + \frac{1}{7}x + 5 + \frac{1}{2}x + 4 = x$; $x = 84$,
so he was 84 years old at death.

Written Exercises, page 227   1. $x = 5$

3. $n = 3\frac{5}{9}$ 5. $a = 2$ 7. $x = -3$ or $x = 2$

9. $y = -\frac{3}{8}$ or $y = 1$ 11. $a = 2$ 13. no solution

15. $x = 5$ 17. $z = 2$ 19. $c = 9$ 21. $h = 8$

23. $x = 4$ or $x = -2$

Written Exercises, page 230   1. 1%; 0.01

3. $\frac{1}{25}$; 4%   5. $\frac{1}{10}$; 0.1   7. 20%; 0.2   9. $\frac{1}{2}$; 50%

11. $\frac{3}{4}$; 0.75   13. $83\frac{1}{3}$%; $0.83\frac{1}{3}$ 15. $\frac{9}{10}$; 90%

Problems, page 231   1. 400 people

3. 9.6 minutes   5. $3000   7. 150 employees

9. 48%   11. 18%   13. 5%   15. 300 votes

17. $104.49

Problems, page 235   1. 20 kg   3. 8.6 kg   5. 48 kg

7. 20 g   9. 25 kg of milk, 75 kg of cream

Problems, page 237   1. $121.50   3. $2750

5. $1272   7. $3500   9. $2000 at 4%,
$5000 at 5%

Consumer Note, page 239   1. $160   3. $1.85

Problems, page 242   1. 2.5 hours   3. 84 km/h

5. 400 km   7. 11:12 A.M.   9. 40 km

Problems, pages 244–245   1. 6 hours

3. $3\frac{3}{7}$ hours   5. 40 minutes   7. 30 minutes

9. 5 hours   11. 36 hours

Cumulative Review, pages 251–252   1. 24

3. -6 5. 18   7. 10   9. 12   11. -16 13. -2

15. $y = -2$ 17. $x = 4$ 19. $x = 3$ 21. $t = 0$

23. $4x^2 - 5x + 3$ 25. $-8x^3y^4$ 27. $-6z^2 - 15z$

29. $15n^4 - 6n^3 + 9n^2$ 31. $x^2 - 2x - 3$
33. $4n^2 - 9$ 35. $9x^2 + 9x + 2$
37. $7rs(2r + 4 - 3s)$ 39. $(3x - 2)(x - 6)$
41. $(6m + 7n)(6m - 7n)$ 43. $\{0, 3\}$ 45. $\{0, \frac{8}{3}\}$
47. $\dfrac{a - b}{3}$ 49. $\frac{1}{4}$ 51. $\dfrac{c - 1}{12}$ 53. $z = -\frac{2}{3}$
55. 24, 26, 28 57. 5 cm by 7 cm 59. $5000
61. 24 km/h

Maintaining Skills, page 253 1. -2 3. 4
5. -290 7. -58 9. 794 11. 17 13. -12
15. 14 17. -3 19. -9 21. 19 23. 1
25. -12 27. -16 29. -2

CHAPTER 7 INEQUALITIES

Written Exercises, page 257 1. $<$ 3. $<$ 5. $<$
7. $<$ 9. $5 < 10$ 11. $-3 > -7$
13. $4 < 6 < 8$ 15. $-20 < -16 < -10$
17. $-5 < -4.5$ and $-4.5 < 4$
19. $6 < 8.5$ and $8.5 < 10.25$
21. $7 > 1$ and $1 > -25$
23. $-2.5 < -2$ and $-2 < -1.75$
25. $7.5 < 8.2$ and $8.2 < 9.5$
27. $0 > -2$ and $-2 > -150$ 29. 2, 3, 4
31. 1, 2, 3 33. $-99, -98, -97, -96$

Written Exercises, page 260 1. $\in$ 3. $>$ 5. $\subset$

7.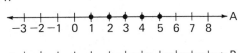

9. (number line: -3 to 5, open circle at 3)

11. (number line: -3 to 5, open circles at -1 and 3)

Written Exercises, page 265

1. $z < 20$ (number line: 15 to 23, open circle at 20)

3. $z > 9$ (number line: 5 to 13, open circle at 9)

5. $y < 4$ (number line: 0 to 8, open circle at 4)

7. $s > 2$ (number line: -2 to 6, open circle at 2)

9. $k > -6$ (number line: -8 to 0, open circle at -6)

11. $x < -7$ (number line: -10 to -2, open circle at -7)

13. $x < 9$ 15. $t < -3$ 17. $z < 1$
19. $v < -\frac{1}{2}$ 21. $x > 4$ 23. $t > -12$
25. $x < 8$ 27. $t > -2$ 29. $r > -4$ 31. $a < \frac{1}{2}$

Extra for Experts, page 266 1. 20 3. 28 5. $2\frac{7}{8}$
7. 11000 9. 0.0101 11. 1.1

Problems, page 268 1. 22 and 24 3. 3 and 5
5. $\{1, 3, 5, 7\}$, $\{3, 5, 7, 9\}$, $\{5, 7, 9, 11\}$,
$\{7, 9, 11, 13\}$, $\{9, 11, 13, 15\}$, $\{11, 13, 15, 17\}$

Applications, page 269 1. 16.1 watts
3. about 120 volts 5. about $3.29

Puzzle Time, page 269 The original price was $100.

Written Exercises, pages 272–273
1. union: $\{0, 1, 2, 3, 4\}$; intersection: $\{2, 3\}$
3. union: $\{1, 2, 3, 4, 5, 6\}$; intersection:
$\varnothing$ (disjoint) 5. union: $\{1, 2, 3, 5, 7, 9, 11\}$;
intersection: $\{3, 5, 7\}$ 7. union: {the natural
numbers and the non-positive even integers};
intersection: {the even natural integers}
9. union: {all real numbers except 0};
intersection: $\varnothing$ (disjoint)

11.

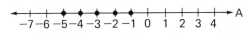

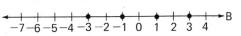

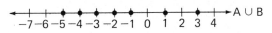

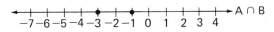

13.

(number lines for 13, A, B, A ∪ B, A ∩ B on scale -7 to 4)

15.

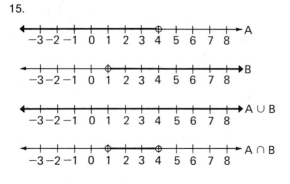

17.

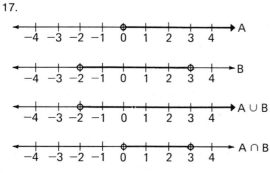

19.

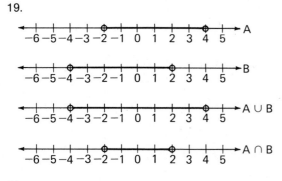

21.

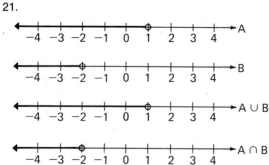

23.

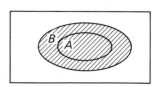

25.

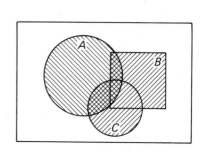

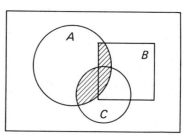

27. $A \cap (B \cup C) = (A \cap B) \cup (A \cap C)$

29.

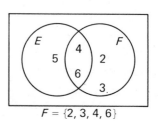

$F = \{2, 3, 4, 6\}$

Puzzle Time, page 273

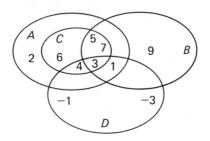

Written Exercises, pages 277–278

1. $1 < x < 6$

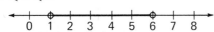

3. $-4 \le t < 0$

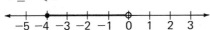

5. $-2 \le r \le 4$

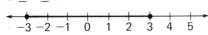

7. $x \le -4$ or $x \ge 2$

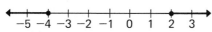

9. $u < 0$ or $3 < u$

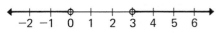

11. $2 > x > -3$

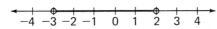

13. $t > 3$ or $t < -3$

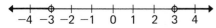

15. $2 > t > -1$

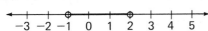

17. all real numbers   19. Ø

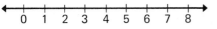

21. all real numbers   23. Ø

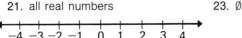

25. $v > 0$

27. all real numbers

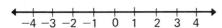

29. $z \le 4$

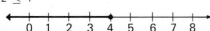

Extra for Experts, page 281

1. $x - 3 = 2$ or $x - 3 = -2$ 3. $-7 \le z \le 7$
5. $-1 < s + 2 < 1$
7. $2 - t \ge 3$ or $2 - t \le -3$
9. $3 + 2a = 1$ or $3 + 2a = -1$
11. $-3 < 2x - 7 < 3$
13. $x = 5$ or $x = 1$

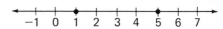

15. $-7 \le z \le 7$

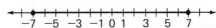

17. $-3 < s < -1$

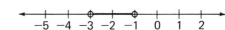

19. $t \le -1$ or $t \ge 5$

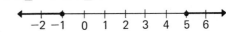

21. $a = -1$ or $a = -2$

23. $2 < x < 5$

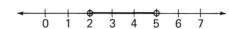

25. $1 < x < 5$

27. $z \ge 1$ or $z \le 0$

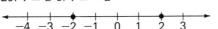

29. $t = 2$ or $t = -2$ 31. Ø

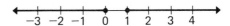

33. $z = 2$

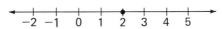

35. $z < 2$

Puzzle Time, page 281

$a(3 - a) > (3 - a)(3 + a)$ is equivalent to $a > 3 + a$ only if $3 - a > 0$ or $3 > a$. But we are given $a > 3$.

Consumer Note, page 284 4.5%; 4.5%; 85% of 83% = 70.55%; 79.55%; $7.50

Maintaining Skills, page 285 1. $5t - 7$
3. $12x + y$ 5. $3x^2 - 4x + 8$ 7. $-5t^2 - 5$
9. $7b^3 + 2b^2 - b - 3$ 11. -18
13. $144 - 10b$ 15. $2t - 33$ 17. $-17s + 1$
19. $-2z^2 - 18z$ 21. $x^2 - x - 6$
23. $2a^2 + 5a - 3$ 25. $4k^2 - 1$
27. $6x^2 - 5x - 6$ 29. $10m^2 - 17m + 3$

CHAPTER 8 FUNCTIONS AND RELATIONS

Written Exercises, page 290 1. $\{-1, 2, 5\}$
3. $\{7, 3, -1\}$ 5. $\{-1, 5\}$ 7. $\{6, 3, 2\}$
9. $\{0, 2\}$ 11. $\{6, 2, 0\}$ 13. 0 15. 0 17. -2
19. 1 21. 0 23. 4 25. 4 27. 4 29. 4
31. 0 33. 0 35. 64 37. 5 39. 9 41. 7
43. -2

Written Exercises, page 294
1. $D = \{$Africa, Asia, Australia, Europe, North America, South America$\}$;
$R = \{5900, 8800, 2200, 5600, 6200, 6900\}$

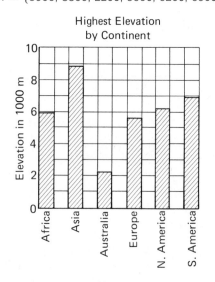

Highest Elevation
by Continent

3. $D = \{1860, 1880, 1900, 1920, 1940, 1960\}$;
$R = \{50,000, 150,000, 320,000, 410,000, 380,000, 350,000\}$

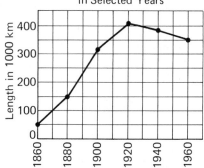

Length of Railroad Track
in Selected Years

5. $D = \{$Jan., Feb., Mar., Apr., May, June, July, Aug., Sept., Oct., Nov., Dec.$\}$;
$R = \{-3, -2, 2, 9, 16, 22, 24, 23, 19, 13, 4\}$

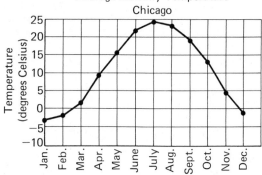

Average Monthly Temperature
Chicago

7. $D = $ same as Ex. 5;
$R = \{13, 14, 15, 17, 18, 20, 23, 22, 19\}$

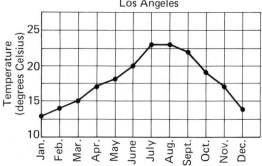

Average Monthly Temperature
Los Angeles

Written Exercises, page 300

1.–11.

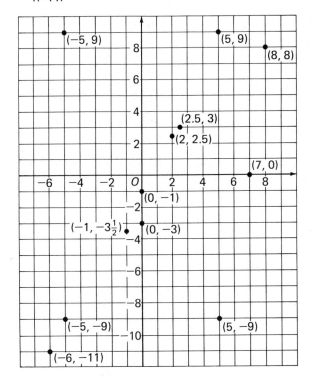

13. *A, Q*   15. *F*

17. *B, C, D, G, I, J, K, M, N, R*

19. *A, B*

21.

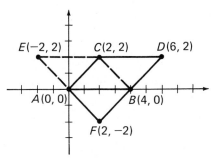

ACDB, AECB, and *ACBF* are parallelograms.

23.

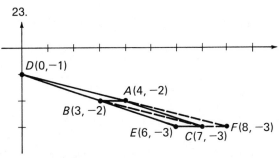

ABEC, ABCF, and *ADBC* are parallelograms.

Written Exercises, page 304

1. $D = \{1, 2, 3, 4, 7\}$; $R = \{2, 3, 5, 6, 8\}$; function

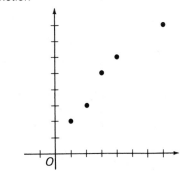

3. $D = \{1, 2, 3\}$; $R = \{0, 3, 4, 5\}$; not a function

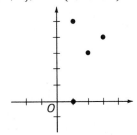

5. $D = \{-2, -1, 0, 1, 2\}$; $R = \{0, 1, 2\}$; function

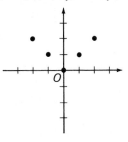

7. $D = \{-2, -1, 0, 1, 2, 3, 4\}$;
   $R = \{-6, -1, 0, 1, 8, 16, 18\}$; function

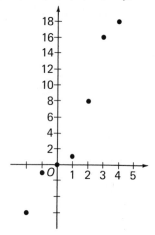

13. $D = \{-5, -4, -3, -2, -1, 0\}$;
    $R = \{-1, 0, 3, 8\}$; function

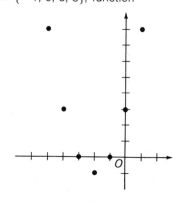

Consumer Note, page 305   1. 105%   3. 12%

9. $D = \{-5, -4, -1, 4\}$;
   $R = \{-3, -2, -1, 0, 1, 2, 3\}$; not a function

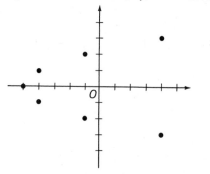

Written Exercises, pages 308–309   1. 6; 7; 4
3. 2; −5; −2   **5.** 1; −1; $\frac{1}{2}$ **7.** 2; 6; 4
9. 1; −2; −6   **11.** 2; 3; 4   **13.** $\{(-1, 1), (0, 2),$
$(1, 3)\}$ **15.** $\{(-1, -\frac{3}{2}), (0, 0), (1, \frac{3}{2})\}$
17. $\{(-1, 1), (0, 0), (1, 1)\}$ **19.** $\{(-1, 3), (0, 0),$
$(1, -1)\}$ **21.** $\{(0, 4), (1, 3), (2, 2), (3, 1), (4, 0)\}$
23. $\{(1, 3), (3, 2), (5, 1), (7, 0)\}$ **25.** $\{(1, 6),$
$(4, 4), (7, 2), (10, 0)\}$ **27.** $\{(0, 4), (3, 2), (6, 0)\}$

29. $\{(-1, 2), (0, 1),$
$(0, 2), (1, 0), (1, 1),$
$(1, 2)\}$

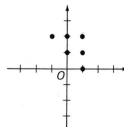

11. $D = \{-4, -3, 0, 3\}$; $R = \{-2, -1, 0, 1, 2\}$;
    not a function

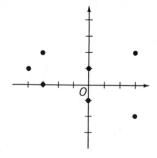

31. $\{(0, -2), (0, -1),$
$(0, 0), (0, 1),$
$(1, -2), (1, -1),$
$(1, 0), (1, 1), (1, 2)\}$

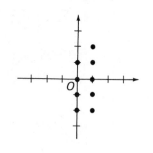

33. {(−1, −1),
(−1, 0), (−1, 1),
(−1, 2), (0, −1),
(0, 0), (0, 1), (0, 2),
(1, −1), (1, 0),
(1, 1), (1, 2)}

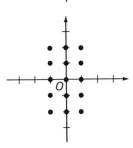

35. {(−1, −2),
(−1, −1), (−1, 0),
(−1, 1), (−1, 2),
(0, −2), (0, −1),
(0, 0), (0, 1), (0, 2),
(1, −2), (1, −1),
(1, 0), (1, 1), (1, 2)}

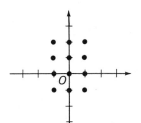

37. {(1, 0), (3, 0), (2, −1), (0, 3), (4, 3)}

Written Exercises, page 314 **1.** above **3.** on
5. below **7.** left **9.** right **11.** on **13. a.** (7, 0)
b. (0, 6) **15. a.** (0, 0) **b.** (0, 0)
17.   **19.**

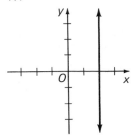
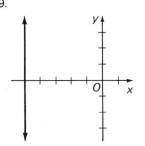

21.   **23.**

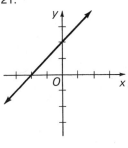
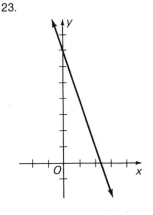

25.   **27.**

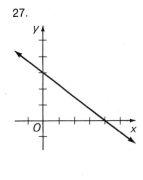

29.   **31.**

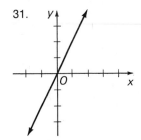

33. (5, 7);
$5 + 7 = 12$ and
$2 \cdot 5 - 7 = 3$

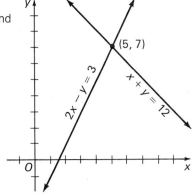

35. (−3, 4);
$2(-3) + 4 = -2$
    and
$-3 + 3 \cdot 4 = 9$

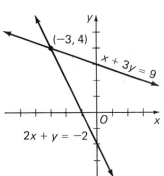

Just for Fun, page 314

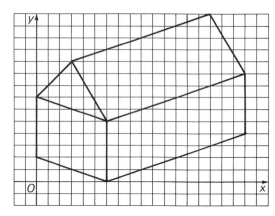

39.

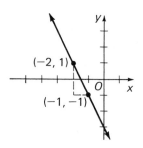

41.

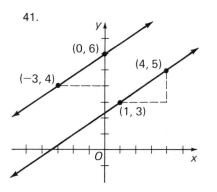

43. 1; $x = 3$

Written Exercises, pages 317–319 1. $-\frac{7}{4}$ 3. $\frac{3}{4}$
5. 7 7. 1 9. 1 11. $\dfrac{2}{a - 2}$ 13. $-\frac{1}{2}$ 15. $\frac{1}{4}$
17. $-\frac{4}{5}$ 19. 3 21. $\frac{1}{2}$ 23. $-\frac{2}{3}$ 25. yes; 3
27. yes; 1 29. yes; -1 31. no

45. $b = 3$

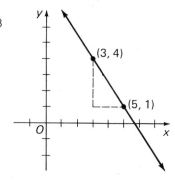

33.

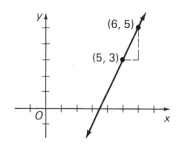

35.   **37.**

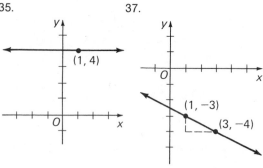

47. $b = 7$

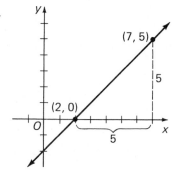

49. $b = 2$

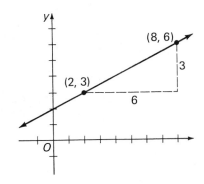

23. $y = x - 2$ 25. $y = 3x + 3$

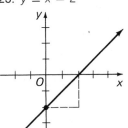

27. Each has slope $-\frac{1}{2}$.   29. $b = 3; b = 1$

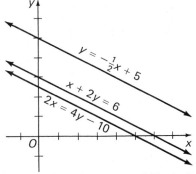

Written Exercises, page 323   1. $x - y = -4$
3. $3x + y = -2$ 5. $x - 2y = -12$ 7. $y = 2$
9. $14x + 21y = -3$ 11. $4x - 5y = 100$
13. $y = x - 7$

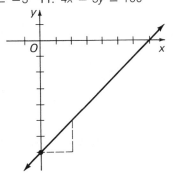

15. $y = 2x - 5$ 17. $y = -x - 5$

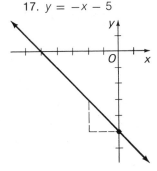

19. $y = \frac{2}{3}x$ 21. $y = -\frac{5}{3}$

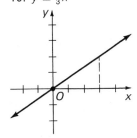   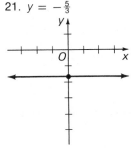

Written Exercises, page 325   1. $3x - y = 1$
3. $2x + y = -1$ 5. $3x - 4y = 3$
7. $x + 2y = 6$ 9. $x + y = 5$
11. $4x + y = -7$ 13. $2x + y = 4$
15. $2x - y = 2$ 17. $x - y = -3$
19. $3x + 2y = 13$ 21. $5x - y = -7$
23. $3x + 4y = -13$

Written Exercises, page 330   1. 3   3. $\frac{1}{2}$ 5. 4
7. $w = 12$ 9. $v = 3437.5$ 11. 125   13. 2
15. $\frac{1}{8}$ 17. $x = 10$ 19. $y = \frac{12}{7}$ 21. $x = \frac{7}{4}$
23. $r = 3$ 25. $p = ks$ 27. $T = km$

Problems, page 331   1. \$720   3. 15 mm   5. \$75
7. 37 divisions

Maintaining Skills, page 335   1. $x(a + b + 2)$
3. $x(x^2 - x + 1)$ 5. $6(4t^2 + 2t - 1)$
7. $3r^2s^2(5s + 8s^4 - 6)$ 9. $6rs(6s + 3r - 2rs)$
11. $(n + 2)(n - 2)$ 13. $(n + 5)^2$
15. $(5 + 3a)(5 - 3a)$ 17. $(y - 9)^2$
19. $(2t - 3)^2$ 21. $(n - 7)(n - 1)$
23. $(r + 7)(r - 5)$ 25. $(t - 8)(t + 1)$
27. $(x - 4y)(x - 5y)$ 29. $(p - 13q)(p - 2q)$
31. $(3b + 1)(b + 1)$ 33. $(2y + 1)^2$
35. $(2t + 1)(t - 1)$ 37. $(4c + 5)(c - 1)$
39. $(4m + 1)(4m - 5)$

CHAPTER 9 SYSTEMS OF OPEN SENTENCES IN TWO VARIABLES

Written Exercises, page 339

1.

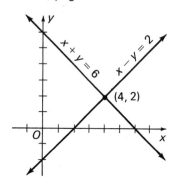

3.

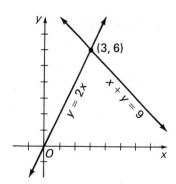

5.

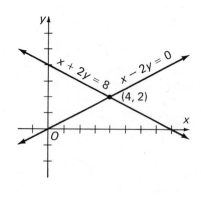

7.

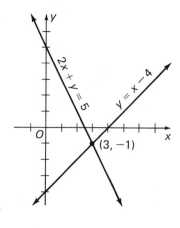

9.

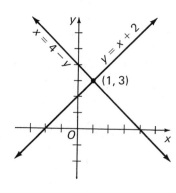

11.

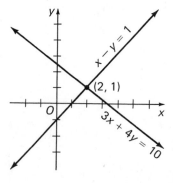

13. $y = \frac{1}{2}x - 2$ 15. $y = -\frac{4}{3}x + 3$

17.

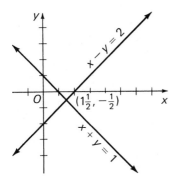

19.

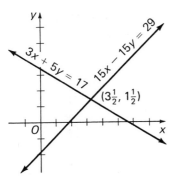

21. $(-6, -6)$

23. 27 square units

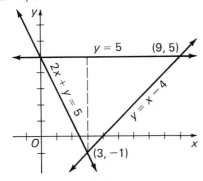

Written Exercises, page 342 **1.** $(2, 2)$
3. $(-3, -1)$ **5.** $(1, 1)$ **7.** $(2, 1)$ **9.** $(3, 1)$
11. $(-3, 2)$ **13.** $(11, 7)$ **15.** $(16, 2)$
17. $(20, -6)$ **19.** $(4, -3)$

Applications, pages 342–343 **1.** 4 m by 3 m
3. 24,000 cm, or 240 m **5.** 400 km **7.** 150 km
9. 120 km **11.** 25 km **13.** 2.5 km

Problems, page 345 **1.** 170 cm²
3. engineer: \$40; assistant: \$30 **5.** 10 and 15
7. 75 on second, 89 on third

Written Exercises, page 347 **1.** $(5, 1)$
3. $(3, -1)$ **5.** $(-4, 2)$ **7.** $(-1, 2)$ **9.** $(5, -1)$
11. $(-2, 0)$ **13.** $(5, -3)$ **15.** $(4, 2)$ **17.** $(7, 2)$
19. $(7, -2)$

Problems, page 347 **1.** 19 and 15 **3.** 18 and 38
5. 22 and 38 **7.** 3 large cans, 4 small cans
9. 57 psychologists, 33 sociologists

Applications, pages 348–349 **1.** Not possible,
since you must know the total number of coins.
3. 2 dimes, 2 quarters **5.** the C.O.D. charges
7. the number of rolls per bag

Written Exercises, pages 351–352 **1.** $(4, -1)$
3. $(-\frac{3}{2}, -2)$ **5.** $(-3, -4)$ **7.** $(\frac{5}{2}, -3)$
9. $(3, 4)$ **11.** $(2, 3)$ **13.** $(\frac{1}{5}, \frac{1}{2})$ **15.** $(\frac{1}{8}, \frac{1}{10})$

Problems, pages 352–353 **1.** 15 and 20
3. \$6000 at 5%, \$4800 at 4% **5.** oil: 80¢
gasoline: 15¢ **7.** \$2000 in stock A,
\$3000 in stock B **9.** \$1000 at 7%, \$700 at 8%

Problems, page 356 (top) **1.** 54 **3.** 27 **5.** 84

Problems, page 356 (bottom) **1.** Julian: 16;
brother: 14 **3.** Bruce: 14; John: 18
5. father: 36; son: 10

Problems, page 357 **1.** $\frac{15}{25}$ **3.** $\frac{20}{30}$ **5.** $\frac{8}{16}$ **7.** $\frac{35}{20}$

Problems, pages 358–359 **1.** current: 5 km/h;
boat: 9 km/h **3.** plane: 210 km/h; wind:
70 km/h **5.** current: 5 km/h; boat: 15 km/h
7. about 315.2 km **9.** plane: 250 km/h;
wind: 50 km/h **11.** $s = 5c$

Written Exercises, page 363
1.   **3.**

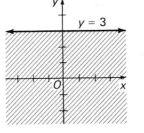

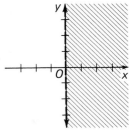

5.

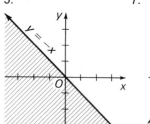

7.

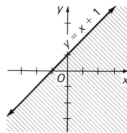

15.

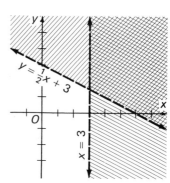

9.

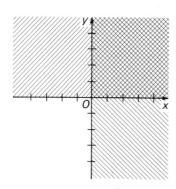

17.

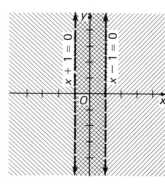

11.

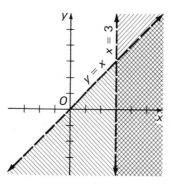

19.

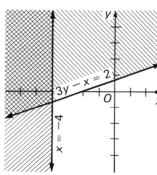

13.

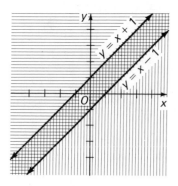

21.

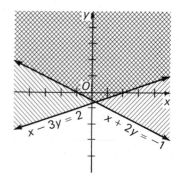

23.

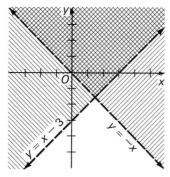

25.

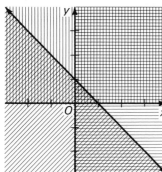

27.

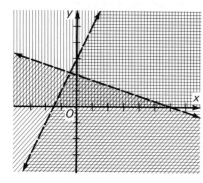

41. $y \leq 84$

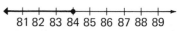

43. 88 calories   45. 6 dimes, 6 quarters

47. $4\frac{4}{5}$ hours   49.

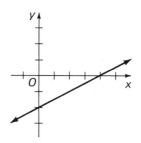

51.   53.

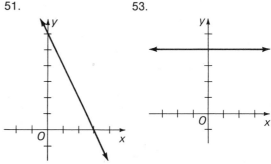

55. slope: $\frac{1}{2}$; y-intercept: -2 57. $(5, -3)$
59. $(2, 3)$ 61. all real numbers   63. $\frac{3}{5}$

Maintaining Skills, page 369   1. $4x$ 3. $\frac{a}{2}$

5. $\frac{3a + 15}{2a + 20}$ 7. $\frac{x - 2}{2x}$ 9. $\frac{x - y}{x - 4}$ 11. $\frac{1}{xy}$

13. $\frac{s}{8t}$ 15. $\frac{3}{4}$ 17. $\frac{r + 2}{r + 3}$ 19. $\frac{x^2 + xy}{x - 4}$

Cumulative Review, pages 367–368   1. 2   3. $\frac{28}{9}$
5. 26   7. $t^2 - 4t$ 9. $2r - 1$ 11. 7   13. 4
15. -29 17. $(2y + 1)(y + 1)$
19. $(2r + s)(2r - s)$ 21. $(y - 1)(y^2 + 1)$
23. $\frac{9k^3}{4}$ 25. $\frac{11 + 2x}{6}$ 27. $\frac{-8y + 6}{y^2 - 4}$ 29. $\{3\}$
31. $\{-5, -3\}$ 33. $\{\frac{7}{2}, -\frac{7}{2}\}$ 35. $\{\frac{1}{3}, -\frac{1}{2}\}$

37. $z > 6$

39. $t \geq 4$

CHAPTER 10   RATIONAL AND IRRATIONAL
NUMBERS

Written Exercises, page 375   1. $<$ 3. $>$ 5. $>$
7. $<$ 9. $-\frac{3}{4}, \frac{1}{3}, \frac{7}{8}$ 11. $-3.2, -\frac{24}{9}, -1.0$
13. $\frac{2}{15}, \frac{3}{16}, \frac{5}{24}, \frac{1}{2}$ 15. $\frac{29}{112}$ 17. $-\frac{13}{200}$ 19. $\frac{35}{36}$
21. increases   23. decreases   25. increases
27. $\frac{21}{32}$ 29. $\frac{r + s}{2}$ 31. -7 is the next larger
integer after -8, since $-8 + 1 = -7$; it is the
least integer greater since there is no integer
between -8 and -7.

Extra for Experts, page 377   1. $1 - 3 = -2$, a negative number   3. $(-1) \times (-2) = 2$, a positive number   5. If $0 < a < 1$ and $0 < b < 1$, then $0 \cdot 0 < ab < 1 \cdot 1$; hence the product is between 0 and 1.

7. $(2n + 1)(2m + 1) = 4mn + 2m + 2n + 1 = 2(2mn + m + n) + 1$, an odd number.

9.

+	−1	0	1
−1	−2	−1	0
0	−1	0	1
1	0	1	2

not closed

×	−1	0	1
−1	1	0	−1
0	0	0	0
1	−1	0	1

closed

11.

×	1
1	1

closed

Written Exercises, page 381   1. $0.\overline{2}$ 3. 0.375
5. -0.24 7. $-0.2\overline{7}$ 9. -0.625 11. $-0.\overline{19}$
13. $\frac{21}{100}$ 15. $\frac{19}{33}$ 17. $-1\frac{16}{45}$ 19. $\frac{1}{2}, \frac{1}{3}; \frac{1}{6}$
21. $\frac{8}{3}, -\frac{16}{3}; -14\frac{2}{9}$ 23. $0.00\overline{3}; 0.333$
25. $0.002; 0.126$ 27. $\frac{1}{8} = 0.125$;
$\frac{2}{8} = 0.25 = 2(0.125); \frac{3}{8} = 0.375 = 3(0.125); \dots$;
$\frac{7}{8} = 0.875 = 7(0.125)$
29. $\frac{1}{17} = 0.\overline{0588235294117647}$;
$\frac{2}{17} = 2(0.0588235294117647); \dots$;
$\frac{16}{17} = 16(0.0588235294117647)$

Written Exercises, page 384   1. 20 3. 32
5. -45 7. $-\frac{14}{5}$ 9. $\pm\frac{1}{16}$ 11. $\pm\frac{6}{13}$ 13. $\frac{1}{5}$
15. $-\frac{6}{5}$ 17. $\pm\frac{9}{100}$ 19. 0.3 21. -1.1
23. ±0.18 25. $\frac{2}{3}$ 27. $-\frac{3}{4}$ 29. $\pm\frac{4}{3}$

Written Exercises, page 390   1. 1.8 3. 44
5. -17.4 7. 6.43 9. -11.36 11. 14.93
13. 4.58 15. -17.32 17. 0.08

Written Exercises, page 392   1. $\{7, -7\}$
3. $\{5, -5\}$ 5. $\{\frac{3}{2}, -\frac{3}{2}\}$ 7. $\{2, -2\}$
9. $\{26.4, -26.4\}$ 11. $\{2.8, -2.8\}$
13. $\{11.2, -11.2\}$ 15. $\{0.2, -0.2\}$
17. $\{2.5, -2.5\}$ 19. $\{7.1, -7.1\}$
21. $\{7.8, -7.8\}$

Problems, page 393   1. 22.4 cm   3. width: 6.4 cm; length: 19.2 cm   5. 10.4 cm   7. 6.5 km

Written Exercises, page 396   1. 10 3. 4.58
5. 2.45 7. yes   9. yes
11. $c^2 = a^2 + b^2 = 1 + 3 = 4$, so $c = \sqrt{4} = 2$.

Problems, page 397   1. 8.60 cm   3. 16.2 cm
5. 6 cm, 8 cm, 10 cm   7. no

Written Exercises, pages 399–400   1. 10 3. 6
5. $2\sqrt{30}$ 7. 1 9. 1 11. $\frac{5\sqrt{3}}{3}$ 13. 2
15. $6\sqrt{3}$ 17. $49\sqrt{3}$ 19. 8 21. $26\sqrt{2}$ 23. $\frac{5}{2}$
25. $-4xy$ 27. $3\sqrt{b} + b$ 29. -48
31. $3x^2\sqrt{26x}$ 33. $12x$ 35. $-\frac{7\sqrt{13}}{2}$

Consumer Note, page 400   1. $s = \$2000$
2. $s = \$2500$

Problems, page 401   1. 5 and 15, or -5 and -15
3. base $= 12$, height $= 18$ 5. 124.2 cm
7. $r = 3$ cm, $c = 15$ cm   9. 2.2 m   11. 5.7 cm

Written Exercises, page 403   1. $8\sqrt{2}$ 3. $\sqrt{10}$
5. $3\sqrt{2}$ 7. $4 - 4\sqrt{2}$ 9. $\frac{47\sqrt{7}}{5}$ 11. $\frac{\sqrt{2}}{2}$
13. $16\sqrt{3}$ 15. $\frac{4\sqrt{10}}{5}$ 17. $\frac{\sqrt{3}}{3}$ 19. $\frac{7\sqrt{10}}{10}$
21. $\frac{13\sqrt{3}}{3}$ 23. $15\sqrt{2} + 20\sqrt{6}$
25. $(x^4 + 3x^3)\sqrt{bx}$ 27. $\frac{5a}{24}$ 29. $b = \sqrt{3}$

Written Exercises, page 405   1. 1 3. 1
5. $12 - 3\sqrt{7}$ 7. $3 + 2\sqrt{2}$ 9. $16 - 8\sqrt{3}$
11. $15\sqrt{2} + 15$ 13. $95 - 5\sqrt{21}$
15. $-36 - 16\sqrt{3}$ 17. $16 + 7\sqrt{10}$
19. $\frac{1 - \sqrt{5}}{-4}$ 21. $\frac{5 + 3\sqrt{5}}{-4}$ 23. $-3 - \sqrt{7}$
25. $\frac{14\sqrt{5} - 7}{19}$ 27. $4 - 3\sqrt{3}$ 29. $4 + \sqrt{5}$
31. $(5 + \sqrt{2})^2 - 10(5 + \sqrt{2}) + 23 = 25 + 10\sqrt{2} + 2 - 50 - 10\sqrt{2} + 23 = 0$; $(5 - \sqrt{2})^2 - 10(5 - \sqrt{2}) + 23 = 25 - 10\sqrt{2} + 2 - 50 + 10\sqrt{2} + 23 = 0$
33. $x - y^2$ 35. $15a^2b + 4ac\sqrt{b} - 3c^2$

Written Exercises, page 407 1. {9} 3. {$\frac{1}{160}$}
5. {16} 7. {$\frac{25}{4}$} 9. {18} 11. {8} 13. {$\frac{25}{12}$}
15. {3} 17. {2} 19. {80} 21. {$\frac{17}{2}$}
23. {50} 25. {$2\sqrt{3}, -2\sqrt{3}$} 27. {0} 29. {3}

Problems, page 407 1. 144 3. 6 5. $\dfrac{5\sqrt{21}}{3}$ m

7. 8 9. 11 and 12

Extra for Experts, page 412 1. 9 3. 10 5. 7.8
7. 8.5 9. 9 11. 14.2 13. Let $A = (0, 3)$,
$B = (3, 9)$, $C = (6,0)$, and $D = (9, 6)$;
$AB = \sqrt{(3 - 0)^2 + (9 - 3)^2} = \sqrt{45}$;
$BD = \sqrt{(9 - 3)^2 + (6 - 9)^2} = \sqrt{45}$;
$DC = \sqrt{(9 - 6)^2 + (6 - 0)^2} = \sqrt{45}$;
$AC = \sqrt{(6 - 0)^2 + (0 - 3)^2} = \sqrt{45}.$

Maintaining Skills, page 413 1. $\dfrac{2x - y}{2y}$ 3. $\dfrac{-3}{10 z}$

5. 4 7. $\dfrac{2 - 2a}{az}$ 9. $\dfrac{11}{3a}$ 11. $\dfrac{a^2 - a + 3}{a - 1}$

13. $\dfrac{c^2 + c}{c - 1}$ 15. $x - 5 + \dfrac{11}{x + 2}$

17. $a + 1 + \dfrac{4}{a - 1}$

CHAPTER 11 QUADRATIC FUNCTIONS AND RELATIONS

Written Exercises, page 418
1. 3.

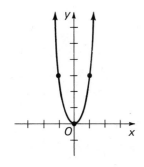
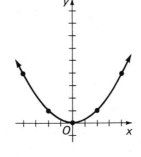

5.

7.

9.

11.

Problems, page 418 1. $\frac{1}{4}$ 3. 312 m
5. 706.86 m 7. 9π cm^2 9. 3 cm

Written Exercises, page 422
1. 3.

5. $\frac{1}{2}$ 7. 8 9. t is cut in half.

Problems, pages 422–423 1. 6 hours 3. 3 m
5. 120 plants 7. 26.7 cm 9. It is halved.
11. about 0.4 m

Written Exercises, page 425 1. 4 3. $\frac{135}{4}$ 5. 40

Problems, page 425 1. $\frac{2}{3}$ m 3. $\frac{4}{9}$

Written Exercises, pages 428–429

1. $(0, -1)$ 3. $(0, -4)$

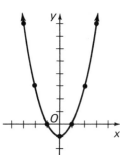   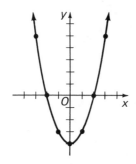

5. $(0, 3)$ 7. $(\frac{1}{2}, -\frac{1}{4})$

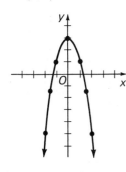   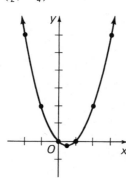

9. $(1\frac{1}{2}, -6\frac{1}{4})$ 11. $(2, 0)$

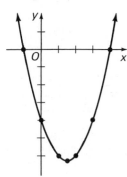   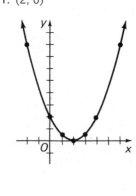

13. 4 15. 1 17. 7 19. -3 21. -4 23. -5

Written Exercises, page 431

1.   3.

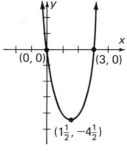   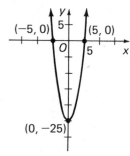

5.

Written Exercises, pages 433–434 1. ± 2
3. ± 3 5. ± 6 7. $\pm\sqrt{7}$ 9. $\pm\frac{1}{4}$ 11. ± 3
13. no real solution 15. ± 2 17. $\pm\sqrt{2}$
19. no real solution 21. $4 \pm \sqrt{3}$
23. $-1 \pm \sqrt{2}$ 25. 11, 3 27. 5, -1
29. 4, -6 31. 8, 6 33. $\pm\frac{4}{3}$ 35. $\pm\frac{3}{4}$
37. $2\frac{1}{7}$, $1\frac{6}{7}$ 39. $\dfrac{-1 \pm \sqrt{2}}{2}$ 41. $\{0, -2, 2\}$
43. $\{0, -7, 7\}$ 45. $\{0, -3, 3\}$ 47. $\{\frac{7}{2}, \frac{3}{2}\}$
49. $\{\sqrt{6}\}$

Written Exercises, page 437 1. $\{7, -5\}$
3. $\{9, -5\}$ 5. $\{4 \pm \sqrt{30}\}$ or $\{9.5, -1.5\}$
7. $\{11, -13\}$ 9. $\left\{\dfrac{-1 \pm \sqrt{13}}{2}\right\}$ or $\{1.3, -2.3\}$
11. $\left\{\dfrac{4 \pm \sqrt{26}}{2}\right\}$ or $\{4.5, -0.5\}$ 13. $\left\{\dfrac{5 \pm 3\sqrt{3}}{2}\right\}$
or $\{5.1, -0.1\}$ 15. $\left\{\dfrac{1 \pm \sqrt{17}}{4}\right\}$ or $\{1.3, -0.8\}$
17. $\{7, 5\}$ 19. $\{8, -2\}$ 21. $\{\frac{5}{3}, -2\}$
23. $\{6, -2\}$ 25. $\{\frac{3}{2}, -6\}$ 27. $\left\{\dfrac{1 \pm \sqrt{6}}{5}\right\}$
29. $\{-1 \pm \sqrt{2}\}$ 31. $x = 1, \pm \sqrt{1 - c}$
33. $x = \dfrac{-b \pm \sqrt{b^2 - 4c}}{2}$

Written Exercises, pages 439–441

1. $\left\{\dfrac{-3 \pm \sqrt{5}}{2}\right\}$ or $\{-0.4, -2.6\}$

3. $\{-3 \pm \sqrt{2}\}$ or $\{-1.6, -4.4\}$

5. $\left\{\dfrac{7 \pm \sqrt{85}}{6}\right\}$ or $\{2.7, -0.4\}$ 7. $\left\{\dfrac{-5 \pm \sqrt{73}}{8}\right\}$

or $\{0.4, -1.7\}$ 9. $\left\{\dfrac{9 \pm \sqrt{21}}{6}\right\}$ or $\{2.3, 0.7\}$

11. $\{2, \frac{1}{5}\}$ 13. $\{-3\}$ 15. $\{0, 1\}$

17. $\{7 \pm \sqrt{3}\}$ 19. $\left\{\dfrac{8 \pm 4\sqrt{10}}{3}\right\}$

21. $\left\{\dfrac{-2 \pm \sqrt{15}}{4}\right\}$ 23. 29; 2 real roots 25. 37;

2 real roots 27. 17; 2 real roots 29. 25;
2 real roots 31. -11; no real roots 33. 0;
1 real root 35. Since $b^2 - 4ac$ is a square,
$\sqrt{b^2 - 4ac}$ is a rational number. By closure,
$\dfrac{-b \pm \sqrt{b^2 - 4ac}}{2a}$ is also rational.

Written Exercises, page 444 1. $\{5, 7\}$
3. $\{3.7, -1.2\}$ 5. $\{3, -\frac{2}{3}\}$ 7. $\{5 \pm \sqrt{6}\}$
9. $\{-\frac{1}{2}, 1\}$ 11. $\{5 \pm 5\sqrt{5}\}$ 13. Let $y = x^2$:
$4y^2 - 13y + 9 = 0$; $(4y - 9)(y - 1) = 0$; $y = \frac{9}{4}$
or $y = 1$; hence $x^2 = \frac{9}{4}$ or $x^2 = 1$, and $x = \pm\frac{3}{2}$
or $x = \pm 1$.

Problems, pages 444–445 1. 8 and 3 3. 4 m
5. Alice: 9 km; Bobby Jo: 12 km 7. 2 km/h

Extra for Experts, page 446
1.

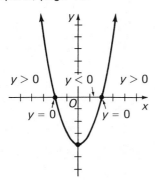

3.

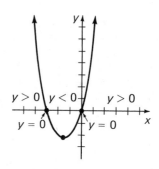

5.

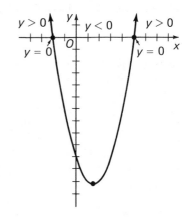

7.

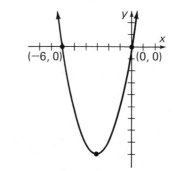

$\sqrt{x^2 + 6x}$ is real when $x^2 + 6x \geq 0$; from the
graph, this is true when $x \leq -6$ or $x \geq 0$.

Maintaining Skills, page 451 1. -4 3. -4
5. -5 7. 1 9. -2 11. 3 13. -4 15. 23
17. 1 19. 6 21. $-11\frac{2}{3}$ 23. -6

CHAPTER 12 GEOMETRY AND
TRIGONOMETRY

Written Exercises, page 455 1. any five of: $\overline{AB}$, $\overline{AC}$, $\overline{AD}$, $\overline{BC}$, $\overline{BD}$, $\overline{CD}$ 3. any five of: $\overline{EI}$, $\overline{EJ}$, $\overline{EM}$, $\overline{IJ}$, $\overline{IM}$, $\overline{JM}$, $\overline{FI}$, $\overline{IG}$, $\overline{FG}$, $\overline{HJ}$, $\overline{JK}$, $\overline{HK}$ 5. right
7. obtuse 9. acute
11. point

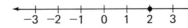

13. segment

Written Exercises, page 458 1. $\angle DCF$, $\angle FGE$, $\angle HGJ$ 3. $140°$

Problems, page 458 1. $45°$ and $135°$ 3. $50°$

Written Exercises, page 460 1. not a right triangle 3. right triangle 5. not a right triangle
7. 6 9. $60°$ 11. $50°$

Problems, page 460 1. $10°$ and $80°$
3. $25°$, $50°$, $105°$ 5. $30°$
7. $30°$, $70°$, $120°$, $140°$

Written Exercises, page 462 1. $\dfrac{DE}{XY} = \dfrac{EF}{YZ} = \dfrac{DF}{XZ}$
3. 20 m 5. 24 cm 7. 600 m 9. 52 cm

Written Exercises, page 466

1. $\frac{4}{5}, \frac{3}{5}, \frac{3}{4}; \frac{3}{5}, \frac{4}{5}, \frac{4}{3}$ 3. $\dfrac{4\sqrt{17}}{17}, \dfrac{\sqrt{17}}{17}, \frac{1}{4};$
$\dfrac{\sqrt{17}}{17}, \dfrac{4\sqrt{17}}{17}, 4$ 5. $\dfrac{\sqrt{2}}{2}, \dfrac{\sqrt{2}}{2}, 1; \dfrac{\sqrt{2}}{2}, \dfrac{\sqrt{2}}{2}, 1$
7. $\sin A = \dfrac{BC}{AB} = \cos B$ 9. $(\sin A)^2 + (\cos A)^2 =$
$\left(\dfrac{BC}{AB}\right)^2 + \left(\dfrac{AC}{AB}\right)^2 = \dfrac{BC^2 + AC^2}{AB^2} = \dfrac{AB^2}{AB^2} = 1$

Puzzle Time, page 466
$\tan \angle ABC = \dfrac{FG}{BG} = \dfrac{FG}{1} = FG; \overline{FG}$

Written Exercises, page 468
1. a. 0.2588 b. 0.9659 c. 0.2679
3. a. 0.6157 b. 0.7880 c. 0.7813
5. a. 0.7771 b. 0.6293 c. 1.2349
7. a. 0.9455 b. 0.3256 c. 2.9042
9. a. 0.0523 b. 0.9986 c. 0.0524
11. a. 0.5299 b. 0.8480 c. 0.6249
13. $42°$ 15. $64°$ 17. $11°$ 19. $8°$

Written Exercises, page 470 1. 23 3. 13 5. 33

Problems, pages 471–472 1. 141 m 3. 4 m
5. $61°$ 7. 338.6 m 9. 146.5 m

Cumulative Review, pages 476–478 1. -1
3. $5t^2 - 4t + 9$ 5. $5x^2 - 11x + 2$
7. $1 - 4r + 4r^2$ 9. $-7x^2 + 6ax - a^2$
11. $-15a - 7$ 13. $3a^2(8a - 1)$ 15. $2ar(2r - h)$
17. $(b - 6)^2$ 19. $(9a + 1)(4a - 1)$
21. $(y + 4)(y - 4)(y + 3)(y - 3)$
23. $3t(3t - 1)(2t + 5)$ 25. $\dfrac{2}{x + 4}$ 27. $\dfrac{c + 3}{c}$
29. $\dfrac{-2y}{x^2 - y^2}$ 31. $z = -5$ 33. $a = -\frac{17}{10}$
35. $m = 3$ 37. $x = 7$ 39. $t = 12$ or $t = 7$
41. $4\sqrt{2}$ 43. $\sqrt{2}$ 45. $\dfrac{\sqrt{35}}{14}$ 47. $24\sqrt{2} - 18$
49. 51.

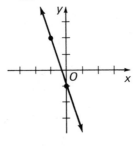
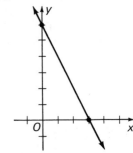

53.

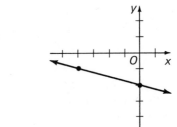

55. $(1, 1)$ 57. $(2, 1)$ 59. $a = 7$
61. $3x + 4y = 20$ 63. a. 960 b. 3 c. -15
65. $\pm\dfrac{9\sqrt{10}}{5}$

67.

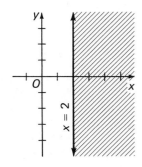

69. 65¢   71. $b = 12$, $a = 7$ or $b = 7$, $a = 12$
73. $22\frac{1}{2}$ minutes

EXTRA PRACTICE IN PROBLEM SOLVING

Section 6-13, page 479   1. $2250 at 6%,
$3000 at $4\frac{1}{2}$%   3. $6000   5. $5600 at 5%,
$4400 at 6%   7. $3500 at 6% and $7000 at 4%

Section 6-14, pages 479–481   1. 500 m
3. 8 hours   5. 100 km/h and 120 km/h
7. 25 km/h   9. 70 km/h   11. 52.5 km/h and
87.5 km/h   13. For editions with facts 1 km up
river, rate of motorboat 22 km/h, time 1 h, 5 min,
speed of current is 2 km/h.

15. Lon: 105 km/h; Connie: 70 km/h

Section 6-15, page 481   1. $\frac{1}{4}$ hour
3. Anthony: $12\frac{1}{2}$ hours; brother: $3\frac{4}{7}$ hours

Section 9-6, pages 481–483
Digit Problems   1. 65   3. 74 and 47
5. $10t + u + (10u + t) = 11t + 11u = 11(t + u)$
Age Problems   1. Ramona: 15; street
number: 90   3. father: 50; mother: 46; son: 14
5. $c = 4b$ 7. man: 39; son: 16
Fraction Problems   1. $\frac{9}{18}$ 3. $\{\frac{1002}{2001}, \frac{2004}{4002}, \frac{3006}{6003}, \frac{4008}{8004}\}$

Section 10-6, page 483   1. $l^2 + l^2 = H^2$; $l^2 = \frac{H^2}{2}$;
$l = \sqrt{\frac{H^2}{2}} = \frac{H}{\sqrt{2}}$ 3. 24 km   5. $z\sqrt{3}$

Section 11-9, pages 483-484   1. 8 cm
3. **a.** $A = 2 \cdot x^2 + 4 \cdot 4x = 2x^2 + 16x$
b. 2.3 cm   5. after 1 second; after 4 seconds;
after 5 seconds   7. 42 or 48

Section 12-4, pages 484–485   1. 13.3 m   3. 18 m

Section 12-7, page 485   1. 9°

ANNOTATED ANSWERS

(Answers too long to be included on the student pages.)

Written Exercises, page 130

25. $a^4 - 1$ **26.** $s^4 - 8s^2 + 16$
27. $u^4 - 4u^2v^2 + 4v^4$ **28.** $9a^4 - 4b^4$
29. $a^3 + 3a^2 - a - 3$ **30.** $x^3 - 2x^2 - x + 2$
31. $r^3 + r^2 - 7r - 3$ **32.** $s^3 - 3s^2 + 5s - 6$
33. $2x^3 + x^2 + 5x - 3$
34. $h^3 - h^2k + hk^2 + 3k^3$
35. $s^3 + s^2t - st^2 + 2t^3$
36. $2a^3 - 5a^2b + 3ab^2 - 2b^3$
37. $3x^2 + 5x - 5$ **38.** $4c^2 - 4c + 3$
39. $x^4 + x^3 - x^2 - 7x - 6$
40. $y^4 + y^3 + 3y^2 + 4y + 6$ **41.** $a^3 - b^3$
42. $a^3 + b^3$ **43.** $s^4 - t^4$ **44.** $s^4 - t^4$
45. $x^4 + 3x^3y + x^2y^2 - 2xy^3 - y^4$
46. $3c^4 - 4c^3d - c^2d^2 + 3cd^3 - d^4$

Just for Fun, page 130

When $x = -1$:   9

5	4	6	15
10	3	2	15
0	8	7	15
15	15	15	15

When $x = 2$:   9

14	−5	6	15
1	3	11	15
0	17	−2	15
15	15	15	15

Written Exercises, page 141

Note: In the answers for Exs. 25–36, only the positive pairs are given. In the answers for Exs.

37–48, only one of the two possible positive/negative pairs is given (i.e., $(-1)(21)$, but not $(1)(-21)$).

25. $1 \cdot 21, 3 \cdot 7$ **26.** $1 \cdot 35, 5 \cdot 7$
27. $1 \cdot 70, 2 \cdot 35, 5 \cdot 14, 7 \cdot 10$
28. $1 \cdot 42, 2 \cdot 21, 3 \cdot 14, 6 \cdot 7$
29. $1 \cdot 72, 2 \cdot 36, 3 \cdot 24, 4 \cdot 18, 6 \cdot 12, 8 \cdot 9$
30. $1 \cdot 96, 2 \cdot 48, 3 \cdot 32, 4 \cdot 24, 6 \cdot 16, 8 \cdot 12$
31. $1 \cdot 48, 2 \cdot 24, 3 \cdot 16, 4 \cdot 12, 6 \cdot 8$
32. $1 \cdot 250, 2 \cdot 125, 5 \cdot 50, 10 \cdot 25$
33. $1 \cdot 88, 2 \cdot 44, 4 \cdot 22, 8 \cdot 11$
34. $1 \cdot 56, 2 \cdot 28, 4 \cdot 14, 7 \cdot 8$
35. $1 \cdot 45, 3 \cdot 15, 5 \cdot 9$
36. $1 \cdot 84, 2 \cdot 42, 3 \cdot 28, 4 \cdot 21, 6 \cdot 14, 7 \cdot 12$

37. $-1 \cdot 21, -3 \cdot 7$ **38.** $-1 \cdot 35, -5 \cdot 7$
39. $-1 \cdot 70, -2 \cdot 35, -5 \cdot 14, -7 \cdot 10$
40. $-1 \cdot 42, -2 \cdot 21, -3 \cdot 14, -6 \cdot 7$
41. $-1 \cdot 72, -2 \cdot 36, -3 \cdot 24, -4 \cdot 18, -6 \cdot 12, -8 \cdot 9$
42. $-1 \cdot 96, -2 \cdot 48, -3 \cdot 32, -4 \cdot 24, -6 \cdot 16, -8 \cdot 12$
43. $-1 \cdot 48, -2 \cdot 24, -3 \cdot 16, -4 \cdot 12, -6 \cdot 8$
44. $-1 \cdot 250, -2 \cdot 125, -5 \cdot 50, -10 \cdot 25$
45. $-1 \cdot 88, -2 \cdot 44, -4 \cdot 22, -8 \cdot 11$
46. $-1 \cdot 56, -2 \cdot 28, -4 \cdot 14, -7 \cdot 8$
47. $-1 \cdot 45, -3 \cdot 15, -5 \cdot 9$
48. $-1 \cdot 84, -2 \cdot 42, -3 \cdot 28, -4 \cdot 21, -6 \cdot 14, -7 \cdot 12$

Written Exercises, page 169

1. $(z + 1)(z + 6)$ **2.** $(w + 1)(w + 10)$
3. $(c + 1)(c + 5)$ **4.** $(t - 1)(t - 5)$
5. $(r - 1)(r - 7)$ **6.** $(m + 9)(m + 1)$
7. $(x + 3)(x + 4)$ **8.** $(y + 2)(y + 3)$
9. $(k - 4)(k - 5)$ **10.** $(u - 2)(u - 12)$
11. $(7 + s)(3 + s)$ **12.** $(8 + v)(2 + v)$
13. $(x + y)(x + 4y)$ **14.** $(u + v)(u + 9v)$
15. $(r - s)(r - 19s)$ **16.** $(a - b)(a - 15b)$
17. $(m - 13n)(m - 2n)$ **18.** $(s - 7t)(s - 3t)$

19. $(x + 5a)(x + 8a)$ **20.** $(x + 6z)(x + 8z)$
21. $(z + 5w)(z + 20w)$ **22.** $(y - 6z)(y - 7z)$
23. $(b - 4c)(b - 13c)$ **24.** $(x + 5y)(x + 10y)$

Written Exercises, page 171

1. $(x + 4)(x - 2)$ **2.** $(y + 4)(y - 1)$
3. $(h + 9)(h - 1)$ **4.** $(z + 5)(z - 2)$
5. $(u - 11)(u + 1)$ **6.** $(s - 10)(s + 1)$
7. $(r + 5)(r - 4)$ **8.** $(t + 3)(t - 2)$
9. $(k - 5)(k + 4)$ **10.** $(m - 3)(m + 2)$
11. $(t - 10)(t + 2)$ **12.** $(r + 8)(r - 2)$
13. $(z + 6)(z - 5)$ **14.** $(k + 6)(k - 3)$
15. $(y - 10)(y + 3)$ **16.** $(x - 10)(x + 5)$
17. $(c - 6)(c + 4)$ **18.** $(a - 8)(a + 3)$
19. $(x + 8y)(x - y)$ **20.** $(m + 6n)(m - n)$
21. $(u - 6v)(u + 4v)$ **22.** $(h - 8k)(h + 3k)$
23. $(a + 9b)(a - 5b)$ **24.** $(r + 15s)(r - 3s)$

Written Exercises, page 178

1. $3(t + 1)(t - 1)$ **2.** $2(x + 2)(x - 2)$
3. $(2 + r)^2$ **4.** $3(s^2 + 4)$ **5.** $2(y - 1)^2$
6. $5(t + 1)(t + 2)$ **7.** $v(u^2 + u + 1)$
8. $x(x + 1)(x - 2)$ **9.** $2x(1 + y)(1 - y)$
10. $2z(3 + z)^2$ **11.** $ax(x^2 + 3x + 4)$
12. $-4c(1 - c)^2$ **13.** $k^2(5k - 2)(k + 2)$
14. $-a(b^2 + 4)$ **15.** $2y(-3 + x)(2 + x)$
16. $(2s - 5)(2s + 1)$ **17.** $(11 + t)(1 + 10t)$
18. $(1 - 9x)(1 - 4x)$ **19.** $(8a + 7b^2)(8a - 7b^2)$
20. $(9u^2 + 13v)(9u^2 - 13v)$
21. $5t(t - 3)(t + 1)$ **22.** $x(100x + 1)(x - 1)$
23. $(a + 4b)(a + b)$ **24.** $(3x + y)(2x - y)$
25. $2(c - d)^2$ **26.** $mn^2(2 - m)^2$
27. $(x^2 + y)(x^2 - y)$ **28.** $x^2(x + y)(x - y)$
29. $u^2v^2(1 + 2uv)(1 - 2uv)$
30. $ab(a + 2b)(a - 2b)$
31. $2hk(k + 2h)(k - 2h)$
32. $7r^2s^2(s + 3r)(s - 3r)$ **33.** $2y(3 + 4y)(2 - y)$
34. $5t(2t - 5)(t + 1)$ **35.** $ax(2x^2 + 3ax + 4a^2)$
36. $-2uv(u^2 - 2uv + 3v^2)$
37. $(x + 2)(x - 2)(x^2 + 1)$
38. $(v + 1)(v - 1)(v + 2)(v - 2)$
39. $(z^2 + 1)(z + 1)(z - 1)$
40. $(y^2 + 4)(y + 2)(y - 2)$

41. $x^2(y^2 + x^2)(y + x)(y - x)$
42. $(a + b)^2(a - b)^2$
43. $(r + 2s)(r - 2s)(r + 3s)(r - 3s)$
44. $(3 + 2z)(3 - 2z)(1 + z^2)$
45. $x^2(x + 2)^2(x - 2)^2$
46. $(2t + 1)(2t - 1)(t + 2)(t - 2)$
47. $x^2(xy - 5)^2$ **48.** $3(a^2 + 4)(a + 2)(a - 2)$
49. $(s - 1)(s + 10)(s + 1)$
50. $(y + 1)(y + 2)(y + 3)$
51. $(h + 3)(2h - 1)(h + 3)$ **52.** $(2z - 1)^3$
53. $(x - 2)(x + 2)^3$ **54.** $(1 + t)(1 - 2t)(1 - t)^2$
55. $(t - 1)(t + 1)^2$ **56.** $(x - 1)(x + 2)(x - 2)$
57. $(u + v - 1)(u - v - 1)$
58. $(2s - t + 2)(2s + t - 2)$
59. $(x - y + z)(x - y - z)$
60. $(y^2 + z^2)(x + 1)(x - 1)$

Written Exercises, page 185

1. $\{1, 3\}$ **2.** $\{1, 4\}$ **3.** $\{3, -2\}$ **4.** $\{-4, 2\}$
5. $\{-7, 7\}$ **6.** $\{-5, 5\}$ **7.** $\{0, 9\}$ **8.** $\{0, 16\}$
9. $\{0, -2, 2\}$ **10.** $\{0, -1, 1\}$ **11.** $\{1, 9\}$
12. $\{6, -5\}$ **13.** $\{-8, 3\}$ **14.** $\{2\}$
15. $\{-\frac{1}{2}, 1\}$ **16.** $\{\frac{1}{3}, -1\}$ **17.** $\{\frac{1}{2}, 2\}$ **18.** $\{\frac{2}{3}, 2\}$
19. $\{-\frac{1}{5}, 4\}$ **20.** $\{\frac{5}{2}, -\frac{1}{2}\}$ **21.** $\{0, -2, 2\}$
22. $\{0, -4, 4\}$ **23.** $\{-1, 1\}$ **24.** $\{-2, 2\}$
25. $\{0, 2, 4\}$ **26.** $\{0, 8, 4\}$ **27.** $\{0, 3\}$
28. $\{0, -5\}$ **29.** $\{0, -5, 2\}$ **30.** $\{0, -8, 7\}$
31. $\{-3, 3, -1, 1\}$ **32.** $\{-3, 3, -2, 2\}$
33. $\{-2, 2\}$ **34.** $\{-1, 1\}$ **35.** $\{-1, 1\}$
36. $\{-1, -2, 2\}$

Written Exercises, page 219

1. $\dfrac{b^2 - b + 6}{b - 1}$ **2.** $\dfrac{ab + a^2 + 2b}{b + a}$ **3.** $\dfrac{4a - b}{a - b}$

4. $\dfrac{12a + 7b}{a + b}$ **5.** $\dfrac{x^2 - y^2 + 1}{x + y}$ **6.** $\dfrac{h^2 - 2}{h - 1}$

7. $\dfrac{x + 7}{x + 2}$ **8.** $\dfrac{5 - m}{m - 2}$ **9.** $\dfrac{7ab + 3b + 6a}{ab}$

10. $\dfrac{m^2 + 3mn + n^2}{mn}$ **11.** $\dfrac{d^2 + 3d - 7}{d - 2}$

12. $\dfrac{h^2 - 3}{h - 1}$

Written Exercises, page 222

9. $x - 1 + \dfrac{4}{x - 3}$ **10.** $r + 1 + \dfrac{5}{r - 4}$

11. $t - 4$ **12.** $m + 5$ **13.** $x + 2 + \dfrac{8}{x - 2}$

14. $d - 3 + \dfrac{21}{d + 3}$ **15.** $x - 3 + \dfrac{1}{2x + 1}$

16. $c + 2$ **17.** $3r + 5 + \dfrac{10}{2r - 3}$

18. $2a + 2 + \dfrac{5}{3a - 1}$ **19.** $3t - 2 + \dfrac{5}{3t + 2}$

20. $2s - 1 + \dfrac{2}{2s + 1}$ **21.** $3x - a - \dfrac{a^2}{2x + a}$

22. $2u + 3v$ **23.** $3s - 4t + \dfrac{2t^2}{s + 2t}$

24. $3c - 2a + \dfrac{3a^2}{2c + a}$

Written Exercises, page 257

17. $-5 < -4.5$ and $-4.5 < 4$
18. $-1.5 < 0$ and $0 < 25$
19. $6 < 8.5$ and $8.5 < 10.25$
20. $25 < 145$ and $145 < 1000$
21. $7 > 1$ and $1 > -25$
22. $8 > -7$ and $-7 > -32$
23. $-2.5 < -2$ and $-2 < -1.75$
24. $-25 > -1007$ and $-1007 > -1100$
25. $7.5 < 8.2$ and $8.2 < 9.5$
26. $-7.5 > -8.2$ and $-8.2 > -9.5$
27. $0 > -2$ and $-2 > -150$
28. $0 < 25$ and $25 < 150$

Oral Exercises, page 259

1. 2 is a member of the set whose members are 1, 2, and 3. **2.** The set whose member is 2 is a subset of the set whose members are 2, 4, and 6. **3.** The set whose members are -3, -2, and -1 is a subset of the set of negative integers. **4.** The set of odd integers is a subset of the set of integers. **5.** The set of prime numbers is a subset of the set of positive integers. **6.** The set of negative integers is a subset of the set of integers. **7.** If A is a subset of B and B is a subset of C, then A is a subset of C. **8.** If A is a subset of B and B is a subset of A, then A equals B.

Extra for Experts, page 281

1. $x - 3 = 2$ or $x - 3 = -2$
2. $t + 1 = 5$ or $t + 1 = -5$ **3.** $-7 \le z \le 7$
4. $u > 3$ or $u < -3$ **5.** $-1 < s + 2 < 1$
6. $-4 \le y - 3 \le 4$
7. $2 - t \ge 3$ or $2 - t \le -3$
8. $6 - t > 2$ or $6 - t < -2$
9. $3 + 2a = 1$ or $3 + 2a = -1$
10. $2s + 3 = 3$ or $2s + 3 = -3$
11. $-3 < 2x - 7 < 3$
12. $-1 - 3r \ge 2$ or $-1 - 3r \le -2$
13. $x = 5$ or $x = 1$ **14.** $t = 4$ or $t = -6$
15. $-7 \le z \le 7$ **16.** $u > 3$ or $u < -3$
17. $-3 < s < -1$ **18.** $-1 \le y \le 7$
19. $t \le -1$ or $t \ge 5$ **20.** $t < 4$ or $t > 8$
21. $a = -1$ or $a = -2$ **22.** $s = 0$ or $s = -3$
23. $2 < x < 5$ **24.** $r \le -1$ or $r \ge \frac{1}{3}$

Written Exercises, page 309

21. $\{(0, 4), (1, 3), (2, 2), (3, 1), (4, 0)\}$
22. $\{(0, 8), (1, 6), (2, 4), (3, 2), (4, 0)\}$
23. $\{(1, 3), (3, 2), (5, 1), (7, 0)\}$
24. $\{(0, 4), (3, 3), (6, 2), (9, 1), (12, 0)\}$
25. $\{(1, 6), (4, 4), (7, 2), (10, 0)\}$
26. $\{(3, 4), (7, 1)\}$
27. $\{(0, 4), (3, 2), (6, 0)\}$
28. $\{(0, 6), (5, 3), (10, 0)\}$
29. $\{(-1, 2), (0, 1), (0, 2), (1, 0), (1, 1), (1, 2)\}$
30. $\{(0, -2), (0, -1), (1, -2), (1, -1), (1, 0), (1, 1)\}$
31. $\{(0, -2), (0, -1), (0, 0), (0, 1), (1, -2), (1, -1), (1, 0), (1, 1), (1, 2)\}$
32. $\{(0, 1), (0, 2), (1, -1), (1, 0), (1, 1), (1, 2)\}$
33. $\{(-1, -1), (-1, 0), (-1, 1), (-1, 2), (0, -1), (0, 0), (0, 1), (0, 2), (1, -1), (1, 0), (1, 1), (1, 2)\}$

34. $\{(-1, 1), (-1, 2), (0, 0), (0, 1), (0, 2),$
$\quad (1, -1), (1, 0), (1, 1), (1, 2)\}$
35. $\{(-1, -2), (-1, -1), (-1, 0), (-1, 1),$
$\quad (-1, 2), (0, -2), (0, -1), (0, 0), (0, 1), (0, 2),$
$\quad (1, -2), (1, -1), (1, 0), (1, 1), (1, 2)\}$
36. $\{(0, -2), (0, -1), (1, -2), (1, -1), (1, 0)\}$

Extra for Experts, page 377

5. If $0 < a < 1$ and $0 < b < 1$, then
$0 \cdot 0 < ab < 1 \cdot 1$; hence, the product is between
0 and 1.   **6.** $2m + 2n = 2(m + n)$, which is
even; $2m \cdot 2n = 2(2mn)$, which is even.
7. $(2m + 1)(2n + 1) = 4mn + 2m + 2n + 1 =$
$2(2mn + m + n) + 1$, an odd number.
8. $\dfrac{a}{b} \div \dfrac{c}{d} = \dfrac{ad}{bc}$. Since a, b, c, d are integers,

so are ad and bc; thus, $\dfrac{ad}{bc}$ is rational.

Written Exercises, page 437

1. $\{7, -5\}$ **2.** $\{7, -13\}$ **3.** $\{9, -5\}$
4. $\{6 \pm \sqrt{37}\}$ or $\{12.1, -0.1\}$
5. $\{4 \pm \sqrt{30}\}$ or $\{9.5, -1.5\}$
6. $\{-5 \pm 4\sqrt{2}\}$ or $\{0.7, -10.7\}$ **7.** $\{11, -13\}$
8. $\{-3 \pm 13\sqrt{5}\}$ or $\{26.0, -32.0\}$
9. $\left\{\dfrac{-1 \pm \sqrt{13}}{2}\right\}$ or $\{1.3, -2.3\}$
10. $\left\{\dfrac{-5 \pm \sqrt{29}}{2}\right\}$ or $\{0.2, -5.2\}$
11. $\left\{\dfrac{4 \pm \sqrt{26}}{2}\right\}$ or $\{4.5, -0.5\}$
12. $\left\{\dfrac{-6 \pm \sqrt{57}}{3}\right\}$ or $\{0.5, -4.5\}$
13. $\left\{\dfrac{5 \pm 3\sqrt{3}}{2}\right\}$ or $\{5.1, -0.1\}$
14. $\left\{\dfrac{9 \pm \sqrt{105}}{6}\right\}$ or $\{3.2, -0.2\}$
15. $\left\{\dfrac{1 \pm \sqrt{17}}{4}\right\}$ or $\{1.3, -0.8\}$
16. $\left\{\dfrac{1 \pm \sqrt{5}}{4}\right\}$ or $\{0.8, -0.3\}$

Written Exercises, pages 439–441

1. $\left\{\dfrac{-3 \pm \sqrt{5}}{2}\right\}$ or $\{-0.4, -2.6\}$
2. $\{-1 \pm \sqrt{2}\}$ or $\{0.4, -2.4\}$
3. $\{-3 \pm \sqrt{2}\}$ or $\{-1.6, -4.4\}$
4. $\left\{2, -\dfrac{1}{2}\right\}$
5. $\left\{\dfrac{7 \pm \sqrt{85}}{6}\right\}$ or $\{2.7, -0.4\}$
6. $\left\{\dfrac{4 \pm \sqrt{26}}{5}\right\}$ or $\{1.8, -0.2\}$
7. $\left\{\dfrac{-5 \pm \sqrt{73}}{8}\right\}$ or $\{0.5, -1.7\}$
8. $\left\{\dfrac{3 \pm \sqrt{33}}{2}\right\}$ or $\{4.4, -1.4\}$
9. $\left\{\dfrac{9 \pm \sqrt{21}}{6}\right\}$ or $\{2.3, 0.7\}$
10. $\left\{\dfrac{3 \pm \sqrt{14}}{5}\right\}$ or $\{1.3, -0.1\}$
11. $\left\{2, \dfrac{1}{5}\right\}$
12. $\left\{\dfrac{-3 \pm \sqrt{69}}{12}\right\}$ or $\{0.4, -0.9\}$

35. Since $b^2 - 4ac$ is a square, $\sqrt{b^2 - 4ac}$ is
also rational. By closure, $\dfrac{-b \pm \sqrt{b^2 - 4ac}}{2a}$ is
rational.
36. Since $b^2 - 4ac$ is not a square, $\sqrt{b^2 - 4ac}$ is
irrational. Thus, the roots are irrational.